BUSINESS MATHEMATICS IN CANADA

Custom Edition for SAIT Polytechnic

Mc Graw Hill Custom Publishing

MCGRAW-HILL RYERSON LIMITED

Toronto Montréal Boston Burr Ridge, IL Dubuque, IA Madison, WI New York San Francisco
St. Louis Bangkok Bogotá Caracas Kuala Lumpur Lisbon London Madrid Mexico City Milan
New Delhi Santiago Seoul Singapore Sydney Taipei

Business Mathematics in Canada, Seventh Edition, by F. Jerome, ISBN 0-07-000989-9. Published by McGraw-Hill, a business unit of the McGraw-Hill Companies, Inc., 1221 Avenue of the Americas, New York, NY, 10020. Copyright © 2011 by the McGraw-Hill Companies, Inc. All rights reserved.

Product Development Manager, Learning Solutions: Jason Giles
Learning Solutions Custom Print Specialist: Corinne Mohr

ISBN-10: 0-07-132004-0
ISBN-13: 978-0-07-132004-7

Printed and bound in Canada

Table of Contents

Business Mathematics in Canada, Seventh Edition
by F. Jerome

CHAPTER 6

Simple Interest

LEARNING OBJECTIVES

After completing this chapter, you will be able to:

LO1 Calculate interest, maturity value (future value), and present value in a simple interest environment

LO2 Present details of the amount and timing of payments in a time diagram

LO3 Calculate the equivalent value on any date of a single payment or a stream of payments

EVERY DAY MONEY IS BORROWED and loaned in tens of thousands of transactions. The transaction amounts range from a few dollars on credit-card purchases to multibillion-dollar refinancings of federal government debt.

Interest is the fee or rent that lenders charge for the use of their money. For many individuals and corporations, and for most provincial and federal governments, interest on debt is one of the largest expenditures in their annual budgets.

Clearly, debt plays a key role in our personal finances and our economic system. As a fundamental skill, you must be able to calculate interest on debt. But to be a truly effective participant in financial decision-making, you must be able to analyze the broader effects that prevailing interest rates have on the value of personal investments and business assets. The remainder of the text is devoted to developing these skills and techniques.

In this chapter you will first learn how to calculate interest in the simple-interest system. We will then take the first step toward answering a central question in finance: "What is an investment worth?" This step involves the concept of "equivalent value." It is a far-reaching concept that will carry forward to the compound-interest system in later chapters.

6.1 BASIC CONCEPTS

Borrowing and lending are two sides of the same transaction. The amount borrowed/loaned is called the **principal**. To the borrower, the principal is a *debt*; to the lender, the principal represents an *investment*.

The interest paid by the borrower is the lender's investment income. There are two systems[1] for calculating interest.

- **Simple interest** is used mainly for short-term loans and investments. (By "short-term," we mean durations of up to one year.) Chapters 6 and 7 cover the mathematics and applications of simple interest.

- *Compound* interest is used mainly for durations longer than one year. Chapters 8 and beyond cover the mathematics and applications of compound interest.

The **rate of interest** is the amount of interest (expressed as a percentage of the principal) charged per period. Simple interest rates are usually calculated and quoted for a one-year period. Such a rate is often called a *per annum rate.* That is,

$$\text{Interest rate (per annum)} = \frac{\text{Annual interest}}{\text{Principal}} \times 100\%$$

Note: If a time interval (such as "per month") is not indicated for a quoted interest rate, assume the rate is an annual or per annum rate.

The rate of interest charged on a loan is the lender's rate of return on investment. (It seems more natural for us to take the borrower's point of view because we usually become borrowers before we become lenders.)

If you "go with your intuition," you will probably correctly calculate the amount of simple interest. For example, how much interest will $1000 earn in six months if it earns an 8% rate

---

[1] We are *not* referring to two alternative methods for obtaining the same answer to an interest calculation. Rather, the two "systems" usually result in different amounts of interest being calculated.

of interest? Your thinking probably goes as follows: "In one year, $1000 will earn $80 (8% of $1000). In six months ($\frac{1}{2}$ year), $1000 will earn only $40 ($\frac{1}{2}$ of $80)."

LO1   Now write an equation for the preceding calculation, but in terms of the following symbols:

I = Amount of interest paid or received
P = Principal amount of the loan or investment
r = Annual rate of simple interest
t = Time period (term), in years, of the loan or investment

To obtain the $40 ($I$) amount, you multiplied $1000 ($P$) by 0.08 ($r$) and by $\frac{1}{2}$ year (t). In general,

AMOUNT OF SIMPLE INTEREST

$$I = Prt \tag{6-1}$$

TIP   **Interest Rates in Algebraic Formulas**

When substituting the numerical value for an interest rate into any equation or formula, you must use the decimal equivalent of the interest rate.

TIP   **Avoid "Formula Clutter"**

Don't try to memorize other versions of formula (6-1) that have different variables isolated on the left-hand side. In any problem requiring formula (6-1), just substitute the three known variables and then solve for the remaining unknown variable.

EXAMPLE 6.1A   **CALCULATING THE AMOUNT OF INTEREST**

What amount of interest will be charged on $6500 borrowed for five months at a simple interest rate of 11%?

SOLUTION

Given: $P = \$6500$, $t = \frac{5}{12}$ year, $r = 11\%$

Since no time period is given for the 11% rate, we understand that the rate is per year.

The amount of interest payable at the end of the loan period is

$$I = Prt = \$6500(0.11)\left(\tfrac{5}{12}\right) = \$297.92$$

EXAMPLE 6.1B   **CALCULATING THE PRINCIPAL AMOUNT**

If a three-month term deposit at a bank pays a simple interest rate of 4.5%, how much will have to be deposited to earn $100 of interest?

SOLUTION

Given: $t = \frac{3}{12}$ year, $r = 4.5\%$, $I = \$100$. Substitute these values into $I = Prt$.

$$\$100 = P(0.045)\tfrac{3}{12}$$
$$\$100 = 0.01125P$$

Solving for P, $P = \dfrac{\$100}{0.01125} = \$8888.89$

$8888.89 must be placed in the three-month term deposit to earn $100 of interest.

EXAMPLE 6.1C | **CALCULATING THE INTEREST RATE**

Interest of $429.48 was charged on a loan of $9500 for seven months. What simple annual rate of interest was charged on the loan?

SOLUTION

Given: $I = \$429.48$, $P = \$9500$, and $t = \frac{7}{12}$ year. Substitute these values into $I = Prt$.

$$\$429.48 = \$9500(r)\tfrac{7}{12}$$
$$\$429.48 = \$5541.67r$$

Solving for r, $\qquad\qquad\qquad r = \dfrac{\$429.48}{\$5541.67} = 0.0775 = 7.75\%$

An interest rate of 7.75% was charged on the loan.

EXAMPLE 6.1D | **CALCULATING THE TIME PERIOD**

The interest earned on a $6000 investment was $240. What was the term in months if the interest rate was 6%?

SOLUTION

Given: $P = \$6000$, $I = \$240$, and $r = 6\%$. Substitute these values into $I = Prt$.

$$\$240 = \$6000(0.06)t$$

Solving for t, $\qquad\qquad \dfrac{\$240}{\$6000(0.06)} = t$

$$t = 0.66667 \text{ year} = 0.66667(12 \text{ months}) = 8 \text{ months}$$

The term of the investment was 8 months.

EXAMPLE 6.1E | **USING MONTHS AS THE UNIT OF TIME**

The simple interest rate being charged on a $5000 loan is three-quarters of 1% per month. If the principal and interest are to be paid in nine months, how much interest will be charged?

SOLUTION

Given: $P = \$5000$, term = 9 months, interest rate = 0.75% per month

We normally use formula (6-1) with r representing the *annual* rate of interest and t representing the term in *years*. However, we can substitute the *monthly* interest rate for r if the term t is measured in *months*. We will present both approaches.

Method 1: With time expressed in years,

$$t = \frac{9}{12} = 0.75 \text{ year} \quad \text{and} \quad r = 12(0.75\%) = 9\% \text{ per } year$$
$$I = Prt = \$5000 \times 0.09 \times 0.75 = \$337.50$$

Method 2: With time expressed in months,

$$t = 9 \text{ months} \quad \text{and} \quad r = 0.75\% \text{ per month}$$
$$I = Prt = \$5000 \times 0.0075 \times 9 = \$337.50$$

The interest that will be charged on the loan is $337.50.

SPREADSHEET STRATEGIES   A Simple-Interest Calculator

Connect provides a template for creating a Simple-Interest Calculator. Go to the Student Edition of Connect and find "Simple-Interest Calculator."

To complete the template, you must program each of the blue cells in the "Output section" with a version of $I = Prt$ that isolates the desired variable.

We use the template here to solve Example 6.1D. In this problem, we are given: $P = \$6000$, $I = \$240$, and $r = 6\%$. The question asks "What was the term in months?" After entering the given values, the answer appears in cell C13. In cell D13, we show the Excel "translation" of the right-hand side of the formula $t = \frac{I}{Pr}$ that is actually programmed into cell C13. (Ignore the contents of the other output cells.)

	A	B	C	D	E
1					
2	Using a spreadsheet to create a Simple Interest Calculator.				
3	Example 6.1D:				
4		**Input section:**			
5		Principal ($), $P =$	$6,000.00		
6		Interest rate per annum (%), $r =$	6.00%		
7		Time period or term (years), $t =$			
8		Interest paid or received ($), $I =$	$240.00		
9					
10		**Output section:**			
11		Principal ($), $P =$	#DIV/0!		
12		Interest rate per annum (%), $r =$	#DIV/0!	Formula in C13:	
13		Time period or term (years), $t =$	0.666666667	=C8/(C5*C6)	
14		Interest paid or received ($), $I =$	$0.00		
15					

The term of the investment was $t = 0.66667$ year $= 0.66667(12$ months$) = 8$ months.

EXERCISE 6.1

 connect

Spreadsheet template: Connect presents a partially completed Excel template for a Simple-Interest Calculator. Go to the Student Edition of Connect and find "Simple-Interest Calculator." After you program the output cells in the template, you can use it for solving any of the following problems.

An open bullet (○) next to a problem indicates "intermediate difficulty;" a closed bullet (●) means "most challenging."

Answers to the odd-numbered problems are at the end of the book.

1. How much interest was paid on a $1500 loan for seven months at an annual interest rate of 9.5%?

2. Montel loaned $6800 to a friend for 13 months at an annual rate of 7.7% simple interest. How much interest did the borrower owe?

3. A $25,000 investment earned 1.1% per month simple interest for a three-month term. What total amount of interest was earned?

4. What was the term of a $4850 loan at 4.5% if the interest due at the end was $145.50?

5. The interest paid at the end of the term of a $9125 loan at 0.8% per month was $511.00. Calculate the term of the loan.

6. The interest paid on an 11-month loan at $10\frac{1}{4}\%$ was $328.85. What was the principal amount of the original loan?

7. What annual rate of interest was earned if a $15,000 investment for five months earned $546.88 in interest?

8. $890 interest was charged on $8900 borrowed on a simple interest basis for eight months. What was the interest rate per month on the loan?

9. How much interest will be earned on $5000 in five months if the interest rate is 5.5%?

10. An invoice states that interest will be charged on overdue accounts at the rate of $1\frac{1}{2}$% per month. What will the interest charges be on a $3760 billing that is three months overdue?

11. The interest owed on a loan after five months was $292.50. If the simple interest rate charged on the loan was 0.9% per month, what was the amount borrowed?

12. How much must be placed in a five-month term deposit earning 4.3% simple interest in order to earn $500 interest?

13. A five-month term deposit of $10,000 at the Scotiabank earned $175 in interest. What annual rate of simple interest did the deposit earn?

14. Indira paid interest charges of $169.05 on a $4830 invoice that was two months overdue. What monthly rate of simple interest was she charged?

15. Morgan loaned $3100 to Rolf at a simple interest rate of 0.65% per month. What was the term of the loan if the total interest came to $221.65?

16. Asher cashed in a one-year term deposit after only five months had elapsed. In order to do so, he accepted an interest rate penalty—a reduction from the scheduled 5.5% rate of simple interest. If he was paid $145.83 interest on the $10,000 term deposit, what reduction was made in the per annum rate of simple interest?

∘17. Sumer put $10,000 in a three-month term deposit at TD Canada Trust, earning a simple interest rate of 3.9%. After the three months, she invested the entire amount of the principal and interest from the first term deposit in a new three-month term deposit earning the same rate of interest. How much interest did she earn on each term deposit? Why are the two interest amounts not equal?

•18. Sergon has $5000 to invest for six months. The rates offered on three-month and six-month term deposits at his bank are 5.5% and 5.8%, respectively. He is trying to choose between the six-month term deposit and two consecutive three-month term deposits. What would the simple interest rate on three-month term deposits have to be, three months from now, for Sergon to end up in the same financial position with either alternative? Assume that he would place both the principal and the interest from the first three-month term deposit in the second three-month term deposit.

6.2 DETERMINING THE TIME PERIOD (TERM)

Whenever possible, the time period t should be determined using the *exact* number of days in the term. If the only information you are given is that a loan was for a three-month term, the best that you can do is to use $t = \frac{3}{12} = 0.25$ year. But if you know that the three-month loan was advanced on September 21, you should determine the exact number of days to the December 21 repayment date.

The most common practice among Canadian financial institutions is to count the starting date (September 21 in this case) *but not the ending date* (December 21). The reason for doing this is that they base their interest calculations on each day's *closing* balance on a loan or savings account. There is a non-zero balance on the day you receive a loan or make a deposit, but zero balance on the day you repay the loan in full or withdraw the deposit.

The numbers of days in each month are listed in Table 6.1. The three-month loan period from September 21 to December 21 includes 10 days in September (September 21 to 30 inclusive), 31 days in October, 30 days in November, and 20 days in December (December 1 to 20 inclusive), giving a total of 91 days. The value that should be used for t is $\frac{91}{365} = 0.24932$ year.

TABLE 6.1   The Number of Days in Each Month

Month	Days	Month	Days	Month	Days
January	31	May	31	September	30
February	28 or 29	June	30	October	31
March	31	July	31	November	30
April	30	August	31	December	31

NET @ssets

There are hundreds of financial calculators available on the Internet. However, it is rare to find one that will handle simple interest calculations. Pine Grove Software has a versatile calculator program (Loan*Calculator! Plus) that you can download free.

Run the program. In the "Calculators" menu, select "Comp/Simple Int". Click on the drop-down list next to "Compounding Period?" and select "Simple." In the drop-down list for the "Rate Basis?" select "Actual/365."

The cells for entering the start and end dates, the annual interest rate, and the principal (referred to as the "Amount") are in the upper half of the calculator window. The calculator will compute both the number of days in the interval and the simple interest earned (called "Interest For Term"). If you already know the number of days in the term, just enter that value in the "Number of Days" cell.

Figure 6.4 in Appendix 6A presents a technique for determining which months have 31 days.

Most years that are divisible by four are leap years. The exceptions are century years (those divisible by 100), which are leap years only if they are divisible by 400. Therefore, 2000, 2004, and 2008 are leap years, with February having 29 days, but 1900 and 2100 are not leap years. When the term of a short-term loan or investment includes part of a leap year, there is no uniform practice across financial institutions for adjusting the length of the year in the denominator of t. The majority of them continue to use 365 days as the length of the year. In this text we will follow the majority and always use 365 days in the denominator.[2] If a loan period includes February 29, that day should be counted in the numerator of t.

Instead of using Table 6.1, another method for calculating the number of days in a loan period employs Table 6.2. In Table 6.2, the days of the year are numbered serially. The number of days in the interval between any two dates in the same calendar year is simply the difference between the serial numbers for the dates. When the term of a loan or investment includes a year-end, the use of Table 6.2 is somewhat tricky. Example 6.2A includes two such cases.

Some financial calculator models have a "Days" or "Date" function that provides a third approach for determining the number of days between two dates. Instructions for using the "DATE" worksheet of the Texas Instruments BA II PLUS are presented in Appendix 6B. This worksheet will be employed as Method 3 in Example 6.2A.

---

[2] The "ordinary interest method" sometimes used in the United States is based on 30-day months and a 360-day year.

TABLE 6.2   The Serial Numbers for Each Day of the Year

Day of Month	Jan	Feb	Mar	Apr	May	Jun	Jul	Aug	Sep	Oct	Nov	Dec	Day of Month
1	1	32	60	91	121	152	182	213	244	274	305	335	1
2	2	33	61	92	122	153	183	214	245	275	306	336	2
3	3	34	62	93	123	154	184	215	246	276	307	337	3
4	4	35	63	94	124	155	185	216	247	277	308	338	4
5	5	36	64	95	125	156	186	217	248	278	309	339	5
6	6	37	65	96	126	157	187	218	249	279	310	340	6
7	7	38	66	97	127	158	188	219	250	280	311	341	7
8	8	39	67	98	128	159	189	220	251	281	312	342	8
9	9	40	68	99	129	160	190	221	252	282	313	343	9
10	10	41	69	100	130	161	191	222	253	283	314	344	10
11	11	42	70	101	131	162	192	223	254	284	315	345	11
12	12	43	71	102	132	163	193	224	255	285	316	346	12
13	13	44	72	103	133	164	194	225	256	286	317	347	13
14	14	45	73	104	134	165	195	226	257	287	318	348	14
15	15	46	74	105	135	166	196	227	258	288	319	349	15
16	16	47	75	106	136	167	197	228	259	289	320	350	16
17	17	48	76	107	137	168	198	229	260	290	321	351	17
18	18	49	77	108	138	169	199	230	261	291	322	352	18
19	19	50	78	109	139	170	200	231	262	292	323	353	19
20	20	51	79	110	140	171	201	232	263	293	324	354	20
21	21	52	80	111	141	172	202	233	264	294	325	355	21
22	22	53	81	112	142	173	203	234	265	295	326	356	22
23	23	54	82	113	143	174	204	235	266	296	327	357	23
24	24	55	83	114	144	175	205	236	267	297	328	358	24
25	25	56	84	115	145	176	206	237	268	298	329	359	25
26	26	57	85	116	146	177	207	238	269	299	330	360	26
27	27	58	86	117	147	178	208	239	270	300	331	361	27
28	28	59	87	118	148	179	209	240	271	301	332	362	28
29	29	*	88	119	149	180	210	241	272	302	333	363	29
30	30		89	120	150	181	211	242	273	303	334	364	30
31	31		90		151		212	243		304		365	31

*__Note:__ For leap years, February 29 becomes day number 60 and the serial number for each subsequent day in the table must be increased by 1.

EXAMPLE 6.2A   **CALCULATING AND USING THE EXACT NUMBER OF DAYS**

a. Calculate the term for each of the following loans.

b. Calculate the interest due on the repayment date for each loan.

	Loan principal ($)	Date advanced	Date repaid	Interest rate
(i)	3000	March 31, 2011	September 4, 2011	$7\frac{3}{4}\%$
(ii)	14,600	January 11, 2012	June 4, 2012	$9\frac{1}{4}\%$
(iii)	23,000	November 29, 2008	April 1, 2009	6.9%

SOLUTION

a. The term will be calculated by three methods:

Method 1: Counting the number of days of each partial and full month within the interval (using Table 6.1).

Method 2: Using the serial numbers of the beginning date and the ending date (from Table 6.2).

Method 3: Using the "DATE" worksheet of the Texas Instruments BA II PLUS calculator.

Method 1: (using Table 6.1)

	(i)		(ii)		(iii)
Month	**Days**	**Month**	**Days**	**Month**	**Days**
March	1	January	21	November	2
April	30	February	29	December	31
May	31	March	31	January	31
June	30	April	30	February	28
July	31	May	31	March	31
August	31	June	3	April	0
September	3				
Total	157	Total	145	Total	123

Method 2: (using Table 6.2) Particularly when the term of the loan includes a year-end, it is helpful to draw a time line showing the dates on which the loan was advanced and repaid. Look up the serial numbers for these dates in Table 6.2, and write them on the time line.

(i)

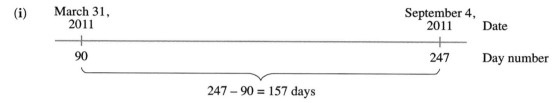

March 31, 2011   September 4, 2011   Date

90   247   Day number

247 − 90 = 157 days

The term of the loan is 157 days.

(ii) When a date falls after February 29 of a leap year, you must add one day to the serial number obtained from Table 6.2.

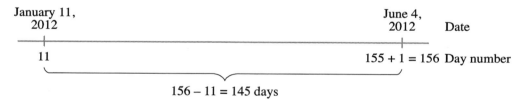

January 11, 2012   June 4, 2012   Date

11   155 + 1 = 156   Day number

156 − 11 = 145 days

The term of the loan is 145 days.

(iii)

Nov. 29, 2008   Dec. 31, 2008   April 1, 2009   Date

333 + 1 = 334   365 + 1 = 366   91   Day number

366 − 334 = 32 days   91 days

The term of the loan is 32 + 91 = 123 days.

Method 3:   Using the "DATE" worksheet of the Texas Instruments BA II PLUS calculator as described in Appendix 6B.

(i) `2nd` `DATE`

3.3111 `ENTER` ①

`↓` 9.0411 `ENTER` ②

`↓` `CPT`

Answer: DBD =   157

(ii) `↑` `↑`

1.1112 `ENTER`

`↓` 6.0412 `ENTER`

`↓` `CPT`

Answer: DBD =   145

(iii) `↑` `↑`

11.2908 `ENTER`

`↓` 4.0109 `ENTER`

`↓` `CPT`

Answer: DBD =   123

`2nd` `QUIT`

① This enters March 31, 2011 as the beginning of the interval.

② This enters September 4, 2011 as the end of the interval.

b. Each loan's term should be expressed as a fraction of a year when substituted in formula (6-1).

(i) $I = Prt = \$3000(0.0775)\left(\dfrac{157}{365}\right) = \$100.01$

(ii) $I = Prt = \$14,600(0.0925)\left(\dfrac{145}{365}\right) = \$536.50$

(iii) $I = Prt = \$23,000(0.069)\left(\dfrac{123}{365}\right) = \$534.80$

Variable or Floating Interest Rates The interest rate on short-term loans is often linked to the "prime rate" charged by the chartered banks. The **prime rate of interest** is the banks' lowest lending rate—it is available only on the most secure loans. Less secure loans are charged anywhere from $\frac{1}{2}$% to 5% more than the prime rate. The chartered banks change the prime rate from time to time in response to interest rate movements in the financial markets. When a loan's interest rate is linked to the prime rate (for example, prime + 2%), it is described as a *variable* interest rate or a *floating* interest rate.

EXAMPLE 6.2B   **FLOATING INTEREST RATES**

Lajos borrowed $5000 on April 7 at prime + 1%. The prime rate was initially $5\frac{1}{2}$%. It increased to 6% effective May 23, and $6\frac{1}{4}$% effective July 13. What amount was required to repay the loan on August 2?

SOLUTION

The statement that the interest rate "increased to 6% effective May 23" means that interest was charged for May 23 (and subsequent days) at the new 6% rate. We need to break the overall loan period into intervals within which the interest rate is constant.

In the following table, the beginning and ending dates have been given for each interval. Since we count the first day but not the last day in an interval, May 23 is counted only in the second interval and July 13 is counted only in the third interval. This is consistent with the new interest rates taking effect on May 23 and July 13.

Interval	Number of days	Interest rate	Interest ($)
April 7 to May 23	24 + 22 = 46	5.5 + 1 = 6.5%	40.96 ①
May 23 to July 13	9 + 30 + 12 = 51	6.0 + 1 = 7.0%	48.90 ②
July 13 to August 2	19 + 1 = 20	6.25 + 1 = 7.25%	19.86
		Total:	109.72

① Interest $= Prt = \$5000(0.065)\dfrac{46}{365} = \$40.96$

② Interest $= Prt = \$5000(0.07)\dfrac{51}{365} = \$48.90$

The amount required to repay the loan on August 7 was $5000 + $109.72 = $5109.72.

SPREADSHEET STRATEGIES   A Days-Between-Dates Calculator

Connect provides a template for calculating the number of days between two dates. Go to the Student Edition of Connect and find "Days-Between-Dates Calculator."

The main features of the Days-Between-Dates Calculator are presented below. Cell C8 must be programmed to make the template operational.

We use the template here to determine the term of the loan in Part (a.iii) of Example 6.2A. In this part, a loan was advanced on November 29, 2008 and repaid on April 1, 2009. After we enter the given dates in the yellow input cells, the answer appears in cell C8.

	A	B	C	D	E
1					
2	Using a spreadsheet to create a Days-Between-Dates Calculator.				
3	Example 6.2A, Part a(iii)				
4				Contents of column C:	
5		Earlier date:	29-Nov-08	November 29, 2008	
6		Later date:	1-Apr-09	April 1, 2009	
7					
8		Number of days in the interval:	123	=C6-C5	
9					

The term of the loan is 123 days.

POINT OF INTEREST

Card Tricks, Part 2—Taking More Interest

If you always pay your credit-card balance in full during the *grace period* (the time between the statement date and the payment due date), you pay no interest on retail purchases made on your credit card. The minimum grace period (set by government regulations) is 21 days. Approximately two-thirds of Canadians pay in full during the grace period. In effect, they receive an interest-free loan on each retail purchase from the date of purchase to the date on which the credit card's balance is paid.

The other third of Canadians who make only partial payments each month are usually aware of the interest rates charged by credit cards—9.4% to 14% on "low-rate" cards, 18% to 20% on "regular" cards. (Aren't we fortunate there are no "high-rate" cards?) But most people are unaware of the details of how these rates are applied—details that make credit-card debt more costly than consumers think.

Trick #1: *The Vanishing Interest-Free Period* There are a couple scenarios under which the interest-free period will vanish. Scenario A: After many months of paying your full balance before the due date, you pay only half the balance in a particular month. You might reasonably assume that no interest will

be charged for the portion of your retail purchases covered by the partial payment. Wrong! In the following month's statement, you will be charged interest on all of the previous statement's purchases right from their purchase dates. Partial payments are not entitled to any interest-free period.

Scenario B: You have been making only partial payments for several months. You now have your financial act together and pay off the entire balance on the current October statement. You might reasonably expect that no interest charges will appear on your November statement for the purchases listed in the preceding October statement. Not necessarily so! Some credit card issuers require that the September statement *also* had to be paid in full for you not to be charged interest in the November statement for purchases appearing on the October statement. (You can obtain a vast amount of information about credit cards from the Web site of the Financial Consumer Agency of Canada (www.fcac-acfc.gc.ca). It describes two methods employed for determining interest-free status, and indicates the method used by each credit card.)

Trick #2: *The Disappearing Grace Period* If you withdraw cash from your credit card account, you will be charged interest (at your credit card's high rate) for *every* day from the date of withdrawal to the date of repayment. In addition, you may be charged a service fee and an ABM fee. The grace period does not apply to a cash advance even if you pay your balance in full.

Trick #3: *The Illusion of Convenience Cheques* The credit-card issuer will sometimes mail "convenience cheques" to you. If you use one to make a payment, the transaction is treated as a cash advance—no interest-free period, no grace period (and really no convenience!)

Trick #4: *The Interest-Rate Switch* Many credit-card issuers offer a six-month low-interest-rate inducement for you to transfer your balance from another credit card. But if you are late on a single payment, the low rate is replaced by a much higher one.

Trick #5: *Psychic Powers* Electronic messaging occurs at millisecond speed in cyberspace. You might reasonably expect that the processing of electronic payments is virtually instantaneous. This would allow you to make your online credit card payment on the due date or, just to be safe, on the preceding day. Some people who have done this later discovered late-payment finance charges on their subsequent statement. It turns out that the processing of online payments can be surprisingly slow. But that's the card issuer's problem, not yours—right? Wrong! The fine print of the typical Cardholder Agreement points out that "it is *your* responsibility to ensure that payments are received by us by each Payment Due Date." How are you supposed to know how long it will take—some sort of psychic power? One credit card issuer cautions that it can take three to five days.

EXERCISE 6.2

connect

Spreadsheet template: *Connect presents a partially completed Excel template for a Days-Between-Dates Calculator. Go to the Student Edition of Connect and find "Days-Between-Dates Calculator." After you program the output cell in the template, you can use it in the solutions for Problems 1–10, and 19–24.*

Answers to the odd-numbered problems are at the end of the book.

1. A \$3800 loan at $10\frac{3}{4}$% was advanced on June 17, 2011. How much interest was due when the loan was repaid on October 1, 2011?

2. How much interest accrued from November 30, 2010, to March 4, 2011, on a \$7350 loan at 7.5%?

3. An \$85,000 investment earned a 6.9% rate of simple interest from December 1, 2010, to May 30, 2011. How much interest was earned?

4. \$850 borrowed on January 7, 2008, was repaid with interest at an annual rate of 7% on July 1, 2008. What was the amount of interest?

5. The interest rate on \$27,000 borrowed on October 16, 2011, was 8.7%. How much interest was owed on the April 15, 2012, repayment date?

6. A \$14,400 loan taken out on May 21, 2010, was repaid with interest at $11\frac{1}{4}$% per annum on July 19, 2011. How much interest was paid?

7. If \$40.52 interest accrued on a \$1000 certificate of deposit from January 15, 2008, to July 7, 2008, what rate of simple interest did the certificate of deposit earn?

8. What was the principal amount of a loan at $9\frac{1}{2}$% if \$67.78 of interest accrued from October 28, 2010, to April 14, 2011?

9. On June 26 Laura put \$2750 into a term deposit until September 3, when she needs the money for tuition, books, and other expenses to return to college. For term deposits in the 60 to 89-day range, her credit union pays an interest rate of $4\frac{1}{4}$%. How much interest will she earn on the term deposit?

10. Raimo borrowed $750 from Chris on October 30 and agreed to repay the debt with simple interest at the rate of 12.3% on May 10. How much interest was owed on May 10? Assume that February has 28 days.

11. Joyce had $2149 in her daily interest savings account for the entire month of June. Her account was credited with interest of $2.65 on June 30 (for the exact number of days in June). What annual rate of simple interest did her balance earn?

12. Maia's chequing account was $329 overdrawn beginning on September 24. On October 9 she made a deposit that restored a credit balance. If she was charged overdraft interest of $2.50, what annual rate of simple interest was charged?

13. In addition to a $2163 refund of her income tax overpayment, the Canada Revenue Agency (CRA) paid Raisa $13.36 of interest on the overpayment. If the simple interest rate paid by the CRA was 5.5%, how many days' interest was paid?

14. Megan was charged $124.83 interest on her bank loan for the period September 18 to October 18. If the rate of interest on her loan was 8.25%, what was the outstanding principal balance on the loan during the period?

∘15. On June 26, 2011, $1000 was borrowed at an interest rate of $10\frac{3}{4}$%. On what date was the loan repaid if the amount of accrued interest was $63.91?

∘16. $1000 was invested on April 18, 2011, in a certificate of deposit earning 7.7% per annum. On its maturity date, the certificate paid $32.28 interest. On what date did it mature?

∘17. On what date was a $1000 loan granted if the interest accrued as at November 16, 2011, was $50.05? The interest rate on the loan was $7\frac{1}{4}$%.

∘18. The $1000 principal amount of a loan was repaid on March 13, 2011, along with accrued interest in the amount of $49.42. If the interest rate on the loan was 11%, on what date was the loan advanced?"

∘19. Bruce borrowed $6000 from Darryl on November 23. When Bruce repaid the loan, Darryl charged $203.22 interest. If the rate of simple interest on the loan was $10\frac{3}{4}$%, on what date did Bruce repay the loan? Assume that February has 28 days.

∘20. Sharon's $9000 term deposit matured on March 16, 2008. Based on a simple interest rate of 3.75%, she received $110.96 in interest. On what date did she originally make the term deposit?

∘21. Mario borrowed $6000 on March 1 at a variable rate of interest. The interest rate began at 7.5%, increased to 8% effective April 17, and then fell by 0.25% effective June 30. How much interest will be owed on the August 1 repayment date?

∘22. Penny invested $4500 on October 28 at a floating rate of interest that initially stood at 6.3%. Effective December 2, the rate dropped by $\frac{1}{2}$%, and then it declined another $\frac{1}{4}$% effective February 27. What total amount of principal plus interest will Penny receive when the investment matures on March 15? Assume that the new year is a leap year.

∘23. How much will be required on February 1 to pay off a $3000 loan advanced on the previous September 30 if the variable interest rate began the interval at 10.7%, rose to 11.2% effective November 2, and then dropped back to 11% effective January 1?

∘24. The total accrued interest owed as of August 31 on a loan advanced the preceding June 3 was $169.66. If the variable interest rate started at $8\frac{3}{4}$%, rose to 9% effective July 1, and increased another $\frac{1}{2}$% effective July 31, what was the principal amount of the loan?

6.3 MATURITY VALUE (FUTURE VALUE) OF A LOAN OR INVESTMENT

LO1 When a loan or investment reaches the end of its term, we say it "matures." The last day of the term is called the **maturity date**. The **maturity value** (or **future value**) is the total of the original principal plus interest due on the maturity date. Using the symbol S to represent the maturity value (or future value), we have

$$S = P + I$$

Substituting $I = Prt$, we obtain

$$S = P + Prt$$

Extracting the common factor P yields:

MATURITY VALUE (FUTURE VALUE)

$$S = P(1 + rt) \qquad (6\text{-}2)$$

EXAMPLE 6.3A CALCULATING THE MATURITY VALUE

Celia invests \$1500 by lending it to Adnan for eight months at an interest rate of $9\frac{1}{4}\%$. What is the maturity value of the loan?

SOLUTION

This problem reminds us that the borrower's debt is the lender's investment.

Given: $P = \$1500$, $t = \frac{8}{12}$ year, $r = 9.25\%$

The maturity value of the loan is:

$$\begin{aligned} S &= P(1 + rt) \\ &= \$1500\left[1 + 0.0925\left(\tfrac{8}{12}\right)\right] \\ &= \$1500(1.061667) \\ &= \$1592.50 \end{aligned}$$

Note that this answer can be obtained just as easily by first calculating the interest due at maturity using $I = Prt$. Then simply add the principal to obtain the maturity value ($S = P + I$). The choice of method is a matter of personal preference.

The maturity value that Adnan must pay to Celia at the end of the eight months is \$1592.50.

EXAMPLE 6.3B CALCULATING THE PRINCIPAL

What amount of money would have to be invested at $10\frac{3}{4}\%$ to grow to \$10,000 after 91 days?

SOLUTION

Given: $r = 10.75\%$, $S = \$10,000$, $t = \frac{91}{365}$ year

Substitute the known values into formula (6-2) and then solve for P.

$$\begin{aligned} S &= P(1 + rt) \\ \$10,000 &= P\left[1 + 0.1075\left(\tfrac{91}{365}\right)\right] \\ &= P(1.026801) \end{aligned}$$

The reasoning for showing seven figures in the value for $(1 + rt)$ is as follows. Common sense tells us that P will be less than \$10,000 (the maturity value of the deposit.) To obtain P accurate to the cent, we require six-figure accuracy in the final result. Therefore, we must maintain at least one more figure (for a total of seven figures) in intermediate results.

Solving for P,

$$P = \frac{\$10,000}{1.026801} = \$9738.99$$

The required investment is \$9738.99.

> **TIP**   Solving for "r" or "t"
>
> If any three of the four variables S, P, r, and t are known, formula (6-2) can be used to solve for the remaining variable. However, the manipulations required to solve for r or t are not trivial. In these cases it is usually simpler to first calculate $I = S - P$ and then solve $I = Prt$ for r or t. The following example illustrates the latter approach.

EXAMPLE 6.3C   **CALCULATING THE INTEREST RATE**

Liam put \$9500 in a term deposit on May 22. It matured on September 4 at \$9588.82. What interest rate did he earn on his term deposit?

SOLUTION

Given: $P = \$9500$; $S = \$9588.82$; the term runs from May 22 to September 4

Hence,

$$I = S - P = \$9588.82 - \$9500 = \$88.82$$

and, using Table 6.2,

$$t = 247 \text{ (September 4)} - 142 \text{ (May 22)} = 105 \text{ days}$$

The annual rate of simple interest is

$$r = \frac{I}{Pt} = \frac{\$88.82}{\$9500 \times \frac{105}{365}} = 0.03250 = 3.25\%$$

Liam earned an interest rate of 3.25% on his term deposit.

EXAMPLE 6.3D   **REINVESTING SIMPLE INTEREST PROCEEDS**

Kyle has a 90-day \$5000 term deposit about to mature at the Bank of Nova Scotia. The interest rate on the term deposit is 3%. Since he does not need the money for at least another 90 days, Kyle instructs the bank to "roll over" the proceeds of the maturing term deposit into a new 90-day term deposit. The prevailing rate for 90-day deposits is now 2.75%. What will be the maturity value of the second term deposit?

SOLUTION

The maturity value of the first term deposit is

$$S = P(1 + rt) = \$5000(1 + 0.03 \times \tfrac{90}{365}) = \$5036.99$$

The entire maturity value of the maturing deposit becomes the beginning principal for the second term deposit. The maturity value of Kyle's second term deposit will be

$$S = P(1 + rt) = \$5036.99(1 + 0.0275 \times \tfrac{90}{365}) = \$5071.14$$

SPREADSHEET STRATEGIES Solving $S = P(1 + rt)$

Connect presents four partially completed templates for this section. Go to the Student Edition of Connect and find "Calculator for $S = P(1 + rt)$." Each template is intended to solve for one of the four variables in the future value formula, $S = P(1 + rt)$.

The main features of the particular template designed to solve for r are presented below. To complete the template, the output cell C9 must be programmed with a version of the future value formula rearranged to isolate r. After some algebraic manipulation, we obtain $r = \dfrac{S - P}{Pt}$. The Excel "translation" of the right-hand side of this derived formula is shown in cell C10.

Let us use the template to solve Example 6.3C. In this example, we are given: $P = \$9500$, $S = \$9588.82$, and the dates on which the $9500 was deposited (May 22) and matured (September 4). The question asks us to calculate the interest rate earned. From the given end-dates, we determine that $t = 105$ days. Enter the values for S, P, and t in the input cells C5, C6, and C7. The value for t must be in years—you have a choice on how to enter it. Either do the division "on the side" and then enter the quotient, or just enter "=105/365" (without the quotes) in C7 and let the spreadsheet perform the division. The answer appears in cell C9.

	A	B	C	D	E
1					
2	Using a spreadsheet to calculate a variable in the future value formula.				
3	Example 6.3C:				
4					
5		Future value, S	$9,588.82		
6		Principal, P	9,500.00		
7		Time period [or term] (yr), t	0.2876712		
8					
9		Annual interest rate (%), r	3.25006%		
10		Formula in cell C9:	=(C5-C6)/(C6*C7)		
11					

The interest rate earned on the term deposit was 3.25%.

EXERCISE 6.3

Spreadsheet templates: *The solutions for all of the following problems can employ one or another of the four partially completed Excel templates available in Connect. Go to the Student Edition of Connect and find "Calculator for $S = P(1+rt)$." The templates come with instructions for completing them.*

Answers to the odd-numbered problems are at the end of the book.

1. What will be the maturity value after seven months of $2950 earning interest at the rate of $4\frac{1}{2}\%$?

2. $12,800 was invested in a 237-day term deposit earning $3\frac{3}{4}\%$. What was its maturity value?

3. What will be the maturity value in 15 months of a $4500 loan at a simple interest rate of 11.9%?

4. Cecille placed $17,000 in a 270-day term deposit earning 4.25%. How much will the bank pay Cecille on the maturity date?

5. What was the principal amount of a loan at $10\frac{1}{2}\%$, if total amount owed after 23 days was $785.16?

6. The maturity value of an investment earning 7.7% per annum for a 360-day term was $2291.01. What amount was originally invested?

7. The balance after 11 months, including interest, on a loan at 9.9% is $15,379.58. What are the principal and interest components of the balance?

8. $7348.25 was the amount required to pay off a loan after 14 months. If the loan was at $8\frac{1}{4}\%$ per annum simple interest, how much of the total was interest?

9. What was the interest rate on a $1750 loan, if the amount required to pay off the loan after five months was $1828.02?

10. A $2875.40 investment grew to $3000 after eight months. What annual rate of simple interest did it earn?

11. Marliss made a $780.82 purchase on her Visa card. Including 45 days' interest, the amount billed on her credit card was $798.63. What annual interest rate does her card charge?

12. The amount required to settle a $680 debt after 300 days was $730.30. What rate of interest was charged on the debt?

13. Janesh has savings of $9625.63. If he can invest this amount to earn 7.8%, how many days will it take for the investment to grow to $10,000?

14. The amount required to pay off a $3500 loan at 8.4% was $3646.60. What was the term (in days) of the loan?

15. A $7760 investment earning $6\frac{1}{4}\%$ matured at $8083.33. What was the term (in months) of the investment?

16. The interest rate on an $859.50 debt was $10\frac{1}{4}\%$. For how many months was the loan outstanding if it was settled with a payment of $907.22?

17. Judit received the proceeds from an inheritance on March 25. She wants to set aside enough on March 26 so that she will have $20,000 available on October 1 to purchase a car when the new models are introduced. If the current interest rate on 181- to 270-day term deposits is 3.75%, what amount should she place in the term deposit?

18. The bookkeeper for Durham's Garage is trying to allocate to principal and interest a payment that was made to settle a loan. The cheque stub has the note "$3701.56 for principal and 7 months' interest at 12.5%." What are the principal and interest components of the payment?

19. The annual $3600 membership fee at the Oak Meadows Golf Club is due at the beginning of the year. Instead of a single "lump" payment, a member can pay $1600 at the start of the year and defer the $2000 balance for five months by paying a $75 surcharge at the time of the second payment. Effectively, what annual rate of simple interest is Oak Meadows charging on the $2000 deferred payment?

20. The snow tires that you are planning to buy next October 1 at the regular price of $107.50 each are advertised at $89.95 in a spring clearance special that will end on the preceding March 25. What annual rate of simple interest will you earn if you "invest" in the new snow tires at the sale price on March 25 instead of waiting until October 1 to buy them at the regular price?

21. A&B Appliances sells a washer-dryer combination for $1535 cash. C&D Appliances offers the same combination for $1595 with no payments and no interest for six months. Therefore, you can pay $1535 now or invest the $1535 for six months and then pay $1595. What value would the annual rate of return have to exceed for the second alternative to be to your advantage?

22. How many days will it take $2500 to grow to $2614.47 at an annual rate of 8.75%?

○23. Karin borrowed $2000 at $10\frac{1}{4}\%$ on July 13. On what date would the amount owed first exceed $2100?

○24. On what date did a corporation borrow $350,000 at 7.5% from its bank if the debt was settled by a payment of $356,041 on February 28?

○**25.** Village Finance Co. advanced three loans to Kamiko—$2200 on June 23, $1800 on August 5, and $1300 on October 31. Simple interest at 7.25% was charged on all three loans, and all were repaid on December 31 when some bonds that she owned matured. What total amount was required to pay off the loans?

○**26.** The cash balance in Amalia's account with her stockbroker earns interest on the daily balance at an annual rate of 4%. Accrued interest is credited to her account every six months—on June 30 and December 31. As a result of the purchase and sale of securities from time to time, the account's balance changed as follows:

Period	Balance
January 1 to March 3	$3347
March 4 to May 23	$8687
May 24 to June 16	$2568
June 17 to June 30	$5923

What interest was credited to Amalia's account on June 30? The brokerage firm includes interest for both January 1 and June 30 in the June 30 payment. Assume that February had 28 days.

○**27.** Dominion Contracting invested surplus funds in term deposits. All were chosen to mature on April 1 when the firm intends to purchase a new grader.

Investment date	Amount invested	Interest rate	Maturity date
November 16	$74,000	6.3%	April 1
December 30	$66,000	5.9%	April 1
February 8	$92,000	5.1%	April 1

What total amount will be available from the maturing term deposits on April 1 (of a leap year)?

TIP   **Now Hear This …**

The concepts that will be developed in Sections 6.4 and 6.5 are fundamental to many other topics and applications in later chapters. If you invest extra effort at this stage to gain a thorough understanding of these concepts, it will pay substantial dividends later.

6.4 EQUIVALENT PAYMENTS

Suppose you can choose to receive either $100 today or $105 one year from now. Suppose further that you can invest money at 5%. From a strict economic point of view, the alternatives are equivalent. If you choose $100 today, you can invest it at 5% and receive $105 after one year. With either alternative, you *can* end up with $105 one year from now.

LO3   This simple example illustrates the concept of *economically equivalent* payments (which we usually shorten to "equivalent payments"). Alternative payments that enable you to end up with the same dollar amount at a later date are called **equivalent payments**. Note the key role played by the interest rate at which money may be invested. If the interest rate had been 6% instead of 5% in our example, you would require $106 one year from now as the amount equivalent to $100 today.

In the terminology of Section 6.3, the later equivalent payment ($105) is just the future value of the alternative payment ($100) after one year. That is,

$$S = P(1 + rt) = \$100(1 + 0.05 \times 1) = \$100(1.05) = \$105$$

In Section 6.3, formula (6-2) described the mathematical relationship between the principal (P) and the maturity value (S). We now see that it *also* represents the relationship between a **P**rior equivalent payment (P) and a **S**ubsequent equivalent payment (S). In this context, r represents the interest rate that invested funds can earn during the time interval, t, between the alternative payments. In our word problems, we use expressions such as "Money can earn $x\%$" or "Money is worth $x\%$" or "Money can be invested at $x\%$" to specify this interest rate.[3]

LO1   The term **present value** is commonly used to refer to an economically equivalent amount at a *prior* date; **future value** is used for an equivalent amount at a *later* date.

EXAMPLE 6.4A   **CALCULATING THE EQUIVALENT PAYMENT AT A LATER DATE**

Herb is supposed to pay $1500 to Ranjit on September 20. Herb wishes to delay payment until December 1.

a. What amount should Herb expect to pay on December 1 if Ranjit can earn 8.25% on a low-risk investment?

b. Show why Ranjit should not care whether he receives the scheduled payment or the delayed payment.

SOLUTION

a. Herb is seeking a postponement of

$$11 + 31 + 30 = 72 \text{ days}$$

He should expect to pay an amount that is equivalent to $1500, 72 days later, allowing for an 8.25% rate of return. That is, he should expect to pay the future value of $1500, 72 days later.

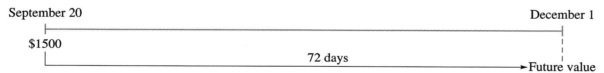

September 20   December 1

$1500

72 days

Future value

Substituting $P = \$1500$, $t = \frac{72}{365}$, and $r = 8.25\%$ into formula (6-2), the future value is

$$S = P(1 + rt) = \$1500[1 + 0.0825(\tfrac{72}{365})] = \$1524.41$$

Herb should expect to pay $1524.41 on December 1 instead of $1500 on September 20.

b. Suppose that Herb makes the $1500 payment as scheduled on September 20. Since Ranjit can earn an 8.25% rate of return, by December 1 the $1500 will grow to

$$S = P(1 + rt) = \$1500[1 + 0.0825(\tfrac{72}{365})] = \$1524.41$$

Ranjit should, therefore, be indifferent between receiving $1500 on September 20 or $1524.41 on December 1 because he can end up with $1524.41 on December 1 with either alternative.

---

[3] You may be thinking: "There are many different interest rates depending on the investment I choose. A savings account earns a very low interest rate, a Guaranteed Investment Certificate earns a higher rate, Canada Savings Bonds earn yet another rate, and so on. What interest rate should I pick for equivalent-payment calculations in a 'real-world' situation?" In a real-world scenario, you should choose the interest rate based on the following thinking.

   Normally, equivalent payments are viewed as *riskless* alternatives. In other words, you will definitely receive the later equivalent payment if you do not choose the earlier equivalent payment. Alternatively, if you choose the earlier payment, the outcome from investing it must be known with *certainty*. The investment question becomes: "What is the *best* interest rate I can earn with complete certainty during the time interval?" If you take a finance course, you will learn that this "risk-free rate" is the prevailing rate of return earned by federal government Treasury Bills (Section 7.3) or bonds (Section 15.1). Select Treasury Bills or bonds that have a term equal to the time interval between the equivalent payments.

EXAMPLE 6.4B   **CALCULATING AN EQUIVALENT PAYMENT AT AN EARLIER DATE**

What payment on March 12 is equivalent to a $1000 payment on the subsequent July 6, if money is worth 6.8% per year?

SOLUTION

Since we want an equivalent payment at an earlier date, we should calculate the *present* value of $1000 on March 12.

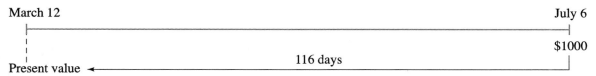

March 12   July 6

$1000

116 days

Present value

The number of days in the interval is

$$20 \text{ (for March)} + 30 + 31 + 30 + 5 \text{ (for July)} = 116$$

Substituting $S = \$1000$, $r = 6.8\%$, and $t = \frac{116}{365}$ into formula (6-2), we obtain

$$P = \frac{S}{1 + rt} = \frac{\$1000}{1 + 0.068\left(\frac{116}{365}\right)} = \$978.85$$

$978.85 on March 12 is equivalent to $1000 on the subsequent July 6.

EXAMPLE 6.4C   **CALCULATING A PRIOR EQUIVALENT PAYMENT**

A furniture store advertises a dining table and chairs for $1495 with nothing down, no payments, and no interest for six months. What cash price should the store be willing to accept if, on a six-month investment, it can earn a rate of return of

a. 4%?   **b.** 9%?

SOLUTION

The store faces the choice between the cash offer and $1495 to be received six months from now (if a customer takes the credit terms). The store should be willing to accept a cash amount that is today's equivalent of $1495. In other words, the store should accept the present value of $1495.

a. If money can earn 4%, $P = \dfrac{S}{1 + rt} = \dfrac{\$1495}{1 + 0.04\left(\frac{6}{12}\right)} = \dfrac{\$1495}{1.02} = \$1465.69$

The store should accept a cash offer of $1465.69.

b. If money can earn 9%, $P = \dfrac{\$1495}{1 + 0.09\left(\frac{6}{12}\right)} = \$1430.62$

The store should accept $1430.62 cash.

Figure 6.1 presents a graph of equivalent values (present value and future value) of $100. Numerical values are indicated at two-month intervals before and after the scheduled payment date (zero on the time axis). We have chosen a simple interest rate of 12% because it is easy to work with 1% per month. The future value increases by $1 every month in a straight-line pattern. The present value decreases for longer time periods in advance of the scheduled payment. However, the rate of decrease is less than linear. This is evident from the widening gap between the present-value curve and the dashed straight line sloping downward to the left (at the rate of $1 per month) in the present value region.

FIGURE 6.1 Graphs of Present Values and Future Values of $100

Equivalent Value of $100 Payment

Present values $115.00   Future values

$110.00

$105.00

$96.15 $100.00 $110.00

$92.59 $106.00

$89.29 $95.00 $102.00

$90.00

$88.00

| 12 | 10 | 8 | 6 | 4 | 2 | 0 | 2 | 4 | 6 | 8 | 10 | 12 |

Months prior to the scheduled payment   Months after the scheduled payment

Comparing Payments If money can earn 5.5%, is $65 today equivalent to $67 eight months from now?

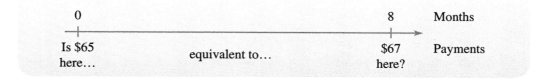

```
0                                          8      Months

Is $65                                    $67    Payments
here...        equivalent to...           here?
```

Trust your instincts. Two methods for answering this question may occur to you. One method is to calculate the future value of $65 after eight months and compare it to $67. The other approach is to calculate the present value of $67 eight months earlier and compare it to $65. If we do the latter, we obtain

$$P = \frac{S}{1 + rt} = \frac{\$67}{1 + 0.055 \times \frac{8}{12}} = \$64.63$$

Since the present value differs from $65, the two payments are not equivalent. Furthermore, $65 paid today is worth

$$\$65.00 - \$64.63 = \$0.37$$

more than $67 paid eight months from now.

Suppose you are asked to compare the economic values of three or four or more alternative payments. What should you do? In general, you can compare the economic values of any number of alternative payments by calculating their equivalent values all at the *same* date. (The date at which the equivalent values are calculated is often referred to as the **focal date**.) The alternative payments can then be ranked on the basis of their equivalent values.

EXAMPLE 6.4D   **COMPARING THE ECONOMIC VALUES OF ALTERNATIVE PAYMENTS**

Marcus can purchase an airplane ticket now on the airline's Early Bird Sale for $459, or he can wait and pay $479 in three months. If he can earn a 9% rate of return on his money, which option should he choose?

SOLUTION

To compare today's economic values of the two alternatives, first calculate the present value of the regular price of $479.

$$P = \frac{S}{1 + rt} = \frac{\$479}{1 + 0.09(\frac{3}{12})} = \$468.46$$

Marcus should choose the alternative having the *lower* economic value. That is, he should buy the ticket at the Early Bird price. However, his true saving is not $479 − $459 = $20, but rather $468.46 − $459.00 = $9.46.

EXAMPLE 6.4E   **FINDING THE RATE OF RETURN THAT MAKES TWO PAYMENTS EQUIVALENT**

Extending the problem in Example 6.4D, what rate of return would Marcus have to earn in order to be indifferent between the two prices?

SOLUTION

He will be indifferent between the two prices if $459 invested for three months will grow to $479. In other words, he will be indifferent if $459 can earn $479 − $459 = $20 in three months. The rate of return that would cause this to occur is

$$r = \frac{I}{Pt} = \frac{\$20}{\$459 \times \frac{3}{12}} = 0.174 = 17.4\%$$

If Marcus could earn a 17.4% rate of return, he could invest the $459 for three months and it would mature at $479, providing exactly the right amount to buy the ticket. (If Marcus could earn more than 17.4%, it would be to his advantage to invest the $459 now and buy the ticket three months later.)

 CONCEPT QUESTIONS

1. What is meant by "equivalent payments"?

2. Under what circumstance is $100 paid today equivalent to $110 paid one year from now?

3. How can you determine whether two payments are equivalent to each other?

4. What is meant by the "present value" of a payment that is scheduled for a future date?

5. How can you determine which of three payments on different dates has the largest economic value?

6. If the interest rate money can earn is revised upward, will a scheduled payment's new present value be higher or lower than before? Explain.

EXERCISE 6.4   *Answers to the odd-numbered problems are at the end of the book.*

1. What amount of money paid today is equivalent to $560 paid five months from now if money can earn $10\frac{3}{4}\%$ per annum?

2. What amount, seven months from now, is equivalent to $1215 today if money can be invested to earn $8\frac{1}{2}\%$?

3. What payment, 174 days from now, is equivalent to $5230 paid today? Assume that money is worth 9.25% per annum.

4. What amount should be accepted as equivalent, 60 days before an obligation of $1480 is due, if money can earn $6\frac{3}{4}\%$?

5. What amount paid on September 24 is equivalent to $1000 paid on the following December 1 if money can earn 5%?

6. What amount received on January 13 is equivalent to $1000 received on the preceding August 12 if money can earn 9.5%?

7. Rasheed wishes to postpone for 90 days the payment of $450 that he owes to Roxanne. If money now earns 6.75%, what amount can he reasonably expect to pay at the later date?

8. Avril owes Value Furniture $1600, which is scheduled to be paid on August 15. Avril has surplus funds on June 15 and will settle the debt early if Value Furniture will make an adjustment reflecting the current short-term interest rate of 7.25%. What amount should be acceptable to both parties?

9. What annual rate of return would money have to earn for $1975.00 to be equivalent to $1936.53 paid 100 days earlier?

10. At what rate can money be invested if $2370.00 is equivalent to $2508.79 paid 190 days later?

11. A late payment of $850.26 was considered equivalent to the originally scheduled payment of $830.00, allowing for interest at 9.9%. How many days late was the payment?

12. What is the time interval (in months) separating equivalent payments of $3500.00 and $3439.80 if money is worth $5\frac{1}{4}\%$ per annum?

13. An early payment of $4574.73 was accepted instead of a scheduled payment of $4850.00, allowing for interest at the rate of $8\frac{3}{4}\%$. How many days early was the payment?

14. How many days separate equivalent payments of $2755.20 and $2740.00 if money can earn $4\frac{1}{2}\%$?

15. If money can be invested at 0.6% per month, which has the greater economic value: $5230 on a specific date or $5500 exactly five months later? At what rate (per month) would the two amounts be economically equivalent?

16. Compare the economic values of $1480 today vs. $1515 in 150 days. Assume money can earn 6.75%. At what rate would the two amounts be equivalent?

17. To settle a $570 invoice, Anna can pay $560 now or the full amount 60 days later. Which alternative should she choose if money can earn $10\frac{3}{4}\%$? What rate would money have to earn for Anna to be indifferent between the alternatives?

18. Jonas recently purchased a one-year membership at Gold's Gym. He can add a second year to the membership now for $1215, or wait 11 months and pay the regular single-year price of $1280. Which is the better economic alternative if money is worth 8.5%? At what discount rate would the alternatives be equivalent?

19. Nicholas can purchase the same furniture from Store A for $2495 cash or from Store B for $2560 with nothing down and no payments or interest for 8 months. Which option should Nicholas choose if he can pay for the furniture by cashing in Canada Savings Bonds currently earning 3.9% per annum?

20. A $5000 payment is scheduled for 120 days from now. If money can earn 7.25%, calculate the payment's equivalent value at each of nine different dates—today and every 30 days for the next 240 days.

21. A $3000 payment is scheduled for six months from now. If money is worth 6.75%, calculate the payment's equivalent values at two-month intervals beginning today and ending one year from now.

22. During its 50-50 Sale, Marpole Furniture will sell its merchandise for 50% down, with the balance payable in six months. No interest is charged for the first six months. What 100% cash price should Marpole accept on a $1845 chesterfield and chair set if Marpole can earn a rate of return of 10.75% on its funds?

23. Mr. and Mrs. Chan have listed for sale a residential building lot they own in a nearby town. They are considering two offers. The offer from the Smiths is for $145,000 consisting of $45,000 down and the balance to be paid in six months. The offer from the Kims is for $149,000 consisting of $29,000 down and $120,000 payable in one year. The Chans can earn an interest rate of 4.5% on low-risk short-term investments.

  a. What is the current economic value to the Chans of each offer?

  b. Other things being equal, which offer should the Chans accept? How much more is the better offer worth (in terms of current economic value)?

○**24.** Westwood Homes is beginning work on its future College Park sub-division. Westwood is now pre-selling homes that will be ready for occupancy in nine months. Westwood is offering $5000 off the $295,000 selling price to anyone making an immediate $130,000 down payment (with the balance due in nine months.) The alternative is a $5000 deposit with the $290,000 balance due in nine months. Mr. and Mrs. Symbaluk are trying to decide which option to choose. They currently earn 4.8% on low-risk short-term investments.

  a. What is the current economic cost of buying on the $130,000-down $5000-off option?

  b. What is the current economic cost of buying on the $5000-deposit full-price option?

  c. Which alternative should the Symbaluks choose? In current dollars, what is the economic advantage of the preferred alternative?

○**25.** What interest rate must money earn for a payment of $1389 on August 20 to be equivalent to a payment of $1348 on the previous March 29?

6.5 THE EQUIVALENT VALUE OF A PAYMENT STREAM

A **payment stream** is a series of two or more payments required by a single transaction or contract. To get their combined value, you might be inclined to add the payments. If you do that, then every dollar, regardless of when it is paid, has an equal influence on the sum. In other words, the simple addition of payments occurring on different dates implies that a dollar on one date has the same economic value as a dollar on any other date. But we have seen that the *economic* value of a dollar depends on when it is paid. This property of money is often referred to as the **time value of money**. The simple addition of the payments ignores the time value of money.

LO3 In Section 6.4, you learned how to calculate the equivalent value, on any date, of a *single* payment. A logical extension of this basic idea allows us to determine the equivalent value of a payment *stream*. We simply add the equivalent values (at the chosen focal date) of the individual payments. The following example illustrates the procedure.

Consider a payment stream consisting of three payments: $1000, $2000, and $3000, scheduled for March 1, May 1, and December 1 of the same year. Let us calculate the single payment on August 1 that is economically equivalent to the three scheduled payments. Suppose money can earn a simple interest rate of 8%.

LO2 For problems involving multiple payments, a **time diagram** is virtually essential. It consists of a time axis or *time line* showing the dollar amounts and the dates of the payments. Figure 6.2 presents a time diagram for the problem at hand. The first benefit of a timeline is that it helps you organize the data. Indicate the payment dates above the time line and the amounts of the corresponding payments below the line. Do not make your diagram too small—use the full width of your page. Attempt to draw reasonably proportionate time intervals between the dates.

FIGURE 6.2 Entering Given Data on a Time Diagram

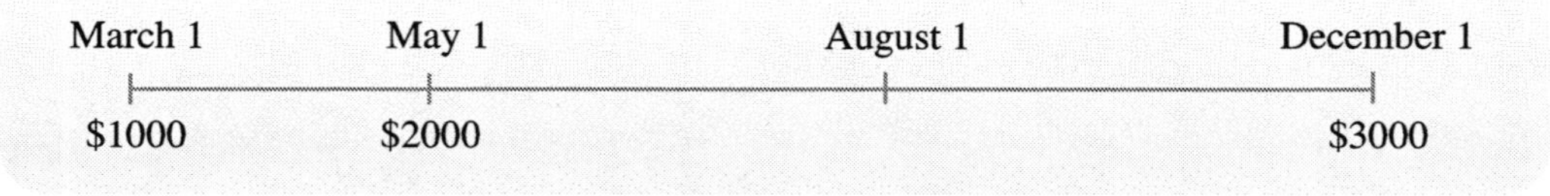
March 1
May 1
August 1
December 1
$1000
$2000
$3000

The solution idea for this problem is:

$$\begin{pmatrix}\text{The equivalent payment}\\ \text{on August 1}\end{pmatrix} = \begin{pmatrix}\text{The sum of the equivalent values on}\\ \text{August 1 of the individual payments}\end{pmatrix}$$

The second benefit of a time diagram is that it allows you to indicate the steps needed to carry out the solution idea. In Figure 6.3, an arrow is drawn from each payment to the August 1 focal date (on which you want the equivalent value). On each arrow you can write the number of days in the time interval. An appropriate symbol (S for future value, P for present value) is entered for each equivalent value. Finally, you can indicate on the diagram that the three equivalent values are to be added. The written solution is now a matter of following the steps outlined in the diagram.

FIGURE 6.3 Showing the Solution Steps on a Time Diagram

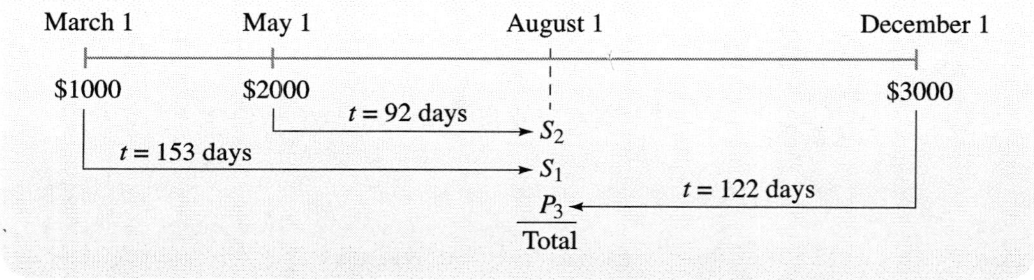
March 1
May 1
August 1
December 1
$1000
$2000
$3000
t = 92 days
S2
t = 153 days
S1
t = 122 days
P3
Total

$$\begin{aligned} S_1 &= \text{Future value on August 1 of the \$1000 payment} \\ &= \$1000(1 + 0.08 \times \tfrac{153}{365}) \\ &= \$1033.53 \end{aligned}$$

$$\begin{aligned} S_2 &= \text{Future value on August 1 of the \$2000 payment} \\ &= \$2000(1 + 0.08 \times \tfrac{92}{365}) \\ &= \$2040.33 \end{aligned}$$

$$\begin{aligned} P_3 &= \text{Present value on August 1 of the \$3000 payment} \\ &= \frac{\$3000}{1 + 0.08 \times \frac{122}{365}} \\ &= \$2921.87 \end{aligned}$$

The equivalent value on August 1 of the payment stream is

$$S_1 + S_2 + P_3 = \$1033.53 + \$2040.33 + \$2921.87 = \$5995.73$$

The significance of this equivalent value is that a payment of \$5995.73 on August 1 is economically equivalent to the three scheduled payments. The recipient will be in the same economic position whether he accepts \$5995.73 on August 1, or he receives the three payments as scheduled.

EXAMPLE 6.5A **COMPARING THE ECONOMIC VALUE OF TWO PAYMENT STREAMS**

Compare the economic values today of the following two payment streams if money can earn 6.5%: \$700 in four months plus \$300 in ten months, vs. \$400 in six months plus \$600 in eights months.

SOLUTION

Construct a time line for each payment stream, indicating the scheduled payments and their equivalent values, P_1 to P_4, today. The stream with the larger total equivalent value today has the greater economic value.

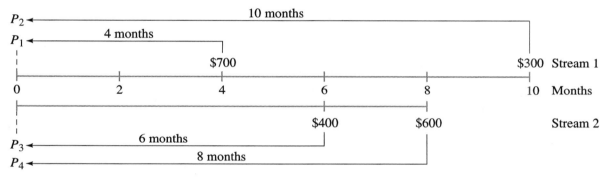

$$\text{Equivalent value of Stream 1} = P_1 + P_2$$
$$= \frac{\$700}{1 + 0.065(\frac{4}{12})} + \frac{\$300}{1 + 0.065(\frac{10}{12})}$$
$$= \$685.155 + \$284.585$$
$$= \$969.74$$

Note that we keep six figures in the second-to-last line in order to obtain five-figure accuracy in the final result.

$$\text{Equivalent value of Stream 2} = P_3 + P_4$$
$$= \frac{\$400}{1 + 0.065(\frac{6}{12})} + \frac{\$600}{1 + 0.065(\frac{8}{12})}$$
$$= \$387.409 + \$575.080$$
$$= \$962.49$$

Even though the sum of the nominal payments in each stream is \$1000, the first stream's economic value today is \$7.25 more than the second stream's value. This happens because, on average, the money in the first stream is received sooner (5.8 months for Stream 1 vs. 7.2 months for Stream 2).

Note: The date on which the economic values of the payment streams are calculated is commonly referred to as the *focal date*. The difference between the economic values of two payment streams depends, weakly, on the choice of the focal date.

EXAMPLE 6.5B   **CALCULATING A PAYMENT EQUIVALENT TO INTEREST-EARNING OBLIGATIONS**

Four months ago Hassan borrowed $1000 from Sean and agreed to repay the loan in two payments to be made five and ten months after the date of the agreement. Each payment is to consist of $500 of principal, and interest at the rate of 9% on that $500 from the date of the agreement. Today Hassan is asking Sean to accept instead a single payment three months from now to settle the debt. What payment should Sean require if money can now earn 7%?

SOLUTION

In this problem we do not initially know the dollar amounts of the scheduled payments because we do not know how much interest must be paid along with each $500 of principal. The first step, then, is to calculate the maturity value of each $500 payment on its scheduled payment date.

The maturity values are represented by S_1 and S_2 in the following time diagram.

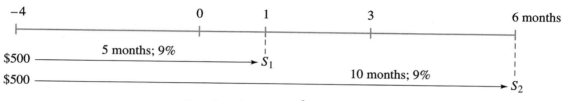

$$S_1 = \$500[1 + 0.09(\tfrac{5}{12})] = \$518.75$$

$$S_2 = \$500[1 + 0.09(\tfrac{10}{12})] = \$537.50$$

Now we can construct a time diagram presenting the scheduled payments and their equivalent values, S and P, on the date of the replacement payment.

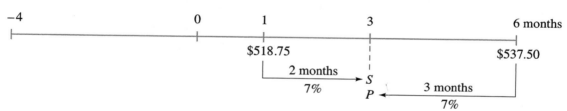

The *current* rate that money can earn, 7%, is used to calculate the equivalent values of the scheduled payments.

$S =$ Future value of $518.75 on a date two months later
$ = \$518.75[1 + 0.07(\tfrac{2}{12})]$
$ = \$524.802$

$P =$ Present value of $537.50 on a date three months earlier
$$ = \frac{\$537.50}{1 + 0.07(\tfrac{3}{12})}$$
$ = \$528.256$

The single equivalent payment is

$$S + P = \$524.802 + \$528.256 = \$1053.06$$

Sean should require a payment of $1053.06 on a date three months from now.

| EXAMPLE 6.5C | CALCULATING AN UNKNOWN PAYMENT IN AN EQUIVALENT PAYMENT STREAM |

Payments of $5000 due four months ago and $3000 due two months from now are to be replaced by a payment of $4000 today and a second payment in six months. What must the second payment be in order to make the replacement payment stream equivalent to the scheduled payment stream? Money in short-term investments can earn 5%. Use six months from now as the focal date.

SOLUTION

Each alternative payment stream is shown below on its own time line. We must determine the size of the payment x so that both payment streams have the same economic value six months from now. The equivalent values, at the focal date of the three known payments, are indicated by S_1, S_2, and S_3. The unknown payment, x, is already at the focal date.

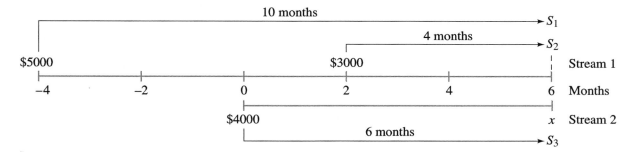

$$\text{Equivalent value of Stream 1} = S_1 + S_2$$
$$= \$5000(1 + 0.05 \times \tfrac{10}{12}) + \$3000(1 + 0.05 \times \tfrac{4}{12})$$
$$= \$5208.333 + \$3050.000$$
$$= \$8258.333$$

$$\text{Equivalent value of Stream 2} = x + S_3$$
$$= x + \$4000(1 + 0.05 \times \tfrac{6}{12})$$
$$= x + \$4100.000$$

For the two streams to be economically equivalent,

$$x + \$4100.000 = \$8258.333$$

Hence, $$x = \$4158.33$$

For the two streams to be equivalent, the second payment must be $4158.33.

POINT OF INTEREST

Consumers Often Defy Common Sense

Imagine two refrigerators in the appliance section of a department store. One sells for $1400 and uses $170 worth of electricity a year. The other is $200 more expensive but costs only $50 a year to run, saving the owner $120 per year. Given that either refrigerator should last at least 10 years without repair, consumers would overwhelmingly buy the second model, right?

Well, not exactly. Many studies by economists have shown that in a wide range of decisions about money—from paying taxes to buying major appliances—consumers consistently make decisions that defy common sense.

In some cases—as in the refrigerator example—this means that people are generally unwilling to pay a little more money up front to save a lot of money in the long run. At times, psychological studies have shown, consumers appear to assign entirely whimsical values to money, values that change depending on time and circumstances.

In recent years, these apparently irrational patterns of human behaviour have become a subject of intense interest among economists and psychologists, both for what they say about the way the human mind works and because of their implications for public policy. How, for example, can we move toward a more efficient use of electricity if so many consumers refuse to buy energy-efficient appliances even when such a move is in their own best interest?

At the heart of research into the economic behaviour of consumers is a concept known as the *discount rate.* It is a measure of how consumers compare the value of a dollar received today with a dollar received a year from now.

Suppose, for example, you win $1000 in a lottery. How much more money would officials have to give you before you would agree to postpone cashing the cheque for a year? Some people might ask for an extra $60, or 6%, since that is roughly how much it would take to make up for the combined effects of a year's worth of inflation and lost interest.

But the studies show that someone who wants immediate gratification might not be willing to postpone receiving the $1000 for 20% or 30% or even 40% more money. In the language of economists, this type of person has a high discount rate: He or she discounts the value of $1000 so much over a year that it would take hundreds of extra dollars to make waiting as attractive as getting the money immediately.

Waiting a year for $1300 is clearly more rational than taking the $1000 now. Why would people turn down $1300 next year in favour of $1000 today? Even if they need the $1000 immediately, they would be better off borrowing it from a bank, even at 15% or 20% interest. Then, a year later, they could pay off the loan—including the interest—with the $1300 and pocket the difference.

The fact is, however, that economists found numerous examples of such high discount rates implicit in consumer behaviour. Although consumers were very much aware of savings to be made at the point of purchase, they so heavily discounted the value of monthly electrical costs they would pay over the lifetime of their dryer or freezer that they were oblivious of the potential for greater savings.

Gas water heaters, for example, were found to carry an implicit discount rate of 100 percent. This means that in deciding which model was cheapest over the long run, consumers acted as if today's value of a $100 gas bill due in one year was only

$$P = \frac{S}{1 + rt} = \frac{\$100}{1 + 1.00 \times 1} = \frac{\$100}{2} = \$50$$

The next $100 gas bill due two years from now was worth $25 ($100 cut in half for each of two years), and so on through the life of the appliance. Few consumers actually make this formal calculation, of course. But, on average, they behave this way.

Other experiments have shown that the way consumers make decisions about money depends a great deal on how much is at stake. Few people are willing to give up $10 now for $15 next year. But most will give up $100 now for $150 next year, a fact that helps explain why consumers appear to care less about many small electricity and gas bills—even if they add up to a lot—than one big initial outlay.

CONCEPT QUESTIONS

1. What is meant by the "time value of money?"

2. We frequently hear a news item that goes something like: "Joe Superstar signed a five-year deal worth $25 million. Under the contract he will be paid $3 million, $4 million, $5 million, $6 million and $7 million in successive years." In what respect is the statement incorrect? How should the value of the contract be calculated?

3. How do you determine the economic value on a particular date of a series of payments?

4. How can you determine whether two payment streams are equivalent to each other?

5. If the interest rate money can earn is revised upward, is today's economic value of a given stream of future payments higher or lower? Explain.

EXERCISE 6.5 *Answers to the odd-numbered problems are at the end of the book.*

1. Calculate the combined equivalent value, six months from now, of $500 due today and $300 due in three months. Assume that money can earn $9\frac{1}{2}$%.

2. A payment stream consists of $1000 payable today and $1500 payable in five months. What is the equivalent value of the payment stream two months from now if money is worth 5.5%?

3. Payments of $900 and $1000 are due in 30 days and 210 days, respectively. If money can be invested at $7\frac{3}{4}$%, what single payment 90 days from now is equivalent to the payment stream?

4. What is the equivalent value, 30 days from now, of a payment stream comprised of $2500 due in 70 days and $4000 due in 200 days? Assume money can earn $6\frac{1}{4}$%.

5. A payment stream consists of three payments: $1000 today, $1500 in 70 days, and $2000 in 210 days. What single payment, 60 days from now, is economically equivalent to the payment stream if money can be invested at a rate of 8.5%?

6. What single payment, 45 days from now, is economically equivalent to the combination of three payments of $1750 each: one due 75 days ago, the second due today, and the third due in 75 days? Money is worth 9.9% per annum.

7. Two payments of $2000 each are to be received six and twelve months from now. If money is worth 10%, what is the total equivalent value of the payments:
   a. Today?
   b. Six months from today?
   c. Explain why the answer in Part (b) is larger.

8. Two payments of $3000 each are due in 50 and 100 days. What is their combined economic value today if money can earn:
   a. 9%?
   b. 11%?
   c. Explain why the answer in Part (b) is smaller.

9. Payments of $850 and $1140 were scheduled to be paid today and nine months from now, respectively. What total payment today would place the payee in the same financial position as the scheduled payments? Money can earn $8\frac{1}{4}$%.

10. Two payments of $1300 and $1800 were scheduled to be paid five months ago and three months from now, respectively. The $1300 payment has not yet been made. What single payment at a focal date one month from now would be equivalent to the two scheduled payments if money can earn $4\frac{1}{2}$%?

11. If money earns 9.5%, calculate and compare the economic value today of the following payment streams:

    Stream 1: Payments of $900 and $1400 due 150 and 80 days ago, respectively.

    Stream 2: Payments of $800, $600, and $1000 due 30, 75, and 125 days from now, respectively.

12. What is the economic value today of each of the following payment streams if money can earn 7.5%? (Note that the two streams have the same total nominal value.)

    a. $1000, $3000, and $2000 due in one, three, and five months, respectively.

    b. Two $3000 payments due two and four months from now.

○13. Eight months ago, Louise agreed to pay Thelma $750 and $950, six and twelve months respectively from the date of the agreement. With each payment, Louise agreed to pay interest on the respective principal amounts at the rate of 9.5% from the date of the agreement. Louise failed to make the first payment and now wishes to settle her obligations with a single payment four months from now. What payment should Thelma be willing to accept if money can earn 7.75%?

○14. Ninety days ago Stella signed an agreement with Manon requiring her to make three payments of $400 plus interest 90, 150, and 210 days, respectively, from the date of the agreement. Each payment was to include interest on the $400 principal at the rate of 13.5% from the date of the agreement. Stella now wants Manon to renegotiate the agreement and accept a single payment 30 days from now, instead of the three scheduled payments. What payment should Manon require in the new agreement if money is worth 8.5%?

○15. Payments of $2600, due 50 days ago, and $3100, due in 40 days, are to be replaced by $3000 today and another payment in 30 days. What must the second payment be if the payee is to end up in an equivalent financial position? Money now earns 8.25%. Use 30 days from now as the focal date.

○16. Three payments of $2000 (originally due six months ago, today, and six months from now) have been renegotiated to two payments: $3000 one month from now and a second payment due in four months. What must the second payment be for the replacement payments to be equivalent to the originally scheduled payments? Assume that money can earn an interest rate of 4%. Choose a focal date four months from now.

6.6 LOANS: A PRINCIPLE ABOUT PRINCIPAL

LO3   In Section 8.3, we will develop (in the context of compound interest) an important relationship between the principal amount of a loan and the payments required to pay off the loan. The relationship applies to *all* compound interest loans and to *some* loans[4] at simple interest. Section 8.3 is covered in virtually all business math courses but Section 6.6 is commonly omitted. Therefore, we will simply state the relationship at this point and demonstrate its use.

---

[4] In general, a loan payment consists of a principal portion and an interest portion. Most loans are structured so that the interest portion of a payment is the accrued interest on the *entire* principal balance still outstanding. However, for the relationship presented in this section to apply precisely to a simple interest loan, the following condition must be met. The interest portion of a simple interest loan payment must be the accrued interest on *only the principal portion of that payment.* Accrued interest on other outstanding principal must be paid only when that principal is repaid. Instances of loans meeting this condition are rare.

> **A General Principle Concerning Loans**
> The original principal amount of a loan is equal to the sum of the present values of all the payments required to pay off a loan. The interest rate used for the present-value calculations is the interest rate charged on the loan.

EXAMPLE 6.6A CALCULATING THE SIZE OF THE FINAL LOAN PAYMENT

A \$5000 loan advanced on April 1 at a $10\frac{1}{2}\%$ interest rate requires payments of \$1800 on each of June 1 and August 1, and a final payment on October 1. What must the final payment be to satisfy the loan in full?

SOLUTION

Let x represent the amount of the final payment. The payments and their equivalent (present) values, P_1, P_2, and P_3, are shown in the following time diagram.

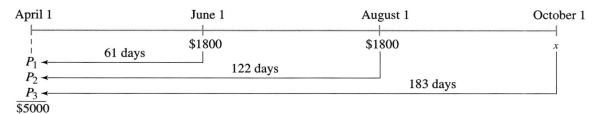

Since the original loan equals the combined present value of all of the payments, then

$$\$5000 = P_1 + P_2 + P_3$$

where

$$P_1 = \frac{\$1800}{1 + 0.105(\frac{61}{365})} = \frac{\$1800}{1.0175479} = \$1768.958$$
$$P_2 = \frac{\$1800}{1 + 0.105(\frac{122}{365})} = \frac{\$1800}{1.0350959} = \$1738.969$$
$$P_3 = \frac{x}{1 + 0.105(\frac{183}{365})} = \frac{x}{1.0526438} = 0.9499889x$$

We maintain seven-figure precision in order to ensure six-figure accuracy in the final result.

Thus

$$\$5000 = \$1768.958 + \$1738.969 + 0.9499889x$$
$$\$1492.073 = 0.9499889x$$
$$x = \frac{\$1492.073}{0.9499889} = \$1570.62$$

The final payment on October 1 must be \$1570.62.

EXAMPLE 6.6B CALCULATING THE SIZE OF EQUAL LOAN PAYMENTS

A \$4000 loan made at 11.75% is to be repaid in three equal payments, due 30, 90, and 150 days, respectively, after the date of the loan. Determine the size of the payments.

SOLUTION

Let the amount of each payment be represented by x. The payments and their equivalent (present) values are presented in the following time diagram.

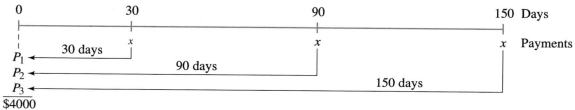

The original loan is equal to the sum of the present values of all of the payments. Therefore,

$$\$4000 = P_1 + P_2 + P_3$$

where

$$P_1 = \frac{x}{1 + 0.1175(\frac{30}{365})} = \frac{x}{1.0096575} = 0.9904349x$$

$$P_2 = \frac{x}{1 + 0.1175(\frac{90}{365})} = \frac{x}{1.0289726} = 0.9718432x$$

$$P_3 = \frac{x}{1 + 0.1175(\frac{150}{365})} = \frac{x}{1.0482877} = 0.9539366x$$

Thus,

$$\$4000 = 0.9904349x + 0.9718432x + 0.9539366x$$
$$= 2.916215x$$
$$x = \frac{\$4000}{2.916215} = \$1371.64$$

Each payment should be $1371.64.

EXERCISE 6.6   *Answers to the odd-numbered problems are at the end of the book.*

∘1. A $3000 loan at 11% was made on March 1. Two payments of $1000 each were made on May 1 and June 1. What payment on July 1 will pay off the loan?

∘2. $5000 was borrowed at $9\frac{1}{2}\%$ on March 1. On April 1 and June 1, the borrower made payments of $2000 each. What payment was required on August 1 to pay off the loan's balance?

∘3. The interest rate on a $3000 loan advanced on March 1 was 10.2%. What must the first payment on April 13 be in order that two subsequent payments of $1100 on May 27 and $1100 on July 13 settle the loan?

∘4. A $3000 loan on March 1 was repaid by payments of $500 on March 31, $1000 on June 15, and a final payment on August 31. What was the third payment if the interest rate on the loan was $8\frac{1}{4}\%$?

∘5. A $1000 loan at 9% was repaid by two equal payments made 30 days and 60 days after the date of the loan. Determine the amount of each payment.

∘6. Two equal payments, 50 days and 150 days after the date of the loan, paid off a $3000 loan at $10\frac{1}{4}\%$. What was the amount of each payment?

∘7. What should be the amount of each payment if a $2500 loan at $8\frac{3}{4}\%$ is to be repaid by three equal payments due two months, four months, and seven months following the date of the loan?

∘**8.** $8000 was borrowed at an interest rate of $11\frac{1}{2}$%. Calculate the amount of each payment if the loan was paid off by three equal payments made 30, 90, and 150 days after the date of the loan.

∘**9.** The simple interest rate on a $5000 loan is 7%. The loan is to be repaid by four equal payments on dates 100, 150, 200, and 250 days from the date on which the loan was advanced. What is the amount of each payment?

∘**10.** A $7500 loan will be paid off by four equal payments to be made 2, 5, 9, and 12 months after the date of the loan. What is the amount of each payment if the interest rate on the loan is 9.9%?

∘**11.** Maurice borrowed $6000 from Heidi on April 23 and agreed to make payments of $2000 on June 1 and $2000 on August 1, and to pay the balance on October 1. If simple interest at the rate of 10% was charged on the loan, what is the amount of the third payment? Use April 23 as the focal date.

∘**12.** A loan of $10,000 is to be repaid by three payments of $2500 due in two, four, and six months, and a fourth payment due in eight months. What should be the size of the fourth payment if an interest rate of 11% is charged on the loan? Use today as the focal date.

∘**13.** A loan of $4000 at 13% is to be repaid by three equal payments due four, six, and eight months after the date on which the money was advanced. Calculate the amount of each payment. Use the loan date as the focal date.

∘**14.** Anthony borrowed $7500 on September 15 and agreed to repay the loan by three equal payments on the following November 10, December 30, and February 28. Calculate the payment size if the interest rate on the loan was $11\frac{3}{4}$%. Use September 15 as the focal date.

KEY TERMS

SUMMARY OF NOTATION AND KEY FORMULAS

P = Principal amount of the loan or investment; present value
r = Annual rate of simple interest
t = Time period (term), in years, of the loan or investment
I = Amount of interest paid or received
S = Maturity value of a loan or investment; future value

FORMULA (6-1) $I = Prt$ Finding the amount of simple interest earned

FORMULA (6-2) $S = P(1 + rt)$ Finding the maturity value or future value

REVIEW PROBLEMS

Answers to the odd-numbered review problems are at the back of the book.

1. **(LO1)** What amount invested at $4\frac{1}{2}$% on November 19, 2007, had a maturity value of $10,000 on March 3, 2008?

2. **(LO1)** If $3702.40 earned $212.45 interest from September 17, 2004, to March 11, 2005, what rate of interest was earned?

3. **(LO1)** A loan of $3300 at $9\frac{1}{4}$% simple interest was made on March 27. On what date was it repaid if the interest cost was $137.99?

4. **(LO1)** Marta borrowed $1750 from Jasper on November 15, 2008, and agreed to repay the debt with simple interest at the rate of 7.4% on June 3, 2009. How much interest was owed on June 3?

5. **(LO1)** Petra has forgotten the rate of simple interest she earned on a 120-day term deposit at Scotiabank. At the end of the 120 days, she received interest of $327.95 on her $21,000 deposit. What rate of simple interest was her deposit earning?

6. **(LO1)** Jacques received the proceeds from an inheritance on March 15. He wants to set aside, in a term deposit on March 16, an amount sufficient to provide a $45,000 down payment for the purchase of a home on November 1. If the current interest rate on 181-day to 270-day deposits is $5\frac{3}{4}$%, what amount should he place in the term deposit?

7. **(LO3)** Sheldrick Contracting owes Western Equipment $60,000 payable on June 14. In late April, Sheldrick has surplus cash and wants to settle its debt to Western Equipment, if Western will agree to a fair reduction reflecting the current 3.6% interest rate that short-term funds can earn. What amount on April 29 should Sheldrick propose to pay to Western?

8. **(LO3)** Peter and Reesa can book their Horizon Holiday package at the early-booking price of $3900, or wait four months and pay the full price of $3995.
   a. Which option should they select if money can earn a 5.25% rate of return?
   b. At what interest rate would they be indifferent between the two prices?

9. **(LO3)** What amount on January 23 is equivalent to $1000 on the preceding August 18 if money can earn $6\frac{1}{2}$%?

10. **(LO2) (LO3)** Three payments are scheduled as follows: $1200 is due today, $900 is due in five months, and $1500 is due in eight months. The three payments are to be replaced by a single equivalent payment due ten months from now. What should the payment be if money is worth 5.9%? Use ten months from now as the focal date.

11. **(LO3)** Two payments of $5000 are to be received four and eight months from now.
    a. What is the combined equivalent value of the two payments today if money can earn 6%?
    b. If the rate of interest money can earn is 4%, what is the payments' combined equivalent value today?

12. **(LO3)** Thad is planning to buy a rototiller next spring at an expected price of $579. In the current fall "flyer" from Evergreen Lawn and Garden, the model he wants is advertised at $499.95 in a Fall Clearance Special.
    a. If money can earn 4%, what is the economic value on the preceding September 15 of the $579 that Thad will pay to purchase the rototiller next April 1? (Assume that February has 28 days.)
    b. What are his true economic savings if he purchases the rototiller at the sale price of $499.95 on September 15?
    c. What interest rate would money have to earn for Thad to be indifferent between buying the rototiller at $499.95 on September 15 or buying it for $579 on the subsequent April 1?

13. **(LO1)** Evelyn put $15,000 into a 90-day term deposit at Laurentian Bank that paid a simple interest rate of 3.2%. When the term deposit matured, she invested the entire amount of the principal and interest from the first term deposit into a new 90-day term deposit that paid the same rate of interest. What total amount of interest did she earn on both term deposits?

14. **(LO1)** Umberto borrowed $7500 from Delores on November 7, 2008. When Umberto repaid the loan, Delores charged him $190.02 interest. If the rate of simple interest on the loan was $6\frac{3}{4}\%$, on what date did Umberto repay the loan?

15. **(LO3)** Payments of $1000 and $7500 were originally scheduled to be paid five months ago and four months from now, respectively. The first payment was not made. What payment two months from now is equivalent to the scheduled payments if money can earn $6\frac{1}{4}\%$?

16. **(LO2) (LO3)** If money earns 7.5%, calculate and compare the economic value today of the following payment streams:

    Stream 1: Payments of $1800 and $2800 made 150 and 90 days ago, respectively.

    Stream 2: Payments of $1600, $1200, and $2000 due 30, 75, and 120 days from now, respectively.

◦17. **(LO3)** Mr. & Mrs. Parsons are considering two offers to purchase their summer cottage. Offer A is for $200,000 consisting of an immediate $40,000 down payment with the $160,000 balance payable one year later. Offer B is for $196,500 made up of a $30,000 down payment and the $166,500 balance payable in six months.

   a. If money can earn 4%, what is the current economic value of each offer?

   b. Other things being equal, which offer should the Parsons accept? What is the economic advantage of the preferred offer over the other offer?

   c. If money can earn 6%, which offer should the Parsons accept? What is the economic advantage of the preferred offer?

◦18. **(LO3)** A $9000 loan is to be repaid in three equal payments occurring 60, 180, and 300 days, respectively, after the date of the loan. Calculate the size of these payments if the interest rate on the loan is $7\frac{1}{4}\%$. Use the loan date as the focal date.

◦19. **(LO2) (LO3)** Nine months ago, Muriel agreed to pay Aisha $1200 and $800 on dates 6 and 12 months, respectively, from the date of the agreement. With each payment Muriel agreed to pay interest at the rate of $8\frac{1}{2}\%$ from the date of the agreement. Muriel failed to make the first payment and now wishes to settle her obligations with a single payment four months from now. What payment should Aisha be willing to accept if money can earn $6\frac{3}{4}\%$?

APPENDIX 6A   **AN AID FOR DETERMINING THE NUMBER OF DAYS IN EACH MONTH**

Figure 6.4 presents a method for determining which months have 31 days. The knuckles and the spaces between them are assigned the names of the months as shown in the figure. Then each knuckle corresponds to a month with 31 days and each space corresponds to a short month.

FIGURE 6.4   "Knuckle Months" Have 31 Days

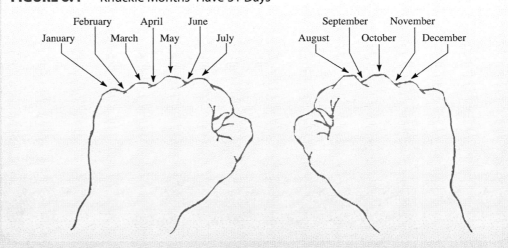

| APPENDIX 6B | **THE TEXAS INSTRUMENTS BA II PLUS DATE WORKSHEET** |

The BA II PLUS's Owner's Manual uses the term "worksheet" to refer to a list of settings and functions designed for a particular application. Usually, a worksheet is the second function of a key. For example, the word **DATE** appears above the ⌑ 1 ⌑ key. You can access the **DATE** worksheet by pressing ⌑ 2nd ⌑ ⌑ 1 ⌑ in sequence (rather than at the same time). Hereafter, we will represent these keystrokes as ⌑ 2nd ⌑ ⌑DATE⌑. The calculator's display then has the form:[5]

$$DT1 = \quad \text{mm-dd-yyyy}$$

The components of the display have the following meanings:

DT1 is the symbol used by the calculator for the *start* date (**DaTe 1**)

In place of "mm", you will see one or two digits representing the month.

In place of "dd", you will see two digits for the day of the month.

In place of "yyyy", you will see four digits for the year.

For example, the display | *DT1* =   12-31-1990 | means that the start date of the interval is December 31, 1990.

You should think of a worksheet as a single column of items that you can view one-at-a-time in the display. The DATE worksheet's column consists of the following four items:

| *DT1* =   mm-dd-yyyy |
| *DT2* =   mm-dd-yyyy |
| *DBD* =   nnn |
| *ACT* |

The solid line around the first item denotes that the display currently provides a "window" to the first item in the column. You can use the scroll keys ⌑ ↓ ⌑ and ⌑ ↑ ⌑ to move up or down the list. *DT2* is the symbol used by the calculator for the *end* date (**DaTe 2**). *DBD* is the symbol for the number of **D**ays **B**etween **D**ates (that is, the number of days between *DT1* and *DT2*, counting the start date but not the end date). *ACT*[6] is short for **ACT**ual. This means that calculations are based on the *actual* number of days in each month. This is the *only* method used in Canada. Some calculations in the United States treat all months as having 30 days.

The DATE worksheet allows you to enter values for any two of the three quantities—*DT1*, *DT2*, and *DBD*—and then compute the value of the third quantity. (The calculator automatically makes adjustments for leap years.) Examples 6BA and 6BB will demonstrate how to do this. But first close the worksheet by pressing ⌑ 2nd ⌑ ⌑QUIT⌑. (By the ⌑QUIT⌑ key, we mean the key having **QUIT** as its second function.)

After reading Examples 6BA and 6BB, use the DATE Worksheet to calculate your age in days, and then to calculate the calendar date on which you will be 20,000 days old.

---

[5] This assumes that the calculator is using the default setting (*US*) for the date format. In the calculator's "Format" worksheet, you can change to the alternative "dd-mm-yyyy" format (*EUR*).

[6] If your display shows "360" at this point, you should switch to "ACT" by pressing ⌑ 2nd ⌑ ⌑SET⌑. By the ⌑SET⌑ key, we mean the key having **SET** as its second function.

EXAMPLE 6BA   **CALCULATING "DBD" GIVEN "DT1" AND "DT2"**

Calculate the number of days in the interval November 8, 2007 to April 23, 2008.

SOLUTION

Here are the keystrokes with brief explanations.

| 2nd | DATE | ⇒ Open the DATE worksheet. |

11.0807 ENTER   ⇒ Key in and save the value for *DT1*. Date information is entered in the format *mm.ddyy* where *mm* is the one- or two-digit number for the month, *dd* is the *two*-digit number for the day of the month, and *yy* is the *last* two digits of the year. Pressing the ENTER key saves this new value for *DT1*.

↓   ⇒ Scroll down to *DT2*.

4.2308 ENTER   ⇒ Key in and save the value for *DT2*.

↓   ⇒ Scroll down to *DBD*.

CPT   ⇒ Compute the value of *DBD*, the number of days in the interval. The answer that appears is 167 days. The calculator automatically handles leap years.

2nd QUIT   ⇒ Close the worksheet.

EXAMPLE 6BB   **CALCULATING "DT1" GIVEN "DT2" AND "DBD"**

Determine the date that is 257 days before June 23, 2012.

SOLUTION

2nd DATE   ⇒ Open the DATE worksheet.

↓   ⇒ Scroll down to *DT2*.

6.2312 ENTER   ⇒ Key in and save the value for *DT2*.

↓   ⇒ Scroll down to *DBD*.

257 ENTER   ⇒ Key in and save the value for *DBD*.

↑ ↑   ⇒ Scroll up to *DT1*.

CPT   ⇒ Compute the value of *DT1*. The answer "*MON* = 10-10-2011" appears in the display. Hence, the beginning date of the interval is Monday, October 10, 2011.

2nd QUIT   ⇒ Close the worksheet.

CHAPTER 7

Applications of Simple Interest

LEARNING OBJECTIVES

After completing this chapter, you will be able to:

LO1 Calculate the interest paid on savings accounts and short-term guaranteed investment certificates

LO2 State the Valuation Principle and apply it to the calculation of the fair market value of an investment with known future cash flows

LO3 Calculate the market price and rate of return for Treasury bills and commercial paper

LO4 Describe typical terms, conditions, and repayment arrangements for revolving (demand) loans, fixed-payment (demand) loans, and Canada Student Loans

LO5 Prepare loan repayment schedules for revolving loans, fixed-payment loans, and Canada Student Loans

HAVE YOU HEARD OF TERM deposits, short-term Guaranteed Investment Certificates (GICs), and Treasury bills? Perhaps not, because these short-term simple-interest investments do not get the media attention received by more volatile and exciting long-term investments such as stocks and bonds. But short-term (or "money market") investments represent a much larger part of the investment "picture" than their low profile suggests. For example, the average size of Canadian money market mutual funds (that hold short-term investments) is similar to the average size of mutual funds that invest in stocks and bonds. When a "bear" market hits stocks, many investors move their money from stocks to these low-risk short-term investments.

Our discussion of short-term investments raises the question: "How much should you pay for an investment?" Answering the question leads us to the Valuation Principle—a very important concept having broad application.

Next we will study arrangements and calculations for demand loans. Most businesses and many individuals have a line of credit or demand loan facility with a financial institution. Over half of college and university graduates face repayment of student loans. We conclude the chapter by describing the features and the calculation of interest on such loans.

7.1 SAVINGS ACCOUNTS AND SHORT-TERM GICS

NET @ssets

Most financial institutions post on their Web sites the current interest rates they pay on savings and investment products.

Banks, trust companies, and credit unions use $I = Prt$ for calculating the interest on a variety of savings accounts and short-term investment products. Interest on most **savings accounts** is calculated on the daily closing balance and paid monthly. This means that you earn one day's interest on each day's closing balance, but the interest is not credited to your account until the last day of the month or the first day of the following month. Some savings accounts have a tiered scale of interest rates, with higher rates paid when the account's balance reaches certain higher levels. The interest rates on savings accounts are floating; they are adjusted to follow the trend of short-term rates in the financial markets. Interest on a few savings and chequing accounts is calculated on only the *minimum monthly* balance and paid monthly or semiannually.

Depositors can earn a higher interest rate if they are prepared to forego access to their funds for at least 30 days. Banks, trust companies, life insurance companies, and credit unions offer **Guaranteed Investment Certificates**, usually referred to as "GICs." Typically, a GIC is issued by a mortgage-lending subsidiary of a financial institution, and is *unconditionally guaranteed* by the parent company. The Canada Deposit Insurance Corporation also guarantees up to $100,000 per depositor. Short-term GICs are issued with maturities of 30 to 364 days. (Long-term GICs, with maturities of one to seven years, will be discussed in Section 8.5.)

LO1 Most banks, trust companies, and credit unions offer both *non-redeemable* and *redeemable* versions of short-term GICs. Redeemable GICs may be redeemed or "cashed-in" before the scheduled maturity date. Non-redeemable GICs do not permit you to recover your money before the maturity date except under extraordinary circumstances. (Some institutions use the term "cashable GIC" and others use "term deposit" instead of "redeemable GIC." At these institutions, any mention of a Guaranteed Investment Certificate is understood to refer to the non-redeemable variety.)

Interest on short-term GICs is calculated on a simple-interest basis and is paid on the maturity date. Normally, the interest rates offered exhibit the following patterns:

- Higher rates are paid on non-redeemable GICs than on redeemable GICs.

- Higher rates are paid for longer terms (within the 30- to 364-day range).

- Higher rates are paid on larger principal amounts.

EXAMPLE 7.1A   **SAVINGS ACCOUNT INTEREST BASED ON A TIERED INTEREST RATE**

Mr. and Mrs. Hernandez have a Performance 55 bank account that pays a slightly higher rate to depositors aged 55 or older. Interest is calculated on the daily closing balance and received monthly as follows:

Portion of balance	Interest rate (%)
From 0 to $1000.00	1.5
From $1000.01 to $3000.00	1.75
Over $3000.00	2.0

On April 1, their balance was $1416.32. They withdrew $500 on April 9, deposited $1200 on April 15, and deposited another $1200 on April 29. Calculate the interest that they will receive for the month of April.

SOLUTION

The following table organizes the given information in preparation for the interest calculation:

Period	Number of days	Balance ($)	Amount ($) subject to a rate of: 1.5%	1.75%	2.0%
April 1–8	8	1416.32	1000.00	416.32	—
April 9–14	6	916.32	916.32	—	—
April 15–28	14	2116.32	1000.00	1116.32	—
April 29–30	2	3316.32	1000.00	2000.00	316.32

The interest earned for the period April 1 to 8 inclusive is

$$\begin{aligned} I(\text{April }1\text{–}8) &= P_1r_1t + P_2r_2t \\ &= (P_1r_1 + P_2r_2)t \\ &= [\$1000(0.015) + \$416.32(0.0175)](\tfrac{8}{365}) \\ &= (\$15.00 + \$7.286)(0.02192) \\ &= \$0.489 \end{aligned}$$

Maintain four-figure precision for three-figure accuracy in the final answer.

Similarly, $I(\text{April }9\text{–}14) = \$916.32(0.015)(\tfrac{6}{365}) = \$0.226$

$$\begin{aligned} I(\text{April }15\text{–}28) &= [\$1000(0.015) + \$1116.32(0.0175)](\tfrac{14}{365}) \\ &= (\$15.00 + \$19.54)(0.03836) \\ &= \$1.325 \end{aligned}$$

$$\begin{aligned} I(\text{April }29\text{–}30) &= [\$1000(0.015) + \$2000(0.0175) + \$316.32(0.02)](\tfrac{2}{365}) \\ &= (\$15.00 + \$35.00 + \$6.33)(0.005479) \\ &= \$0.309 \end{aligned}$$

Total interest for April = $0.489 + $0.226 + $1.325 + $0.309 = $2.349

Mr. and Mrs. Hernandez will earn $2.35 interest in April.

EXAMPLE 7.1B   **CALCULATION OF INTEREST ON SHORT-TERM GICS**

For amounts of $5000 to $99,999 and terms of 90 to 179 days, the RBC Royal Bank pays an interest rate of 2.70% on redeemable GICs and 2.95% on non-redeemable GICs. In order to retain the redemption privilege, how much interest (in dollars) must Edith forgo on an investment of $25,000 for 150 days?

SOLUTION

On a non-redeemable GIC, Edith would earn

$$I = Prt = \$25{,}000(0.0295)(\tfrac{150}{365}) = \$303.08$$

On a redeemable GIC, she would earn

$$I = Prt = \$25{,}000(0.0270)(\tfrac{150}{365}) = \$277.40$$

Edith must forgo $303.08 − $277.40 = $25.68 of interest earnings to retain the redemption privilege.

EXERCISE 7.1   *Answers to the odd-numbered problems are at the end of the book.*

1. a. What will be the maturity value of $15,000 placed in a 120-day term deposit paying an interest rate of 2.25%?

    b. If, on the maturity date, the combined principal and interest are "rolled over" into a 90-day term deposit paying 2.15%, what amount will the depositor receive when the second term deposit matures?

2. For amounts between $10,000 and $24,999, a credit union pays a rate of 2.5% on term deposits with maturities in the 91- to 120-day range. However, early redemption will result in a rate of 1.75% being applied. How much more interest will a 91-day $20,000 term deposit earn if it is held until maturity than if it is redeemed after 80 days?

3. For 90- to 365-day GICs, TD Canada Trust offered a rate of 3.00% on investments of $25,000 to $59,999 and a rate of 3.20% on investments of $60,000 to $99,999. How much more will an investor earn from a single $60,000, 270-day GIC than from two $30,000, 270-day GICs?

4. On a $10,000 principal investment, a bank offered interest rates of 3.45% on 270- to 364-day GICs and 3.15% on 180- to 269-day GICs. How much more will an investor earn from a 364-day GIC than from two consecutive 182-day GICs? (Assume that the interest rate on 180- to 269-day GICs will be the same on the renewal date as it is today. Remember that both the principal and the interest from the first 182-day GIC can be invested in the second 182-day GIC.)

5. For investments of $5000 to $24,999, a bank quotes interest rates of 2.65% on 90-day GICs and 2.85% on 180-day GICs. How much more interest will an investor earn by placing $15,000 in a 180-day GIC than by purchasing two consecutive 90-day GICs? (Assume that interest rates do not change over the next 90 days. Remember that interest earned from the first 90-day GIC can be invested in the second 90-day GIC.)

○6. Suppose that the current rates on 90- and 180-day GICs are 3.25% and 3.50%, respectively. An investor is weighing the alternatives of purchasing a 180-day GIC versus purchasing a 90-day GIC and then reinvesting its maturity value in a second 90-day GIC. What would the interest rate on 90-day GICs have to be 90 days from now for the investor to end up in the same financial position with either alternative?

○7. Joan has savings of $12,000 on June 1. Since she may need some of the money during the next three months, she is considering two options at her bank. (1) An Investment Builder account earns a 2.25% rate of interest. The interest is calculated on the daily closing balance and paid on the first day of the following month. (2) A 90- to 179-day cashable term deposit earns a rate of 2.8%, paid at maturity. If interest rates do not change and Joan does not withdraw any of the funds, how much more will she earn from the term deposit option up to September 1? (Keep in mind that savings account interest paid on the first day of the month will itself earn interest during the subsequent month.)

8. A savings account pays interest of 1.5%. Interest is calculated on the daily closing balance and paid at the close of business on the last day of the month. A depositor had a $2239 opening balance on September 1, deposited $734 on September 7 and $327 on September 21, and withdrew $300 on September 10. What interest will be credited to the account at the month's end?

○9. An Investment Savings account offered by a trust company pays a rate of 1.25% on the first $1000 of daily closing balance, 1.5% on the portion of the balance between $1000 and $3000, and 1.75% on any balance in excess of $3000. What interest will be paid for the month of April if the opening balance was $2439, $950 was deposited on April 10, and $500 was withdrawn on April 23?

10. The Moneybuilder account offered by a chartered bank calculates interest daily based on the daily closing balance as follows:

Interest rate (%)	Amount to which the rate applies
0.00	Balance when it is below $1000
1.25	Entire balance when it is between $1000 and $3000
1.75	Portion of balance above $3000

The balance at the beginning of March was $1678. On March 5, $700 was withdrawn. Then $2500 was deposited on March 15, and $900 was withdrawn on March 23. What interest will be credited to the account for the month of March?

○11. The Super Savings account offered by a trust company calculates interest daily based on the *lesser* of each day's opening or closing balance as follows:

Interest rate (%)	Amount to which the rate applies
0.50	Entire balance when it is between $0 and $2999.99
1.00	Entire balance when it is between $3000 and $4999.99
1.25	Entire balance when it is between $5000 and $9999.99
1.50	Entire balance when it is between $10,000 and $24,999.99
1.75	Entire balance when it is between $25,000 and $49,999.99
2.25	Entire balance when it is $50,000 or more

September's opening balance was $8572. The transactions in the account for the month were a $9500 deposit on September 6, a deposit of $8600 on September 14, and a withdrawal of $25,000 on September 23. What interest will be credited to the account at the end of September?

○12. For principal amounts of $5000 to $49,999, a bank pays an interest rate of 2.95% on 180- to 269-day non-redeemable GICs, and 3.00% on 270- to 364-day non-redeemable GICs. Ranjit has $10,000 to invest for 364 days. Because he thinks interest rates will be higher six months from now, he is debating whether to choose a 182-day GIC now (and reinvest its maturity value in another 182-day GIC) or to choose a 364-day GIC today. What would the interest rate on 182-day GICs have to be on the reinvestment date for both alternatives to yield the same maturity value 364 days from now?

■ connect

13. Access the Royal Bank's Web page for current interest rates. In this page's navigation bar, select "Redeemable GIC" or "Non-Redeemable GIC" to obtain current rates for these simple-interest investments.

    a. For each type of GIC, how much interest will you earn on $10,000 invested for 100 days?

    b. How much interest will you earn on the Redeemable GIC if you redeem it after:
       (i) 29 days?   **(ii)** 31 days?

    Hint: Scroll down the Redeemable GIC page to find the "Prior Redemption Rates" table.

7.2 THE VALUATION PRINCIPLE

LO2   Consider an investment that will deliver a single payment of $110 one year from today. What is the most you should pay to buy the investment if you require a minimum rate of return of 10%? (In other words, what is the current value of the investment to you?) After a little thought, you probably answer "$100" for the following reason. The $10 difference between the amount you pay ($100) and the amount you will receive ($110) represents a 10% rate of return on your $100 investment.

But how would you calculate the price to pay if the given numbers are not so "nice?" For example, what maximum price should you pay for an investment that will pay you $129 after 247 days, if you require a rate of return of 5.5%? Let us think about where the $100 came from in the first example. Note that $100 invested for one year at 10% will grow to $110. Since $110 is the *future* value of $100, then $100 is the *present* value of $110. That is,

$$P = \frac{S}{1 + rt} = \frac{\$110}{1 + 0.10 \times 1} = \$100$$

This demonstrates that the present value calculation gives a price that "builds in" the required 10% rate of return. If your minimum required rate of return is only 8%, then you should be willing to pay up to

$$P = \frac{S}{1 + rt} = \frac{\$110}{1 + 0.08 \times 1} = \$101.85$$

The $8.15 ($110.00 − $101.85) you will earn during the next year provides a rate of return (on your $101.85 investment) of

$$\frac{\$8.15}{\$101.85} \times 100\% = 8.00\%$$

The lower the rate of return you are prepared to accept, the higher the price you can pay now for a given future payment.

In the language of finance, the process of calculating a payment's present value is often called "**discounting a payment.**" (When you calculate the present value of a payment, you get a smaller number than the payment.) The interest rate used in the present value calculation is then called the **discount rate.**

To determine the price to pay for an investment that promises two or more future payments, we simply extend our basic idea. That is, first calculate the present value of each of the payments (using the required rate of return as the discount rate). Then add the present values.

For investments purchased privately, you have some flexibility to negotiate a *higher* rate of return by bargaining *down* the price. But for various types of investments available to the general public, the rates of return are determined by market forces of supply and demand. When an investment's price is established by competitive bidding among many buyers and sellers, we refer to the price as the **fair market value**. A particular fair market value corresponds to a specific rate of return from the investment. This rate of return is what we mean by the *market-determined rate of return*. For publicly traded investments, your only decision is whether or not to accept the prevailing price and the corresponding market-determined rate of return.

These ideas are so important and of such wide application in finance that they are formally embodied in the Valuation Principle.

> **Valuation Principle**
> The fair market value of an investment is the sum of the present values of the cash flows expected from the investment. The discount rate used in the present value calculations should be the prevailing market-determined rate of return on this type of investment.

If the expected cash flows are received as forecast, the investor's actual rate of return on the amount invested will be precisely the discount rate used in the fair market value calculation.

EXAMPLE 7.2A   **VALUATION OF A NON-INTEREST-BEARING OBLIGATION**

An investment contract calls for a payment of $1000 five months from now and another payment, 10 months from now, of $1500.

a. What price will an investor be prepared to pay for the investment today if the required rate of return is 12%?

b. Demonstrate that the investor will realize a 12% rate of return on this price if the payments are received as expected.

SOLUTION

a. According to the Valuation Principle,

$$\text{Price} = \text{Present value of } \$1000 + \text{Present value of } \$1500$$
$$= \frac{\$1000}{1 + 0.12(\frac{5}{12})} + \frac{\$1500}{1 + 0.12(\frac{10}{12})}$$
$$= \$952.381 + \$1363.636$$
$$= \$2316.02$$

An investor requiring a 12% rate of return should be willing to pay $2316.02 today for the contract.

b. Think of the $952.38 and $1363.64 components of the $2316.02 price as separately buying the future cash flows of $1000 and $1500, respectively.

$952.38 invested for five months at 12% will grow to

$$S = P(1 + rt) = \$952.38[1 + 0.12(\tfrac{5}{12})] = \$1000.00$$

Therefore, the $1000 payment received after five months recovers the $952.38 investment along with five months' interest on $952.38 at 12%.

Similarly, it can be shown that the $1500 payment received after 10 months pays back the $1363.64 component of the initial investment plus 10 months' interest on $1363.64 at 12%.

EXAMPLE 7.2B **VALUATION OF AN INTEREST-BEARING OBLIGATION**

On March 1, Murray signed a contract to pay Anton or his designate $2000 plus interest at 8% on June 1, and $3000 plus interest at 8% on September 1. Anton sold the contract to Randy on May 1 at a price negotiated to provide Randy with a 10% rate of return. What price did Randy pay?

SOLUTION

According to the Valuation Principle, the price paid by Randy should be the present value on May 1 of the two scheduled payments discounted at 10%. Unlike Example 7.2A, we do not know at the outset the dollar amounts of the scheduled payments. As indicated in the following time diagram, we must first calculate the maturity value of each obligation using the contract's 8% interest rate. Then we can determine the present value of each scheduled payment using a discount rate of 10%. (The present value calculations thereby build in a 10% rate of return to Randy.)

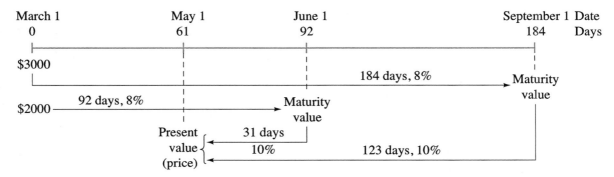

$$\text{Payment due on June 1} = \text{Maturity value of } \$2000 = \$2000[1 + 0.08(\tfrac{92}{365})] = \$2040.33$$

$$\text{Payment due on September 1} = \text{Maturity value of } \$3000 = \$3000[1 + 0.08(\tfrac{184}{365})] = \$3120.99$$

$$
\begin{aligned}
\text{Price} &= \text{Present value of scheduled payments} \\
&= \frac{\$2040.33}{1 + 0.10(\tfrac{31}{365})} + \frac{\$3120.99}{1 + 0.10(\tfrac{123}{365})} \\
&= \$2023.147 + \$3019.246 \\
&= \$5042.39
\end{aligned}
$$

Randy paid $5042.39 for the contract.

CONCEPT QUESTIONS

1. What do you need to know to be able to calculate the fair market value of an investment that will deliver two future payments?

2. If the market-determined rate of return on an investment declines, what happens to the investment's fair market value? Explain. (Assume the expected cash flows from the investment do not change.)

3. If you purchase an investment privately, how do you determine the maximum price you are prepared to pay?

4. Assume that the expected cash flows from an investment and the market-determined rate of return do not change as time passes.

   a. What will happen to the investment's fair market value leading up to the first scheduled payment? Explain.

   b. If the first scheduled payment is $500, what will happen to the fair market value of the investment immediately after the payment is made? Explain.

Answers to the odd-numbered problems are at the end of the book.

1. An investment promises two payments of $500, on dates three and six months from today. If the required rate of return on the investment is 9%:

    a. What is the value of the investment today?

    b. What will its value be in one month if the required rate of return remains at 9%?

    c. Give an explanation for the change in value as time passes.

2. An investment promises two payments of $1000, on dates 60 and 90 days from today. What price will an investor pay today:

    a. If her required rate of return is 10%?

    b. If her required rate of return is 11%?

    c. Give an explanation for the lower price at the higher required return.

3. Certificate A pays $1000 in four months and another $1000 in eight months. Certificate B pays $1000 in five months and another $1000 in nine months. If the current rate of return required on this type of investment certificate is 5.75%, determine the current value of each of the certificates. Give an explanation for the lower value of B.

4. A contract requires payments of $1500, $2000, and $1000 in 100, 150, and 200 days, respectively, from today. What is the value of the contract today if the payments are discounted to yield a 10.5% rate of return?

5. An agreement stipulates payments of $4000, $2500, and $5000 in three, six, and nine months, respectively, from today. What is the highest price an investor will offer today to purchase the agreement if he requires a minimum rate of return of 9.25%?

∘6. An assignable loan contract executed three months ago requires two payments to be paid five and ten months after the contract date. Each payment consists of a principal portion of $1800 plus interest at 10% on $1800 from the date of the contract. The payee is offering to sell the contract to a finance company in order to raise cash. If the finance company requires a return of 15%, what price will it be prepared to pay today for the contract?

∘7. Claude Scales, a commercial fisherman, bought a new navigation system for $10,000 from Coast Marine Electronics on March 20. He paid $2000 in cash and signed a conditional sale contract requiring a payment on July 1 of $3000 plus interest on the $3000 at a rate of 11%, and another payment on September 1 of $5000 plus interest at 11% from the date of the sale. The vendor immediately sold the contract to a finance company, which discounted the payments at its required return of 16%. What proceeds did Coast Marine receive from the sale of the contract?

7.3 TREASURY BILLS AND COMMERCIAL PAPER

LO3   Treasury bills (T-bills) are paper contracts issued to lenders by the federal government and several provincial governments when they borrow money for terms of less than one year. At the end of 2009, $183 billion of the Government of Canada's net federal debt of $565 billion was borrowed through T-bills.

The Bank of Canada conducts auctions of Government of Canada T-bills every second Tuesday. At each auction, the Government of Canada typically borrows between $15 billion and $25 billion. Three T-bill maturities are available at each auction, but in two patterns at alternating auctions. If 98-day, 182-day, and 364-day maturities are offered in Week 1, then

98-day, 168-day, and 350-day maturities[1] are offered in Week 3. The same maturities are offered on Week 5 as on Week 1, on Week 7 as on Week 3, and so on. (Provincial governments tend to issue 91-day, 182-day, and 364-day maturities on more irregular schedules.) In financial markets, we refer to both 91- and 98-day maturities as three-month T-bills, both 168- and 182-day maturities as six-month T-bills, and both 350- and 364-day maturities as one-year T-bills.

The initial lenders (purchasers of the T-bills) are major investment dealers and chartered banks. In turn, these financial institutions sell most of the T-bills to their client-investors in multiples of $1000, with a minimum face value of $5000.

In everyday loan transactions, we normally stipulate the principal amount and then calculate the payment or payments required to repay the principal plus interest. With T-bills, the arrangement is different. The denomination or **face value** of a T-bill is the full amount, *including interest,* payable at maturity of the T-bill. The purchase price (or amount loaned) will be less than the face value—the difference represents the interest that will be earned on the loan. In investment language, T-bills are "issued at a discount to their face value."

How do you decide how much to pay (lend) for the right to receive a T-bill's face value on a known future date? This is the same type of question you were asked at the beginning of Section 7.2. You calculate the present value of the T-bill's face value, using your required rate of return as the discount rate.[2]

The purchaser of a T-bill is not required to hold it until it matures. There is an active market for the sale/purchase of T-bills that are partway through their terms. On any day, the price at which a T-bill may be bought or sold is the present value of its face value. The face value should be discounted at the *current* market-determined rate of return on T-bills over the *time remaining* until maturity. Typical market rates for a few maturities are listed in the financial pages of major newspapers each day. An example of T-bill quotations is presented in the middle column of Table 7.1.

Rates of return (or yields) on T-bills and commercial paper for the most recent five business days are available on the Bank of Canada's Web site.

NET @ssets

TABLE 7.1 Treasury Bill and Commercial Paper Rates (August 15, 2008)

Time remaining until maturity	Rate of return on Treasury bills (%)	Rate of return on commercial paper (%)
1 month	2.22	3.10
3 months	2.42	3.25
6 months	2.65	na
1 year	2.68	na

Some large corporations also borrow money for short periods by selling contracts called **commercial paper.** Commercial paper is essentially a corporation's version of T-bills. Common maturities are 30, 60, and 90 days (usually referred to as one-month, two-month, and three-month maturities). The minimum face value is usually $100,000. Like Treasury bills, commercial paper is priced at its discounted present value. The required rate of return (discount rate) on commercial paper is usually 0.4% to 0.8% higher than that on T-bills. (See Table 7.1.) The higher rate of return is required because of the small risk that the corporation might be unable to pay the face value on the due date.

---

[1] The 168-day maturity is technically not a new issue, but rather a re-opening of the 182-day issue offered two weeks earlier. Similarly, the 350-day maturity is a re-opening of the 364-day issue offered two weeks earlier.

[2] For the initial auction of T-bills, participating financial institutions submit price bids just prior to the auction. The institutions use their own required rate of return as the discount rate when determining the present value of the face value. An institution arrives at its required rate of return based on prevailing short-term interest rates in financial markets, and on the expected demand for T-bills from its clients. The Bank of Canada accepts bids in order of decreasing prices until the government's borrowing requirements for the week are met. The *delivery date* for bids accepted on Tuesday is the subsequent Thursday. This means that the Bank of Canada must receive payment by Thursday, and the "clock" for the T-bills' terms starts on Thursday.

> **EXAMPLE 7.3A** **VALUATION OF A T-BILL ON ITS ISSUE DATE**
>
> Suppose the average rate of return or yield on 168-day Government of Canada Treasury bills sold at a Tuesday auction was 4.68%. At this yield, what price was paid for a T-bill with a face value of $100,000?
>
> **SOLUTION**
>
> $$\text{Price} = \text{Present value of \$100,000 discounted at 4.68\% for 168 days}$$
> $$= \frac{\$100,000}{1 + 0.0468 \times \frac{168}{365}}$$
> $$= \$97,891.34$$
>
> To obtain a yield of 4.68%, $97,891.34 was paid for the 168-day, $100,000 face value T-bill.

> **EXAMPLE 7.3B** **VALUATION OF A T-BILL**
>
> The institutional purchaser of the T-bill in Example 7.3A immediately sells it to a client at a higher price that represents a (lower) yield to the client of 4.48%. What profit did the institution make on the transaction?
>
> **SOLUTION**
>
> $$\text{Selling price to the client} = \frac{\$100,000}{1 + 0.0448 \times \frac{168}{365}} = \$97,979.63$$
>
> $$\text{Profit} = \text{Price charged to the client} - \text{Acquisition price}$$
> $$= \$97,979.63 - \$97,891.34$$
> $$= \$88.29$$
>
> The institution's profit on the resale of the T-bill was $88.29.

> **EXAMPLE 7.3C** **CALCULATION OF THE RATE OF RETURN ON A T-BILL SOLD BEFORE MATURITY**
>
> Suppose the client who purchased the 168-day, $100,000 T-bill in Example 7.3B for $97,979.63, sold the T-bill after 73 days in order to invest the proceeds elsewhere.
>
> **a.** What price would she receive if the short-term interest rate for this maturity had risen to 4.92% by the date of sale?
>
> **b.** What rate of return (per annum) did the client realize while holding the T-bill?
>
> **SOLUTION**
>
> **a.** Days remaining to maturity $= 168 - 73 = 95$
>
> $$\text{Selling price} = \text{Present value of \$100,000 discounted at 4.92\% for 95 days}$$
> $$= \frac{\$100,000}{1 + 0.0492 \times \frac{95}{365}}$$
> $$= \$98,735.64$$
>
> The client sold the T-bill for $98,735.64.
>
> **b.** The client purchased an investment for $97,979.63 and sold it 73 days later for $98,735.64. We need to calculate the rate of return when $97,979.63 grows to $98,735.64 in 73 days. In effect, the initial investment of $97,979.63 earned interest amounting to
>
> $$I = \$98,735.64 - \$97,979.63 = \$756.01$$

Formula (6-1) may now be used to obtain the corresponding rate of return.

$$r = \frac{I}{Pt} = \frac{\$756.01}{\$97,979.63(\frac{73}{365})} = 0.03858 = 3.858\%$$

The client's rate of return during the 73-day holding period was 3.858%.

EXAMPLE 7.3D   **CALCULATION OF THE RATE OF RETURN ON COMMERCIAL PAPER**

Sixty-day commercial paper with face value $100,000 was issued by Suncor Inc. for $99,190. What rate of return will be realized if the paper is held until maturity?

SOLUTION

In effect, the interest earned on an investment of $99,190 for 60 days is

$$\$100,000 - \$99,190 = \$810$$

Using formula (6-1) rearranged to solve for r, we have

$$r = \frac{I}{Pt} = \frac{\$810}{\$99,190(\frac{60}{365})} = 0.04968 = 4.968\%$$

A 4.968% rate of return will be realized if the paper is held until it matures.

CONCEPT QUESTIONS

1. Is the price of a 98-day $100,000 T-bill higher or lower than the price of a 168-day $100,000 T-bill? Why?

2. If short-term interest rates have increased during the past week, will investors pay more this week (than last week) for T-bills of the same term and face value? Explain.

3. If short-term interest rates do not change, what happens to a particular T-bill's fair market value as time passes?

EXERCISE 7.3   *Answers to the odd-numbered problems are at the end of the book.*

Calculate T-bill prices accurate to the nearest dollar and rates of return accurate to the nearest 0.001%.

Note: *A few problems in this and later Exercises have been extracted (with permission) from course materials created by the **Canadian Institute of Financial Planning** (CIFP) for its program leading to the Certified Financial Planner (CFP) designation. The CIFP and associated bodies (see www.ifse.ca) are leading providers of financial services education in Canada. Problems derived from CIFP materials are identified in our Exercises by placing the organization's logo in the margin adjacent to the problems.*

1. Calculate the price of a $25,000, 91-day Province of British Columbia Treasury bill on its issue date if the current market rate of return is 3.672%.

2. Calculate the price on its issue date of $100,000 face value, 90-day commercial paper issued by GE Capital Canada if the prevailing market rate of return is 3.932%.

3. A money market mutual fund purchased $1 million face value of Honda Canada Finance Inc. 90-day commercial paper 28 days after its issue. What price was paid if the paper was discounted at 4.10%?

4. A $100,000, 91-day Province of Ontario Treasury bill was issued 37 days ago. What will be its purchase price today in order to yield the purchaser 3.14%?

5. Calculate and compare the issue-date prices of $100,000 face value commercial paper investments with 30-, 60-, and 90-day maturities, all priced to yield 5.5%.

6. Calculate and compare the market values of a $100,000 face value Government of Canada Treasury bill on dates that are 91 days, 61 days, 31 days, and one day before maturity. Assume that the rate of return required in the market stays constant at 3% over the lifetime of the T-bill.

7. Jake purchased a $100,000 182-day T-bill discounted to yield 5.5%. When he sold it 30 days later, yields had dropped to 5.0%. How much did Jake earn? (Taken from CIFP course materials.)

8. A $100,000, 90-day commercial paper certificate issued by Wells Fargo Financial Canada was sold on its issue date for $99,250. What rate of return will it yield to the buyer?

9. Debra paid $99,615 for a $100,000 T-bill with 30 days remaining until maturity. What (annual) rate of interest will she earn? (Taken from CIFP course materials.)

○10. Lydia purchased a $100,000 150-day T-bill when the prevailing yield on T-bills was 4.5%. She sold the T-bill 60 days later when the prevailing yield was 4.2%. What interest rate did Lydia earn during the 60-day period? (Taken from CIFP course materials.)

○11. A 168-day, $100,000 T-bill was initially issued at a price that would yield the buyer 5.19%. If the yield required by the market remains at 5.19%, how many days before its maturity date will the T-bill's market price first exceed $99,000?

○12. An investor purchased a 182-day, $25,000 Province of Alberta Treasury bill on its date of issue for $24,610 and sold it 60 days later for $24,750.

    a. What rate of return was implied in the original price?

    b. What rate of return did the market require on the sale date?

    c. What rate of return did the original investor actually realize during the 60-day holding period?

○13. A $100,000, 168-day Government of Canada Treasury bill was purchased on its date of issue to yield 3.1%.

    a. What price did the investor pay?

    b. Calculate the market value of the T-bill 85 days later if the rate of return then required by the market has:
        (i) risen to 3.4%.
        (ii) remained at 3.1%.
        (iii) fallen to 2.8%.

    c. Calculate the rate of return actually realized by the investor if the T-bill is sold at each of the three prices calculated in Part (b).

14. Over the past 35 years, the prevailing market yield or discount rate on 90-day T-bills has ranged from a low of 0.20% in May 2009 to a high of 20.82% in August of 1981. (The period from 1979 to 1990 was a time of historically high inflation rates and interest rates.) How much more would you have paid for a $100,000 face value 90-day T-bill at the May 2009 discount rate than at the August 1981 discount rate?

7.4 DEMAND LOANS

Most businesses arrange demand loans or lines of credit to meet short-term financing requirements. Many individuals obtain personal lines of credit, set up on a demand basis, to meet their short-term borrowing needs.

COMMON TERMS AND CONDITIONS

LO4 The name **demand loan** comes from the lender's right to demand full repayment of the loan at any time without notice. This rarely happens if the borrower fulfills the terms of the loan (unless the lender has reason to believe the borrower's financial condition is deteriorating). The borrower may repay any portion of the loan at any time without penalty.

The interest rate charged on demand loans is usually "floating." This means that the rate is linked to the prime rate of interest in the banking system. Interest rates are then quoted as "prime plus" some additional amount. For example, if a small business is viewed by the lender as a moderate risk, the business might be charged a rate of prime plus 2% or prime plus 3%.

Interest on a demand loan is paid on the same date each month. The most common approach is to calculate interest *from (and including)* the previous interest payment date *up to (but not including)* the current interest payment date. This procedure is consistent with the count-the-first-day-but-not-the-last-day rule for determining the length of the time interval in simple-interest calculations. The interest rate in effect each day is applied to each day's *closing* loan balance.

Arrangements for repaying the loan principal are negotiated between the borrower and lender. Acceptable terms will depend upon the purpose of the loan, the nature of the security given, and the seasonality of the borrower's income. The two most common demand loan arrangements are:

- A revolving loan.
- A fixed-payment loan.

REVOLVING LOANS

LO4 Revolving loans are preferred by businesses and individuals whose short-term borrowing requirements vary over the year. These loans give borrowers the flexibility to borrow additional funds at their discretion and to reduce their debt whenever extra funds are available. Most *lines of credit* and business *operating loans* are set up as revolving loans.[3]

The borrower and the lending institution negotiate the terms and conditions of the loan—the credit limit, the security required, the interest rate, and so on. Subject to the credit limit and a few general guidelines, draws (or advances) of principal and repayments of principal are at the borrower's discretion.

For *fully-secured* revolving loans, the minimum monthly payment may be only the accrued interest on the outstanding loan balance. In most other cases, the minimum monthly payment is something like "the greater of $100 or 3% of the *current* balance." The "current balance" in this context includes accrued interest. The lender usually requires that the borrower have a chequing account (sometimes called a *current account* for a business) with the lending institution. The required monthly payment is then automatically withdrawn from the chequing account on the interest payment date.

---

[3] Visa and MasterCard accounts are in many respects similar to revolving lines of credit. Interest rates are usually fixed rather than floating. Interest (based on $I = Prt$ and the daily closing balance) is paid monthly. However, the calculations are complicated by special rules concerning waiver of interest when the balance is paid in full, different treatment for cash advances than for credit purchases, days of grace, etc. These rules make the interest calculations considerably more tedious (but not more mathematically instructive) than calculations for demand loans.

EXAMPLE 7.4A   **CALCULATION OF INTEREST ON A REVOLVING LOAN**

On March 20, Hank's Cycle Shop received an initial advance of $10,000 on its revolving demand loan. On the fifteenth of each month, interest is calculated (up to but not including the fifteenth) and deducted from Hank's bank account. The floating rate of interest started at 9.75% and dropped to 9.5% on April 5. On April 19, another $10,000 was drawn on the line of credit. What interest was charged to the bank account on April 15 and May 15?

SOLUTION

The one-month period ending on an interest payment date (April 15 and May 15) must be broken into intervals within which the balance on the loan *and* the interest rate are constant. In the following table, we should count the first day but not the last day in each interval. This will cause April 5 (the first day at the 9.5% interest rate) to be included in the second interval but not in the first interval.

Interval	Days	Principal ($)	Rate (%)	Amount of Interest
March 20–April 5	16	10,000	9.75	$\$10{,}000(0.0975)\left(\dfrac{16}{365}\right) = \$42.74$
April 5–April 15	10	10,000	9.5	$\$10{,}000(0.095)\left(\dfrac{10}{365}\right) = 26.03$
				Interest charged on April 15: $\underline{\$68.77}$
April 15–April 19	4	10,000	9.5	$\$10{,}000(0.095)\left(\dfrac{4}{365}\right) = \$10.41$
April 19–May 15	26	20,000	9.5	$\$20{,}000(0.095)\left(\dfrac{26}{365}\right) = 135.34$
				Interest charged on May 15: $\underline{\$145.75}$

The interest charged to Hank's bank account on April 15 was $68.77 and on May 15 was $145.75.

LO6   **Repayment Schedule For a Revolving Loan** A **loan repayment schedule** is a table in which interest charges, loan draws and payments, and outstanding balances are recorded. The schedule helps us organize our calculations and properly allocate payments to interest and principal.

    Figure 7.1 presents a format for a demand loan repayment schedule. You enter a row in the schedule when any of the following three events takes place:

- A principal amount is advanced or repaid.

- The interest rate changes.

- Interest (and possibly principal) is paid on an interest payment date.

FIGURE 7.1   Demand Loan Repayment Schedule

(1)	(2)	(3)	(4)	(5)	(6)	(7)	(8)
Date	Number of days	Interest Rate	Interest	Accrued interest	Payment (Advance)	Principal portion	Balance

The columns in the table are used as follows. (Each item in the following list refers to the corresponding numbered column in Figure 7.1.)

1. In chronological order down Column (1), enter the **Dates** on which payments are made, the interest rate changes, or principal amounts are advanced to the borrower.

2. Enter into Column (2) the **number of days** in the interval *ending* on each date in Column (1). In any particular row, record the number of days from (and including) the *previous* row's date to (but not including) the date in the row *at hand*.

3. Enter into Column (3) the **interest rate** that applies to each interval in Column (2). When the date in Column (1) is the date on which a new interest rate takes effect, the interest rate in Column (3) is still the *previous rate*. The reason is that the days in Column (2) are for the period *up to but not including* the date in Column (1).

4. In Column (4), enter the **Interest** charge ($I = Prt$) for the number of days (t) in Column (2) at the interest rate (r) in Column (3) on the balance (P) from Column (8) of the *preceding* line.

5. In Column (5), enter the cumulative total of unpaid or **Accrued interest** as of the current row's date. This amount is the interest just calculated in Column (4) plus any previously accrued but unpaid interest [from Column (5) in the *preceding* line].

6. In Column (6), enter the amount of any **Payment** (of principal and/or interest). A loan **Advance** is enclosed in brackets to distinguish it from a loan payment.

7. On an interest payment date, the accrued interest in Column (5) is deducted from the payment to obtain the **Principal portion** of the payment. Put a single stroke through the accrued interest in Column (5) as a reminder that it has been paid and should not be carried forward to the next period.

   If an *unscheduled* payment is entered in Column (6), the entire amount is usually applied to principal. Enter it again in Column (7). Similarly, the amount of any loan advance in Column (6) should be duplicated in Column (7).

8. The new loan **Balance** is the previous line's balance *less* any principal repaid or *plus* any principal advanced [the amount in Column (7)].

EXAMPLE 7.4B   REPAYMENT SCHEDULE FOR A REVOLVING OPERATING LOAN

The Bank of Montreal approved a $50,000 line of credit on a demand basis to Tanya's Wardrobes to finance the store's inventory. Interest at the rate of prime plus 3% is charged to Tanya's chequing account at the bank on the twenty-third of each month. The initial advance was $25,000 on September 23 when the prime rate stood at 5.25%. There were further advances of $8000 on October 30 and $10,000 on November 15. Payments of $7000 and $14,000 were applied against the principal on December 15 and January 15, respectively. The prime rate rose to 5.75% effective December 5. What was the total interest paid on the loan for the period September 23 to January 23?

SOLUTION

A large amount of information is given in the statement of the problem. The best way to organize the data is to construct a repayment schedule using the format in Figure 7.1. In the date column, list in chronological order all of the dates on which a transaction or an event affecting the loan occurs. These are the dates of advances, payments of principal or interest, and interest rate changes. Next, enter the information that is given for each transaction or event. At this point the schedule has the following entries:

Date	Number of days	Interest rate (%)	Interest ($)	Accrued interest ($)	Payment (Advance) ($)	Principal portion ($)	Balance ($)
Sept 23	—	—	—	—	(25,000)	(25,000)	25,000
Oct 23		8.25				0	
Oct 30		8.25			(8000)	(8000)	
Nov 15		8.25			(10,000)	(10,000)	
Nov 23		8.25				0	
Dec 5		8.25				0	
Dec 15		8.75			7000	7000	
Dec 23		8.75				0	
Jan 15		8.75			14,000	14,000	
Jan 23		8.75				0	

Note that 8.25% (5.25% + 3%) has been entered on the December 5 line. Although the interest rate changes to 8.75% *effective* December 5, the "Number of days" entry on this line will be the number of days from (and including) November 23 to (but not including) December 5. These 13 days are still charged interest at the 8.25% rate. The 8.75% rate will first apply to the December 5 to December 15 period, which is handled on the December 15 line.

The "Number of days" column may be completed next. Then the calculations can proceed row by row to obtain the full schedule. The circled numbers (①, ②, etc.) in the following schedule refer to sample calculations listed after the schedule. Draw a stroke through an accrued interest figure when the interest is paid.

Date	Number of days	Interest rate (%)	Interest ($)	Accrued interest ($)	Payment (Advance) ($)	Principal portion ($)	Balance ($)
Sept 23	—	—	—	—	(25,000)	(25,000)	25,000
Oct 23	30	8.25	169.52 ①	~~169.52~~	169.52	0	25,000
Oct 30	7	8.25	39.55	39.55	(8000)	(8000)	33,000
Nov 15	16	8.25	119.34 ②	158.89 ③	(10,000)	(10,000)	43,000
Nov 23	8	8.25	77.75 ④	~~236.64~~ ⑤	236.64	0	43,000
Dec 5	12	8.25	116.63	116.63		0	43,000
Dec 15	10	8.75	103.08	219.71	7000	7000	36,000
Dec 23	8	8.75	69.04	~~288.75~~	288.75	0	36,000
Jan 15	23	8.75	198.49	198.49	14,000	14,000	22,000
Jan 23	8	8.75	42.19	~~240.68~~	240.68	0	22,000

① $I = Prt = \$25{,}000(0.0825)(\frac{30}{365}) = \$169.52$

② $I = \$33{,}000(0.0825)(\frac{16}{365}) = \$119.34$

③ Accrued interest = $\$39.55 + \$119.34 = \$158.89$

④ $I = \$43{,}000(0.0825)(\frac{8}{365}) = \$77.75$

⑤ Accrued interest = $\$158.89 + \$77.75 = \$236.64$

The total interest paid on the loan for the period September 23 to January 23 was

$$\$169.52 + \$236.64 + \$288.75 + \$240.68 = \$935.59$$

EXAMPLE 7.4C   **REPAYMENT SCHEDULE FOR A REVOLVING PERSONAL LINE OF CREDIT**

Warren Bitenko has a $20,000 personal line of credit with the RBC Royal Bank. The interest rate is prime + 2.5%. On the last day of each month, a payment equal to the greater of $100 or 3% of the current balance (including the current month's accrued interest) is deducted from his chequing account.

On July 6, he took his first advance of $2000. On August 15, he took another draw of $7500. The prime rate started at 6%, and rose to 6.25% on September 9. Prepare a loan repayment schedule up to and including September 30.

SOLUTION

Begin a schedule by entering, in chronological order, the dates of advances, interest rate changes, and payments. Information known about these events should also be entered. At this point, the schedule has the following entries and you are ready to begin the calculations.

Date	Number of days	Interest rate (%)	Interest ($)	Accrued interest ($)	Payment (Advance) ($)	Principal portion ($)	Balance ($)
July 6	—	8.5	—	—	(2000)	(2000)	2000
July 31		8.5					
Aug 15		8.5			(7500)	(7500)	
Aug 31		8.5					
Sept 9		8.5					
Sept 30		8.75					

Now proceed row by row to construct the loan schedule. The circled numbers (①, ②, etc.) in the following schedule refer to the sample calculations listed immediately after the schedule.

Date	Number of days	Interest rate (%)	Interest ($)	Accrued interest ($)	Payment (Advance) ($)	Principal portion ($)	Balance ($)
July 6	—	8.5	—	—	(2000.00)	(2000.00)	2000.00
July 31	25	8.5	11.64 ①	11.64	100.00 ②	88.36 ③	1911.64
Aug 15	15	8.5	6.68	6.68	(7500.00)	(7500.00)	9411.64
Aug 31	16	8.5	35.07	41.75	283.60 ④	241.85 ⑤	9169.79
Sept 9	9	8.5	19.22	19.22			9169.79
Sept 30	21	8.75	46.16	65.38	277.06	211.68	8958.11

① Interest $= Prt = \$2000(0.085)(\frac{25}{365}) = \$11.64$

② The payment is the greater of \$100 or $0.03 \times \$2011.64 = \$60.35$. The larger amount is \$100.

③ Principal repaid $= \$100 - \$11.64 = \$88.36$

④ Required payment $= 0.03 \times$ Current balance $= 0.03 \times (\$9411.64 + \$41.75) = \$283.60$

⑤ Principal repaid $= \$283.60 - \$41.75 = \$241.85$

FIXED-PAYMENT LOANS

LO6 A fixed-payment loan requires *equal* monthly payments. The interest component of each payment is the interest that has accrued on the outstanding principal balance since the preceding payment. As the outstanding loan balance declines, each successive payment has a smaller interest component and a larger principal component.

EXAMPLE 7.4D   **REPAYMENT SCHEDULE FOR A FIXED-PAYMENT LOAN**

Bailey & Co. borrowed \$4000 at prime plus $1\frac{1}{2}\%$ from its bank on May 29 to purchase a new computer system. The floating-rate demand loan requires fixed monthly payments of \$800 on the first day of each month, beginning July 1. The prime rate was at 7.25% on May 29 and increased to 7.5% effective August 4. Construct a full repayment schedule showing details of the allocation of each payment to interest and principal.

SOLUTION

On a loan repayment schedule, enter the dates of payments and interest rate changes in chronological order. Information known about these events can also be entered. We can anticipate that a sixth payment (of less than \$800) on December 1 will pay off the loan. At this point, the schedule has the following entries:

Date	Number of days	Interest rate (%)	Interest ($)	Accrued interest ($)	Payment (Advance) ($)	Principal portion ($)	Balance ($)
May 29	—	8.75	—	—	(4000)	(4000.00)	4000.00
July 1		8.75			800		
Aug 1		8.75			800		
Aug 4		8.75					
Sept 1		9			800		
Oct 1		9			800		
Nov 1		9			800		
Dec 1		9					

Proceed with the calculations row by row. The circled numbers (①, ②, etc.) in the following schedule refer to sample calculations listed after the schedule. Draw a stroke through an accrued interest figure when the interest has been paid.

Date	Number of days	Interest rate (%)	Interest ($)	Accrued interest ($)	Payment (Advance) ($)	Principal portion ($)	Balance ($)
May 29	—	8.75	—	—	(4000)	(4000.00)	4000.00
July 1	33	8.75	31.64 ①	31.64	800	768.36 ②	3231.64
Aug 1	31	8.75	24.02	24.02	800	775.98	2455.66
Aug 4	3	8.75	1.77	1.77			
Sept 1	28	9	16.95	18.72	800	781.28	1674.38
Oct 1	30	9	12.39	12.39	800	787.61	886.77
Nov 1	31	9	6.78	6.78	800	793.22	93.55
Dec 1	30	9	0.69	0.69	94.24 ③	93.55	0

① $I = Prt = \$4000(0.0875)(\frac{33}{365}) = \$31.64$

② Principal portion = $\$800 - \$31.64 = \$768.36$

③ Final payment = $\$93.55 + \$0.69 = \$94.24$

SPREADSHEET STRATEGIES   Demand Loan Repayment Schedules

Connect provides two partially completed templates for revolving loan and fixed-payment loan schedules. Go to the Student Edition of Connect and find "Demand Loan Schedules."

The main features of the loan schedules are presented below. The "Introduction" page of the "Demand Loan Schedule" workbook describes how to handle rounding using Excel's ROUND function. Detailed instructions for programming and completing the templates are provided with each template.

Here we present the completed spreadsheets for Examples 7.4B and 7.4D. A sample of the formula used in each programmed column is provided under each schedule.

	A	B	C	D	E	F	G	H
1								
2	Using a spreadsheet for a Revolving Loan Schedule.							
3	Example 7.4B:							
4								
5		Number	Interest			Accrued	Payment	Principal	
6	Date	of days	rate	Interest	interest	(Advance)	portion	Balance
7	23-Sep	– –	– –	– –	– –	($25,000.00)	($25,000.00)	$25,000.00
8	23-Oct	30	8.25%	$169.52	$169.52		$169.52	$0.00	$25,000.00
9	30-Oct	7	8.25%	$39.55	$39.55	($8,000.00)	($8,000.00)	$33,000.00
10	15-Nov	16	8.25%	$119.34	$158.89	($10,000.00)	($10,000.00)	$43,000.00
11	23-Nov	8	8.25%	$77.75	$236.64		$236.64	$0.00	$43,000.00
12	5-Dec	12	8.25%	$116.63	$116.63		$0.00	$43,000.00
13	15-Dec	10	8.75%	$103.08	$219.71	$7,000.00	$7,000.00	$36,000.00
14	23-Dec	8	8.75%	$69.04	$288.75		$288.75	$0.00	$36,000.00
15	15-Jan	23	8.75%	$198.49	$198.49	$14,000.00	$14,000.00	$22,000.00
16	23-Jan	8	8.75%	$42.19	$240.68		$240.68	$0.00	$22,000.00
17								
18	Sample Formulas	Cell B8:	=A8-A7			Cell D8:	=ROUND(H7*C8*B8/365,2)	
19			Cell E8:	=D8			Cell H8:	=H7-G8
20			Cell E10:	=D10+E9				
21								
22	Using a spreadsheet for a Fixed-Payment Loan Schedule.							
23	Example 7.4D:							
24								
25		Number	Interest			Accrued	Payment	Principal	
26	Date	of days	rate	Interest	interest	(Advance)	portion	Balance
27	29-May	– –	– –	– –	– –	($4,000.00)	($4,000.00)	$4,000.00
28	1-Jul	33	8.75%	$31.64	$31.64	$800.00	$768.36	$3,231.64
29	1-Aug	31	8.75%	$24.02	$24.02	$800.00	$775.98	$2,455.66
30	4-Aug	3	8.75%	$1.77	$1.77			$2,455.66
31	1-Sep	28	9.00%	$16.95	$18.72	$800.00	$781.28	$1,674.38
32	1-Oct	30	9.00%	$12.39	$12.39	$800.00	$787.61	$886.77
33	1-Nov	31	9.00%	$6.78	$6.78	$800.00	$793.22	$93.55
34	1-Dec	30	9.00%	$0.69	$0.69	$94.24	$93.55	$0.00
35								
36	Sample Formulas	Cell B28:	=A28-A27			Cell D28:	=ROUND(H27*C28*B28/365,2)	
37			Cell E28:	=D28			Cell G28:	=F28-E28
38			Cell E31:	=D31+E30			Cell H28:	=H27-M28
39							Cell F34:	=H33+E34
40								

POINT OF INTEREST

Improving the Score on Your Credit Report

Personal debt is soaring as more and more people become bogged down in loans and credit card debt. In late 2009, the Bank of Canada reported that total residential mortgage debt passed the $930 billion mark. Other consumer debt (mainly personal loans, personal lines of credit and credit card balances) exceeded $445 billion. Together these represent a debt of over $41,000 for every adult and child in the country! All of these measures of debt more than doubled during the preceding ten years.

As personal debt levels rise faster than income, personal credit reports and credit scores are increasingly important to the lenders providing consumer credit. Anyone who has ever borrowed money or applied for a credit card is likely to have a personal file with one or both of Canada's two main credit bureaus: Equifax Canada and TransUnion Canada. These are independent companies whose business is maintaining records on how every individual and business in Canada manages their debt.

Most businesses granting credit are members of one or both of these credit bureaus, and they supply the bureaus with information on how customers handle their credit. Any business thinking of granting credit to you, or providing you with a service that you will receive before you pay for it (such as telephone service or apartment rental) can obtain a comprehensive credit report on you from the credit bureau.

Your credit report contains information about every loan or credit card you've had in the previous six years, the credit limit on each account, how much you owe, whether you pay on time, and a list of authorized credit grantors that have accessed your file. Each account or loan has a *credit rating* notation. For example, revolving loans are rated from R1 (meaning that you have made payments "as agreed" or within 30 days of billing) to R9 (meaning your account has been classified as a "bad debt" or has been "placed for collection").

The credit bureau also assigns a single comprehensive *credit score* (often referred to as the FICO score or Beacon score). This score is based on a formula that takes into account several factors indicating credit-worthiness. The score can range from 300 to 900—the higher the number the better. About 27% of the population have a score within the range 750 to 799. Statistically, only 2% of borrowers in this category will default on a debt within the next two years. Consequently, anyone with this score is very likely to get the loan or credit for which he/she applies.

You can (and probably should) periodically obtain a copy of your credit report. Stories of inaccuracies in credit reports abound. CBC Television's Marketplace program once asked 100 people to check their credit reports for errors. More than 40 found mistakes—13 were serious enough to affect the individual's ability to obtain credit. For a fee of $20 to $25, you can apply online to see your credit report. Alternatively, you can obtain one free credit report per year by a mail-in request. (This basic report does not include your all-important FICO score—you have to pay extra to get that.) There is a standard (though not necessarily speedy) process for correcting errors in the report.

Here are the main factors (with their weightings) that affect your FICO credit score:

- *Payment history* (35%). Pay your debts on time.
- *Amounts owed* (30%). Try not to run up the balances to your credit limit. Keeping balances below 75% of the credit limit can help your score.
- *Length of credit history* (15%). A longer experience with a creditor and a record of paying down revolving account balances will help your score.
- *New credit* (10%). Don't apply for credit unless you have a genuine need. Too many inquiries by potential creditors in a short period of time is a sign of financial difficulties.
- *Number and types of credit/loan accounts* (10%). A large number of accounts (credit cards, retail accounts, mortgage, and car loan) can reduce your score. Pay off your credit card balance instead of moving it to a new account. Such "balance transfers" can hurt your score.

EXERCISE 7.4

≋ connect

Spreadsheet templates: Connect presents two partially completed Excel templates for demand loan repayment schedules. Go to the Student Edition of Connect and find "Demand Loan Schedules." You can use the Revolving Loan template for Problems 1 to 9 and the Fixed-Payment Loan template for Problems 10 to 14.

Answers to the odd-numbered problems are at the end of the book.

Revolving Demand Loans

○**1.** Dr. Robillard obtained a $75,000 operating line of credit at prime plus 1%. Accrued interest up to but not including the last day of the month is deducted from his bank account on the last day of each month. On February 5 (of a leap year) he received the first draw of $15,000. He made a payment of $10,000 toward principal on March 15, but took another draw of $7000 on May 1. Prepare a loan repayment schedule showing the amount of interest charged to his bank account on the last days of February, March, April, and May. Assume that the prime rate remained at 7.5% through to the end of May.

○**2.** Mr. Michaluk has a $50,000 personal (revolving) line of credit with the Canadian Imperial Bank of Commerce (CIBC). The loan is on a demand basis at a floating rate of prime plus 1.5%. On the fifteenth of each month, a payment equal to the greater of $100 or 3% of the combined principal and accrued interest is deducted from his chequing account. The principal balance after a payment on September 15 stood at $23,465.72. Prepare the loan repayment schedule from September 15 up to and including the payment on January 15. Assume that he makes the minimum payments and the prime rate remains at 5.25%.

○**3.** McKenzie Wood Products negotiated a $200,000 revolving line of credit with the Bank of Montreal at prime plus 2%. On the twentieth of each month, interest is calculated (up to but not including the twentieth) and deducted from the company's chequing account. If the initial loan advance of $25,000 on July 3 was followed by a further advance of $30,000 on July 29, how much interest was charged on July 20 and August 20? The prime rate was at 8% on July 3 and fell to 7.75% on August 5.

○**4.** On the June 12 interest payment date, the outstanding balance on Delta Nurseries' revolving loan was $65,000. The floating interest rate on the loan stood at 6.25% on June 12, but rose to 6.5% on July 3, and to 7% on July 29. If Delta made principal payments of $10,000 on June 30 and July 31, what were the interest charges to its bank account on July 12 and August 12? Present a repayment schedule supporting the calculations.

○**5.** Scotiabank approved a $75,000 line of credit for Curved Comfort Furniture on the security of its accounts receivable. Curved Comfort drew down $30,000 on October 7, another $15,000 on November 24, and $20,000 on December 23. The bank debited interest at the rate of prime plus 1.5% from the business's bank account on the fifteenth of each month. The prime rate was 6.25% on October 7, and dropped by 0.25% on December 17. Present a loan repayment schedule showing details of transactions up to and including January 15.

○**6.** Shoreline Yachts has a $1 million line of credit with the RBC Royal Bank, secured by its inventory of sailboats. Interest is charged at the floating (naturally!) rate of prime plus 2% on the tenth of each month. On February 10 (of a non-leap year), the loan balance stood at $770,000 and the prime rate at 6.5%. Shoreline took an additional $100,000 draw on March 1. Spring sales enabled Shoreline to make payments of $125,000 and $150,000 against the principal on March 30 and April 28. The prime rate rose by

0.5% on April 8. What total interest was Shoreline charged for the three months from February 10 to May 10? Present a repayment schedule showing how this interest figure was determined.

○**7.** Hercules Sports obtained a $60,000 operating line of credit on March 26. Interest charges at the rate of prime plus 2.5% were deducted from its chequing account on the eighteenth of each month. Hercules took an initial draw of $30,000 on March 31, when the prime rate was 5%. Further advances of $10,000 and $15,000 were taken on April 28 and June 1. Payments of $5000 and $10,000 were applied against the principal on June 18 and July 3. The prime rate rose to 5.25% effective May 14. Present a repayment schedule showing details of transactions up to and including July 18.

○**8.** Benjamin has a $20,000 personal line of credit at prime plus 2% with his credit union. His minimum end-of-month payment is the greater of $100 or 3% of the combined principal and accrued interest. After his payment on April 30, his balance was $3046.33. On May 23, he used his income tax refund to make a principal payment of $1000. On July 17, he took a $7000 advance to purchase a car. The prime rate began at 6%, rose 0.25% on June 25, and jumped another 0.25% on July 18. Prepare a loan repayment schedule showing details of payments on May 31, June 30, and July 31.

○**9.** Bronwyn's $15,000 line of credit is at prime plus 2.5%. The minimum payment (the greater of $100 or 3% of the combined principal and accrued interest) is automatically deducted from her chequing account on the fifteenth of each month. After the payment on August 15, her balance was $3589.80. To reduce the loan faster, she makes an additional discretionary payment of $300 on the last day of each month. Each $300 payment is applied entirely to principal. Prepare a repayment schedule for the August 15 to November 15 period. The prime rate was at 6.25% on August 15 but dropped 0.25% effective October 11.

Fixed-Payment Demand Loans

○**10.** A $5000 demand loan was advanced on June 3. Fixed monthly payments of $1000 were required on the first day of each month beginning July 1. Prepare the full repayment schedule for the loan. Assume that the interest rate remained at 8.75% for the life of the loan.

○**11.** Giovando, Lindstrom & Co. obtained a $6000 demand loan at prime plus 1.5% on April 1 to purchase new office furniture. The company agreed to fixed monthly payments of $1000 on the first of each month, beginning May 1. Calculate the total interest charges over the life of the loan if the prime rate started at 6.75% on April 1, decreased to 6.5% effective June 7, and returned to 6.75% on August 27. Present a repayment schedule in support of your answer.

○**12.** Doina borrowed $7000 from her credit union on a demand loan on July 20 to purchase a motorcycle. The terms of the loan require fixed monthly payments of $1400 on the first day of each month, beginning September 1. The floating rate on the loan is prime plus 3%. The prime rate started at 5.75%, but rose 0.5% on August 19, and another 0.25% effective November 2. Prepare a loan repayment schedule presenting the amount of each payment and the allocation of each payment to interest and principal.

○**13.** Beth borrowed $5000 on demand from TD Canada Trust on February 23 for a Registered Retirement Savings Plan (RRSP) contribution. Because she used the loan proceeds to purchase the bank's mutual funds for her RRSP, she received a special interest rate of prime plus 0.5%. Beth was required to make fixed monthly payments of $1000 on the fifteenth of each month, beginning April 15. The prime rate was initially

4.75%, but it jumped to 5% effective June 15 and increased another 0.25% on July 31. (It was not a leap year.) Construct a repayment schedule showing the amount of each payment and the allocation of each payment to interest and principal.

○**14.** Dr. Chan obtained a $15,000 demand loan at prime plus 1.5% on September 13 from the Bank of Montreal to purchase a new dental X-ray machine. Fixed payments of $700 will be deducted from the dentist's chequing account on the twentieth of each month, beginning October 20. The prime rate was 7.5% at the outset, dropped to 7.25% on the subsequent November 26, and rose to 7.75% on January 29. Prepare a loan repayment schedule showing the details of the first five payments.

7.5 **CANADA STUDENT LOANS**

LO4

The first significant debt incurred by many who pursue post-secondary education is a student loan. All provincial governments and the federal government offer student loan programs. Only the federal government's Canada Student Loans Program (CSLP) is discussed in this section. Currently about 450,000 students (representing over half of post-secondary enrolment) borrow over $2.1 billion per year under the program.

No interest is charged on Canada Student Loans as long as you retain full-time student status (at least 60% of a full course load) under the CSLP. Six months after you cease to be a student, you must begin to make monthly loan payments. For example, if final examinations end on May 7 and you do not return to college the following September, the six-month grace period runs from June 1 to November 30. Interest accrues at the floating rate of prime + $2\frac{1}{2}$% during this six-month grace period. You may pay the accrued interest at the end of the grace period or have it *capitalized* (that is, converted to principal).

Before the end of the grace period, you must make arrangements with the National Student Loans Service Centre to consolidate all Canada Student Loans into a single loan. The first payment on a consolidated loan is due one month after the end of the grace period. In the preceding example, the first payment is due December 31.

At the time of consolidation, you choose either a *floating* interest rate of prime plus $2\frac{1}{2}$% or a *fixed* rate equal to the prime rate (at the time of consolidation) plus 5%. The choice may not be changed later. You also choose the amount of the *fixed* monthly payment subject to a maximum term of 114 months.

The interest portion of each monthly payment is calculated using the daily-interest method with the exact number of days since the previous payment. A loan repayment schedule can be constructed using the same format as for demand loans in Section 7.4. (Canada Student Loans are not demand loans from the lender's point of view. However, the borrower

LO5 may prepay additional principal at any time without penalty.)

NET @ssets

Human Resources and Social Development Canada maintains a Web site for the Canada Student Loans Program (CSLP).

Here, you can calculate the monthly payment you will face on your combined CSLs, *not* including any capitalized interest from the grace period.

POINT OF INTEREST

Repaying Student Loans Is a Must

After you graduate, do you have plans to travel or buy a new car or rent a better apartment? Such expenditures should be weighed against repaying your student loan. Paying off student loans is probably the most pressing financial matter facing a graduate, even ahead of as financially virtuous a move as starting a Registered Retirement Savings Plan.

If you are unable to manage your student debt, it could ruin your credit rating and make it difficult to get a mortgage or car loan in the future. Delinquent student loans are reported to credit bureaus and will affect your credit rating. On the other hand, smooth repayment of your student debts will help to establish you as a preferred borrower.

To partially offset the cost of interest on your student loan, there are federal and provincial tax credits you can claim on your personal tax return. The provincial tax credit varies somewhat from province to province, but the outcome is approximately this— for every $100 of interest you pay on a student loan, the amount of income tax you pay will be reduced by about $22.

If you are going to have difficulty making payments on your Canada Student Loan because you have a low-paying job or you are unable to find work for a few months, the federal student loan Repayment Assistance Program, introduced in August of 2009, can provide help. Based upon the borrower's family income and family size, the program establishes the amount of an affordable monthly student-loan payment. The upper limit for an affordable monthly payment is 20% of family income; it could be as low as $0! If the affordable monthly payment is less than the prescribed monthly payment, the federal government will pay the interest on the student loan for up to five years. All of the borrower's payments will be applied directly to reducing the principal balance on the loan.

If the borrower's financial difficulties remain after the five years, the federal government may continue to cover the interest on the loan. In addition, the government may pay a portion of the monthly principal payment if the borrower's affordable monthly payment is insufficient to pay off the loan over the next ten years.

For the first few years after leaving school, declaring personal bankruptcy is not an option for shedding student-loan debt. Seven years must pass for student loans to be discharged in personal bankruptcy. (In a case of undue hardship, a bankrupt may apply to the Court for a discharge of student loans after five years.)

EXAMPLE 7.5A   **CONSTRUCTING A REPAYMENT SCHEDULE FOR A CANADA STUDENT LOAN**

Heidi had Canada Student Loans totalling $10,600 when she graduated from college. Her six-month grace period ended on November 30, and she chose to have the grace period's accrued interest converted to principal. Heidi selected the floating interest rate option (prime plus 2.5%) when the prime rate was at 5.5%. Monthly payments beginning December 31 were set at $150.

Prepare a loan repayment schedule up to and including the payment on the following March 31. The intervening February had 29 days. The prime rate increased from 5.5% to 5.75% effective August 3, and rose another 0.5% effective January 14.

SOLUTION

The period from June 1 to August 3 has $215 - 152 = 63$ days, and the period from August 3 to (and including) November 30 has $334 + 1 - 215 = 120$ days. The accrued interest at the end of the grace period was

$$
\begin{aligned}
I &= Pr_1t_1 + Pr_2t_2 \\
&= \$10,600(0.08)\left(\tfrac{63}{365}\right) + \$10,600(0.0825)\left(\tfrac{120}{365}\right) \\
&= \$146.37 + \$287.51 \\
&= \$433.88
\end{aligned}
$$

The consolidated loan balance at the end of November was

$$\$10,600.00 + \$433.88 = \$11,033.88$$

Date	Number of days	Interest rate (%)	Interest ($)	Accrued interest ($)	Payment (Advance) ($)	Principal portion ($)	Balance ($)
Dec 1	—	—	—	—	—	—	11,033.88
Dec 31	30	8.25	74.82 ①	74.82	150	75.18	10,958.70
Jan 14	14	8.25	34.68	34.68			
Jan 31	17	8.75	44.66	79.34	150	70.66	10,888.04
Feb 29	29	8.75	75.69	75.69	150	74.31	10,813.73
Mar 31	31	8.75	80.36	80.36	150	69.64	10,744.09

① Interest $= Prt = \$11,033.88(0.0825)\left(\tfrac{30}{365}\right) = \$74.82$

EXERCISE 7.5

Spreadsheet templates: The Fixed-Payment Loan template provided for Exercise 7.4 in Connect may be used for Canada Student Loan repayment schedules in Exercise 7.5. Go to the Student Edition of Connect and find "Demand Loan Schedules." Select the "Fixed-Payment Loan" worksheet.

Answers to the odd-numbered problems are at the end of the book.

○1. Sarah's Canada Student Loans totalled $9400 by the time she graduated from Georgian College in May. She arranged to capitalize the interest on November 30 and to begin monthly payments of $135 on December 31. Sarah elected the floating rate interest option (prime plus 2.5%). The prime rate stood at 6.75% on June 1, dropped to 6.5% effective September 3, and then increased by 0.25% on January 17. Prepare a repayment schedule presenting details of the first three payments. February has 28 days.

○2. Harjap completed his program at Nova Scotia Community College in December. On June 30, he paid all of the interest that had accrued (at prime plus 2.5%) on his $5800 Canada Student Loan during the six-month grace period. He selected the fixed rate option (prime plus 5%) and agreed to make end-of-month payments of $95 beginning July 31. The prime rate was 8% at the beginning of the grace period and rose by 0.5% effective March 29. On August 13, the prime rate rose another 0.5%. The relevant February had 28 days.

    a. What amount of interest accrued during the grace period?

    b. Calculate the total interest paid in the first three regular payments, and the balance owed after the third payment.

○3. Monica finished her program at New Brunswick Community College on June 3 with Canada Student Loans totalling $6800. She decided to capitalize the interest that accrued (at prime plus 2.5%) during the grace period. In addition to regular end-of-month payments of $200, she made an extra $500 lump payment on March 25 that was applied entirely to principal. The prime rate dropped from 6% to 5.75% effective

September 22, and declined another 0.5% effective March 2. Calculate the balance owed on the floating rate option after the regular March 31 payment. The relevant February had 28 days.

○**4.** Kari had Canada Student Loans totalling $3800 when she completed her program at Niagara College in December. She had enough savings at the end of June to pay the interest that had accrued during the six-month grace period. Kari made arrangements with the National Student Loans Service Centre to start end-of-month payments of $60 in July. She chose the fixed interest rate option (at prime plus 5%) when the prime rate was at 5.5%. Prepare a loan repayment schedule up to and including the September 30 payment.

○**5.** Seth had accumulated Canada Student Loans totalling $5200 by the time he graduated from Mount Royal College in May. He arranged with the National Student Loans Service Centre to select the floating-rate option (at prime plus $2\frac{1}{2}$%), to capitalize the grace period's accrued interest, and to begin monthly payments of $110 on December 31. Prepare a loan repayment schedule up to and including the February 28 payment. The prime rate was initially at 7.25%. It dropped by 0.25% effective January 31. Seth made an additional principal payment of $300 on February 14.

KEY TERMS

Commercial paper **p. 243**

Demand loan **p. 247**

Discounting a payment **p. 239**

Discount rate **p. 239**

Face value **p. 243**

Fair market value **p. 240**

Guaranteed Investment Certificate **p. 235**

Loan repayment schedule **p. 248**

Savings account **p. 235**

Treasury bill **p. 242**

SUMMARY OF NOTATION AND KEY FORMULAS

Valuation Principle

The fair market value of an investment is the sum of the present values of the cash flows expected from the investment. The discount rate used in the present value calculations should be the prevailing market-determined rate of return on this type of investment.

REVIEW PROBLEMS

Answers to the odd-numbered review problems are at the end of the book.

1. **(LO3)** Calculate the price of a $50,000, 91-day Province of Nova Scotia Treasury bill on its issue date when the market rate of return was 4.273%.

2. **(LO3)** A $100,000, 182-day Province of New Brunswick Treasury bill was issued 66 days ago. What will it sell at today to yield the purchaser 4.48%?

3. **(LO3)** A $100,000, 90-day commercial paper certificate issued by Bell Canada Enterprises was sold on its issue date for $98,950. What annual rate of return (to the nearest 0.001%) will it yield to the buyer?

4. **(LO1)** A chartered bank offers a rate of 5.50% on investments of $25,000 to $59,999 and a rate of 5.75% on investments of $60,000 to $99,999 in 90- to 365-day GICs. How much more will an investor earn from a single $80,000, 180-day GIC than from two $40,000, 180-day GICs?

5. **(LO1)** An Investment Savings account offered by a trust company pays a rate of 1.00% on the first $1000 of daily closing balance, 1.75% on the portion of the balance between $1000 and $3000, and 2.25% on any balance in excess of $3000. What interest will be paid for the month of January if the opening balance was $3678, $2800 was withdrawn on the fourteenth of the month, and $950 was deposited on the twenty-fifth of the month?

6. **(LO2)** An agreement stipulates payments of $4500, $3000, and $5500 in 4, 8, and 12 months, respectively, from today. What is the highest price an investor will offer today to purchase the agreement if he requires a minimum rate of return of 10.5%?

7. **(LO1)** Paul has $20,000 to invest for six months. For this amount, his bank pays 3.3% on a 90-day GIC and 3.5% on a 180-day GIC. If the interest rate on a 90-day GIC is the same three months from now, how much more interest will Paul earn by purchasing the 180-day GIC than by buying a 90-day GIC and then reinvesting its maturity value in a second 90-day GIC?

8. **(LO1)** Suppose that the current rates on 60- and 120-day GICs are 5.50% and 5.75%, respectively. An investor is weighing the alternatives of purchasing a 120-day GIC versus purchasing a 60-day GIC and then reinvesting its maturity value in a second 60-day GIC. What would the interest rate on 60-day GICs have to be 60 days from now for the investor to end up in the same financial position with either alternative?

○9. **(LO3)** A $100,000, 168-day Government of Canada Treasury bill was purchased on its date of issue to yield 3.7%.

    a. What price did the investor pay?

    b. Calculate the market value of the T-bill 85 days later if the annual rate of return then required by the market has:
      (i) risen to 4.0%.
      (ii) remained at 3.7%.
      (iii) fallen to 3.4%.

    c. Calculate the rate of return actually realized by the investor if the T-bill is sold at each of the three prices calculated in Part (b).

○10. **(LO3)** A $25,000, 91-day Province of Newfoundland Treasury bill was originally purchased at a price that would yield the investor a 5.438% rate of return if the T-bill is held until maturity. Thirty-four days later, the investor sold the T-bill through his broker for $24,775.

    a. What price did the original investor pay for the T-bill?

    b. What rate of return will the second investor realize if she holds the T-bill until maturity?

    c. What rate of return did the first investor realize during his holding period?

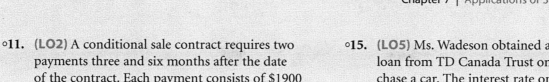

○11. **(LO2)** A conditional sale contract requires two payments three and six months after the date of the contract. Each payment consists of $1900 principal plus interest at 12.5% on $1900 from the date of the contract. One month into the contract, what price would a finance company pay for the contract if it requires an 18% rate of return on its purchases?

○12. **(LO2)** An assignable loan contract executed 3 months ago requires two payments of $3200 plus interest at 9% from the date of the contract, to be paid 4 and 8 months after the contract date. The payee is offering to sell the contract to a finance company in order to raise urgently needed cash. If the finance company requires a 16% rate of return, what price will it be prepared to pay today for the contract?

13. **(LO5)** Ruxandra's Canada Student Loans totalled $7200 by the time she finished Conestoga College in April. The accrued interest at prime plus 2.5% for the grace period was converted to principal on October 31. She chose the floating interest rate option and began monthly payments of $120 on November 30. The prime rate of interest was 5.5% on May 1, 5.25% effective July 9, and 5% effective December13. Prepare a repayment schedule presenting details of the first three payments.

○14. **(LO5)** George borrowed $4000 on demand from CIBC on January 28 for an RRSP contribution. Because he used the loan proceeds to purchase CIBC's mutual funds for his RRSP, the interest rate on the loan was set at the bank's prime rate. George agreed to make monthly payments of $600 (except for a smaller final payment) on the twenty-first of each month, beginning February 21. The prime rate was initially 6.75%, dropped to 6.5% effective May 15, and decreased another 0.25% on July 5. It was not a leap year. Construct a repayment schedule showing the amount of each payment and the allocation of each payment to interest and principal.

○15. **(LO5)** Ms. Wadeson obtained a $15,000 demand loan from TD Canada Trust on May 23 to purchase a car. The interest rate on the loan was prime plus 2%. The loan required payments of $700 on the fifteenth of each month, beginning June 15. The prime rate was 7.5% at the outset, dropped to 7.25% on July 26, and then jumped by 0.5% on September 14. Prepare a loan repayment schedule showing the details of the first four payments.

○16. **(LO5)** Mayfair Fashions has a $90,000 line of credit from the Bank of Montreal. Interest at prime plus 2% is deducted from Mayfair's chequing account on the twenty-fourth of each month. Mayfair initially drew down $40,000 on March 8 and another $15,000 on April 2. On June 5, $25,000 of principal was repaid. If the prime rate was 5.25% on March 8 and rose by 0.25% effective May 13, what were the first four interest deductions charged to the store's account?

○17. **(LO5)** Duncan Developments Ltd. obtained a $120,000 line of credit from its bank to subdivide a parcel of land it owned into four residential lots and to install water, sewer, and underground electrical services. Amounts advanced from time to time are payable on demand to its bank. Interest at prime plus 4% on the daily principal balance is charged to the developer's bank account on the twenty-sixth of each month. The developer must apply at least $30,000 from the proceeds of the sale of each lot against the loan principal. Duncan drew down $50,000 on June 3, $40,000 on June 30, and $25,000 on July 17. Two lots quickly sold, and Duncan repaid $30,000 on July 31 and $35,000 on August 18. The initial prime rate of 5% changed to 5.25% effective July 5 and 5.5% effective July 26. Prepare a repayment schedule showing loan activity and interest charges up to and including the interest payment on August 26.

CASE Debt Consolidation

Graham and Stacy are having difficulty stretching their salaries to pay their bills. Before their marriage three months ago, they purchased new furnishings for their apartment. Then they paid for their honeymoon with "plastic." Now the bills are all in. The following table lists their debts.

Debt	Balance ($)	Interest rate	Monthly payment Minimum	Fixed ($)
Car loan	6000	9.5%	—	300
Canada Student Loan	6800	Prime + 2.5%	—	100
Visa	4700	17.5%	5%	—
MasterCard	3900	15.9%	5%	—
Sears	3850	28.8%	4%	—
Canadian Tire	1250	28.8%	5%	—

The minimum monthly payment on each credit card is the indicated percentage of the *combined* principal balance plus accrued interest. The prime rate of interest is 6.5%.

With a view to consolidating their debts, Stacy and Graham have discussed their personal financial position with the Personal Banking Representative (PBR) at the bank close to their new apartment. The PBR is prepared to approve a $20,000 joint line of credit at prime plus 3% on the condition that $6000 be used immediately to pay off the car loan (obtained from another bank). The minimum monthly payment would be 3% of the combined principal balance plus accrued interest.

QUESTIONS

1. Assuming 30 days' interest on the indicated (principal) balances, what is the next minimum payment on each of the four credit cards?
2. If all the debt balances except the Canada Student Loan are consolidated in the new line of credit, what will be the first minimum payment? (Again assume a full 30 days' accrued interest on the principal for the fairest comparison with the "status quo.")
3. Based on the preceding results, what is the reduction in the first month's total debt service payments?
4. With respect to credit card debt only, what is the reduction in the first month's interest charges?
5. What (weighted) average interest rate are Graham and Stacy currently paying? What (weighted) average interest rate will they be paying after loan consolidation? (Include the Canada Student Loan in both calculations.)
6. Give two reasons why the PBR set the condition that Graham and Stacy use part of the line of credit to pay off the car loan.
7. Give two reasons why the PBR did not suggest a $27,000 line of credit and require that Graham and Stacy use the extra $7000 to pay off the Canada Student Loan.

APPENDIX 7A   # PROMISSORY NOTES

CONCEPTS AND DEFINITIONS

A promissory note is a written promise by one party to pay an amount of money to another party on a specific date, or on demand.

The required elements and the general rules of law that apply to promissory notes are set out in the federal Bills of Exchange Act. The basic information required in a promissory note is illustrated in Figure 7.2. A *demand* promissory note that might be used by a financial institution in connection with a demand loan is shown in Figure 7.3. The bracketed numbers in Figures 7.2 and 7.3 refer to the following terms.

1. The **maker** of the note is the debtor promising the payment.
2. The **payee** is the creditor to whom the payment is to be made.
3. The **face value** is the principal amount of the debt.
4. The **issue date** is the date on which the note was written or "made" and the date from which interest, if any, is computed.
5. The **term** of the note is the length of the loan period. (A demand note is payable at any time the payee chooses.)
6. The Bills of Exchange Act provides that, unless otherwise specified,[4] an extra **three days of grace** are added at the end of a note's term to determine the note's legal due date. The maker is not in default until after the **legal due date.** No days of grace are allowed in the case of demand notes.

FIGURE 7.2   Term Promissory Note

> PROMISSORY NOTE
>
> (3)   (4)
> $7200.00   Edmonton, Alberta   November 30, 2010
>
> ↑ (5)   Three months   after date   ___I___ promise to pay to the order of
>   (2)   Western Builders Supply Ltd.
> the sum of   seventy-two hundred and   – – – – – – – – – – – 00 /100 Dollars
> at   (8)   RBC Royal Bank, Terminal Plaza Branch
> for value received, with interest at   (7) ___12%___ per annum.
>
> Due: (6) March 3, 2011   Signed: (1)   J. Anderson

---

[4]   To extinguish the normal three days of grace, "NO DAYS OF GRACE" should be indicated on the note by the payee.

FIGURE 7.3 Demand Promissory Note

(3)		(4)
$5000.00	Hamilton, Ontario	April 30, 2010

ON DEMAND after date for value received, ____I____ promise to pay to the order of

(2) _____ Acme Distributing Ltd. _____ at

(8) _____ the RBC Royal Bank of Canada, Limeridge Mall Branch _____ the sum of

(3) __ five thousand __ – __ 00 __ /100 Dollars

(7) with interest thereon calculated and payable monthly at a rate equal to the RBC Royal Bank of Canada's prime interest rate per annum in effect from time to time plus __2__% per annum as well after as before maturity, default and judgment. At the date of this note, such prime interest rate is __8__% per annum.

Prime interest rate is the annual rate of interest announced from time to time by the RBC Royal Bank of Canada as a reference rate then in effect for determining interest rates on Canadian dollar commercial loans in Canada.

Signed: ___(1)___ *R. A. Matthews*

7. If interest is to be charged on the face value, the interest rate must be specified on the note. This makes it an interest-bearing promissory note. The days of grace are included in the interest period for calculating the maturity value (face value plus interest) of the note on the legal due date.[5] For terms of one year or less, it is understood that the simple-interest method should be used. (The maturity value of a non-interest-bearing note is the same as its face value.)

8. The note can specify the location at which the maker is to make the payment to the payee's account.

EXAMPLE 7AA | **DETERMINING THE LEGAL DUE DATE**

Show how the due date of the promissory note in Figure 7.2 is obtained.

SOLUTION

When the term of the note is specified in months, the end of the term is normally on the same numbered day in the expiry month as the date of issue. This particular instance is different, as there is no February 30. In such cases the last day of the expiry month is used as the end of the term. The legal due date is then three days later.

For the note in Figure 7.2, the term expires on February 28, 2011, and the legal due date is March 3, 2011.

---

[5] The Bills of Exchange Act provides that, whenever the last day of grace falls on a Saturday, Sunday, or legal holiday, the next following business day becomes the last day of grace. Technically, any extra calendar days added as a consequence of this provision should be included in the interest period. We will ignore this fine point of law to avoid the extra complication. The dollar amount involved (in relation to the maturity value otherwise calculated) is not material.

| EXAMPLE 7AB | **CALCULATING AN INTEREST-BEARING NOTE'S MATURITY VALUE** |

What is the maturity value of the note in Figure 7.2?

> **SOLUTION**
>
Even though the term is specified in months, the interest is calculated to the exact number of days, including the three days of grace.

Month	Days of interest
November	1
December	31
January	31
February	28
March	2
	93

$$\text{Maturity value} = P(1 + rt)$$
$$= \$7200[1 + 0.12(\tfrac{93}{365})]$$
$$= \$7420.14$$

The maturity value required to settle the note on March 3, 2011 is $7420.14.

| EXAMPLE 7AC | **LEGAL DUE DATE AND MATURITY VALUE OF AN INTEREST-BEARING NOTE** |

What would be the legal due date of the promissory note in Figure 7.2 if the term were 120 days instead of three months? What would be the maturity value of the note?

> **SOLUTION**
>
The legal due date will occur 123 days after the issue date.

Interval	Number of days of interest in the interval	Remaining days of interest in the term
Nov 30 and December	32	123 − 32 = 91
January	31	91 − 31 = 60
February	28	60 − 28 = 32
March	31	32 − 31 = 1
April 1 to April 2	1 ①	0

① We have counted the first day (Nov 30) of the term but not the last day (Apr 2).

The legal due date falls on April 2, 2011.

$$\text{Maturity value} = \$7200[1 + 0.12(\tfrac{123}{365})] = \$7491.16$$

The maturity value on the legal due date is $7491.16.

DISCOUNTING PROMISSORY NOTES

Promissory notes are *negotiable.* This means that the payee can transfer ownership of the note by *endorsing* it—that is, by signing his name on the back of the note. The payee will do this if he sells the note to an investor at any time before the note's legal due date. The maker is then obliged to pay the maturity value to the holder of the endorsed note on its due date.

The usual reason for selling a note is that the payee needs cash before the due date of the note. The price received for the note is often referred to as the **proceeds** of the note. The general case is presented in Figure 7.4. The face value P of an interest-bearing note earns interest at the rate r_1 (specified in the note) for the time period t_1 until its legal due date. That maturity value will be

$$S = P(1 + r_1 t_1)$$

We want to calculate the value of the note on the date of sale, a time period t_2 prior to the due date.

FIGURE 7.4   Calculating the Proceeds of a Promissory Note

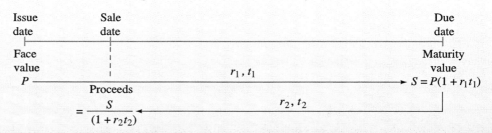

According to the Valuation Principle, the purchase price should be the present value of the maturity value discounted at the buyer's required rate of return. That is,

$$\text{Purchase price (Proceeds)} = \frac{S}{1 + r_2 t_2}$$

In summary, the calculation of the purchase price or proceeds of a promissory note is a two-step procedure.

1. Calculate the maturity value on the due date using the interest rate *specified in the note.* If the note does not bear interest, its maturity value is the same as its face value.
2. Calculate the present value, on the date of sale, of the maturity value using the discount rate agreed upon by the buyer and the seller.

N

EXAMPLE 7AD   **CALCULATING THE PROCEEDS OF A NON-INTEREST-BEARING NOTE**

A 150-day non-interest-bearing note for $2500 was made on June 15. The note was sold on August 21 at a price reflecting a discount rate of 12.5%. What were the proceeds of the note?

SOLUTION

There are 153 days from the issue date until the legal due date. By August 21, $16 + 31 + 20 = 67$ of the days have passed and $153 - 67 = 86$ days remain.

This information and the solution approach are presented in the following time diagram.

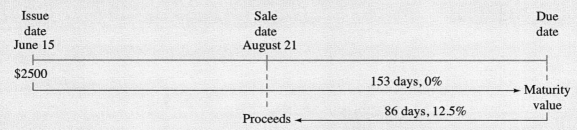

Since the face value does not earn interest, the maturity value will equal the face value of $2500.

The proceeds of the note will be the present value, 86 days earlier, of the maturity value discounted at the rate of 12.5%.

$$\text{Proceeds} = \frac{S}{1 + rt} = \frac{\$2500}{1 + 0.125(\frac{86}{365})} = \$2428.48$$

Note: By paying this price, the extra

$$\$2500 - \$2428.48 = \$71.52$$

received on the note's legal due date provides a 12.5% rate of return for 86 days on the investment of $2428.48. To verify this, calculate

$$r = \frac{I}{Pt} = \frac{\$71.52}{\$2428.48(\frac{86}{365})} = 0.125 = 12.5\%$$

EXAMPLE 7AE   **CALCULATING THE PROCEEDS OF AN INTEREST-BEARING NOTE**

Old Country Antiques accepted a six-month promissory note from a customer for the $2850 balance owed on the purchase of a dining room suite. The note was dated November 8, 2011, and charged interest at 13%. The store's proprietor sold the promissory note 38 days later to a finance company at a price that would yield the finance company an 18% rate of return on its purchase price. What price did the finance company pay?

SOLUTION

The note's legal due date was May 11, 2012 (May 8 + 3 days). The total number of days from the issue date to the due date was

$$23 + 31 + 31 + 29 + 31 + 30 + 10 = 185 \text{ days}$$

When the note was sold, $185 - 38 = 147$ days remained until the due date. The given information and the steps in the solution can be presented in a time diagram.

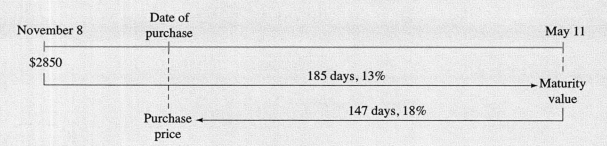

$$\text{Maturity value of note} = \$2850\left[1 + 0.13\left(\tfrac{185}{365}\right)\right] = \$3037.79$$

The price paid by the finance company was the present value, 147 days earlier, of the maturity value discounted at 18%.

$$\text{Price} = \frac{\$3037.79}{1 + 0.18\left(\tfrac{147}{365}\right)} = \$2832.46$$

The finance company paid $2832.46 for the promissory note.

EXERCISE 7A   *Answers to the odd-numbered problems are at the end of the book.*

Calculate the missing values for the promissory notes described in Problems 1 through 22.

Problem	Issue date	Term	Legal due date
1.	May 19	120 days	?
2.	June 30	90 days	?
3.	July 6	? days	Oct 17
4.	Nov 14	? days	Jan 31
5.	?	4 months	Feb 28
6.	?	9 months	Oct 3
7.	?	180 days	Sept 2
8.	?	60 days	March 1(leap year)

Problem	Issue date	Face value ($)	Term	Interest rate (%)	Maturity value ($)
9.	April 30	1000	4 months	9.50	?
10.	Feb 15	3300	60 days	8.75	?
11.	July 3	?	90 days	10.20	2667.57
12.	Aug 31	?	3 months	7.50	7644.86
13.	Jan 22	6200	120 days	?	6388.04
14.	Nov 5	4350	75 days	?	4445.28
15.	Dec 31	5200	? days	11.00	5275.22
16.	March 30	9400	? days	9.90	9560.62

Problem	Face value ($)	Issue date	Interest rate (%)	Term	Date of sale	Discount rate (%)	Proceeds ($)
17.	1000	March 30	0	50 days	April 8	10	?
18.	6000	May 17	0	3 months	June 17	9	?
19.	2700	Sept 4	10	182 days	Dec 14	12	?
20.	3500	Oct 25	10	120 days	Dec 14	8	?
21.	9000	July 28	8	91 days	Sept 1	?	9075.40
22.	4000	Nov 30	8	75 days	Jan 1	?	4015.25

23. Determine the legal due date for:

   a. A five-month note dated September 29, 2010.

   b. A 150-day note issued September 29, 2010.

24. Determine the legal due date for:

   a. A four-month note dated April 30, 2011.

   b. A 120-day note issued April 30, 2011.

25. Calculate the maturity value of a 120-day, $1000 face value note dated November 30, 2011, and earning interest at 10.75%.

26. Calculate the maturity value of a $1000 face value, five-month note dated December 31, 2011, and bearing interest at 9.5%.

27. A 90-day non-interest-bearing note for $3300 is dated August 1. What would be a fair selling price of the note on September 1 if money can earn 7.75%?

28. A six-month non-interest-bearing note issued on September 30, 2010 for $3300 was discounted at 11.25% on December 1. What were the proceeds of the note?

29. A 100-day $750 note with interest at 12.5% was written on July 15. The maker approaches the payee on August 10 to propose an early settlement. What amount should the payee be willing to accept on August 10 if short-term investments can earn 8.25%?

30. The payee on a three-month $2700 note earning interest at 8% wishes to sell the note to raise some cash. What price should she be prepared to accept for the note (dated May 19) on June 5 in order to yield the purchaser an 11% rate of return?

31. A six-month note dated June 30 for $2900 bears interest at 13.5%. Determine the proceeds of the note if it is discounted at 9.75% on September 1.

32. An investor is prepared to buy short-term promissory notes at a price that will provide him with a return on investment of 12%. What amount would he pay on August 9 for a 120-day note dated July 18 for $4100 with interest at 10.25%?

8

Compound Interest: Future Value and Present Value

LEARNING OBJECTIVES

After completing this chapter, you will be able to:

LO1 Calculate the future value and present value in compound interest applications, by both the algebraic method and the preprogrammed financial calculator method

LO2 Calculate the maturity value of compound-interest Guaranteed Investment Certificates (GICs)

LO3 Calculate the price of strip bonds

LO4 Calculate the redemption value of a compound-interest Canada Savings Bond

LO5 Adapt the concepts and equations from compound interest to compound growth

LO6 Calculate the payment on any date that is equivalent to one or more payments on other dates

LO7 Calculate the economic value of a payment stream

EXAMPLES OF COMPOUND INTEREST ARE easy to find. If you obtain a loan to purchase a car, interest will be compounded monthly. The advertised interest rates on mortgage loans are semiannually compounded rates. Interest is always compounded in long-term financial planning. So if you wish to take control of your personal financial affairs or to be involved in the financial side of a business, you must thoroughly understand compound interest and its applications. The remainder of this textbook is devoted to the mathematics and applications of compound interest.

You will be able to hit the ground running! In Chapters 6 and 7, you learned the concepts of maturity value, time value of money, future value, and present value for the case of simple interest. These ideas transfer to compound interest. Now we just need to develop new mathematics for calculating future value and present value when interest is compounded. And there is good news in this regard! Most compound interest formulas are permanently programmed into financial calculators. After you become competent in the algebraic method for solving compound interest problems, your instructor may allow you to use a financial calculator to perform the computations. Before long, you will be impressed at the range of applications you can handle!

8.1 | BASIC CONCEPTS

The *simple* interest method discussed in Chapter 6 is restricted primarily to loans and investments having terms of less than one year. The *compound* interest method is employed in virtually all instances where the term exceeds one year. It is also used in some cases where the duration is less than one year.

In the **compound interest method**, interest is *periodically* calculated and *converted* to principal. "Converting interest to principal" means that the interest is added to the principal and is thereafter treated as principal. Consequently, interest earned in one period will itself earn interest in all subsequent periods. The time interval between successive interest conversion dates is called the **compounding period**. Suppose, for example, you invest $1000 at 10% compounded annually. "Compounded annually" means that "interest is compounded once per year." Therefore, the compounding period is one year. On each anniversary of the investment, interest will be calculated and converted to principal. The process is indicated in Figure 8.1. The original $1000 investment is represented by the column located at "0" on the time axis. During the first year, you will earn $100 interest (10% of $1000). At the end of the first year, this $100 will be converted to principal. The new principal ($1100) will earn $110 interest (10% of $1100) in the second year. Note that you earn $10 more interest in the second year than in the first year because you have $100 more principal invested at 10%. How much interest will be earned in the third year? Do you see the pattern developing? Each year you will earn more interest than in the preceding year—$100 in the first year, $110 in the second year, $121 in the third year, and so on. Consequently, the growth in value of the investment will accelerate as the years pass.

FIGURE 8.1   Converting Interest to Principal at the End of Each Compounding Period

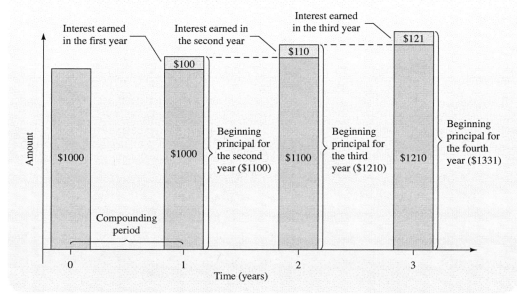

In contrast, if the $1000 earns 10% per annum *simple* interest, only the *original* principal will earn interest ($100) each year. A $1000 investment will grow by just $100 each year. After two years, your investment will be worth only $1200 (compared to $1210 with annual compounding).

In many circumstances, interest is compounded more frequently than once per year. The number of compoundings per year is called the **compounding frequency**. The commonly used frequencies and their corresponding compounding periods are listed in Table 8.1.

TABLE 8.1   Compounding Frequencies and Periods

Compounding frequency	Number of compoundings per year	Compounding period
Annually	1	1 year
Semiannually	2	6 months
Quarterly	4	3 months
Monthly	12	1 month

A compound interest rate is normally quoted with two components:

- A number for the annual interest rate; and

- Words stating the compounding frequency.

The two components together are called the **nominal[1] interest rate**. For example, an interest rate of 8% compounded semiannually means that half of the 8% nominal annual rate is earned and compounded each six-month compounding period. A rate of 9% compounded monthly means that 0.75% (one-twelfth of 9%) is earned and compounded each month. We

---

[1]   As you will soon understand, you cannot conclude that $100 invested for one year at 8% compounded semiannually will earn exactly $8.00 of interest. Therefore, we use the word "nominal," meaning "in name only," to describe the quoted rate.

use the term **periodic interest rate** for the interest rate per compounding period. In the two examples at hand, the periodic interest rates are 4% and 0.75%, respectively. In general,

$$\text{Periodic interest rate} = \frac{\text{Nominal interest rate}}{\text{Number of compoundings per year}}$$

If we define the following symbols:

$$j = \text{Nominal interest rate}$$
$$m = \text{Number of compoundings per year}$$
$$i = \text{Periodic interest rate}$$

the simple relationship between the periodic interest rate and the nominal interest rate is:

PERIODIC INTEREST RATE

$$i = \frac{j}{m} \qquad\qquad \text{(8-1)}$$

TRAP   *"m"* for Quarterly Compounding

What is the value of m for quarterly compounding? Sometimes students incorrectly use $m = 3$ with quarterly compounding because $\frac{1}{4}$ year = 3 months. But m represents the number of compoundings per year (4), not the length of the compounding period.

TIP   Give the Complete Description of an Interest Rate

Whenever you are asked to calculate or state a nominal interest rate, it is understood that you should include the compounding frequency in your response. For example, an answer of just "8%" is incomplete. Rather, you must state "8% compounded quarterly" if interest is compounded four times per year.

EXAMPLE 8.1A   **CALCULATING THE PERIODIC INTEREST RATE**

Calculate the periodic interest rate corresponding to:

a. 10.5% compounded annually.

b. 9.75% compounded semiannually.

c. 9.0% compounded quarterly.

d. 9.5% compounded monthly.

SOLUTION

Employing formula (8-1), we obtain:

a. $i = \dfrac{j}{m} = \dfrac{10.5\%}{1} = 10.5\%$ (per year)

b. $i = \dfrac{9.75\%}{2} = 4.875\%$ (per half year)

c. $i = \dfrac{9.0\%}{4} = 2.25\%$ (per quarter)

d. $i = \dfrac{9.5\%}{12} = 0.791\overline{6}\%$ (per month)

EXAMPLE 8.1B   **CALCULATING THE COMPOUNDING FREQUENCY**

For a nominal interest rate of 8.4%, what is the compounding frequency if the periodic interest rate is:

a. 4.2%?   **b.** 8.4%?

c. 2.1%?   **d.** 0.70%?

SOLUTION

The number of compoundings or conversions in a year is given by the value of m in formula (8-1).

Rearranging this formula to solve for m, we obtain $m = \dfrac{j}{i}$

a. $m = \dfrac{8.4\%}{4.2\%} = 2$ which corresponds to semiannual compounding.

b. $m = \dfrac{8.4\%}{8.4\%} = 1$ which corresponds to annual compounding.

c. $m = \dfrac{8.4\%}{2.1\%} = 4$ which corresponds to quarterly compounding.

d. $m = \dfrac{8.4\%}{0.7\%} = 12$ which corresponds to monthly compounding.

EXAMPLE 8.1C   **CALCULATING THE NOMINAL INTEREST RATE**

Determine the nominal rate of interest if:

a. The periodic rate is 1.75% per quarter.   **b.** The periodic rate is $0.8\overline{3}\%$ per month.

SOLUTION

Rearranging formula (8-1) to solve for j, the nominal interest rate, we obtain $j = mi$

a. $j = 4(1.75\%) = 7.0\%$ compounded quarterly

b. $j = 12(0.8\overline{3}\%) = 10.0\%$ compounded monthly

CONCEPT QUESTIONS

1. What does it mean to compound interest?

2. Explain the difference between "compounding period" and "compounding frequency."

3. Explain the difference between "nominal rate of interest" and "periodic rate of interest."

EXERCISE 8.1   *Answers to the odd-numbered problems are at the end of the book.*

1. Calculate the periodic rate of interest if the nominal interest rate is 6% compounded:

    a. Monthly.   **b.** Quarterly.   **c.** Semiannually.

2. Determine the periodic interest rate for a nominal interest rate of 4.8% compounded:

    a. Semiannually.   **b.** Quarterly.   **c.** Monthly.

3. What is the periodic rate of interest corresponding to:

    a. 5.4% compounded quarterly?   **b.** 5.4% compounded monthly?

4. Determine the periodic interest rate for a nominal interest rate of:

    a. 8% compounded semiannually.   **b.** 8% compounded monthly.

5. Calculate the nominal interest rate if the periodic rate is:

    a. 3.6% per half year.   **b.** 1.8% per quarter.   **c.** 0.6% per month.

6. Determine the nominal rate of interest if the periodic rate is:

   a. 1.5% per month.   **b.** 1.5% per quarter.   **c.** 1.5% per half year.

7. Determine the nominal interest rate if the periodic rate is:

   a. 1.25% per quarter.   **b.** 0.41$\overline{6}$% per month.

8. What is the nominal rate of interest if the periodic rate is:

   a. 0.58$\overline{3}$% per month?   **b.** 5.8% per year?

9. Calculate the compounding frequency for a nominal rate of 6.6% if the periodic rate of interest is:

   a. 1.65%.   **b.** 3.3%.   **c.** 0.55%.

10. For a nominal rate of 5.9%, determine the compounding frequency if the periodic interest rate is:

    a. 2.95%.   **b.** 0.491$\overline{6}$%.   **c.** 1.475%.

11. What is the compounding frequency for a nominal rate of 4.7% if the periodic interest rate is:

    a. 1.175%?   **b.** 0.391$\overline{6}$%?

12. For a nominal rate of 6.75%, determine the compounding frequency if the periodic interest rate is:

    a. 0.5625%.   **b.** 1.6875%.

8.2   FUTURE VALUE (OR MATURITY VALUE)

CALCULATING FUTURE VALUE

LO1   Remember from our study of simple interest in Chapter 6 that the **maturity value** or **future value** is the combined principal and interest due at the maturity date of a loan or investment. We used $S = P(1 + rt)$ to calculate future value in the simple interest case. Now our task is to develop the corresponding formula for use with compound interest.

Financial calculators, spreadsheet software, and the majority of finance textbooks employ the following symbols in compound interest functions:

$$FV = \text{Future value (or maturity value)}$$
$$PV = \text{Principal amount of a loan or investment; Present value}$$

We want to answer the general question:

"What is the future value, FV, after n compounding periods of an initial principal, PV?"

Let's work toward the future value one period at a time, observing any pattern that arises.

Interest earned during the *first* compounding period $= i \times PV = i(PV)$

Future value after *one* compounding period $=$ Principal $+$ Interest earned
$$= PV + i(PV)$$
$$= PV(1 + i)$$

This amount becomes the beginning principal for the *second* compounding period.

Interest earned during the *second* compounding period $= i \times$ Beginning principal
$$= i(PV)(1 + i)$$

Future value after *two* compounding periods $=$ Beginning principal $+$ Interest earned
$$= PV(1 + i) + i(PV)(1 + i)$$

Extracting the common factor $PV(1 + i)$ from the two terms, we obtain:

$$\text{Future value after } \textit{two} \text{ compounding periods} = PV(1 + i)(1 + i)$$
$$= PV(1 + i)^2$$

Already we notice a pattern. For each compounding period, we multiply the initial principal, PV, by another $(1 + i)$ factor. After n compounding periods, the future value will be

FUTURE VALUE OR MATURITY VALUE (COMPOUND INTEREST)

$$FV = PV(1 + i)^n \qquad \text{(8-2)}$$

Usually, the term of a loan or investment is given in years rather than as the total number of compounding periods, n. To calculate n, first determine m, the number of compoundings per year, from the nominal interest rate. Then,

TOTAL NUMBER OF COMPOUNDING PERIODS

$$n = m \times (\textbf{Number of years in the term}) \qquad \text{(8-3)}$$

EXAMPLE 8.2A   **CALCULATING THE MATURITY VALUE OF AN INVESTMENT**

What will be the maturity value of $10,000 invested for five years at 9.75% compounded semiannually?

SOLUTION

Given: $PV = \$10,000$, Term of investment = 5 years, $j = 9.75\%$, $m = 2$

The interest rate per six-month compounding period is

$$i = \frac{j}{m} = \frac{9.75\%}{2} = 4.875\% \text{ (per half year)}$$
$$n = m \times \text{Term (in years)} = 2(5) = 10$$

The maturity value will be

$$
\begin{aligned}
FV &= PV(1 + i)^n \\
&= \$10,000(1 + 0.04875)^{10} \\
&= \$10,000(1.6096066) \\
&= \$16,096.07
\end{aligned}
$$

The investment will grow to $16,096.07 after five years.

EXAMPLE 8.2B   **COMPARING TWO NOMINAL RATES OF INTEREST**

Other things being equal, would an investor prefer an interest rate of 4.8% compounded monthly or 4.9% compounded annually for a two-year investment?

SOLUTION

The preferred rate will be the one that results in the higher maturity value. Pick an arbitrary initial investment, say $1000, and calculate the maturity value at each rate.

With $PV = \$1000$, $i = \frac{j}{m} = \frac{4.8\%}{12} = 0.4\%$, and $n = m(\text{Term}) = 12(2) = 24$,

$$FV = PV(1 + i)^n = \$1000(1.004)^{24} = \$1100.55$$

With $PV = \$1000$, $i = \frac{j}{m} = \frac{4.9\%}{1} = 4.9\%$, and $n = m(\text{Term}) = 1(2) = 2$,

$$FV = PV(1 + i)^n = \$1000(1.049)^2 = \$1100.40$$

The rate of 4.8% compounded monthly is slightly better. The higher compounding frequency more than offsets the lower nominal rate.

EXAMPLE 8.2C | **CALCULATING THE MATURITY VALUE WHEN THE INTEREST RATE CHANGES**

George invested $5000 at 9.25% compounded quarterly. After 18 months, the rate changed to 9.75% compounded semiannually. What amount will George have three years after the initial investment?

SOLUTION

For the first 18 months,

$$PV = \$5000, \ i = \frac{j}{m} = \frac{9.25\%}{4} = 2.3125\% \text{ (per quarter) and } n = m(\text{Term}) = 4(1.5) = 6$$

For the next 18 months,

$$i = \frac{j}{m} = \frac{9.75\%}{2} = 4.875\% \text{ (per half year) and } n = m(\text{Term}) = 2(1.5) = 3$$

Because of the interest rate change, the solution should be done in two steps, as indicated by the following diagram.

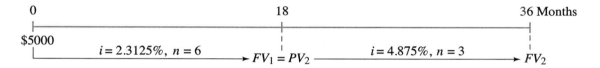

The future value, FV_1, after 18 months becomes the beginning "principal," PV_2, for the remainder of the three years.

Step 1:   Calculate the future value after 18 months.

$$FV_1 = PV(1 + i)^n = \$5000(1.023125)^6 = \$5735.12$$

Step 2:   Calculate the future value, FV_2, at the end of the three years (a further 18 months later).

$$FV_2 = PV_2(1 + i)^n = \$5735.12(1.04875)^3 = \$6615.44$$

George will have $6615.44 after three years.

EXAMPLE 8.2D | **THE BALANCE OWED AFTER PAYMENTS ON A COMPOUND INTEREST LOAN**

Fay borrowed $5000 at an interest rate of 11% compounded quarterly. On the first, second, and third anniversaries of the loan, she made payments of $1500. What payment made on the fourth anniversary will extinguish the debt?

SOLUTION

At each anniversary we will first calculate the amount owed (FV) and then deduct the payment. This difference becomes the principal balance (PV) at the beginning of the next year. The periodic interest rate is

$$i = \frac{j}{m} = \frac{11\%}{4} = 2.75\% \text{ (per quarter)}$$

The sequence of steps is indicated by the following time diagram.

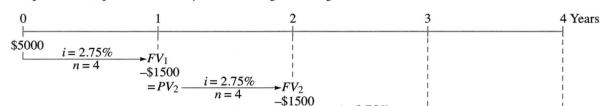

$$FV_1 = PV(1 + i)^n = \$5000(1.0275)^4 = \$5573.11$$
$$PV_2 = FV_1 - \$1500 = \$5573.11 - \$1500 = \$4073.11$$
$$FV_2 = PV_2(1 + i)^n = \$4073.11(1.0275)^4 = \$4539.97$$
$$PV_3 = FV_2 - \$1500 = \$4539.97 - \$1500 = \$3039.97$$
$$FV_3 = PV_3(1 + i)^n = \$3039.97(1.0275)^4 = \$3388.42$$
$$PV_4 = FV_3 - \$1500 = \$3388.42 - \$1500 = \$1888.42$$
$$FV_4 = PV_4(1 + i)^n = \$1888.42(1.0275)^4 = \$2104.87$$

A payment of $2104.87 on the fourth anniversary will pay off the debt.

GRAPHS OF FUTURE VALUE VERSUS TIME

A picture is worth a thousand words, but a graph can be worth more. The best way to develop our understanding of the effects of compounding and the roles of key variables is through the study of graphs.

The Components of Future Value Let us investigate in greater detail the consequences of earning "interest on interest" through compounding. In Figure 8.2, we compare the growth of two investments:

- $100 invested at 10% compounded annually (the upper curve)

- $100 invested at 10% per annum simple interest (the inclined straight line)

For the compound interest investment,

$$FV = PV(1 + i)^n = \$100(1 + 0.10)^n = \$100(1.10)^n$$

The upper curve was obtained by plotting values of FV for n ranging from 0 to 10 compounding periods (years).

For the simple interest investment,

$$S = P(1 + rt) = \$100(1 + 0.10t)$$

This gives an upward-sloping straight line when we plot values of S for t ranging from 0 to 10 years. In this case, the future value increases $10 per year because only the original principal of $100 earns 10% interest each year. At any point, the future value of the simple interest investment has *two* components:

1. The original principal ($100).
2. The interest earned on the original principal. In the graph, this component is the vertical distance from the horizontal line (at $100) to the sloping simple interest line.

FIGURE 8.2   The Components of the Future Value of $100

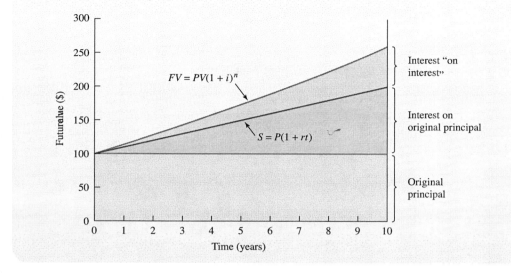

Returning to the compound interest investment, we can think of its future value at any point as having *three* components: the same two listed above for the simple interest investment, plus

3. "Interest earned on interest"—actually interest earned on interest that was previously converted to principal. In the graph, this component is the vertical distance from the inclined simple interest line to the upper compound interest curve. Note that this component increases at an accelerating rate as time passes. Eventually, "interest on interest" will exceed the interest earned on the original principal! How long do you think this will take to happen for the case plotted in Figure 8.2?

The Effect of the Nominal Interest Rate on the Future Value Suppose Investment A earns 10% compounded annually, and Investment B earns 12% compounded annually. B's rate of return (12%) is one-fifth larger than A's (10%). You might think that if $100 is invested in each investment for say, 25 years, the investment in B will grow one-fifth or 20% more than the investment in A. Wrong! Let's look into the outcome more carefully. It has very important implications for long-term financial planning.

In Figure 8.3, the future value of a $100 investment is plotted over a 25-year period for four *annually* compounded rates of interest. The four rates are at 2% increments, and include the rates earned by Investments A (10%) and B (12%). We expect the separation of the curves to increase as time passes—that would happen without compounding. The most important observation you should make is the *disproportionate* effect each 2% increase in interest rate has on the long-term growth of the future value. Compare the future values after 25 years at the 10% and 12% rates. You can see that the future value at 12% compounded annually (Investment B) is about 1.5 times the future value at 10% compounded annually (Investment A). In comparison, the ratio of the two interest rates is only $\frac{12\%}{10\%} = 1.2$!

The contrast between long-term performances of A and B is more dramatic if we compare their *growth* instead of their future values. Over the full 25 years, B grows by

$$FV - PV = PV(1 + i)^n - PV$$
$$= \$100(1.12)^{25} - \$100$$
$$= \$1600.01$$

while A grows by

$$FV - PV = PV(1 + i)^n - PV$$
$$= \$100(1.10)^{25} - \$100$$
$$= \$983.47$$

FIGURE 8.3   Future Values of $100 at Various Compound Rates of Interest

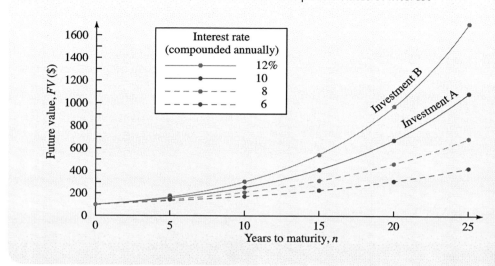

In summary, B's growth is 1.63 times A's growth, even though the interest rate earned by B is only 1.2 times the rate earned by A. What a difference the extra 2% per year makes, especially over longer time periods! The implications for planning and managing your personal financial affairs are:

- You should begin an investment plan early in life in order to realize the dramatic effects of compounding beyond a 20-year time horizon.

- You should try to obtain the best available rate of return (at your acceptable level of risk). An extra 0.5% or 1% added to your annual rate of return has a disproportionate effect on investment growth, particularly in the long run.

The Effect of the Compounding Frequency on the Future Value What difference will it make if we invest $100 at 12% compounded *monthly* instead of 12% compounded *annually*? In the first case, the $1 interest (1% of $100) earned in the first month gets converted to principal at the end of the month. We will then have $101 earning interest in the second month, and so on. With annual compounding, the $1 interest earned in the first month is not converted to principal. Just the original principal ($100) will earn interest in the second through to the twelfth month. Only then will the $12 interest earned during the year be converted to principal. Therefore, the original $100 will grow faster with monthly compounding.

The long-run effect of more frequent compounding is shown in Figure 8.4. As time passes, the higher compounding frequency produces a surprisingly large and ever-increasing difference between the future values. After 15 years, the future value with monthly compounding is about 10% larger than with annual compounding. Thereafter, the gap continues to widen in both dollar and percentage terms. After 20 years, it is almost 13% and after 25 years, it is 16.4%.

FIGURE 8.4 Future Values of $100 at the Same Nominal Rate but Different Compounding Frequencies

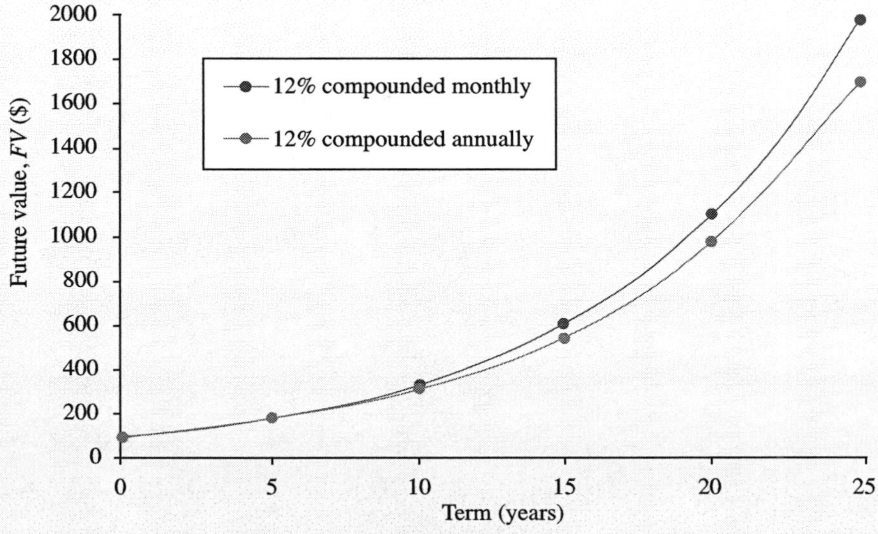

Where do you think the curves for semiannual and quarterly compounding would lie if they were included on the graph?

LO6 **Equivalent Payments** Recall from Section 6.4 that **equivalent payments** are alternative payments that enable you to end up with the same dollar amount at a later date. The concepts we developed in Section 6.4 still apply when the time frame exceeds one year. The only change needed is to use the mathematics of *compound* interest when calculating a present value (an equivalent payment at an earlier date) or a future value (an equivalent payment at a later date). The rate of return employed in equivalent payment calculations should be the rate of return that can be earned from a low-risk investment. In real life, the prevailing rate of return[2] on Government of Canada bonds is the customary standard.

EXAMPLE 8.2E **CALCULATING THE PAYMENT AT A LATER DATE THAT IS EQUIVALENT TO TWO SCHEDULED PAYMENTS**

A small claims court has ruled in favour of Mrs. Peacock. She claimed that Professor Plum defaulted on two payments of $1000 each. One payment was due 18 months ago, and the other 11 months ago. What is the appropriate amount for the court to order Plum to pay immediately if the court uses 6% compounded monthly for the interest rate money can earn?

SOLUTION

The appropriate award is the combined future value of the two payments brought forward from their due dates to today. The periodic rate of interest is

$$i = \frac{j}{m} = \frac{6\%}{12} = 0.5\% \text{ per month}$$

---

[2] This rate of return can be found any day of the week in the financial pages of major newspapers. Government of Canada bonds are covered in detail in Chapter 15.

The solution plan is presented in the diagram below.

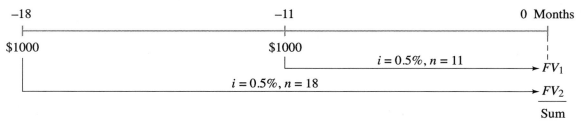

The amount today that is equivalent to the payment due 11 months ago is

$$FV_1 = PV(1 + i)^n = \$1000(1.005)^{11} = \$1056.396$$

Similarly,

$$FV_2 = \$1000(1.005)^{18} = \$1093.929$$
$$FV_1 + FV_2 = \$1056.396 + \$1093.929 = \$2150.33$$

The appropriate amount for Plum to pay is $2150.33.

POINT OF INTEREST

The "Magic" of Compound Interest

"I don't know the names of the Seven Wonders of the World, but I do know the Eighth Wonder: Compound Interest."

— Baron Rothschild

Many books and articles on personal financial planning write with similar awe about the "miracle" or "magic" of compound interest. The authors make it appear that mysterious forces are involved. *The Wealthy Barber*, a Canadian bestseller, says that "it's a real tragedy that most people don't understand compound interest and its wondrous powers."

The book makes a legitimate point, even if it seems overstated once you become familiar with the mathematics of compound interest. Most people really do underestimate the long-term growth of compound-interest investments. Also, they do not take seriously enough the advice to start saving and investing early in life. As we noted in Figure 8.3, compound growth accelerates rapidly beyond the 20-year horizon.

The reason most people underestimate the long-term effects of compounding is that they tend to think in terms of proportional relationships. For example, most would estimate that an investment will earn about twice as much over 20 years as it will earn over 10 years at the same rate of return. Let's check your intuition in this regard.

QUESTIONS

1. How do you think the growth of a $100 investment over 20 years compares to its growth over 10 years? Assume a return of 8% compounded annually. Will the former be twice as large? Two-and-a-half times as large? Make your best educated guess and then work out the actual ratio. Remember, we want the ratio for the *growth*, not the ratio for the *future value*.

2. Will the growth ratio be larger, smaller, or the same if we invest $1000 instead of $100 at the start? After making your choice, calculate the ratio.

3. Will the growth ratio be larger, smaller, or the same if the rate of return is 10% compounded annually instead of 8% compounded annually? After making your choice, calculate the ratio.

CONCEPT QUESTIONS

1. What is meant by the future value of an investment?

2. For a given nominal interest rate (say 10%) on a loan, would the borrower prefer it to be compounded annually or compounded monthly? Which compounding frequency would the lender prefer? Give a brief explanation.

3. For a six-month investment, rank the following interest rates (number one being "most preferred"): 6% per annum simple interest, 6% compounded semiannually, 6% compounded quarterly. Explain your ranking.

4. From a *simple inspection,* is it possible for an investor to rank the four rates of return in each of Parts (a) and (b)? If so, state the ranking. Give a brief explanation to justify your answer.

   a. 9.0% compounded monthly, 9.1% compounded quarterly, 9.2% compounded semiannually, 9.3% compounded annually.

   b. 9.0% compounded annually, 9.1% compounded semiannually, 9.2% compounded quarterly, 9.3% compounded monthly.

5. If an investment doubles in nine years, how long will it take to quadruple (at the same rate of return)? (This problem does not require any detailed calculations.)

6. Suppose it took x years for an investment to grow from $100 to $200 at a fixed compound rate of return. How many more years will it take to earn an additional

   a. $100?   b. $200?   c. $300?

   In each case, pick an answer from:
   (i) more than x years,
   (ii) less than x years,
   (iii) exactly x years.

7. Why is $100 received today worth more than $100 received at a future date?

EXERCISE 8.2   *Answers to the odd-numbered problems are at the end of the book.*

Note: In Section 8.4, you will learn how to use special functions on a financial calculator to solve compound-interest problems. Exercise 8.4 suggests that you return to this Exercise to practise the financial calculator method.

1. What is the maturity value of $5000 invested at 6.0% compounded semiannually for seven years?

2. What is the future value of $8500 after $5\frac{1}{2}$ years if it earns 9.5% compounded quarterly?

3. To what amount would $12,100 grow after $3\frac{1}{4}$ years if it earned 7.5% compounded monthly?

4. What was a $4400 investment worth after $6\frac{3}{4}$ years if it earned 5.4% compounded monthly?

5. Assume that a $10,000 investment can earn 8% compounded quarterly. What will be its future value after:

   a. 15 years?   b. 20 years?   c. 25 years?   d. 30 years?

6. How much will $10,000 be worth after 25 years if it earns:

   a. 6% compounded semiannually?

   b. 7% compounded semiannually?

   c. 8% compounded semiannually?

7. To what amount will $10,000 grow after 25 years if it earns:

   a. 9% compounded annually?   b. 9% compounded semiannually?

   c. 9% compounded quarterly?   d. 9% compounded monthly?

8. $10,000 is invested at 7% compounded annually. Over the next 25 years, how much of the investment's increase in value represents:

   a. Earnings strictly on the original $10,000 principal?

   b. Earnings on re-invested earnings? (This amount reflects the cumulative effect of compounding.)

9. By calculating the maturity value of $100 invested for one year at each rate, determine which rate of return an investor would prefer.

   a. 8.0% compounded monthly   b. 8.1% compounded quarterly

   c. 8.2% compounded semiannually   d. 8.3% compounded annually

10. By calculating the maturity value of $100 invested for one year at each rate, determine which rate of return an investor would prefer.

   a. 12.0% compounded monthly   b. 12.1% compounded quarterly

   c. 12.2% compounded semiannually   d. 12.3% compounded annually

11. What is the maturity value of a $12,000 loan for 18 months at 7.2% compounded quarterly? How much interest is charged on the loan?

12. What total interest will be earned by $5000 invested at 5.4% compounded monthly for $3\frac{1}{2}$ years?

13. How much more will an investment of $10,000 be worth after 25 years if it earns 9% compounded annually instead of 8% compounded annually? Calculate the difference in dollars and as a percentage of the smaller maturity value.

14. How much more will an investment of $10,000 be worth after 25 years if it earns 6% compounded annually instead of 5% compounded annually? Calculate the difference in dollars and as a percentage of the smaller maturity value.

15. How much more will an investment of $10,000 earning 8% compounded annually be worth after 25 years than after 20 years? Calculate the difference in dollars and as a percentage of the smaller maturity value.

16. How much more will an investment of $10,000 earning 8% compounded annually be worth after 15 years than after 10 years? Calculate the difference in dollars and as a percentage of the smaller maturity value.

17. A $1000 investment is made today. Calculate its maturity values for the six combinations of terms and annually compounded rates of return in the following table.

		Term	
Rate of return (%)	20 years	25 years	30 years
8	?	?	?
10	?	?	?

18. Suppose an individual invests $1000 at the beginning of each year for the next 30 years. Thirty years from now, how much more will the first $1000 investment be worth than the sixteenth $1000 investment if both earn 8.5% compounded annually?

19. A $5000 payment due $1\frac{1}{2}$ years ago has not been paid. If money can earn 8.25% compounded annually, what amount paid $2\frac{1}{2}$ years from now would be the economic equivalent of the missed payment?

20. What amount three years from now is equivalent to $3000 due five months from now? Assume that money can earn 7.5% compounded monthly.

21. What amount today is equivalent to $10,000 four years ago, if money earned 5.5% compounded monthly over the last four years?

22. What amount two years from now will be equivalent to $2300 at a date $1\frac{1}{2}$ years ago, if money earns 6.25% compounded semiannually during the intervening time?

23. Payments of $1300 due today and $1800 due in $1\frac{3}{4}$ years are to be replaced by a single payment 4 years from now. What is the amount of that payment if money is worth 6% compounded quarterly?

24. Bjorn defaulted on payments of $2000 due 3 years ago and $1000 due $1\frac{1}{2}$ years ago. What would a fair settlement to the payee be $1\frac{1}{2}$ years from now, if the money could have been invested in low-risk government bonds to earn 4.2% compounded semiannually?

∘25. Faisal borrowed $3000, $3500, and $4000 from his father on January 1 of three successive years at college. Faisal and his father agreed that interest would accumulate on each amount at the rate of 5% compounded semiannually. Faisal is to start repaying the loan one year after the $4000 loan. What consolidated amount will he owe at that time?

26. Interest rates were at historical highs in the early 1980s. In August of 1981, you could earn 17.5% compounded annually on a five-year term deposit with a Canadian bank. Since then, the interest rate offered on five-year term deposits dropped to a low of 2.0% compounded annually in August of 2009. On a $10,000 deposit for a term of five years, how much more would you have earned at the historical high interest rate than at the more recent low rate?

∘27. Mrs. Vanderberg has just deposited $5000 in each of three savings plans for her grandchildren. They will have access to the accumulated funds on their nineteenth birthdays. Their current ages are 12 years, 7 months (Donna); 10 years, 3 months (Tim); and 7 years, 11 months (Gary). If the plans earn 8% compounded monthly, what amount will each grandchild receive at age 19?

∘28. Nelson borrowed $5000 for $4\frac{1}{2}$ years. For the first $2\frac{1}{2}$ years, the interest rate on the loan was 8.4% compounded monthly. Then the rate became 7.5% compounded semiannually. What total amount was required to pay off the loan if no payments were made before the expiry of the $4\frac{1}{2}$-year term?

∘29. Alberto has just invested $60,000 in a five-year Guaranteed Investment Certificate (GIC) earning 6% compounded semiannually. When the GIC matures, he will reinvest its entire maturity value in a new five-year GIC. What will be the maturity value of the second GIC if it yields:

    a. The same rate as the current GIC?

    b. 7% compounded semiannually?

    c. 5% compounded semiannually?

∘30. An investment of $2500 earned interest at 4.5% compounded quarterly for $1\frac{1}{2}$ years, and then 4.0% compounded monthly for two years. How much interest did the investment earn in the $3\frac{1}{2}$ years?

∘31. A debt of $7000 accumulated interest at 9.5% compounded quarterly for 15 months, after which the rate changed to 8.5% compounded semiannually for the next six months. What was the total amount owed at the end of the entire 21-month period?

∘32. Megan borrowed $1900, $3\frac{1}{2}$ years ago at 7% compounded semiannually. Two years ago she made a payment of $1000. What amount is required today to pay off the remaining principal and the accrued interest?

○**33.** Duane borrowed $3000 from his grandmother five years ago. The interest on the loan was to be 5% compounded semiannually for the first three years, and 6% compounded monthly thereafter. If he made a $1000 payment $2\frac{1}{2}$ years ago, what is the amount now owed on the loan?

○**34.** A loan of $4000 at 7.5% compounded monthly requires three payments of $1000 at 6, 12, and 18 months after the date of the loan, and a final payment of the full balance after two years. What is the amount of the final payment?

•**35.** Dr. Sawicki obtained a variable-rate loan of $10,000. The lender required payment of at least $2000 each year. After nine months the doctor paid $2500, and another nine months later she paid $3000. What amount was owed on the loan after two years if the interest rate was 6.6% compounded monthly for the first year, and 7% compounded quarterly for the second year?

36. Follow the instructions in the NET @ssets box earlier in this section to access the interactive chart named "Future Value of $100" on the textbook's Web site. Use the chart to help you answer these questions. What is the percentage increase in an investment's future value every five years if the investment earns:

   a. 7% compounded annually?

   b. 9% compounded annually?

   c. 11% compounded annually?

37. Follow the instructions in the NET @ssets box earlier in this section to access the interactive chart named "Future Value of $100" on the textbook's Web site. Use the chart to help you answer:

   a. Problem 13.

   b. Problem 15.

○**38.** Follow the instructions in the NET @ssets box earlier in this section to access the interactive chart named "Future Value of $100" on the textbook's Web site. Use the chart to help you answer these questions. Over a 25-year period, how much more (expressed as a percentage) will an investment be worth if it earns:

   a. 6% compounded monthly instead of 6% compounded annually?

   b. 9% compounded monthly instead of 9% compounded annually?

   c. 12% compounded monthly instead of 12% compounded annually?

8.3   PRESENT VALUE

LO1   If money can earn 6% compounded annually, what amount *today* is equivalent to $1000 paid five years from now? This is an example of determining a payment's **present value**—an economically equivalent amount at an *earlier* date. In this instance, the present value is the (principal) amount you would have to invest at 6% compounded annually in order to end up with $1000 after five years. To calculate this initial investment, we need only rearrange

$$FV = PV(1 + i)^n$$

to isolate *PV*, and then substitute the values for *FV*, *i*, and *n*. Dividing both sides of the formula by $(1 + i)^n$ leaves *PV* by itself on the right side. We thereby obtain a second version of formula (8-2):

$$PV = \frac{FV}{(1 + i)^n} = FV(1 + i)^{-n}$$

In summary, $PV = FV(1 + i)^{-n}$ applies to two types of problems:

- Calculating the initial investment needed to produce a particular maturity value, FV; and
- Calculating the present value of a scheduled payment, FV.

TIP   Efficient Use of Your Calculator

Calculating PV using $FV(1 + i)^{-n}$ leads to a more efficient calculation than using $\dfrac{FV}{(1 + i)^n}$.

To illustrate, we will evaluate $FV(1 + i)^{-n}$ for the values $FV = \$1000$, $n = 5$, and $i = 6\%$ (from the question posed at the beginning of this section). We have $PV = \$1000(1.06)^{-5}$. The number of keystrokes is minimized if we reverse the order of multiplication and evaluate $1.06^{-5} \times \$1000$. Enter the following keystroke sequence.

$$1.06 \;\boxed{y^x}\; 5 \;\boxed{+/-}\; \boxed{\times}\; 1000 \;\boxed{=}$$

The $\boxed{+/-}$ key must be pressed immediately after entering the number whose sign is to be reversed. After the $\boxed{\times}$ key is pressed, the value of 1.06^{-5} appears in the display. The final $\boxed{=}$ keystroke executes the multiplication, giving $\$747.26$ in the display.

The present value of a future payment will, of course, always be a smaller number than the payment. This is why the process of calculating a payment's present value is sometimes described as **discounting a payment**. The interest rate used in the present value calculation is then referred to as the **discount rate**.

The longer the time period before a scheduled payment, the smaller the present value will be. Figure 8.5 shows the pattern of decreasing present value for longer periods *before* the payment date. The decline is rapid in the first ten years, but steadily tapers off at longer periods. With a discount rate of 10% compounded annually, the present value seven years before the payment is about half the *numerical* value of the payment. Twenty-five years prior to the payment, the present value is less than one-tenth of the payment's size! In practical terms, payments that will be received more than 25 years in the future have little *economic* value today.

How would Figure 8.5 change for a discount rate of 8% compounded annually? And how would it differ for a discount rate of 12% compounded annually?

FIGURE 8.5   The Present Value of $1000 (Discounted at 10% Compounded Annually)

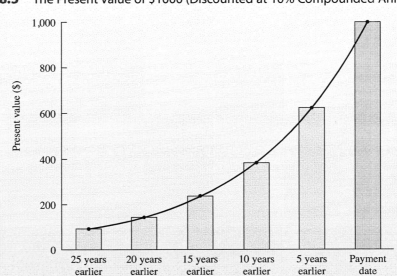

TIP **Numerical Values vs. Economic Values**

In terms of numerical values, a present value is smaller than the payment, and a future value is larger than the payment. However, these *numerically different* amounts all have the *same economic* value. For example, suppose a $100 payment is due one year from now, and money can earn 10% compounded annually. Today's present value is $100(1.10)^{-1} = 90.91. The future value two years from now is $110.00. The three amounts all have the same economic value, namely the value of $90.91 *current* dollars.

EXAMPLE 8.3A **THE INVESTMENT NEEDED TO REACH A PARTICULAR FUTURE VALUE**

If an investment can earn 4% compounded monthly, what amount must you invest now in order to accumulate $10,000 after $3\frac{1}{2}$ years?

SOLUTION

Given: $j = 4\%$, $m = 12$, $FV = $10,000$, and Term = 3.5 years

Then $i = \frac{j}{m} = \frac{4\%}{12} = 0.\overline{3}\%$ per month and $n = m(\text{Term}) = 12(3.5) = 42$

Rearranging formula (8-2) to solve for *PV*,

$$PV = FV(1 + i)^{-n} = $10,000(1.00333333)^{-42} = $8695.61$$

You must invest $8695.61 now in order to have $10,000 after $3\frac{1}{2}$ years.

TIP **Efficient Use of Your Calculator**

If you use any fewer than six 3s in the value for *i* in Example 8.3A, you will have some round-off error in the calculated value for *PV*. For the fewest keystrokes and maximum accuracy in your answer, avoid manual re-entry of calculated values. The most efficient sequence of keystrokes resulting in the highest accuracy of *PV* in Example 8.3A is

0.04 ÷ 12 + 1 = y^x 42 +/− × 10000 =

When you employ the calculated value of *i* in this way, the calculator actually uses more than the seven 3s you see in the display (after pressing the first = in the preceding sequence). The calculator maintains and uses two or three more figures than are shown in the display. In subsequent example problems, this procedure will be assumed but will not be shown.

EXAMPLE 8.3B **CALCULATING AN EQUIVALENT PAYMENT AT AN EARLIER DATE**

Mr. and Mrs. Espedido's property taxes, amounting to $2450, are due on July 1. What amount should the city accept if the taxes are paid eight months in advance and the city can earn 3.6% compounded monthly on surplus funds?

SOLUTION

The city should accept an amount that is equivalent to $2450, allowing for the rate of interest that the city can earn on its surplus funds. This equivalent amount is the present value of $2450, eight months earlier.

Given: $FV = 2450, $j = 3.6\%$ compounded monthly, $m = 12$, and $n = 8$.

Then $\qquad i = \frac{j}{m} = \frac{3.6\%}{12} = 0.3\%$ (per month)

and $\qquad$ Present value, $PV = FV(1 + i)^{-n} = \$2450(1.003)^{-8} = \$2391.99$

The city should be willing to accept $2391.99 on a date eight months before the scheduled due date.

EXAMPLE 8.3C $\quad$ **CALCULATING AN EQUIVALENT VALUE OF TWO PAYMENTS**

Two payments of $10,000 each must be made one year and four years from now. If money can earn 9% compounded monthly, what single payment two years from now would be equivalent to the two scheduled payments?

SOLUTION

When more than one payment is involved in a problem, it is helpful to present the given information in a time diagram. Some of the calculations that need to be done may be indicated on the diagram. In this case, we can indicate the calculation of the equivalent values by constructing arrows from the scheduled payments to the date of the replacement payment. Then we write the relevant values for i ($\frac{9\%}{12} = 0.75\%$) and n on each arrow.

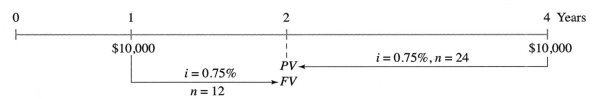

The single equivalent payment is equal to $PV + FV$.

$$
\begin{aligned}
FV &= \text{Future value of \$10,000, 12 months later} \\
&= \$10,000(1.0075)^{12} \\
&= \$10,938.069
\end{aligned}
$$

$$
\begin{aligned}
PV &= \text{Present value of \$10,000, 24 months earlier} \\
&= \$10,000(1.0075)^{-24} \\
&= \$8358.314
\end{aligned}
$$

The equivalent single payment is

$$\$10,938.069 + \$8358.314 = \$19,296.38$$

EXAMPLE 8.3D $\quad$ **DEMONSTRATING ECONOMIC EQUIVALENCE**

Show why the recipient of the payments in Example 8.3C should be indifferent between receiving the scheduled payments and receiving the replacement payment.

SOLUTION

If the recipient ends up in the same economic position with either alternative, then he should not care which alternative is used.

We will calculate how much money the recipient will have four years from now with each alternative, assuming that any amounts received are invested at 9% compounded monthly.

The two alternatives are presented in the two following time diagrams.

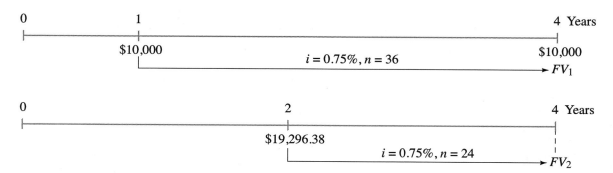

With the scheduled payments, the total amount that the recipient will have after four years is

$$FV_1 + \$10{,}000 = \$10{,}000(1.0075)^{36} + \$10{,}000$$
$$= \$13{,}086.45 + \$10{,}000$$
$$= \$23{,}086.45$$

With the single replacement payment, the recipient will have

$$FV_2 = \$19{,}296.38(1.0075)^{24} = \$23{,}086.45$$

With either alternative, the recipient will have $23,086.45 after four years. Therefore, the replacement payment is economically equivalent to the scheduled payments.

A General Principle Regarding the Present Value of Loan Payments Let us work through a problem that illustrates a very important principle. We will use the data and results from Example 8.2D. In that example, three payments of $1500 each were made on a $5000 loan at one-year intervals after the date of the loan. The interest rate on the loan was 11% compounded quarterly. The problem was to determine the additional payment needed to pay off the loan at the end of the fourth year. The answer was $2104.87.

We will now calculate the sum of the present values of all four payments at the date on which the loan was granted. Use the interest rate on the loan as the discount rate. The calculation of each payment's present value is given in the following table.

Payment	Amount, FV	n	i	$PV = FV(1 + i)^{-n}$
First	$1500.00	4	2.75%	$PV_1 = \$1500(1.0275)^{-4} = \$1345.75$
Second	$1500.00	8	2.75%	$PV_2 = \$1500(1.0275)^{-8} = \$1207.36$
Third	$1500.00	12	2.75%	$PV_3 = \$1500(1.0275)^{-12} = \$1083.20$
Fourth	$2104.87	16	2.75%	$PV_4 = \$2104.87(1.0275)^{-16} = \underline{\$1363.69}$
				Total: $5000.00

Note that the sum of the present values is $5000.00, precisely the original principal amount of the loan. *This outcome will occur for all loans.* The payments do not need to be equal in size or to be at regular intervals. The fundamental principle is highlighted below because we will use it repeatedly in later work.

> **Present Value of Loan Payments**
> The sum of the present values of all of the payments required to pay off a loan is equal to the original principal of the loan. The discount rate for the present-value calculations is the rate of interest charged on the loan.

EXAMPLE 8.3E   CALCULATING TWO UNKNOWN LOAN PAYMENTS

Kramer borrowed $4000 from George at an interest rate of 7% compounded semiannually. The loan is to be repaid by three payments. The first payment, $1000, is due two years after the date of the loan. The second and third payments are due three and five years, respectively, after the initial loan. Calculate the amounts of the second and third payments if the second payment is to be twice the size of the third payment.

SOLUTION

In Example 8.2D, we solved a similar problem but only the last of four loan payments was unknown. In this problem, two payments are unknown and it would be difficult to use the approach of Example 8.2D. However, the fundamental principle developed in this section may be used to solve a wide range of loan problems (including Example 8.2D). Applying this principle to the problem at hand, we have

Sum of the present values of the three payments = $4000

The given data are presented on the time line below. If we let x represent the third payment, then the second payment must be $2x$. Notice how the idea expressed by the preceding word equation can (and should) be indicated on the diagram.

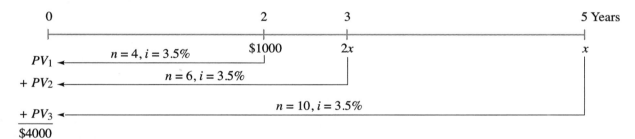

The second and third payments must be of sizes that will make

$$PV_1 + PV_2 + PV_3 = \$4000 \quad ①$$

We can obtain a numerical value for PV_1, but the best we can do for PV_2 and PV_3 is to express them in terms of x. That is just fine—after we substitute these values into equation ①, we will be able to solve for x.

$$PV_1 = FV(1 + i)^{-n} = \$1000(1.035)^{-4} = \$871.442$$
$$PV_2 = 2x(1.035)^{-6} = 1.6270013x$$
$$PV_3 = x(1.035)^{-10} = 0.7089188x$$

Now substitute these values into equation ① and solve for x.

$$\$871.442 + 1.6270013x + 0.7089188x = \$4000$$
$$2.3359201x = \$3128.558$$
$$x = \$1339.326$$

Kramer's second payment will be 2($1339.326) = $2678.65, and the third payment will be $1339.33.

CONCEPT QUESTIONS

1. What is the meaning of the term *discount rate*?

2. Does a smaller discount rate result in a larger or a smaller present value? Explain.

3. The process of discounting is the opposite of doing what?

4. Why does $100 due one year from now have less economic value than $100 has today? What do you need to know before you can determine the difference between the economic values of the two payments?

5. If the present value of $100 due eight years from now is $50, what is the present value of $100 due 16 years from now? Answer without using formula (8-2).

6. Suppose the future value of $1 after x years is $5. What is the present value of $1, x years before its scheduled payment date? (Assume the same interest rate in both cases.)

EXERCISE 8.3   *Answers to the odd-numbered problems are at the end of the book.*

Note: In Section 8.4, you will learn how to use special functions on a financial calculator to solve compound-interest problems. Exercise 8.4 will invite you to return to this Exercise to practise the financial calculator method.

Note: A few problems in some Exercises have been extracted (with permission) from course materials created by the Canadian Institute of Financial Planning (CIFP) for its program leading to the Certified Financial Planner (CFP) designation. The CIFP and associated bodies (see www.ifse.ca) are leading providers of financial services education in Canada. Problems derived from CIFP materials are identified in our Exercises by the organization's logo placed in the margin adjacent to the problems.

1. If money can be invested to earn 6.5% compounded annually, how much would have to be invested today to grow to $10,000 after:

   a. 10 years?   **b.** 20 years?   **c.** 30 years?

2. What amount would have to be invested today for the future value to be $10,000 after 20 years if the rate of return is:

   a. 5% compounded quarterly?   **b.** 7% compounded quarterly?
   c. 9% compounded quarterly?

3. What amount invested today would grow to $10,000 after 25 years, if the investment earns:

   a. 8% compounded annually?   **b.** 8% compounded semiannually?
   c. 8% compounded quarterly?   **d.** 8% compounded monthly?

4. If money is worth 6% compounded annually, what amount today is equivalent to $10,000 paid:

   a. 12 years from now?   **b.** 24 years from now?   **c.** 36 years from now?

5. What is the present value of $10,000 discounted at 4.5% compounded annually over ten years?

6. What principal amount will have a maturity value of $5437.52 after 27 months, if it earns 8.5% compounded quarterly?

7. The maturity value of an investment after 42 months is $9704.61. What was the original investment, if it earned 7.5% compounded semiannually?

8. What amount today is economically equivalent to $8000 paid 18 months from now, if money is worth 5% compounded monthly?

9. If your client's objective is to have $10,000 in four years, how much should he invest today in a product earning 5.5% compounded annually? (Taken from CIFP course materials.)

10. Ross has just been notified that the combined principal and interest on an amount that he borrowed 27 months ago at 11% compounded quarterly is now $2297.78. How much of this amount is principal and how much is interest?

11. Your client has a choice of either receiving $5000 two years from now or receiving a lump payment today. If your client can earn 5.4% compounded semiannually, what amount received today is equivalent to $5000 in two years? (Taken from CIFP course materials.)

12. You owe $6000 payable three years from now. What alternative amount should your creditor be willing to accept today if she can earn 4.2% compounded monthly on a low-risk investment?

13. What amount, $1\frac{1}{2}$ years from now, is equivalent to $7000 due in 8 years, if money can earn 6.2% compounded semiannually?

14. A payment of $1300 is scheduled for a date $3\frac{1}{2}$ years from now. What would be an equivalent payment 9 months from now, if money is worth 5.5% compounded quarterly?

15. What amount 15 months ago is equivalent to $2600, $1\frac{1}{2}$ years from now? Assume money can earn 5.4% compounded monthly.

16. Mustafa can receive a $77 discount if he pays his property taxes early. Alternatively, he can pay the full amount of $2250 when payment is due in nine months. Which alternative is to his advantage if he can earn 6% compounded monthly on short-term investments? In current dollars, how much is the advantage?

17. What single amount, paid three years from now, would be economically equivalent to the combination of $1400 due today and $1800 due in five years, if funds can be invested to earn 6% compounded quarterly?

18. Ramon wishes to replace payments of $900 due today and $500 due in 22 months by a single equivalent payment 18 months from now. If money is worth 5% compounded monthly, what should that payment be?

19. Mohinder has financial obligations of $1000 due in $3\frac{1}{2}$ years and $2000 due in $5\frac{1}{2}$ years. He wishes to settle the obligations sooner with a single payment one year from now. If money is worth 7.75% compounded semiannually, what amount should the payee be willing to accept?

20. What payment $2\frac{1}{4}$ years from now would be a fair substitute for the combination of $1500 due (but not paid) 9 months ago and $2500 due in $4\frac{1}{2}$ years, if money can earn 9% compounded quarterly?

21. What single payment six months from now would be equivalent to payments of $500 due (but not paid) four months ago, and $800 due in 12 months? Assume money can earn 7.5% compounded monthly.

22. What single payment one year from now would be equivalent to $2500 due in three months, and another $2500 due in two years? Money is worth 7% compounded quarterly.

23. A scheduled payment stream consisted of three payments: $2100 due (but not paid) $1\frac{1}{2}$ years ago, $1300 due today, and $800 due in 2 years. What single payment, 6 months from now, would be economically equivalent to the payment stream? Money can earn 4.5% compounded monthly.

24. A debtor owing payments of $750 due today, $1000 due in 2 years, and $1250 due in 4 years requests a payout figure to settle all three obligations by means of a single economically equivalent payment 18 months from now. What is that amount, if the payee can earn 9.5% compounded semiannually?

25. Alicia is considering two offers-to-purchase that she has received on a residential building lot she wishes to sell. One is a cash offer of $145,000. The other offer consists of three payments of $49,000—one now, one in six months, and one in twelve months. Which offer has the larger economic value if Alicia can earn 4.4% compounded quarterly on low-risk investments? How much more (in current dollars) is the better offer worth?

26. A bond pays $1000 interest at the end of every year for the next 30 years. What is the *current* economic value of each of the 15th and 30th payments if we discount the payments at:

    a. 5% compounded semiannually?   b. 8% compounded semiannually?

∘27. Joe Superstar has just signed a "four-year, $68-million deal" with the Toronto Blue Jays. The terms of the contract include a signing bonus of $4.8 million and salaries of $10 million, $17.2 million, $17.5 million, and $18.5 million in successive years of the contract. The news media always ignore the time value of money when they report the "value" of professional athletes' contracts. What is the economic value of Joe's contract on the date it was signed? Assume that the signing bonus was paid on that date, that the annual salaries will be paid in lump amounts $\frac{1}{2}$ year, $1\frac{1}{2}$ years, $2\frac{1}{2}$ years, and $3\frac{1}{2}$ years later, and that money is worth 5% compounded semiannually. Round the answer to the nearest $1000.

28. To motivate individuals to start saving at an early age, financial planners will sometimes present the results of the following type of calculation. How much must a 25-year-old individual invest five years from now to have the same maturity value at age 55 as an immediate investment of $1000? Assume that both investments earn 8% compounded annually.

∘29. Michelle has just received an inheritance from her grandfather's estate. She will be entering college in $3\frac{1}{2}$ years, and wants to immediately purchase three compound-interest investment certificates having the following maturity values and dates: $4000 at the beginning of her first academic year, $5000 at the start of her second year, and $6000 at the beginning of her third year. She can obtain interest rates of 5% compounded semiannually for any terms between three and five years, and 5.6% compounded quarterly for terms between five and seven years. What principal amount should she invest in each certificate?

30. Daniel makes annual payments of $2000 to the former owner of a residential lot that he purchased a few years ago. At the time of the fourth from last payment, Daniel asks for a payout figure that would immediately settle the debt. What amount should the payee be willing to accept instead of the last three payments, if money can earn 8.5% compounded semiannually?

∘31. Commercial Finance Co. buys conditional sale contracts from furniture retailers at discounts that provide a 16.5% compounded monthly rate of return on the purchase price. What total price should Commercial Finance pay for the following three contracts: $950 due in four months, $780 due in six months, and $1270 due in five months?

∘32. Teresita has three financial obligations to the same person: $2700 due in 1 year, $1900 due in $1\frac{1}{2}$ years, and $1100 due in 3 years. She wishes to settle the obligations with a single payment in $2\frac{1}{4}$ years, when her inheritance will be released from her mother's estate. What amount should the creditor accept if money can earn 6% compounded quarterly?

∘33. A $15,000 loan at 11.5% compounded semiannually is advanced today. Two payments of $4000 are to be made one year and three years from now. The balance is to be paid in five years. What will the third payment be?

∘34. A $4000 loan at 10% compounded monthly is to be repaid by three equal payments due 5, 10, and 15 months from the date of the loan. What is the size of the payments?

○**35.** A \$10,000 loan at 8% compounded semiannually is to be repaid by three equal payments due $2\frac{1}{2}$, 4, and 7 years after the date of the loan. What is the size of each payment?

○**36.** A \$6000 loan at 9% compounded quarterly is to be settled by two payments. The first payment is due after nine months and the second payment, half the amount of the first payment, is due after $1\frac{1}{2}$ years. Determine the size of each payment.

○**37.** A \$7500 loan at 9% compounded monthly requires three payments at five-month intervals after the date of the loan. The second payment is to be twice the size of the first payment, and the third payment is to be double the amount of the second payment. Calculate the size of the second payment.

○**38.** Three equal payments were made two, four, and six years after the date on which a \$9000 loan was granted at 10% compounded quarterly. If the balance immediately after the third payment was \$5169.81, what was the amount of each payment?

●**39.** Repeat Problem 31 with the change that each contract accrues interest from today at the rate of 12% compounded monthly.

●**40.** Repeat Problem 32 with the change that each obligation accrues interest at the rate of 9% compounded monthly from a date nine months ago when the obligations were incurred.

●**41.** If the total interest earned on an investment at 8.2% compounded semiannually for $8\frac{1}{2}$ years was \$1175.98, what was the original investment?

●**42.** Peggy has never made any payments on a five-year-old loan from her mother at 6% compounded annually. The total interest owed is now \$845.56. How much did she borrow from her mother?

8.4   USING FINANCIAL CALCULATORS

LO1   The formulas for many compound-interest calculations are permanently programmed into financial calculators. These calculators allow you to enter the numerical values for the variables into memory. Then you select the appropriate financial function to automatically perform the calculation.

Ideally, you should be able to solve compound-interest problems using both the algebraic method and the financial functions on a calculator. The algebraic approach strengthens your mathematical skills and provides more flexibility for handling non-standard cases. It helps prepare you to create spreadsheets for specific applications. Financial calculators make routine calculations more efficient and reduce the likelihood of making arithmetic errors. Most of the example problems from this point onward will present both algebraic and financial calculator solutions.

KEY DEFINITIONS AND CALCULATOR OPERATION

The financial calculator instructions and keystrokes shown in the main body of this text and in the Student's Solutions Manual are for the Texas Instruments BA II PLUS. General instructions for two other models are provided in Appendixes 8A and 12A.

The basic financial keys of the Texas Instruments BA II PLUS calculator are in the third row of its keyboard. The calculator's manual refers to them as the TVM (Time-Value-of-Money) keys. The definitions for these keys are as follows.

N	represents the number of compounding periods, n
IY	represents the nominal (annual) interest rate, j
PV	represents the principal or present value, PV
PMT	represents the periodic annuity payment (not used until Chapter 10)
FV	represents the maturity value or future value, FV

Each of the five keys has two uses:

1. Saving in memory a numerical value for the variable.
2. Computing the value of the variable (based on previously saved values for all other variables).

As an example, let us compute the future value of $1000 invested at 8% compounded semiannually for 3 years. We must first enter values for [N], [I/Y], [PV], and [PMT]. They may be entered in any order. To save $1000 in the [PV] memory, just enter the digits for 1000 and press [PV]. The display then shows[3]

$$\boxed{PV = \qquad\qquad 1{,}000.}$$

Next enter values for the other variables in the same manner. (You do not need to clear your display between entries.) Note that the *nominal interest rate must be entered in percent form* (without the % symbol) rather than in its decimal equivalent form. For all compound interest problems in Chapters 8 and 9, the value "0" must be stored in the [PMT] memory. (This tells the calculator that there is no regular annuity payment.) In summary, the keystrokes for entering these four known values are:

1000 [PV]   6 [N]   8 [I/Y]   0 [PMT]

Do you think the calculator now has enough information to compute the future value? Note that we have not yet entered any information about the compounding frequency. To key in and save the value for the number of compoundings per year, you must first gain access to a particular list of internal settings. Note the *P/Y* symbol above the *I/Y* key. This indicates that the *P/Y* settings worksheet is the second function of the *I/Y* key. Therefore, to open this worksheet, press the key labelled "2nd" followed by the key labelled "*I/Y*." Hereafter, we will represent this keystroke combination by

[2nd] [P/Y]

After pressing these two keys, your calculator's display will show something like

$$\boxed{P/Y = \qquad\qquad 12.}$$

This display is actually a "window" to the first item in a list of just two items as shown below.

$$\boxed{\begin{array}{ll} P/Y = & \qquad 12. \\ C/Y = & \qquad 12. \end{array}}$$

You can scroll down to the second item by pressing the [↓] key. The definitions for these new symbols are:

> *P/Y* represents the number of annuity payments per year
> *C/Y* represents the number of compoundings per year

Therefore, *C/Y* corresponds to the algebraic symbol *m*.

If the calculation does not involve an annuity, *P/Y* must be given the same value as *C/Y*.[4] This requirement applies to all problems in Chapters 8 and 9. In the current example, we

---

[3] The assumption here is that the calculator has previously been set for "floating-decimal format." See the Appendix to this chapter for instructions on setting this format on the "Format worksheet."

[4] This requirement does not come from any logic or line of reasoning. It is just a result of the particular way Texas Instruments has programmed the calculator.

have semiannual compounding. Therefore, we need to set both *P/Y* and *C/Y* equal to 2. To do that, scroll back up to the *P/Y* line in the list. Then press

2 |ENTER|

The calculator display now shows

| *P/Y* =   2. |

Next, scroll down to *C/Y*. Observe that its value has automatically changed to 2. Entering a new value for *P/Y* *always* causes *C/Y* to change automatically to the same value. So for all problems in Chapters 8 and 9, we need only set *P/Y* = *m*. That will produce the desired result of making[5] *C/Y* = *P/Y* = *m*.

Before we can compute the future value of the $1000, we must close the *P/Y* settings worksheet. Note that the second function of the key labelled CPT is QUIT. Pressing

| 2nd | | QUIT |

will close whatever worksheet is open. Then, to execute the future value calculation, press

| CPT | | FV |

The calculator will display

| *FV* =   −1,265.319018 |

Rounded to the nearest cent, the future value of the $1000 investment is $1265.32. The significance of the negative sign will be discussed in the next subsection.

Let's summarize the complete sequence of keystrokes needed for the future value calculation.

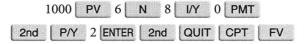

| TIP | **Efficient Use of Your Calculator**

You can operate your calculator more efficiently if you take advantage of the following features.

1. After any computation, all internal settings and numbers saved in memory are retained until you change them or clear them. Therefore, you do not need to re-enter a variable's value if it is unchanged in a subsequent calculation.

2. Whenever you *accidentally* press one of the five financial keys, the number in the display at that moment will be saved as the value of that financial variable. At any time, you can check the value stored in a financial key's memory by pressing | RCL | followed by the key.

3. When you turn the calculator off, it still retains the internal settings and the values in memory. (When the calculator's battery becomes weak, this feature and other calculator operations are unreliable.)

CASH-FLOW SIGN CONVENTION

Cash flow is a term frequently used in finance and accounting to refer to a cash payment. A cash inflow is a cash receipt; a cash outflow is a cash disbursement. A cash *inflow* should be

---

[5] Later in Chapter 10, *P/Y* and *C/Y* will have differing values in some annuity problems. We will deal with this matter when needed.

saved in a financial calculator's memory as a *positive* value. A cash *outflow* should be entered as a *negative* number. These two simple rules have a rather overblown name in finance—the **cash-flow sign convention**.

> **Cash-Flow Sign Convention**
> Cash inflows (receipts) are positive.
> Cash outflows (disbursements) are negative.

All financial calculators use the cash-flow convention. Finance courses and finance textbooks use it. The financial functions in spreadsheet software employ it. The greatest benefits from using the sign convention come in later chapters. However, we will introduce it now so you can become familiar with it before moving on to more complex cases.

To use the cash-flow sign convention, you must treat a compound interest problem as either an investment or a loan. The directions of the cash flows for these two cases are compared in the following table. When you invest money, you pay it (cash outflow) to some institution or individual. Later, you receive cash inflows from investment income and from the sale or redemption of the investment. In contrast, when you receive a loan, it is a cash inflow for you. The subsequent cash flows in the loan transaction are the loan payments (cash outflows).

Transaction	Initial cash flow	Subsequent cash flows
Investment	Outflow (negative)	Inflows (positive)
Loan	Inflow (positive)	Outflows (negative)

Now you can understand why your calculator gave a negative future value earlier in this section. Because we entered 1000 as a positive number in the `PV` memory, the calculator interpreted the $1000 as a loan. The computed future value represents the single payment required to pay off the loan. Since this payment is a cash outflow, the calculator displayed it as a negative number. To properly employ the sign convention for the initial $1000 investment, we should have entered 1000 in `PV` as a negative number. The calculator would then compute a positive future value—the cash inflow we will receive when the investment matures.

To illustrate the use of financial calculators, Example problems 8.3A, 8.3C, and 8.3E will now be repeated as Examples 8.4A, 8.4B, and 8.4C, respectively.

EXAMPLE 8.4A   **THE INVESTMENT NEEDED TO REACH A PARTICULAR FUTURE VALUE**

What amount must you invest now at 4% compounded monthly to accumulate $10,000 after $3\frac{1}{2}$ years?

SOLUTION

Given: $j = 4\%$, $m = 12$, $FV = \$10,000$, Term = 3.5 years

Then $n = m \times \text{Term} = 12(3.5) = 42$

Enter the known variables and then compute the present value.

42 `N` 4 `I/Y` 0 `PMT` 10000 `FV`
`2nd` `P/Y` 12 `ENTER` `2nd` `QUIT` `CPT` `PV` *Answer:* −8,695.606596

Note that we entered the $10,000 as a positive value because it is the cash *inflow* you will receive 3.5 years from now. The answer is negative because it represents the investment (cash outflow) that must be made today. Rounded to the cent, the initial investment required is $8695.61.

EXAMPLE 8.4B   **CALCULATING AN EQUIVALENT VALUE OF TWO PAYMENTS**

Two payments of $10,000 each must be made one year and four years from now. If money can earn 9% compounded monthly, what single payment two years from now would be equivalent to the two scheduled payments?

SOLUTION

Given: $j = 9\%$ compounded monthly making $m = 12$ and $i = \frac{j}{m} = \frac{9\%}{12} = 0.75\%$

Other data and the solution strategy are shown on the time line below. FV_1 represents the future value of the first scheduled payment and PV_2 represents the present value of the second payment.

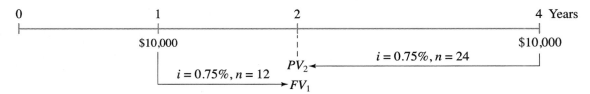

The single equivalent payment is $FV_1 + PV_2$. Before we start crunching numbers, let's exercise your intuition. Do you think the equivalent payment will be greater or smaller than $20,000? It is clear that FV_1 is greater than $10,000 and that PV_2 is less than $10,000. When the two amounts are added, will the sum be more than or less than $20,000? We can answer this question by comparing the time intervals through which we "shift" each of the $10,000 payments. The first payment will have one year's growth added, but the second payment will be discounted by two years' growth.[6] Therefore, PV_2 is farther below $10,000 than FV_1 is above $10,000. Hence, the equivalent payment will be less than $20,000. So if your equivalent payment turns out to be more than $20,000, you will know that your solution has an error. Returning to the calculations,

FV_1: 12 [N] 9 [I/Y] 10000 [PV] 0 [PMT]

    [2nd] [P/Y] 12 [ENTER] [2nd] [QUIT] [CPT] [FV] *Answer:* −10,938.069

PV_2: Do not clear the values and settings currently in memory. Then you need enter only those values and settings that change.

    24 [N] 10000 [FV] [CPT] [PV] *Answer:* −8,358.314

The equivalent payment two years from now is $10,938.069 + $8358.314 = $19,296.38.

Note: An equivalent payment problem is neither a loan nor an investment situation. Loans and investments always involve at least one cash flow in each direction. In contrast, an equivalent payment is a payment that can *substitute for* one or more other payments. The substitute payment will flow in the *same* direction as the payment(s) it replaces. So how should you apply the cash-flow sign convention to equivalent payment calculations? Just enter the scheduled payments as positive numbers and ignore the opposite sign on the calculated equivalent value.

---

[6] You cannot conclude that the difference between $10,000 and FV_1 will be twice the difference between PV_2 and $10,000. To illustrate this sort of effect, consider that at 10% compounded annually, the future value of $100 one year later is $110 but the present value of $100 one year earlier is $90.91. We see that the increase ($10) when compounding ahead one year exceeds the decrease ($9.09) when discounting back one year.

EXAMPLE 8.4C   **CALCULATING TWO UNKNOWN LOAN PAYMENTS**

Kramer borrowed $4000 from George at an interest rate of 7% compounded semiannually. The loan is to be repaid by three payments. The first payment, $1000, is due two years after the date of the loan. The second and third payments are due three and five years, respectively, after the initial loan. Calculate the amounts of the second and third payments if the second payment is to be twice the size of the third payment.

SOLUTION

Given: $j = 7\%$ compounded semiannually making $m = 2$ and $i = \frac{j}{m} = \frac{7\%}{2} = 3.5\%$

Let x represent the third payment. Then the second payment must be $2x$. As indicated in the following diagram, PV_1, PV_2, and PV_3 represent the present values of the first, second, and third payments.

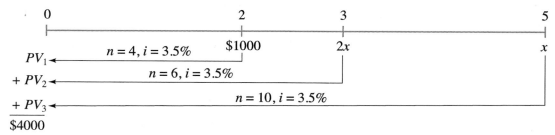

Since the sum of the present values of all payments equals the original loan, then

$$PV_1 + PV_2 + PV_3 = \$4000 \quad \text{①}$$

PV_1:   4 | N | 7 | I/Y | 0 | PMT | 1000 | FV |

   | 2nd | | P/Y | 2 | ENTER | | 2nd | | QUIT | | CPT | | PV | *Answer:* −871.442

At first, we may be stumped as to how to proceed for PV_2 and PV_3. Let's think about the third payment of x dollars. We can compute the present value of just $1 from the x dollars.

   10 | N | 1 | FV | | CPT | | PV | *Answer:* −0.7089188

The present value of $1 paid five years from now is $0.7089188 (almost $0.71). Consider the following questions (Q) and their answers (A).

Q: What is the present value of $2?   A: It's about $2 \times \$0.71 = \$1.42$.

Q: What is the present value of $5?   A: It's about $5 \times \$0.71 = \$3.55$.

Q: What is the present value of x?   A: Extending the preceding pattern, the present value of x is about
$x \times \$0.71 = \$0.71x$. Precisely, it is $PV_3 = \$0.7089188x$.

Similarly, calculate the present value of $1 from the second payment of $2x$ dollars. The only variable that changes from the previous calculation is | N | .

   6 | N | | CPT | | PV | *Answer:* −0.8135006

Hence, the present value of $2x$ is $PV_2 = 2x(\$0.8135006) = \$1.6270012x$

Now substitute the values for PV_1, PV_2 and PV_3 into equation ① and solve for x.

$$\$871.442 + 1.6270012x + 0.7089188x = \$4000$$
$$2.3359200x = \$3128.558$$
$$x = \$1339.326$$

Kramer's second payment will be $2(\$1339.326) = \$2678.65$ and the third payment will be $1339.33.

SPREADSHEET STRATEGIES   Future Value and Present Value

Connect provides two partially completed templates for calculating the future value and the present value of single payments. Go to the Student Edition of Connect and find "FV and PV of a Single Payment."

The Future Value template and the Present Value template each use two methods—one based on the algebraic formula (8-2) and the other based on a built-in Excel function. The "Introduction" page of the "FV and PV of a Single Payment" workbook describes Excel's built-in Future Value (FV) function and Present Value (PV) function.

The main features of a completed Future Value template are presented below. The formulas programmed into cells C9 and C11 are displayed in cells C10 and C12, respectively. Here data are entered to solve Example 8.2A. In this example, we are to determine the maturity value of $10,000 invested for five years at 9.75% compounded semiannually. As an initial "side calculation," we determine that $i = \frac{j}{m} = \frac{9.75\%}{2} = 4.875\%$, and $n = m \times \text{Term} = 2 \times 5 = 10$ compounding periods. After entering these known values into the input cells, the computed future value immediately appears in the output cells.

	A	B	C	D	E
1					
2	Using a spreadsheet for the future value of a single payment.				
3		Example 8.2A:			
4					
5		Present value, PV	10,000.00		
6		Periodic rate of interest, i	4.8750%		
7		Number of cmpding periods, n	10.00		
8					
9		Future value, FV	$16,096.07		
10		Formula in Cell C9:	=C5*(1+C6)^C7		
11		Future value, FV	-$16,096.07		
12		Formula in Cell C11:	=FV(C6,C7,0,C5,0)		
13					

The maturity value of the investment after five years is $16,096.07.

EXERCISE 8.4   *Solve the problems in Exercise 8.2 and 8.3 using the financial functions on a calculator.*

Spreadsheet templates: *Two partially completed Excel templates for calculating present value and future value are provided in Connect. Go to the Student Edition of Connect and find "FV and PV of a Single Payment." One or the other of these templates may be used in solving most of the problems in Exercise 8.2 and Exercise 8.3.*

8.5   OTHER APPLICATIONS OF COMPOUNDING

COMPOUND-INTEREST INVESTMENTS

The two most common types of compound-interest investments owned by Canadians are Guaranteed Investment Certificates and Canada Savings Bonds.

Guaranteed Investment Certificates (GICs) GICs may be purchased from banks, credit unions, life insurance companies, trust companies, and caisses populaires (mostly in Quebec). When you buy a GIC from a financial institution, you are in effect lending money to it or to one of its subsidiaries. The financial institution uses the funds raised from selling GICs to make loans—most commonly, mortgage loans. The interest rate charged on mortgage loans is typically 1.5% to 2% higher than the interest rate paid to GIC investors. The word "Guaranteed" in the name of this investment refers to the *unconditional guarantee* of principal and interest by the parent financial institution. In addition to this guarantee, there is usually some form of government-regulated deposit insurance.

Most Guaranteed Investment Certificates are purchased with maturities in the range of one to five years. Longer maturities (up to 10 years) are available, but are not covered by deposit insurance. Normally, you earn higher interest rates for longer maturities. Early redemption restrictions apply to many types of GICs. You must accept lower interest rates for more liberal redemption privileges. The following diagrams present typical alternatives for redemption privileges, the structure of interest rates, and for the payment of interest.

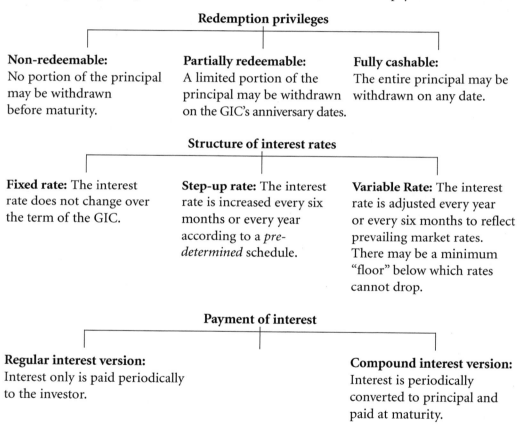

Redemption privileges

Non-redeemable:
No portion of the principal may be withdrawn before maturity.

Partially redeemable:
A limited portion of the principal may be withdrawn on the GIC's anniversary dates.

Fully cashable:
The entire principal may be withdrawn on any date.

Structure of interest rates

Fixed rate: The interest rate does not change over the term of the GIC.

Step-up rate: The interest rate is increased every six months or every year according to a *pre-determined* schedule.

Variable Rate: The interest rate is adjusted every year or every six months to reflect prevailing market rates. There may be a minimum "floor" below which rates cannot drop.

Payment of interest

Regular interest version:
Interest only is paid periodically to the investor.

Compound interest version:
Interest is periodically converted to principal and paid at maturity.

LO2   The regular interest versions of GICs are not mathematically interesting since periodic interest is paid out to the investor instead of being converted to principal. For compound interest versions, there are two mathematically distinct cases.

1. If the interest rate is *fixed*, use $FV = PV(1 + i)^n$ to calculate the maturity value.
2. If the interest rate is either a *variable rate* or a *step-up rate*, the periodic rate i can differ for each compounding period. Then you must use a more general version of formula (8-2) that allows for a different $(1 + i)$ factor for each compounding period. That is, use

FUTURE VALUE (VARIABLE AND STEP-UP INTEREST RATES)

$$FV = PV(1 + i_1)(1 + i_2)(1 + i_3) \ldots (1 + i_n) \qquad \text{(8-4)}$$

EXAMPLE 8.5A   **CALCULATING THE PAYMENT FROM A REGULAR INTEREST GIC**

What periodic payment does an investor receive from a $9000, four-year, monthly payment GIC earning a nominal rate of 5.25% payable monthly? (Only the accrued interest is paid each month.)

SOLUTION

The interest rate per payment interval is

$$i = \frac{j}{m} = \frac{5.25\%}{12} = 0.4375\%$$

The monthly payment is

$$PV \times i = \$9000 \times 0.004375 = \$39.38$$

EXAMPLE 8.5B   **COMPARING GICs HAVING DIFFERENT NOMINAL RATES**

Suppose a bank quotes nominal annual interest rates of 6.6% compounded annually, 6.5% compounded semiannually, and 6.4% compounded monthly on five-year compound-interest GICs. Which rate should an investor choose?

SOLUTION

An investor should choose the rate that results in the highest maturity value. The given information may be arranged in a table.

j	m	$i = \frac{j}{m}$	n
6.6%	1	6.6%	5
6.5	2	3.25	10
6.4	12	$0.5\overline{3}$	60

Choose an amount, say $1000, to invest. Calculate the maturity values for the three alternatives.

$$FV = PV(1 + i)^n$$
$$= \$1000(1.066)^5 \quad = \$1376.53 \quad \text{for } j = 6.6\% \text{ compounded annually}$$
$$= \$1000(1.0325)^{10} = \$1376.89 \quad \text{for } j = 6.5\% \text{ compounded semiannually}$$
$$= \$1000(1.005\overline{3})^{60} = \$1375.96 \quad \text{for } j = 6.4\% \text{ compounded monthly}$$

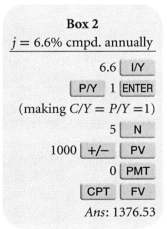

Box 1
$j = 6.6\%$ cmpd. annually

6.6 I/Y
2nd P/Y
1 ENTER
(making $C/Y = P/Y = 1$)
2nd QUIT
5 N
1000 +/− PV
0 PMT
CPT FV
Ans: 1376.53

Box 2
$j = 6.6\%$ cmpd. annually

6.6 I/Y
P/Y 1 ENTER
(making $C/Y = P/Y = 1$)
5 N
1000 +/− PV
0 PMT
CPT FV
Ans: 1376.53

Let's now calculate these same maturity values using our financial calculator. We will switch to a vertical format for presenting the keystrokes. The case $j = 6.6\%$ compounded annually is shown in Box 1. A good habit to develop for calculations in later chapters is to enter the interest rate information first. The first five lines (after the title) do this. The fourth line is just a reminder that, when we enter a new value for P/Y, it also changes C/Y to the same value. The sequence for entering the remaining values does not matter.

Every time we need to change the value of P/Y or C/Y, we will have the same keystrokes 2nd P/Y to access these variables and the same keystrokes 2nd QUIT to return to the calculation. To avoid this repetition in our calculator solutions, we will

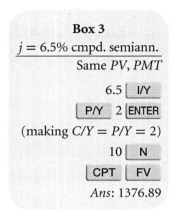

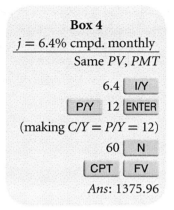

shorten the display hereafter as shown in Box 2. It is left to you to supply the missing keystrokes.

The keystrokes for calculating the maturity values at the other two interest rates are displayed in Boxes 3 and 4. The calculator's memories retain the most recent values if you do not clear the TVM memories. Therefore, we show only those values that change from the preceding calculation.

Answering the initial question, the investor should choose the GIC earning 6.5% compounded semiannually since it produces the highest maturity value.

EXAMPLE 8.5C   **MATURITY VALUE OF A VARIABLE-RATE GIC**

A chartered bank offers a five-year "Escalator Guaranteed Investment Certificate." In successive years it earns annual interest rates of 4%, 4.5%, 5%, 5.5%, and 6%, respectively, *compounded* at the end of each year. The bank also offers regular five-year GICs paying a fixed rate of 5% compounded annually. Calculate and compare the maturity values of $1000 invested in each type of GIC. (Note that 5% is the average of the five successive one-year rates paid on the Escalator GIC.)

SOLUTION

Using formula (8-4), the maturity value of the Escalator GIC is

$$FV = \$1000(1.04)(1.045)(1.05)(1.055)(1.06) = \$1276.14$$

Using formula (8-2), the maturity value of the regular GIC is

$$FV = \$1000(1.05)^5 = \$1276.28$$

The Escalator GIC will mature at $1276.14, but the regular GIC will mature at $1276.28 ($0.14 more). We can also conclude from this example that a series of compound interest rates does not produce the same future value as the *average* rate compounded over the same period.

LO4   **Canada Savings Bonds (CSBs)** Although you may purchase CSBs from most of the same financial institutions that issue GICs, your money goes to the federal government to help finance its debt.[7] The financial institution is merely an agent in the transaction.

Canada Savings Bonds sold in recent years have terms of 10 years. The batch of bonds sold on a particular date is assigned a series number. For example, the CSBs issued on November 1, 2003 are referred to as Series 84 (S84). All CSBs have variable interest rates—the Finance Department changes the interest rate for a particular series on that series' anniversary date. The interest rate is adjusted to bring it into line with prevailing rates. The interest rates paid on CSBs issued on November 1 each year are presented in Table 8.2.

---

[7]   At the end of 2009, the total outstanding amount of CSBs was $12.1 billion. This represented 2.1% of Canada's net federal debt.

NET @ssets

Canada Investment and Savings is an agency of the federal Department of Finance. It maintains a Web site providing information on Canada Savings Bonds and Canada Premium Bonds. Interest rates on all unmatured issues are available on the site.

Canada Savings Bonds are issued in regular-interest versions (called R-bonds) and compound-interest versions (called C-bonds). R-bonds pay a full year's interest to their owners on each anniversary of the issue date. C-bonds convert interest to principal on each anniversary.

Canada Savings Bonds may be redeemed at any time.[8] The following rules apply to calculating the interest for the *partial* year since the most recent anniversary date.

- Interest is accrued to the first day of the month in which redemption occurs. (If you redeem a CSB partway through a month, you receive no interest for the partial month.)

- Interest is calculated on a simple interest basis. That is, the additional interest for the partial year is $I = Prt$ where

  $P =$ The principal (including converted interest on compound-interest bonds) at the preceding anniversary date

  $r =$ The prescribed annual interest rate for the current year

  $t =$ The number of months (from the preceding anniversary date up to the first day of the month in which redemption occurs) divided by 12

TABLE 8.2 Interest Rates (%) on Canada Savings Bonds

Interest rate effective Nov. 1 of:	S72 (issued Nov.1, 2001)	S78 (issued Nov.1, 2002)	S84 (issued Nov.1, 2003)	S90 (issued Nov.1, 2004)	S96 (issued Nov.1, 2005)	S102 (issued Nov.1, 2006)	S108 (issued Nov.1, 2007)	S114 (issued Nov.1, 2008)	S120 (issued Nov.1, 2009)
2001	1.80								
2002	2.00	2.00							
2003	1.75	1.75	1.75						
2004	1.50	1.50	1.50	1.50					
2005	2.50	2.50	2.50	2.50	2.50				
2006	3.00	3.00	3.00	3.00	3.00	3.00			
2007	3.25	3.25	3.25	3.25	3.25	3.25	3.25		
2008	2.00	2.00	2.00	2.00	2.00	2.00	2.00	2.00	
2009	0.40	0.40	0.40	0.40	0.40	0.40	0.40	0.40	0.40
Matures Nov. 1 of:	2011	2012	2013	2014	2015	2016	2017	2018	2019

EXAMPLE 8.5D **CALCULATING THE REDEMPTION VALUE OF A COMPOUND-INTEREST CANADA SAVINGS BOND**

A $1000 face value Series S84 compound-interest Canada Savings Bond (CSB) was presented to a credit union branch for redemption. What amount did the owner receive if the redemption was requested on:

a. November 1, 2008?   **b.** January 17, 2009?

SOLUTION

a. In Table 8.2, we note that Series S84 CSBs were issued on November 1, 2003. November 1, 2008 falls on the fifth anniversary of the issue date. Substituting the annual interest rates for S84 bonds from Table 8.2 into formula (8-4), we have

$$FV = PV(1 + i_1)(1 + i_2)(1 + i_3)(1 + i_4)(1 + i_5)$$
$$= \$1000(1.0175)(1.015)(1.025)(1.03)(1.0325)$$
$$= \$1125.78$$

The owner received $1125.78 on November 1, 2008.

---

[8] In 1998, the Government of Canada started to issue another type of savings bond called Canada Premium Bonds (CPBs). CPBs are issued for a 10-year term with the interest rate for the first three years fixed at the date of issue. They may be redeemed, but *only on an anniversary date and 30 days thereafter*. Because of this restriction on redemption, Canada Premium Bonds pay a higher interest rate than Canada Savings Bonds.

b. For a redemption that took place on January 17, 2009, the bond's owner would have been paid extra interest at the annual rate of 2.00% for November 2008 and December 2008 (but no interest for the days in January). The amount of the extra interest was

$$I = Prt = \$1125.78(0.02)\tfrac{2}{12} = \$3.75$$

Therefore, the total amount the owner received on January 17, 2009 was

$$\$1125.78 + \$3.75 = \$1129.53$$

POINT OF INTEREST

The RRSP Advantage

We will often refer to Registered Retirement Savings Plans (RRSPs) in examples and exercises. For many individuals, particularly those who do not belong to an employer-sponsored pension plan, an RRSP is the central element of their retirement planning. In this discussion, you will begin to appreciate the advantages of investing within an RRSP, rather than investing outside an RRSP.

An RRSP is not a type of investment. Instead, think of an RRSP as a type of trust account in which you can deposit money and then use the money to purchase certain investments. The Income Tax Act sets out strict rules governing the amount of money you may contribute and the type of investments you may hold within an RRSP. There are two main advantages of using an RRSP to accumulate savings for retirement.

1. A contribution to an RRSP is deductible from the contributor's taxable income. In effect, you do not pay income tax on the part of your income that you contribute to an RRSP. (There are some complicated rules that determine the upper limit for your contribution each year.)

2. Earnings on investments held within an RRSP are not subject to income tax until they are withdrawn from the RRSP.

Consider the case of Darren and Cathy, who are both 30 years old and both earning salaries of $65,000 per year. Both intend to invest their $1000 year-end bonuses for their retirement. Being very conservative investors, both intend to build a portfolio of bonds and GICs. But Darren intends to contribute his $1000 to an RRSP trust account, and

invest the money within his RRSP. Cathy intends to hold her investments in her own name.

Let us compare the outcomes, 30 years later, of these alternative approaches for saving this year's $1000 bonuses. We will assume that their investments earn 6% compounded annually for the entire 30 years. Canadians with a $65,000 annual income are subject to a marginal income tax rate of close to 32%. (The figure varies somewhat from province to province.) This means that, if you earn an additional $100, you will pay $32 additional income tax and keep only $68 after tax. We will assume the 32% rate applies to Darren and Cathy for the next 30 years.

The consequence of the first advantage listed above is that Darren will pay no tax on his $1000 bonus. Cathy will pay $320 tax on her bonus, leaving her only $680 to invest. The second advantage means that Darren will not pay tax each year on the interest earned in his RRSP. In contrast, Cathy will have to pay tax at a rate of 32% on her interest income each year. After tax, her savings will grow at a compound annual rate of only

$$6\% - 0.32(6\%) = 6\% - 1.92\% = 4.08\%$$

In summary, Darren has a $1000 investment in his RRSP growing at 6% compounded annually, while Cathy has a $680 investment growing at 4.08% compounded annually after tax. Over the next 30 years, Darren's $1000 will grow to

$$FV = PV(1 + i)^n = \$1000(1.06)^{30} = \$5743.49$$

in his RRSP, while Cathy's $680 will grow to

$$FV = PV(1 + i)^n = \$680(1.0408)^{30} = \$2256.98$$

We should not directly compare these amounts. Before Darren can enjoy the fruits of his RRSP savings, he must withdraw the funds from his RRSP and pay tax on them. Darren's marginal tax rate may well be lower in retirement than while working. But even if we still use the 32% rate, Darren will be left with

$$0.68 \times \$5743.49 = \$3905.57$$

after tax. This is 73% more than the amount Cathy accumulated outside an RRSP!

QUESTIONS

1. Repeat the calculations with the change that Darren and Cathy are in a lower tax bracket with a marginal tax rate of 26%.

2. Repeat the calculations with the change that Darren and Cathy are in a higher tax bracket with a marginal tax rate of 43%.

3. Summarize the pattern you observe. (Is the "RRSP advantage" greater or lesser at higher marginal tax rates?)

VALUATION OF INVESTMENTS

With many types of investments, the owner can sell the investment to another investor. Such investments are said to be transferable.[9] The key question is: What is the appropriate price at which the investment should be sold/purchased? We encountered the same question in Chapter 7 for investments earning simple interest. There we discussed the thinking behind the Valuation Principle (repeated below for ease of reference).

> **Valuation Principle**
> The fair market value of an investment is the sum of the present values of the expected cash flows. The discount rate used should be the prevailing market-determined rate of return on this type of investment.

For an investment with cash inflows extending beyond one year, the market-determined rate of return is almost always a compound rate of return. In this section, we will apply the Valuation Principle to two types of investments.

LO3   **Strip Bonds** Many investors choose to hold strip bonds[10] in their Registered Retirement Savings Plans (RRSPs). You need to know only a few essential features of strip bonds in order to handle strip-bond calculations. If you buy a strip bond, you will receive a *single* payment (called the face value of the bond) on the bond's maturity date. The maturity date could be as much as 30 years in the future. You will receive no interest payments in the interim. Consider a $1000 face-value strip bond that matures 18 years from now. Its owner will receive a single payment of $1000 18 years from now. What is the appropriate price to pay for the bond today? Clearly, it will be substantially less than $1000. The difference between the $1000 you will receive at maturity and the price you pay today represents the earnings on your initial investment (the purchase price). The situation is similar to the pricing of T-bills in Section 7.3.

According to the Valuation Principle, the fair market price is the present value of the payment (of the face value) that will be received on the bond's maturity date. The discount rate you should use for "i" in $PV = FV(1 + i)^{-n}$ is the prevailing rate of return in financial

---

[9]   Guaranteed Investment Certificates and Canada Savings Bonds are normally not transferable.

[10] **Strip bonds** are created when investment dealers (brokers) break up marketable bonds (Chapter 15) into simple components that investors can purchase. Normally, investment dealers do this only with some of the marketable bonds issued by federal and provincial governments.

markets for strip bonds of similar risk and maturity. Table 8.3 presents quotes for a few strip bonds on June 1, 2009. The quoted "Prices" are per $100 of face value. The quoted "Yields" are understood in the financial world to be nominal rates with *semiannual* compounding. To simplify matters at this point, we have selected only strip bonds that have a December 1 or June 1 "Maturity Date." Consequently, the number of six-month compounding periods from June 1, 2009 until maturity is an integer in every case. (The more general circumstance where n is not an integer will be addressed in Section 9.2.)

TABLE 8.3   Strip Bond Price and Yield Quotations (June 1, 2009)

Issuer	Maturity Date	Price ($)	Yield (%)
Province of Ontario	June 1, 2015	83.008	3.128
Province of Quebec	December 1, 2018	65.014	4.584
Bell Canada	December 1, 2021	52.295	5.254
Government of Canada	June 1, 2025	52.402	4.080
Bell Canada	December 1, 2027	34.587	5.822
Province of Quebec	June 1, 2032	30.747	5.194

Consider the Bell Canada strip bond maturing on December 1, 2021. The market-determined rate of return (yield) on this bond late in the afternoon of June 1, 2009 was 5.254% compounded semiannually. This yield can vary by a few hundredths of a percent from hour to hour as investors react to events and economic forces.

We will now show that this market-determined yield is consistent with the quoted price of $52.295 (per $100 of face value). The price on June 1, 2009 should be the present value of the future $100 payment discounted at 5.254% compounded semiannually. With

$$FV = \$100, \ i = \frac{5.254\%}{2} = 2.627\%, \text{ and } n = m(\text{Term}) = 2(12.5) = 25,$$

$$PV = FV(1 + i)^{-n} = \$100(1 + 0.02627)^{-25} = \$52.295$$

The quoted price is $52.295. Since the published yield was rounded to four figures, we can expect no better than four-figure accuracy in our calculated price. The quoted and calculated prices are consistent.

Note: In example problems from this point onward, we will present financial calculator procedures in a "call-out" box adjacent to the algebraic solution. A "curly bracket" will indicate the algebraic calculations that the calculator procedure can replace.

EXAMPLE 8.5E   **CALCULATING THE PRICE OF A STRIP BOND**

A $10,000 face value strip bond has $15\frac{1}{2}$ years remaining until maturity. If the prevailing market rate of return is 6.5% compounded semiannually, what is the fair market value of the strip bond?

SOLUTION

Given: $FV = \$10,000$ $j = 6.5\%$ $m = 2$ Term $= 15\frac{1}{2}$ years

Therefore, $i = \frac{j}{m} = \frac{6.5\%}{2} = 3.25\%$ and $n = m(\text{Term}) = 2(15.5) = 31$

Fair market value = Present value of the face value
$$= FV(1 + i)^{-n}$$
$$= \$10,000(1.0325)^{-31}$$
$$= \$3710.29$$

The fair market value of the strip bond is $3710.29.

6.5 | I/Y
P/Y 2 ENTER
(making C/Y = P/Y = 2)
31 | N
10000 | FV
0 | PMT
CPT | PV
Ans: −3710.29

Long-Term Promissory Notes A promissory note is a simple contract between a debtor and creditor setting out the amount of the debt (face value), the interest rate thereon, and the terms of repayment. A *long-term* promissory note is a note whose term is longer than one year. Such notes usually accrue compound interest on the face value.

The payee (creditor) on a promissory note may sell the note to an investor before maturity. The debtor is then obligated to make the remaining payments to the new owner of the note. To determine the note's selling/purchase price, we need to apply the Valuation Principle to the note's maturity value. The two steps are:

1. Determine the note's maturity value based on the contractual rate of interest on the note.
2. Discount (that is, calculate the present value of) the Step 1 result back to the date of sale/purchase. Since there is no "market" for private promissory notes, the seller and purchaser must negotiate the discount rate.

EXAMPLE 8.5F   **CALCULATING THE SELLING PRICE OF A LONG-TERM PROMISSORY NOTE**

A five-year promissory note with a face value of $3500, bearing interest at 11% compounded semiannually, was sold 21 months after its issue date to yield the buyer 10% compounded quarterly. What amount was paid for the note?

SOLUTION

We should find the maturity value of the note and then discount the maturity value (at the required yield) back to the date of the sale. These two steps are indicated on the following diagram.

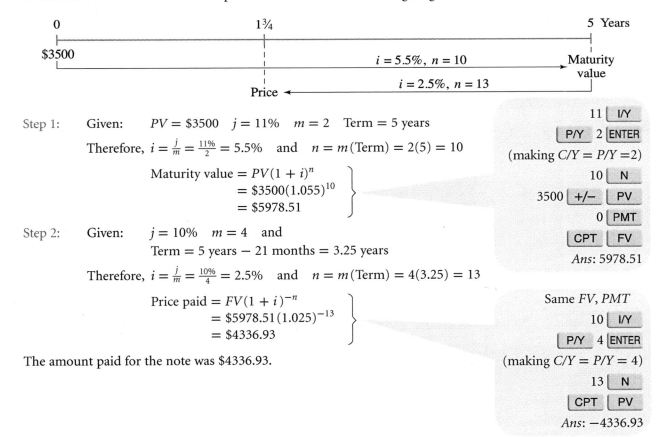

Step 1:   Given: $PV = \$3500$ $j = 11\%$ $m = 2$ Term $= 5$ years

Therefore, $i = \frac{j}{m} = \frac{11\%}{2} = 5.5\%$ and $n = m(\text{Term}) = 2(5) = 10$

$$\text{Maturity value} = PV(1 + i)^n$$
$$= \$3500(1.055)^{10}$$
$$= \$5978.51$$

Step 2:   Given: $j = 10\%$ $m = 4$ and

Term $= 5$ years $- 21$ months $= 3.25$ years

Therefore, $i = \frac{j}{m} = \frac{10\%}{4} = 2.5\%$ and $n = m(\text{Term}) = 4(3.25) = 13$

$$\text{Price paid} = FV(1 + i)^{-n}$$
$$= \$5978.51(1.025)^{-13}$$
$$= \$4336.93$$

The amount paid for the note was $4336.93.

COMPOUND GROWTH

LO5   The formula $FV = PV(1 + i)^n$ may be used in non-financial problems involving compound growth at a fixed periodic rate. Furthermore, you can use the financial functions of your calculator in such cases. Simply place the following interpretations on the variables.

Variable	General interpretation
PV	Beginning value, size, or quantity
FV	Ending value, size, or quantity
i	Fixed periodic rate of growth
n	Number of periods with growth rate i

If a quantity shrinks or contracts at a fixed periodic rate, it can be handled mathematically by treating it as *negative growth*. For example, suppose a firm's annual sales volume is projected to decline for the next four years by 5% per year from last year's level of 100,000 units. The expected sales volume in the fourth year may be obtained using $FV = PV(1 + i)^n$ with $n = 4$ and $i = (-5\%) = (-0.05)$. That is,

$$
\begin{aligned}
\text{Sales (in Year 4)} &= 100{,}000[1 + (-0.05)]^4 \\
&= 100{,}000(0.95)^4 \\
&= 81{,}451 \text{ units}
\end{aligned}
$$

In the financial calculator approach, you would save "−5" in the [I/Y] memory. The answer represents an overall decline of 18.55% in the annual volume of sales. Note that the overall decline is less than 20%, an answer you might be tempted to reach by simply adding the percentage changes.

Inflation and Purchasing Power A useful application of compound growth in financial planning is using forecast rates of inflation to estimate future prices and the purchasing power of money. As discussed in Section 3.6, the rate of inflation measures the annual percent change in the price level of goods and services. By compounding the forecast rate of inflation over a number of years, we can estimate the level of prices at the end of the period.

When prices rise, money loses its purchasing power—these are "two sides of the same (depreciating) coin." If price levels double, a given nominal amount of money will purchase only half as much. We then say that the money has half its former purchasing power. Similarly, if price levels triple, money retains only one-third of its former purchasing power. These examples demonstrate that price levels and purchasing power have an inverse relationship. That is,

$$
\frac{\text{Ending purchasing power}}{\text{Beginning purchasing power}} = \frac{\text{Beginning price level}}{\text{Ending price level}}
$$

Let us push the reasoning one step further to answer this question: If price levels rise 50% over a number of years, what will be the percent *loss* in purchasing power? This gets a little tricky—the answer is *not* 50%. If the ending price level is 50% higher than the beginning price level, the ratio of price levels (on the right side of the preceding proportion) is

$$
\frac{100}{150} \quad \text{or} \quad \frac{2}{3}
$$

Therefore, money will *retain* $\frac{2}{3}$ of its purchasing power and *lose* the other $\frac{1}{3}$ or $33\frac{1}{3}\%$ of its purchasing power.

EXAMPLE 8.5G   **THE LONG-TERM EFFECT OF INFLATION ON PURCHASING POWER**

If the rate of inflation for the next 20 years is 2.5% per year, what annual income (rounded to the nearest $100) will be needed 20 years from now to have the same purchasing power as a $50,000 annual income today?

SOLUTION

The required income will be $50,000 compounded at 2.5% per year for 20 years.

Given: $PV = \$50,000$ $j = 2.5\%$ $m = 1$ Term = 20 years

Hence, $i = \frac{j}{m} = \frac{2.5\%}{1} = 2.5\%$ and $n = m(\text{Term}) = 1(20) = 20$

$$\left.\begin{aligned} FV &= PV(1 + i)^n \\ &= \$50,000(1.025)^{20} \\ &= \$81,930.82 \end{aligned}\right\}$$

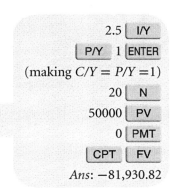

2.5 [I/Y]
[P/Y] 1 [ENTER]
(making $C/Y = P/Y = 1$)
20 [N]
50000 [PV]
0 [PMT]
[CPT] [FV]
Ans: −81,930.82

After 20 years of 2.5% annual inflation, an annual income of $81,900 will be needed to have the same purchasing power as $50,000 today.

EXAMPLE 8.5H   **COMPOUND ANNUAL DECREASE IN POPULATION**

The population of a rural region is expected to fall by 2% per year for the next 10 years. If the region's current population is 100,000, what is the expected population 10 years from now?

SOLUTION

The 2% "negative growth" should be compounded for 10 years.

Given: $PV = 100,000$ $j = -2\%$ $m = 1$ Term = 10 years

Hence, $i = \frac{j}{m} = \frac{-2\%}{1} = -2\%$ and $n = m(\text{Term}) = 1(10) = 10$

$$\left.\begin{aligned} FV &= PV(1 + i)^n \\ &= 100,000[1 + (-0.02)]^{10} \\ &= 100,000(0.98)^{10} \\ &= 81,707 \end{aligned}\right\}$$

2 [+/−] [I/Y]
[P/Y] 1 [ENTER]
(making $C/Y = P/Y = 1$)
10 [N]
100000 [PV]
0 [PMT]
[CPT] [FV]
Ans: −81,707

The region's population is expected to drop to about 81,707 during the next 10 years.

SPREADSHEET STRATEGIES   Future Value Using Formula (8-4)

Connect provides a partially completed template for calculating the future value when the periodic interest rate changes from one compounding period to the next. Go to the Student Edition of Connect and find "Formula (8-4) Calculator."

The main features of the completed template are presented below. The formula programmed into cell C12 is displayed in Row 14. Here data are entered to perform *one* of the calculations required in Example 8.5C. In this example, we need to determine the maturity value of $1000 invested in a five-year GIC that earns annual rates of 4%, 4.5%, 5%, 5.5%, and 6% in successive years. After entering these known values into the input cells, the computed future value ($1276.14) immediately appears in the output cell C12.

	A	B	C	D	E
1					
2		Using a spreadsheet to calculate a future value with formula (8-4).			
3	Example 8.5C:				
4					
5		Principal or Initial value, $PV =$	$1,000.00		
6		Rate for Period 1, $i_1 =$	$4.000%		
7		Rate for Period 2, $i_2 =$	$4.500%		
8		Rate for Period 3, $i_3 =$	$5.000%		
9		Rate for Period 4, $i_4 =$	$5.500%		
10		Rate for Period 5, $i_5 =$	$6.000%		
11					
12		Future value, $FV=$	$1,276.14		
13		Fomula programmed			
14		into cell C12: =C5*(1+C6)*(1+C7)*(1+C8)*(1+C9)*(1+C10)			
15					

CONCEPT QUESTIONS

1. How, if at all, will the future value of a three-year variable-rate GIC differ if it earns 4%, 5%, and 6% in successive years instead of 6%, 5%, and 4% in successive years?

2. Why must the Finance Department keep the interest rates on existing CSBs at least as high as the rate on a new CSB issue?

3. Should we conclude that the owner of a strip bond earns nothing until the full face value is received at maturity? Explain.

4. If a quantity increases by $x\%$ per year (compounded) for two years, will the overall percent increase be more or less than $2x\%$? Explain.

5. If a quantity declines by $x\%$ per year (compounded) for two years, will the overall percent decrease be more or less than $2x\%$? Explain.

EXERCISE 8.5

Spreadsheet template: A partially completed Excel template for calculating a future value using formula (8-4) is provided in Connect. Go to the Student Edition of Connect and find "Formula (8-4) Calculator." You can use this template in any problem in Exercise 8.5 that requires the use of formula (8-4).

Answers to the odd-numbered problems are at the end of the book.

Note: A few problems in some Exercises have been extracted (with permission) from course materials created by the Canadian Institute of Financial Planning (CIFP) for its program leading to the Certified Financial Planner (CFP) designation. The CIFP and associated bodies (see www.ifse.ca) are leading providers of financial services education in Canada. Problems derived from CIFP materials are identified in our Exercises by the organization's logo placed in the margin adjacent to the problems.

1. Krista invested $18,000 in a three-year regular-interest GIC earning 4.2% payable semiannually. What is each semiannual interest payment?

2. Eric invested $22,000 in a five-year regular-interest GIC earning 4.5% payable monthly. What is each monthly interest payment?

3. Mr. Dickson purchased a seven-year, $30,000 compound-interest GIC with funds in his RRSP. If the interest rate on the GIC is 5.25% compounded semiannually, what is the GIC's maturity value?

4. Mrs. Sandhu placed $11,500 in a four-year compound-interest GIC earning 6.75% compounded monthly. What is the GIC's maturity value?

5. A trust company offers three-year compound-interest GICs earning 4.8% compounded monthly or 4.9% compounded semiannually. Which rate should an investor choose?

6. If an investor has the choice between rates of 5.4% compounded quarterly and 5.5% compounded annually for a six-year GIC, which rate should she choose?

∘7. For a given term of compound-interest GIC, the nominal interest rate with annual compounding is typically 0.125% higher than the rate with semiannual compounding and 0.25% higher than the rate with monthly compounding. Suppose that the rates for five-year GICs are 5.00%, 4.875%, and 4.75% for annual, semiannual, and monthly compounding, respectively. How much more will an investor earn over five years on a $10,000 GIC at the most favourable rate than at the least favourable rate?

8. Sun Life Financial offers a five-year compound-interest GIC earning rates of 2.5%, 3%, 3.5%, 4.25%, and 5% in successive years. Manulife offers a similar GIC paying rates of 2.75%, 3.25%, 3.5%, 4%, and 4.25% in successive years. For a $10,000 investment, which GIC will have the greater maturity value after five years? How much greater?

9. Using the information given in Problem 8, calculate the interest earned in the third year from a $10,000 investment in each GIC.

10. Stan purchased a $15,000 compound-interest Series 103 Canada Savings Bond on December 1, 2008. The interest rate in the first year was 2.50% and in the second year was 3.00%. What total interest did Stan receive when he redeemed the CSB on May 1, 2010?

In problems 11 to 13, use Table 8.2 to find the interest rates you need.

11. What amount did the owner of a $5000 face value compound-interest Series S96 Canada Savings Bond receive when she redeemed the bond on:
    a. November 1, 2009?
    b. August 21, 2010?

12. What amount did the owner of a $10,000 face value compound-interest Series S102 CSB receive when he redeemed the bond on:
    a. November 1, 2009?
    b. May 19, 2010?

13. What was the redemption value of a $300 face value compound-interest Series S90 CSB on March 8, 2010?

14. On February 1, 2007, Selma purchased a $50,000 compound-interest CSB. The interest rate on the CSB was 1.55% for each of the first two years and 2.675% for the third year. What was the total interest earned on the CSB by the time Selma redeemed the bond on April 1, 2009? (Taken from CIFP course materials.)

15. Calculate the maturity value of $2000 invested in a five-year compound-interest GIC earning 4.1% compounded annually.

16. A compound-interest GIC will earn 5% compounded annually for the first two years and 6% compounded annually for the last three years of its five-year term. What will be the maturity value of $3000 invested in this GIC?

17. $8000 is invested in a five-year compound-interest GIC earning interest rates of 4%, 4.5%, 5%, 5.5%, and 6% in successive years. What amount will the investor receive at maturity?

18. Western Life's "Move-Up" compound-interest GIC earns 4.125%, 4.25%, 4.5%, 4.875%, and 5% in successive years. What will be the maturity value of $7500 invested in this GIC?

19. The BMO Bank of Montreal advertised rates of 1.8%, 2.25%, 2.6%, 3%, and 3.25% for the five successive years of its five-year compound-interest RateOptimizer GIC. At the same time, the bank was offering fixed-rate five-year compound-interest GICs yielding 2.75% compounded annually. What total interest would be earned during the five-year term on a $5000 investment in each type of GIC?

20. On the same date that the CIBC advertised rates of 2%, 2.5%, 3%, 3.25%, and 7% in successive years of its five-year compound-interest Escalating Rate GIC, it offered 2.75% compounded annually on its five-year fixed-rate GIC. How much more will a $10,000 investment be worth at maturity if the Escalating Rate GIC is chosen instead of the fixed-rate GIC?

21. Using the information given in Problem 20, calculate the interest earned in the fourth year from a $10,000 investment in each GIC.

22. Using the information given in Problem 20, how much would have to be initially invested in each GIC to have a maturity value of $20,000?

23. How much will you need 20 years from now to have the purchasing power of $100 today if the (compound annual) rate of inflation during the period is:
    a. 2%?   **b.** 3%?   **c.** 4%?

24. How much money was needed 15 years ago to have the purchasing power of $1000 today if the (compound annual) rate of inflation has been:
    a. 2%?   **b.** 4%?

25. If the inflation rate for the next 10 years is 3.5% per year, what hourly rate of pay in 10 years will be equivalent to $15/hour today?

26. Zimbabwe's descent into economic chaos during the late 1990s and early 2000s resulted in hyperinflation. By August of 2008, the *monthly* inflation rate stood at 839%! Retailers were increasing their prices more than once each day. The government had to issue currency in ever rising denominations—the highest denomination note circulating in August of 2008 was for $100 billion ($100,000,000,000) Zimbabwean dollars!

    a. Consider a loaf of bread with a price of $4 at the beginning of a month. With an inflation rate of 839% per month, what would the loaf's price be at the end of a month in order to "keep pace" with inflation?

    b. In the scenario in Part (a), what percentage of its purchasing power did a fixed nominal amount of currency retain at the end of the month?

    c. What daily percent price increase, compounded over a 30-day month, would result in an 839% overall price increase during the month?

    d. Consider a piece of candy priced at just one cent ($0.01) at the beginning of a year. If inflation continued at the rate of 839% per month for an entire year, what would be the inflation-adjusted price of the candy at the end of the year?

27. Mr. and Mrs. Rasuli would like to retire in 15 years at an annual income level that would be equivalent to $35,000 today. What is their retirement income goal if, in the meantime, the annual rate of inflation is:

    a. 2%? **b.** 3%? **c.** 5%?

28. In 2002 the number of workers in the forest industry was forecast to decline by 3% per year, reaching 80,000 in 2012. How many were employed in the industry in 2002?

○29. A pharmaceutical company had sales of $28,600,000 in the year just completed. Sales are expected to decline by 4% per year for the next three years until new drugs, now under development, receive regulatory approval. Then sales should grow at 8% per year for the next four years. What are the expected sales for the final year of the seven-year period?

○30. The late 1970s and early 1980s were years of historically high rates of inflation in Canada. For the years 1978, 1979, 1980, 1981, and 1982 the rates of inflation were 8.8%, 9.2%, 10.9%, 12.6%, and 10.0%, respectively.

    a. Suppose your hourly wage at the beginning of 1978 was $10 per hour. What wage did you need to earn at the end of 1982 just to keep pace with inflation?

    b. What percentage of its purchasing power did money lose over these five years?

31. A $1000 face value strip bond has 22 years remaining until maturity. What is its price if the market rate of return on such bonds is 6.5% compounded semiannually?

32. What price should be paid for a $5000 face value strip bond with 19.5 years remaining to maturity if it is to yield the buyer 6.1% compounded semiannually?

○33. Wojtek purchased a $10,000 face value strip bond on a date when it had 14 years left until maturity. The purchase price was based on a market yield of 6.2% compounded semiannually. He sold the bond $4\frac{1}{2}$ years later when the market yield was 5.2% compounded semiannually. What was Wojtek's total gain on the investment? (Taken from CIFP course materials.)

34. Consider a $5000 face value Province of Quebec strip bond from the issue in Table 8.3 that matures on December 1, 2018. If the yield does not change as years go by, what will be the bond's value on:

    a. December 1, 2012?

    b. December 1, 2014?

    c. December 1, 2016?

35. Consider a $10,000 face value Government of Canada strip bond from the issue in Table 8.3 that matures on June 1, 2025. Assume the yield does not change as years go by.

    a. What will be the bond's value on December 1, 2016?

    b. What will be the bond's value on December 1, 2020?

    c. Suppose you invest an amount equal to the answer from Part (a) at 4.08% compounded semiannually for four years. What will its maturity value be?

    d. To three-figure accuracy, why do you get the same answers for Parts (b) and (c)?

36. If the current discount rate on 15-year strip bonds is 4.75% compounded semiannually, how many $1000 face value strips can be purchased with $10,000?

37. Mrs. Janzen wishes to purchase some 13-year-maturity strip bonds with the $12,830 in cash she now has in her RRSP. If these strip bonds are currently priced to yield 5.25% compounded semiannually, how many $1000 denomination bonds can she purchase?

38. Boris recently turned 30, an event causing him to give thought to some long-range financial planning. He believes that, if he owns a home and is debt-free by age 60, he and his partner can retire and live comfortably on an annual income that is equivalent to $40,000 today. Fill in the cells of the following table with the nominal annual income needed to satisfy this criterion at each age under each of three inflation rate scenarios.

	2% annual inflation	3% annual inflation	4% annual inflation
Income at age 60:	?	?	?
Income at age 70:	?	?	?
Income at age 80:	?	?	?

○39. A four-year $8000 promissory note bearing interest at 13.5% compounded monthly was discounted 21 months after issue to yield 12% compounded quarterly. What were the proceeds from the sale of the note?

○40. An eight-year note for $3800 with interest at 11% compounded semiannually was sold after three years and three months to yield the buyer 14% compounded quarterly. What price did the buyer pay?

•41. The contract for a $4000 loan at 9% compounded quarterly requires two payments. The first payment of $2000 is required two years after the date of the loan. (It is applied to the balance owed after conversion of interest to principal.) A second payment in the amount needed to pay off the loan is due one year later. What price would an investor pay for the contract six months after the date of the loan to earn 10% compounded semiannually on the purchase price?

•42. A $5000 loan at 10% compounded annually is to be repaid by two payments three and five years from the date of the loan. The first payment of $3000 will be applied to the balance owed after conversion of interest to principal at the end of the first three years. What would an investor pay for the loan contract 20 months after the date of the loan if she requires a rate of return of 9% compounded monthly?

43. **Redemption Value of a Canada Savings Bond** Go to the textbook's Web site and find "Canada Savings Bonds." From there, you should be able to link to a page that will provide interest rates for all outstanding issues of CSBs. Update Table 8.2 for the Series 108 (S108) CSB. If you own a $1000 face value S108 compound-interest CSB, for what amount could you redeem it at the beginning of next month?

44. **Shopping for GICs** Go to the textbook's Web site. In Chapter 8 of the Student Edition, find "Canoe Money GICs." This Web page provides a comprehensive comparison of current rates available on GICs for terms of one to five years. How much more would you earn on $10,000 invested for five years at the highest available rate than at the lowest rate?

8.6 EQUIVALENT PAYMENT STREAMS

LO7 Sometimes a scheduled payment stream is replaced by another payment stream. This can happen, for example, in re-scheduling payments on a loan. In this section we will learn how to make the new stream of payments economically equivalent to the stream it replaces. In this way, neither the payer nor the payee gains any financial advantage from the change.

The general principle we will develop is an extension of ideas from Sections 8.2 and 8.3. In those sections you learned how to obtain the equivalent value of a multiple-payment stream at a particular focal date. It was a two-step procedure:

1. Calculate the equivalent value of each payment at the focal date.
2. Add up the equivalent values to obtain the stream's equivalent value.

How, then, would you compare the economic values of two payment streams? Your intuition should be a good guide here. First calculate the equivalent value of each stream at the *same* focal date. Then compare the two equivalent values to rank them. For two payment streams to be economically equivalent, they must meet the following condition.

> **Criterion for the Equivalence of Two Payment Streams**
> A payment stream's equivalent value (at a focal date) is the sum of the equivalent values of all of its payments. Two payment streams are economically equivalent if they have the same equivalent value at the same focal date.

You must impose this requirement when designing a payment stream that is to be economically equivalent to a given payment stream. The criterion becomes the basis for an equation that enables us to solve for an unknown payment in the new stream.

> **TIP** **Choosing a Focal Date**
>
> Any interest conversion date may be chosen for the focal date in an equivalent-payment stream problem. If two payment streams are equivalent at one conversion date, they will be equivalent at any other conversion date. Therefore, problems will generally not specify a particular focal date to be used in the solution. Calculations will usually be simplified if you locate the focal date at one of the unknown payments in the new stream. Then that payment's equivalent value on the focal date is simply its nominal value. But be careful to use the *same* focal date for *both* payment streams.

EXAMPLE 8.6A **CALCULATING AN UNKNOWN PAYMENT IN A TWO-PAYMENT REPLACEMENT STREAM**

Payments of $2000 and $1000 were originally scheduled to be paid one year and five years, respectively, from today. They are to be replaced by a $1500 payment due four years from today, and another payment due two years from today. The replacement stream must be economically equivalent to the scheduled stream. What is the unknown payment, if money can earn 7% compounded semiannually?

SOLUTION

The diagram below presents just the given information. Each payment stream has its own time line. The unknown payment is represented by *x*. We must calculate a value for *x* such that the two streams satisfy the Criterion for Equivalence.

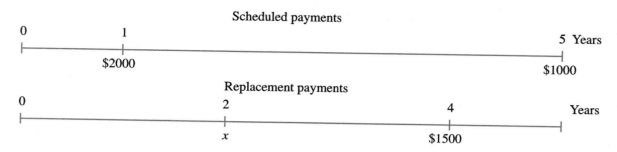

Scheduled payments

Replacement payments

In the next diagram, the date of the unknown payment has been chosen as the focal date. Consequently, the unknown payment's equivalent value on the focal date is just x. The equivalent values of the other payments are represented by FV_1, PV_2, and PV_3.

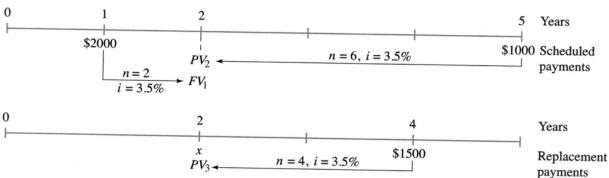

To satisfy the Criterion for Equivalence, we require

$$FV_1 + PV_2 = x + PV_3 \quad \text{①}$$

The equivalent values of the individual payments are calculated in the usual way.

FV_1 = Future value of $2000, 1 year later
$= PV(1 + i)^n$
$= \$2000(1.035)^2$
$= \$2142.450$

7 I/Y
P/Y 2 ENTER
(making C/Y = P/Y = 2)
2 N
2000 PV
0 PMT
CPT FV
Ans: −2142.450

PV_2 = Present value of $1000, 3 years earlier
$= FV(1 + i)^{-n}$
$= \$1000(1.035)^{-6}$
$= \$813.501$

Same I/Y, PMT, P/Y, C/Y
6 N
1000 FV
CPT PV
Ans: −813.501

PV_3 = Present value of $1500, 2 years earlier
$= \$1500(1.035)^{-4}$
$= \$1307.163$

Same I/Y, PMT, P/Y, C/Y
4 N
1500 FV
CPT PV
Ans: −1307.163

Substituting these amounts into equation ①, we have

$$\$2142.450 + \$813.501 = x + \$1307.163$$
$$\$2955.951 - \$1307.163 = x$$
$$x = \$1648.79$$

The first payment in the replacement stream must be $1648.79.

EXAMPLE 8.6B   **CALCULATING TWO PAYMENTS IN A THREE-PAYMENT REPLACEMENT STREAM**

The original intention was to settle a financial obligation by two payments. The first payment of $1500 was due one year ago. The second payment of $2500 is due three years from now. The debtor missed the first payment, and now proposes three payments that will be economically equivalent to the two originally scheduled payments. The replacement payments are $1000 today, a second payment in $1\frac{1}{2}$ years, and a third payment (twice as large as the second) in three years. What should the second and third payments be if money can earn 8% compounded semiannually?

SOLUTION

Let the payment due in $1\frac{1}{2}$ years be x. The scheduled and replacement streams are presented in the following time diagrams. The date of the first unknown payment has been chosen as the focal date, and the symbols for equivalent values on the focal date are indicated.

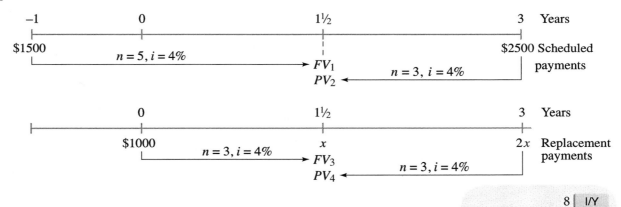

For equivalence of the two payment streams,

$$FV_1 + PV_2 = x + FV_3 + PV_4 \quad ①$$

$$FV_1 = \text{Future value of } \$1500, 2\frac{1}{2} \text{ years later}$$
$$= PV(1 + i)^n$$
$$= \$1500(1.04)^5$$
$$= \$1824.979$$

$$PV_2 = \text{Present value of } \$2500, 1\frac{1}{2} \text{ years earlier}$$
$$= FV(1 + i)^{-n}$$
$$= \$2500(1.04)^{-3}$$
$$= \$2222.491$$

8 I/Y
P/Y 2 ENTER
(making C/Y = P/Y = 2)
5 N
1500 PV
0 PMT
CPT FV
Ans: −1824.979

Same *I/Y, PMT, P/Y, C/Y*
3 N
2500 FV
CPT PV
Ans: −2222.491

FV_3 = Future value of $1000, $1\frac{1}{2}$ years later
$$= \$1000(1.04)^3$$
$$= \$1124.864$$

Same N, I/Y, PMT, P/Y, C/Y

1000 | PV

CPT | FV

Ans: −1124.864

PV_4 = Present value of $2x$, $1\frac{1}{2}$ years earlier
$$= 2x(1.04)^{-3}$$
$$= 1.777993x$$

Find the PV of $2
Same N, I/Y, PMT, P/Y, C/Y

2 | FV

CPT | PV

Ans: −1.777993

Substituting these values into equation ①, we obtain

$$\$1824.979 + \$2222.491 = x + \$1124.864 + \$1.777993x$$
$$\$4047.470 = 2.777993x + \$1124.864$$
$$x = \frac{\$4047.470 - \$1124.864}{2.777993}$$
$$= \$1052.06$$

The payments should be $1052.06 in $1\frac{1}{2}$ years and $2104.12 in three years.

CONCEPT QUESTIONS

1. If two payment streams are equivalent at one discount rate, will they be equivalent at another discount rate?

2. Give two examples of advertisements or news items that routinely ignore the time value of money.

3. What would be the most convincing way to demonstrate that the replacement stream in Example 8.6A is economically equivalent to the given stream?

EXERCISE 8.6   *Answers to the odd-numbered problems are at the end of the book.*

1. Scheduled payments of $3000 due today and $2000 due in 15 months are to be replaced by two payments—$1500 due in 15 months and a second payment of undetermined size due in 24 months. What must the second payment be for the two streams to be economically equivalent? Assume that money can earn 6% compounded quarterly.

2. A two-payment stream consisting of $1750 due today and $2900 due in 18 months is to be replaced by an economically equivalent stream comprised of an undetermined payment due in 9 months and a payment of $3000 due in 19 months. Calculate the unknown replacement payment if money is worth 9% compounded monthly.

3. Patrice defaulted on payments of $1000 due one year ago and $1500 due six months ago. A Small Claims Court orders her to make three payments—$800 one month from now, $900 four months from now, and a third payment seven months from now. The third payment is to be determined so that the creditor will end up in the same economic position as if the original payments had been made on time. The court set the fair rate of return at 4.2% compounded monthly. What should the third payment be?

4. Marvin was supposed to make three payments of $2000 each—the first one year ago, the second one year from now, and the third three years from now. He missed the first payment and proposes to pay $3000 today and a second amount in two years. If money can earn 4.5% compounded semiannually, what must the second payment be to make the proposed payments equivalent to the scheduled payments?

○**5.** Payments of $850 due two years ago and $1760 due six months ago have not been made. The proposed alternative is two equal payments, three months and nine months from now, that will put the payee in an equivalent economic position allowing that money can earn 5.6% compounded quarterly. What is the amount of each of these payments?

○**6.** Jorge is unable to make a $4500 payment due today. He proposes to settle the obligation by making three equal payments—one today, another in four months, and a third in nine months. What must each payment be to make the proposed payment stream equivalent to the scheduled payment if money can earn 7.2% compounded monthly?

○**7.** The scheduled payment stream consists of $5000 due today and $10,000 due in five years. It is proposed to replace this stream by an economically equivalent stream comprised of three equal payments due one, three, and five years from now. Determine the size of each payment if money is worth 5% compounded annually.

○**8.** Payments of $400 due eight months ago and $650 due three months ago were not made. Now the debtor is proposing to "make good" by two future payments that provide for a 7.5% compounded monthly rate of return to the creditor on the missed payments. The first payment will be made in two months. The second payment, *twice* as large as the first, will be made in seven months. Determine the amount of each payment.

○**9.** Two payments of $2000 each are scheduled for six months from now and two years from now. They are to be re-scheduled as follows: a payment one year from now and a second payment, *half* the size of the first payment, three years from now. What must the amount of each payment be for the replacement stream to be equivalent to the originally scheduled stream? Assume that money can earn 7.8% compounded semiannually.

○**10.** The owner of a residential building lot has received two purchase offers. Mrs. A is offering a $20,000 down payment plus $40,000 payable in one year. Mr. B's offer is $15,000 down plus two $25,000 payments due one and two years from now. Which offer has the greater economic value if money can earn 9.5% compounded quarterly? How much more is it worth in current dollars?

○**11.** During its January Sale, Furniture City is offering terms of 25% down with no further payments and no interest charges for six months, when the balance is due. Furniture City sells the conditional sale contracts from these credit sales to a finance company. The finance company discounts the contracts to yield 18% compounded monthly. What cash amount should Furniture City accept on a $1595 item in order to end up in the same financial position as if the item had been sold under the terms of the January Sale?

○**12.** Henri has decided to purchase a $25,000 car. He can either liquidate some of his investments and pay cash, or accept the dealer's proposal that Henri pay $5000 down and $8000 at the end of each of the next three years.

a. Which choice should Henri make if he can earn 7% compounded semiannually on his investments? In current dollars, what is the economic advantage of the preferred alternative?

    b. Which choice should Henri make if he can earn 11% compounded semiannually on his investments? In current dollars, what is the economic advantage of the preferred alternative?

    (*Hint:* When choosing among alternative streams of cash *inflows,* we should select the one with the greatest economic value. When choosing among alternative streams of cash *outflows,* we should select the one with the least economic value.)

○**13.** A lottery prize gives the winner a choice between (1) $10,000 now and another $10,000 in 5 years, or (2) four $6700 payments—now and in 5, 10, and 15 years.

    a. Which alternative should the winner choose if money can earn 6% compounded annually? In current dollars, what is the economic advantage of the preferred alternative?

    b. Which alternative should the winner choose if money can earn 8.5% compounded annually? In current dollars, what is the economic advantage of the preferred alternative?

○**14.** CompuSystems was supposed to pay a manufacturer $19,000 on a date four months ago and another $14,000 on a date two months from now. Instead, CompuSystems is proposing to pay $10,000 today and the balance in five months, when it will receive payment on a major sale to the provincial government. What will the second payment be if the manufacturer requires 12% compounded monthly on overdue accounts?

○**15.** Payments of $5000 and $7000 are due three and five years, respectively, from today. They are to be replaced by two payments due $1\frac{1}{2}$ and four years from today. The first payment is to be half the amount of the second payment. What should the payments be if money can earn 7.5% compounded semiannually?

○**16.** Two payments of $3000 each are due today and five years from today. The creditor has agreed to accept three equal payments due one, three, and five years from now. Assuming that money can earn 7.5% compounded monthly, what payments will the creditor accept?

○**17.** Payments of $8000 due 15 months ago and $6000 due in six months are to be replaced by a payment of $4000 today, a second payment in nine months, and a third payment, three times as large as the second, in $1\frac{1}{2}$ years. What should the last two payments be if money is worth 6.4% compounded quarterly?

○**18.** The principal plus interest at 10% compounded quarterly on a $15,000 loan made $2\frac{1}{2}$ years ago is due in two years. The debtor is proposing to settle the debt by a payment of $5000 today and a second payment in one year that will place the lender in an equivalent financial position, given that money can now earn only 6% compounded semiannually.

    a. What should be the amount of the second payment?

    b. Demonstrate that the lender will be in the same financial position two years from now with either repayment alternative.

•**19.** Three years ago, Andrea loaned $2000 to Heather. The principal with interest at 9% compounded semiannually is to be repaid four years from the date of the loan. Eighteen months ago, Heather borrowed another $1000 for $3\frac{1}{2}$ years at 8% compounded semiannually. Heather is now proposing to settle both debts with two equal payments to be made one and three years from now. What should the payments be if money now earns 6% compounded quarterly?

KEY TERMS

SUMMARY OF NOTATION AND KEY FORMULAS

j = Nominal annual interest rate

m = Number of compoundings per year

i = Periodic rate of interest

PV = Principal amount of the loan or investment; Present value

FV = Maturity value of the loan or investment; Future value

n = Number of compounding periods

FORMULA (8-1) $i = \dfrac{j}{m}$ Obtaining the periodic interest rate from the nominal annual rate

FORMULA (8-2) $\begin{cases} FV = PV(1 + i)^n \\ PV = FV(1 + i)^{-n} \end{cases}$

Finding the maturity value or future value

Finding the principal or present value

FORMULA (8-3) $n = m \times$ (Number of years in the term)   Finding the number of compounding periods

FORMULA (8-4) $FV = PV(1 + i_1)(1 + i_2)(1 + i_3) \dots (1 + i_n)$ Finding the maturity value with compounding at a variable interest rate

---

Cash-Flow Sign Convention

Cash inflows (receipts) are positive.

Cash outflows (disbursements) are negative.

Present Value of Loan Payments

The sum of the present values of all of the payments required to pay off a loan is equal to the original principal of the loan. The discount rate for the present-value calculations is the rate of interest charged on the loan.

Criterion for the Equivalence of Two Payment Streams

A payment stream's equivalent value (at a focal date) is the sum of the equivalent values of all of its payments. Two payment streams are economically equivalent if they have the same equivalent value at the same focal date.

REVIEW PROBLEMS

Answers to the odd-numbered review problems are at the end of the book.

1. **(LO6)** What amount three years ago is equivalent to $4800 on a date $1\frac{1}{2}$ years from now if money earns 8% compounded semiannually during the intervening time?

2. **(LO5)** If the inflation rate for the next 10 years is 3% per year, what hourly rate of pay in 10 years will be equivalent to $15 per hour today?

3. **(LO5)** To satisfy more stringent restrictions on toxic waste discharge, a pulp mill will have to reduce toxic waste by 10% from the previous year's level every year for the next five years. What fraction is the target level of the current discharge level?

4. **(LO2)** If an investor has the choice between rates of 5.5% compounded semiannually and 5.6% compounded annually for a six-year GIC, which rate should be chosen?

5. **(LO5)** A 1995 study predicted that employment in base metal mining would decline by 3.5% per year for the next five years. What percentage of total base metal mining jobs was expected to be lost during the five-year period?

6. **(LO4)** At the same time as compound-interest Canada Savings Bonds were being sold with guaranteed minimum annual rates of 5.25%, 6%, and 6.75% in the first 3 years of their 10-year term, a trust company offered 3-year Bond-Beater GICs paying 5.75%, 6.5%, and 7.25% compounded annually in the 3 successive years. If the CSBs earn their minimum interest rates, how much more will $4000 earn over the 3 years if invested in the GIC?

7. **(LO1)** Jacques has just been notified that the combined principal and interest on an amount he borrowed 19 months ago at 8.4% compounded monthly is now $2297.78. How much of this amount is principal and how much is interest?

8. **(LO1)** Accurate Accounting obtained a private loan of $25,000 for five years. No payments were required, but the loan accrued interest at the rate of 9% compounded monthly for the first $2\frac{1}{2}$ years and then at 8.25% compounded semiannually for the remainder of the term. What total amount was required to pay off the loan after 5 years?

9. **(LO2)** A credit union's Rate-Climber GIC pays rates of 4%, 5%, and 6% compounded semiannually in successive years of a three-year term.
   a. What will be the maturity value of $12,000 invested in this GIC?
   b. How much interest will be earned in the second year?

10. **(LO4)** A $1000 face value compound-interest Series S96 Canada Savings Bond was redeemed on March 14, 2010. What amount did the bond's owner receive? (Obtain the issue date and the interest rates paid on the bond from Table 8.2.)

11. **(LO2)** On the same date that the Alberta Treasury Branches were advertising rates of 2.25%, 3%, 3.75%, 4.5%, and 6.5% in successive years of their five-year compound-interest Springboard GIC, they offered 3.5% compounded annually on their five-year fixed-rate compound-interest GIC.
   a. What will be the maturity values of $10,000 invested in each GIC?
   b. How much interest will each GIC earn in the third year?

12. **(LO6)** Maynard Appliances is holding a "Fifty-Fifty Sale." Major appliances may be purchased for nothing down and no interest to pay if the customer pays 50% of the purchase price in six months and the remaining 50% in 12 months. Maynard then sells the conditional sale contracts at a discount to Consumers Finance Co. What will the finance company pay Maynard for a conditional sale contract in the amount of $1085 if it requires a return of 14% compounded quarterly?

13. **(LO7)** Donnelly Excavating has received two offers on a used backhoe that Donnelly is advertising for sale. Offer 1 is for $10,000 down, $15,000 in 6 months, and $15,000 in 18 months. Offer 2 is for $8000 down, plus two $17,500 payments one and two years from now. What is the economic value today of each offer if money is worth 10.25% compounded semiannually? Which offer should be accepted?

14. **(LO1)** For the five-year period ended June 30, 2009, the Desjardins Environment Fund had one of the best performances of all diversified Canadian equity funds. It effectively earned a compound annual return of 9.5% compared to the average of 4.4% for 287 diversified Canadian equity funds with a five-year history. How much more would an initial $1000 investment in the Desjardins Environment Fund have earned over the five-year period than a $1000 investment in a fund earning the average rate of return?

15. **(LO1)** Isaac borrowed $3000 at 10.5% compounded quarterly $3\frac{1}{2}$ years ago. One year ago he made a payment of $1200. What amount will extinguish the loan today?

16. **(LO1)** For the 10-year period ended March 31, 2007, the Phillips, Hager & North (PH&N) Canadian Equity Fund had a compound annual return of 11.3% whereas the PH&N U.S. Equity Fund had a compound annual return (after converting to Canadian dollars) of 1.3%. How much more would an initial $1000 investment have earned over the 10-year period in the Canadian Equity Fund than in the U.S. Equity Fund?

17. **(LO4)** Use the data in Table 8.2 to determine the redemption value of a $500 face value compound-interest Series S90 Canada Savings Bond on:

    a. November 1, 2009.   **b.** April 15, 2010.

18. **(LO6)** Payments of $2400, $1200, and $3000 were originally scheduled to be paid today, 18 months from today, and 33 months from today, respectively. Using 6% compounded quarterly as the rate of return money can earn, what payment six months from now would be equivalent to the three scheduled payments?

○19. **(LO1)** Jarmila borrowed $3000, $3500, and $4000 from her grandmother on December 1 in each of three successive years at college. They agreed that interest would accumulate at the rate of 4% compounded semiannually. Jarmila is to start repaying the loan on June 1 following the third loan. What consolidated amount will she owe at that time?

○20. **(LO1)** A four-year $7000 promissory note bearing interest at 10.5% compounded monthly was discounted 18 months after issue to yield 9.5% compounded quarterly. What were the proceeds from the sale of the note?

○21. **(LO1) (LO5)** For the 10 years ended December 31, 2008, the annually compounded rate of return on the portfolio of stocks represented by the S&P/TSX Composite Index was 2.66%. For the same period, the compound annual rate of inflation (as measured by the increase in the Consumer Price Index) was 2.39%.

    a. What was $1000 invested in the Index stock portfolio on December 31, 1998, worth 10 years later?

    b. What amount of money was needed on December 31, 2008, to have the same purchasing power as $1000 on December 31, 1998?

    c. For an investment in the Index stock portfolio, what was the percent increase in purchasing power of the original $1000?

○22. **(LO1)** On February 1 of three successive years, Roger contributed $3000, $4000, and $3500, respectively, to his RRSP. The funds in his plan earned 9% compounded monthly for the first year, 8.5% compounded quarterly for the second year, and 7.75% compounded semiannually for the third year. What was the value of his RRSP three years after the first contribution?

○23. **(LO7)** A loan contract called for a payment after two years of $1500 plus interest (on this $1500 only) at 8% compounded quarterly, and a second payment after four years of $2500 plus interest (on this $2500) at 8% compounded quarterly. What would you pay to purchase the contract 18 months after the contract date if you require a return of 10.5% compounded semiannually?

○24. **(LO1)** Payments of $1800 and $2400 were made on a $10,000 variable-rate loan 18 and 30 months after the date of the loan. The interest rate was 11.5% compounded semiannually for the first two years and 10.74% compounded monthly thereafter. What amount was owed on the loan after three years?

○25. **(LO6)** A $6500 loan at 11.25% compounded monthly is to be repaid by three equal payments due 3, 6, and 12 months after the date of the loan. Calculate the size of each payment.

○26. **(LO6) (LO7)** Payments of $2300 due 18 months ago and $3100 due in three years are to be replaced by an equivalent stream of payments consisting of $2000 today and two equal payments due two and four years from now. If money can earn 9.75% compounded semiannually, what should be the amount of each of these two payments?

○27. **(LO3)** A $1000 face value strip bond has 19 years remaining until maturity. What is its price if the market rate of return on such bonds is 5.9% compounded semiannually? At this market rate of return, what will be the increase in the value of the strip bond during the fifth year of ownership?

○28. **(LO7)** Two payments of $5000 are scheduled six months and three years from now. They are to be replaced by a payment of $3000 in two years, a second payment in 42 months, and a third payment, twice as large as the second, in five years. What should the last two payments be if money is worth 9% compounded semiannually?

○29. **(LO2)** A five-year, compound-interest GIC purchased for $1000 earns 6% compounded annually.

   a. How much interest will the GIC earn in the fifth year?

   b. If the rate of inflation during the five-year term is 2.5% per year, what will be the percent increase in the purchasing power of the invested funds over the entire five years?

○30. **(LO7)** Three equal payments were made one, two, and three years after the date on which a $10,000 loan was granted at 10.5% compounded monthly. If the balance immediately after the third payment was $5326.94, what was the amount of each payment?

○31. **(LO1)** If the total interest earned on an investment at 6.6% compounded monthly for $3\frac{1}{2}$ years was $1683.90, what was the original investment?

•32. **(LO1) (LO7)** Four years ago John borrowed $3000 from Arlette. The principal with interest at 10% compounded semiannually is to be repaid six years from the date of the loan. Fifteen months ago, John borrowed another $1500 for $3\frac{1}{2}$ years at 9% compounded quarterly. John is now proposing to settle both debts with two equal payments to be made 2 and $3\frac{1}{2}$ years from now. What should the payments be if money now earns 8% compounded quarterly?

APPENDIX 8A   INSTRUCTIONS FOR SPECIFIC MODELS OF FINANCIAL CALCULATORS

SETTING THE CALCULATOR IN THE FINANCIAL MODE

Texas Instruments BA II Plus	Sharp EL-738C	Hewlett Packard 10B
Calculator is "ready to go" for financial calculations.	Press [MODE] 0	Calculator is "ready to go" for financial calculations.

SETTING THE NUMBER OF DECIMAL PLACES DISPLAYED AT 9

Texas Instruments BA II Plus	Sharp EL-738C	Hewlett Packard 10B
[2nd] [Format] 9 [ENTER] [2nd] [QUIT]	[SETUP] 0 0 9	[____] [DISP] 9

SETTING A FLOATING POINT DECIMAL[11]

Texas Instruments BA II Plus	Sharp EL-738C	Hewlett Packard 10B
Set for 9 decimal places as in the preceding table.	[SETUP] 0 2	[____] [DISP] [•]

CHECKING THE CONTENTS OF A FINANCIAL KEY'S MEMORY (USING THE [PV] KEY AS AN EXAMPLE)

Texas Instruments BA II Plus	Sharp EL-738C	Hewlett Packard 10B
[RCL] [PV]	[RCL] [PV]	[RCL] [PV]

---

[11] With this setting, the calculator will show all of the digits but no trailing zeros for a terminating decimal. Non-terminating decimals will be displayed with 10 digits.

Compound Interest: Further Topics and Applications

LEARNING OBJECTIVES

After completing this chapter, you will be able to:

LO1 Calculate the interest rate and term in compound interest applications

LO2 Given a nominal interest rate, calculate its effective interest rate

LO3 Given a nominal interest rate, calculate its equivalent interest rate at another compounding frequency

LO4 Calculate the income yield, capital gain yield, and rate of total return on stocks and mutual funds

LO5 Combine rates of total return for successive holding periods

IN ALL OF THE COMPOUND interest problems in Chapter 8, the interest rate and the term of the loan or investment were known. With a little reflection, you can think of many situations requiring the calculation of an interest rate, or a rate of return, or a rate of growth. For example, if you invest $1000 in a mutual fund, what rate of return must it earn to grow to $5000 over a 15-year period? If a stock's price rose from $15.50 to $27.40 over the past five years, what has been its equivalent annual percent increase in price? What was the average annual rate of inflation for the last 10 years if the Consumer Price Index rose from 87.4 to 118.3?

In other circumstances, we want to know the time required for an amount to grow from a beginning value to a target value. How long, for example, will it take an investment to double if it earns 10% compounded annually? By the end of Section 2, you will be able to answer such questions.

Compound interest rates on loans and investments may be quoted with differing compounding frequencies. This gives rise to questions such as: "How do we compare 7.9% compounded semiannually to 8% compounded annually? What semiannually compounded rate is equivalent to 6% compounded monthly?" The techniques you will learn in Sections 3 and 4 will enable you to answer these questions. Later on, in Chapters 10 through 14, this ability will be used routinely in calculations involving annuities.

In Section 5 you will first learn some of the terminology used to describe investment returns from stocks and mutual funds. Then we explain how you can use familiar mathematics from earlier chapters to calculate one-year and long-term returns from stocks and mutual funds.

9.1 CALCULATING THE PERIODIC INTEREST RATE, i

In cases where we know values for PV, FV, and n, the periodic and nominal rates of interest may be calculated.

Algebraic Method Rearranging the basic equation $FV = PV(1 + i)^n$ to isolate i is more difficult than isolating PV. First divide both sides of the equation by PV and then interchange the two sides, giving

$$(1 + i)^n = \frac{FV}{PV}$$

Next take the nth root of both sides of the equation. This makes the left side simply $(1 + i)$, and we have

$$1 + i = \sqrt[n]{\frac{FV}{PV}}$$

Therefore,[1]

PERIODIC RATE OF INTEREST

$$i = \sqrt[n]{\frac{FV}{PV}} - 1 = \left(\frac{FV}{PV}\right)^{1/n} - 1 \qquad (9\text{-}1)$$

Financial Calculator Method Enter values for the known variables—PV, FV, n, and m—into the appropriate memories. Then press $\boxed{\text{CPT}}$ $\boxed{\text{I/Y}}$ in sequence to compute j, the nominal annual rate of interest. If the value of i is required, calculate $i = \frac{j}{m}$.

---

[1] It was pointed out in Section 2.2 that the nth root of a quantity is equivalent to raising it to the exponent $1/n$.

> **TRAP** | **Sign Convention Now Mandatory**
>
> When you enter values for both *FV* and *PV*, it is imperative that you employ the cash-flow sign convention. If you fail to use it, an error message will appear in your calculator's display.

EXAMPLE 9.1A | **CALCULATING THE PERIODIC AND NOMINAL RATES OF INTEREST**

The maturity value of a three-year, $5000 compound-interest GIC is $5788.13. To three-figure accuracy, calculate the nominal rate of interest paid on the GIC if interest is compounded:

a. Annually. **b.** Quarterly.

SOLUTION

Given: $PV = \$5000$ and $FV = \$5788.13$

In Part (a), $m = 1$, $n = m(\text{Term}) = 1(3) = 3$ compounding periods.

In Part (b), $m = 4$, $n = m(\text{Term}) = 4(3) = 12$ compounding periods.

Formula (9-1) enables us to calculate the interest rate for one compounding period.

a.
$$i = \left(\frac{FV}{PV}\right)^{1/n} - 1$$
$$= \left(\frac{\$5788.13}{\$5000.00}\right)^{1/3} - 1$$
$$= (1.157626)^{0.\overline{3}} - 1$$
$$= 0.05000$$
$$= 5.000\%$$

The nominal rate of interest on the GIC is
$j = mi = 1(5.000\%) = 5.00\%$ compounded annually.

| P/Y | 1 ENTER |
(making $C/Y = P/Y = 1$)
3	N
5000 +/–	PV
0	PMT
5788.13	FV
CPT	I/Y
Ans: 5.000

b.
$$i = \left(\frac{\$5788.13}{\$5000.00}\right)^{1/12} - 1$$
$$= (1.157626)^{0.08\overline{3}} - 1$$
$$= 0.01227$$
$$= 1.227\%$$

The nominal rate of interest on the GIC is
$j = mi = 4(1.227\%) = 4.91\%$ compounded quarterly.

Same *PV, PMT, FV*
| P/Y | 4 ENTER |
(making $C/Y = P/Y = 4$)
| 12 | N |
| CPT | I/Y |
Ans: 4.909

> **TRAP** | **Don't Leave Out the Final Step**
>
> The calculation of *i* is usually not the last step in a problem. Typically you are asked to determine either the nominal interest rate or the effective interest rate (to be discussed in Section 9.3). Do not forget to complete the extra step needed to directly answer the question.

EXAMPLE 9.1B **CALCULATING A SEMIANNUALLY COMPOUNDED RATE OF RETURN**

Mr. Dunbar paid $10,000 for a $40,000 face value strip bond having $19\frac{1}{2}$ years remaining until maturity. (Recall that a strip bond is an investment that returns just one payment, the face value, at maturity.) What semiannually compounded rate of return will Mr. Dunbar earn on his investment?

SOLUTION

Given: $PV = \$10,000 \quad FV = \$40,000 \quad \text{Term} = 19\frac{1}{2} \text{ years} \quad m = 2$

Then $\qquad n = m(\text{Term}) = 2(19.5) = 39$

$$
\begin{aligned}
i &= \left(\frac{FV}{PV}\right)^{1/n} - 1 \\
&= \left(\frac{\$40,000}{\$10,000}\right)^{1/39} - 1 \\
&= 4^{0.0256410} - 1 \\
&= 0.036185 \\
&= 3.6185\%
\end{aligned}
$$

P/Y 2 ENTER	
(making $C/Y = P/Y = 2$)	
39	N
10000 +/-	PV
0	PMT
40000	FV
CPT	I/Y

Ans: 7.237

$j = mi = 2(3.6185\%) = 7.24\%$ compounded semiannually

Mr. Dunbar will earn 7.24% compounded semiannually on his strip bond investment.

EXAMPLE 9.1C **CALCULATING AN ANNUALLY COMPOUNDED RATE OF RETURN THAT IS EQUIVALENT TO A SERIES OF INDIVIDUAL ANNUAL RETURNS**

In the years 2006, 2007, and 2008, the Excel China Fund earned annual rates of return of 83.2%, 39.5%, and −45.9%, respectively. Calculate the fund's equivalent annually compounded rate of return for the three years. (This is the fixed annual rate of return that would produce the same overall growth.)

SOLUTION

The equivalent annually compounded rate of return for the three-year period cannot be obtained by simply averaging the three individual annual returns. Instead, we must use a two-step procedure:

Step 1: Use $FV = PV(1 + i_1)(1 + i_2)(1 + i_3) \ldots (1 + i_n)$ to calculate how much an investment on December 31, 2005, was worth on December 31, 2008.

Step 2: Calculate the annually compounded rate of return that will produce the *same* growth in three years.

Step 1: For the initial investment, choose a "nice, round" amount such as $100 or $1000.

$$
\begin{aligned}
FV &= PV(1 + i_{2006})(1 + i_{2007})(1 + i_{2008}) \\
&= \$1000(1 + 0.832)(1 + 0.395)(1 - 0.459) \\
&= \$1382.60
\end{aligned}
$$

Step 2:
$$
\begin{aligned}
i &= \left(\frac{FV}{PV}\right)^{1/n} - 1 \\
&= \frac{\$1382.60^{1/3}}{\$1000} - 1 \\
&= 1.38260^{0.333333} - 1 \\
&= 0.11404 \\
&= 11.40\%
\end{aligned}
$$

P/Y 1 ENTER	
(making $C/Y = P/Y = 1$)	
3	N
1000 +/-	PV
0	PMT
1382.60	FV
CPT	I/Y

Ans: 11.404

$j = mi = 1(11.40\%) = 11.40\%$ compounded annually

The mutual fund's equivalent annually compounded rate of return for the 3-year period ended December 31, 2008, was 11.40% compounded annually.

Postscript: At the end of every month, the type of calculation in Example 9.1C is done for about 2000 mutual funds available in Canada. The equivalent compound annual rates of return are calculated for three-year, five-year, and ten-year periods terminating at the month-end. These returns are then published in monthly mutual fund supplements to major newspapers. They are also available on investment Web sites that specialize in mutual funds. (In fact, these equivalent rates of return are easier to find than the year-by-year returns on which they are based.) You may have noticed that mutual fund advertisements commonly quote mutual fund performance in terms of the three-year, five-year, and ten-year compound annual returns. Now you know how they are obtained and how to interpret them.

NET @ssets

The *Globe and Mail* maintains one of the most popular Web sites for mutual fund information and analysis.

Their "Fund Filter" allows you to set criteria for searching a comprehensive Canadian mutual fund database. For example, you can easily obtain a listing of all Canadian Equity funds whose equivalent annually compounded rate of return for the past 10 years has been greater than 7%.

To obtain detailed information about a fund whose name you know, you can choose "Fund Selector" in their list of links.

EXAMPLE 9.1D **CALCULATING AN INFLATION-ADJUSTED (REAL) RATE OF RETURN**

Over a 10-year period, Brooke's investment in Suncor stock grew in value from $9480 to $17,580. During the same period, the Consumer Price Index (CPI) rose from 93.6 to 126.1. What was her *real* compound annual rate of return on the stock during the decade? (The real rate of return is the rate of return net of inflation. It represents the rate of increase in purchasing power.)

SOLUTION

With the CPI up from 93.6 to 126.1, Brooke needed $\frac{126.1}{93.6}$ times as many dollars at the end of the decade to purchase the same goods and services as at the beginning. The $9480 value of the stock at the beginning had to grow to

$$\$9480 \times \frac{126.1}{93.6} = \$12{,}772$$

just to maintain her purchasing power. In fact, it grew to $17,580. In terms of end-of-decade dollars, her purchasing power rose from $12,772 to $17,580. Hence, to obtain the real rate of return, use $PV = \$12{,}772$, $FV = \$17{,}580$, and $n = 10$.

$$
\begin{aligned}
i &= \left(\frac{FV}{PV}\right)^{1/n} - 1 \\
&= \left(\frac{\$17{,}580}{\$12{,}772}\right)^{1/10} - 1 \\
&= 1.37645^{0.1} - 1 \\
&= 0.03247 \\
&= 3.247\%
\end{aligned}
$$

P/Y	1	ENTER

(making $C/Y = P/Y = 1$)

10	N
12772 +/−	PV
0	PMT
17580	FV
CPT	I/Y

Ans: 3.247

$j = mi = 1(3.247\%) = 3.25\%$ compounded annually

The real rate of return on the Suncor stock was 3.25% compounded annually.

Postscript: Two points should be mentioned.

1. The same answer will be obtained if you choose to adjust for inflation by expressing $17,580 in terms of beginning-of-decade dollars.
2. An entirely different approach may have occurred to you. Suppose you separately calculate the rate of return on the stock, and the rate of inflation from the CPI data. (You would obtain 6.37% and 3.03% compounded annually, respectively.) You might think that:

$$\text{Real rate of return} = \text{Actual rate of return} - \text{Rate of inflation}$$
$$= 6.37\% - 3.03\%$$
$$= 3.34\%$$

This is a slightly larger value (by 0.09%) than the strictly correct answer we obtained in the "official solution." The reason for the small difference is quite subtle and technical—we will spare you the details. However, real rates of return are, more often than not, calculated this way. Since nominal rates of return and inflation rates are easily obtained from published data, this approximation is an easier approach and is good enough for most purposes.

SPREADSHEET STRATEGIES   Periodic Rate of Interest

Connect provides a partially completed template for calculating i, the periodic rate of interest. Go to the Student Edition of Connect and find "RATE Function." The "Introduction" page of the workbook describes Excel's built-in RATE function.

The main features of a completed Periodic Rate of Interest template are presented below. The formula programmed into cell C9 is displayed in cell C10. Here data are entered to solve Example 9.1B. In this example, we are asked to determine

the semiannually compounded rate of return on the $10,000 purchase price for a $40,000 face value strip bond with $19\frac{1}{2}$ years remaining until maturity. As an initial "side calculation," we obtain $n = m \times \text{Term} = 2 \times 19.5 = 39$ compounding periods. After entering the known values into the input cells, the computed periodic rate of interest appears immediately in the output cell.

	A	B	C	D
1				
2	Using a spreadsheet to calculate the periodic rate of interest.			
3	Example 9.1B:			
4				
5		Future value, *FV*	40,000.00	
6		Present value, *PV*	-10,000.00	
7		Number of cmpding periods, *n*	39.00	
8				
9		Periodic rate of interest, **RATE**	3.619%	
10		Formula in cell C9:	=RATE(C7,0,C6,C5,0)	
11				

The rate of return on the strip bond is $j = mi = 2(3.619\%) = 7.24\%$ compounded semiannually.

CONCEPT QUESTIONS

1. If *FV* is less than *PV*, what can you predict about the value for *i*?

2. Is *FV* negative if you lose money on an investment?

3. Which scenario had the higher periodic rate of return: "$1 grew to $2" or "$3 grew to $5?" Both investments were for the same length of time at the same compounding frequency. Justify your choice.

EXERCISE 9.1

Spreadsheet template: A partially completed Excel template for calculating the periodic rate of return is provided in Connect. Go to the Student Edition of Connect and find "RATE Function." The completed template may be used wherever you need to calculate i in Exercise 9.1.

Answers to the odd-numbered problems are at the end of the book.

Calculate interest rates accurate to the nearest 0.01%.

1. No payments were made on a $3400 loan during its three-year term. What was the annually compounded nominal interest rate on the loan, if the amount owed at the end of the term was $4297.91?

2. What was the annually compounded nominal rate of growth, if the future value of $1000 after 20 years was $4016.94?

3. An initial $1800 investment was worth $2299.16 after two years and nine months. What quarterly compounded nominal rate of return did the investment earn?

4. A strip bond that will mature $7\frac{1}{2}$ years from now at its $13,000 face value can be purchased today for $9042. What rate of return (compounded semiannually) will this strip bond provide to an investor?

5. The amount owed on a promissory note for $950 after two years and five months is $1165.79. What monthly compounded nominal rate of interest was charged on the debt?

6. Philippe contributed $4300 to an RRSP eight years and six months ago. The money was invested in a Canadian Equity mutual fund. The investment is now worth $10,440.32. Over the entire period, what annually compounded nominal rate of return has the investment delivered?

7. When he died in 1790, Benjamin Franklin left $4600 to the city of Boston, with the stipulation that the money and its earnings could not be used for 100 years. The bequest grew to $332,000 by 1890. What (equivalent) compound annual rate of return did the bequest earn during the 100-year period?

8. In early 2009, the Templeton Growth Fund ran advertisements containing the message:

   $10,000 INVESTED IN TEMPLETON GROWTH FUND IN 1954
   WOULD BE WORTH $5.09 MILLION TODAY.

   What compound annual rate of return did the fund realize over this period (December 31, 1954 to December 31, 2008)?

9. Anders discovered an old pay statement from 11 years ago. His monthly salary at the time was $2550 versus his current salary of $4475 per month. At what (equivalent) compound annual rate has his salary grown during the period?

10. Mr. and Mrs. Markovich note that the home they purchased 20 years ago for $70,000 is now appraised at $340,000. What was the (equivalent) annual rate of appreciation in the value of their home during the 20-year period?

11. A $1000 five-year compound-interest GIC matured at $1234.01. What semiannually compounded rate of interest did it earn?

12. The maturity value of a $5000 four-year compound-interest GIC was $6147.82. What quarterly compounded rate of interest did it earn?

13. Three years ago Mikhail invested $7000 in a three-year compound interest GIC. He has just received its maturity value of $7867.34. What was the monthly compounded rate of interest on the GIC?

14. **a.** The population of Canada grew from 24,343,000 in 1981 to 33,505,000 in 2008. What was the overall compound annual rate of growth in our population during the period?

    b. According to the Canadian Real Estate Association, the average selling price of Canadian homes rose from $67,000 in 1980 to $315,000 in 2008. What has been the overall compound annual appreciation of home prices?

15. The following table contains 1981 and 2008 population figures for five provinces. Calculate each province's equivalent compound annual rate of population change during the period.

Province	1981 Population	2008 Population
Alberta	2,237,700	3,632,000
British Columbia	2,744,500	4,420,000
Newfoundland	567,700	509,000
Nova Scotia	847,400	939,500
Ontario	8,625,100	12,987,000

16. For an investment to double in value during a 10-year period,

    a. What annually compounded rate of return must it earn?

    b. What semiannually compounded rate of return must it earn?

    c. What monthly compounded rate of return must it earn?

17. For an investment to triple in value during a 15-year period,

    a. What annually compounded rate of return must it earn?

    b. What quarterly compounded rate of return must it earn?

    c. What monthly compounded rate of return must it earn?

18. What compound annual rate of return is required for an investment to double in:

    a. 12 years?   **b.** 10 years?

    c. 8 years?   **d.** 6 years?

    For each case, multiply the annual rate of return (in %) by the time period (in years). Compare the four products. Does the comparison suggest a general rule-of-thumb?

19. Monty purchased a strip bond for his RRSP. He paid $3800 for a $5000 face value bond with three years remaining until maturity. What semiannually compounded rate of return will he realize over the three years? (Taken from CIFP course materials.)

20. If the number of workers in the forest industry in Canada declined by 41% from the end of 1993 to the beginning of 2009, what was the compound annual rate of attrition in the industry during the period?

21. The Canadian Consumer Price Index (based on a value of 100 in 1971) rose from 97.2 in 1970 to 210.6 in 1980. What was the (equivalent) annual rate of inflation in the decade of the 1970s?

22. The Consumer Price Index (based on a value of 100 in 1986) rose from 67.2 in 1980 to 119.5 in 1990. What was the (equivalent) annual rate of inflation in the decade of the 1980s?

23. The Consumer Price Index (based on a value of 100 in 1992) rose from 93.3 in 1990 to 113.5 in 2000. What was the (equivalent) annual rate of inflation in the decade of the 1990s?

○24. Using the data given in Problems 21 and 22, calculate the annual rate of inflation for the 1970–1990 period. (Note: Simply averaging the two answers to Problems 21 and 22 will give only an approximation of the correct result.)

25. According to Statistics Canada, undergraduate students paid an average of $4724 in tuition fees for the 2008/2009 academic year compared to fees of $1464 for the 1990/1991 year. During the same period, the Consumer Price Index rose from 78.5 to 115.8.

   a. What would have been the average tuition fees for the 2008/2009 year if tuition fees had grown just at the rate of inflation since the 1990/1991 year?

   b. What was the (equivalent) compound annual rate of increase of tuition fees during the period?

   c. What was the (equivalent) compound annual rate of inflation during the period?

○26. A four-year promissory note for $3800 plus interest at 9.5% compounded semiannually was sold 18 months before maturity for $4481. What quarterly compounded nominal rate of return will the buyer realize on her investment?

○27. A $6000, three-year promissory note bearing interest at 11% compounded semiannually was purchased 15 months into its term for $6854.12. What monthly compounded discount rate was used in pricing the note?

○28. An investor's portfolio increased in value by 93% over a seven-year period in which the Consumer Price Index rose from 95.6 to 115.3. What was the compound annual real rate of return on the portfolio during the period?

○29. An investment grew in value from $5630 to $8485 during a five-year period. The annual rate of inflation for the five years was 2.3%. What was the compound annual real rate of return during the five years?

○30. An investment earned 6% compounded semiannually for two years and 8% compounded annually for the next three years. What was the equivalent annually compounded rate of return for the entire five-year period?

○31. A portfolio earned annual rates of 20%, −20%, 0%, 20%, and −20% in five successive years. What was the portfolio's five-year equivalent annually compounded rate of return?

○32. A portfolio earned annual rates of 20%, 15%, −10%, 25%, and −5% in five successive years. What was the portfolio's five-year equivalent annually compounded rate of return?

○33. At the end of 2009, the RBC Canadian Dividend Fund was the largest equity mutual fund in Canada. The aggregate market value of its holdings at the end of 2009 was $9.995 billion. The fund's annual returns in successive years from 2000 to 2009 inclusive were 28.3%, 4.4%, −0.5%, 23.5%, 12.9%, 21.1%, 15.1%, 3.0%, −27.0%, and 27.3%, respectively. For the 3-year, 5-year, and 10-year periods ended December 31, 2009, what were the fund's equivalent annually compounded returns?

○**34.** At the end of 2009, the Industrial Alliance (IA) Group Dividends Fund had the best 10-year compound annual return of any Canadian diversified equity mutual fund. During the 10-year period, this fund invested primarily in the shares of large Canadian companies. The fund's annual returns in successive years from 2000 to 2009 inclusive were 33.5%, 9.2%, 2.2%, 25.8%, 17.9%, 27.9%, 19.7%, 6.3%, −26.0%, and 32.3%, respectively. For 3-year, 5-year, and 10-year periods ended December 31, 2009, what were the fund's equivalent annually compounded returns?

○**35.** At the end of 2009, the Trans IMS Canadian Growth Fund had one of the worst 10-year compound annual returns of any Canadian diversified equity mutual fund. The fund's annual returns in successive years from 2000 to 2009 inclusive were −12.8%, −38.3%, −24.1%, 25.4%, 9.2%, 18.6%, 12.0%, −0.2%, −38.5%, and 24.5%, respectively. For 3-year, 5-year, and 10-year periods ended December 31, 2009, what were the fund's equivalent annually compounded returns?

○**36.** In June of 2006, AIC Limited published full-page advertisements focused on the fact that its AIC Advantage Mutual Fund was Canada's "Best Performing Canadian Equity Fund over the 20 years" ending May 31, 2006. The equivalent annual rate of return during the 20 years was 11.9% compared to 9.9% for the benchmark S&P/TSX Composite Total Return Index. But the advertisement failed to point out that during the second half of that 20-year period, the fund's 9.4% compounded annual return was actually less than the 10.2% growth rate for the S&P/TSX Composite Total Return Index. Furthermore, in the final 5 years of the 20-year period, the fund's 2.4% annual rate of return was far below the index's 9.5% annual growth. The Advantage Fund's five-year performance was even less than the *median* performance of all Canadian equity mutual funds. In short, AIC was still trying to capitalize on the initial 10 years of truly outstanding performance, even though the Advantage Fund's subsequent 10 years' performance was at best mediocre.

a. What would $10,000 invested in the AIC Advantage Fund on May 31, 1986 have grown to after 20 years?

b. What was this investment worth after the first 10 years?

c. What compound annual rate of return did the AIC Advantage Fund earn during the first 10 years of the 20-year period?

d. What was the overall percent increase in the value of an investment in the AIC Advantage Fund during:
(**i**) The first 10 years?   (**ii**) The second 10 years?

37. Searching a Mutual Fund Data Base Access the *Globe and Mail*'s Web site. When the Globe Investor/Funds page loads, select "Fund Selector" from the links listed at the centre of the page. In the "Option C" area, you can enter the name of a particular fund. Enter "RBC Canadian Dividend" and click on "Go." The table that loads has several tabs along its top. Select "Long-term." This brings up another table with columns giving the fund's compound annual return for 3-year, 5-year, and 10-year periods ending on the last business day of the previous month. How much would $10,000 invested in this fund 10 years earlier be worth at the end of the previous month? Repeat for the "IA Group Dividends" and the "Trans IMS Canadian Growth" funds.

9.2 CALCULATING THE NUMBER OF COMPOUNDING PERIODS, n

LO1 If we know values for PV, FV, and i, we can calculate the number of compounding periods and the term of the loan or investment.

Algebraic Method You can take either of two approaches.

1. If you are familiar with the rules of logarithms, you can substitute the values for PV, FV, and i into $FV = PV(1 + i)^n$ and then solve for n.
2. If you are not comfortable manipulating logarithms, you can use formula (9-2). It is, in fact, just a "dressed-up" version of $FV = PV(1 + i)^n$ in which n is already isolated for you.

NUMBER OF COMPOUNDING PERIODS

$$n = \frac{\ln\left(\frac{FV}{PV}\right)}{\ln(1 + i)} \qquad (9\text{-}2)$$

In Example 9.2A, we will demonstrate both algebraic methods. Thereafter, only the second approach will be used in the text.

Financial Calculator Method Enter values for the four known variables—PV, FV, i, and m—into the appropriate memories. Then press $\boxed{\text{CPT}}$ $\boxed{\text{N}}$ in sequence to execute the calculation.

> **TIP** **Don't Leave Out the Final Step**
>
> The calculation of n is usually not the last step in a problem. Typically you are asked to determine the total time in years and months (rather than the number of compounding periods). Do not forget to complete the extra step necessary to directly answer the problem.

EXAMPLE 9.2A **CALCULATING THE NUMBER OF COMPOUNDING PERIODS**

What is the term of a compound-interest GIC if $4000 invested at 5.5% compounded annually earns interest totalling $1227.84?

SOLUTION

Given: $PV = \$4000$ $i = \frac{j}{m} = \frac{5.5\%}{1} = 5.5\%$ Total interest = $1227.84

The maturity value of the GIC is

$$FV = PV + \text{Total interest} = \$4000 + \$1227.84 = \$5227.84$$

Method 1: Use the basic formula $FV = PV(1 + i)^n$ to calculate the number of compounding periods required for $4000 to grow to $5227.84. Substitute the known values for PV, FV, and i giving

$$\$5227.84 = \$4000(1.055)^n$$

Therefore, $\qquad 1.055^n = \dfrac{\$5227.84}{\$4000} = 1.30696$

Now take logarithms of both sides. On the left side, use the rule that: $\ln(a^n) = n(\ln a)$

Therefore, $\qquad n(\ln 1.055) = \ln 1.30696$

and $\qquad\qquad n = \dfrac{\ln 1.30696}{\ln 1.055} = \dfrac{0.267704}{0.0535408} = 5.000$

Since each compounding period equals one year, the term of the GIC is five years.

Method 2: Substitute the known values into the derived formula (9-2). The number of compounding periods required for $4000 to grow to $5227.84 is

$$n = \frac{\ln\left(\dfrac{FV}{PV}\right)}{\ln(1+i)} = \frac{\ln\left(\dfrac{\$5227.84}{\$4000.00}\right)}{\ln(1.055)}$$

$$= \frac{\ln(1.30696)}{\ln(1.055)}$$

$$= \frac{0.267704}{0.0535408}$$

$$= 5.000$$

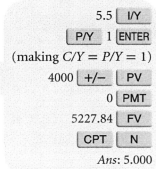

5.5 │ I/Y

│ P/Y │ 1 │ENTER

(making $C/Y = P/Y = 1$)

4000 │ +/− │ │ PV

0 │ PMT

5227.84 │ FV

│ CPT │ │ N

Ans: 5.000

Since each compounding period equals one year, the term of the GIC is five years.

TIP   **Efficient Use of Your Calculator**

The most efficient keystroke sequence for evaluating formula (9-2) in Method 2 of Example 9.2A is:

5227.84 │ ÷ │ 4000 │ = │ │ LN │ │ ÷ │ 1.055 │ LN │ │ = │

On the Sharp EL-738C calculator, the (natural) logarithm function │ ln │ is the second function of the │ 2 │ key.

Noninteger Values for *n* If formula (9-2) or the financial calculator procedure gives a value for *n* that is not an integer, it means (as you would expect) that the term of the loan or investment includes a partial compounding period. In the final answer, we normally convert the fractional part of *n* to months, or to months and days (depending on the requested precision).

EXAMPLE 9.2B   **CALCULATING AND INTERPRETING A NONINTEGER *n***

Rounded to the nearest month, how long will it take a city's population to grow from 75,000 to 100,000 if the annual growth rate is 2%?

SOLUTION

In effect, we are given:

$$PV = 75,000,\ FV = 100,000,\ \text{and}\ i = \frac{j}{m} = \frac{2\%}{1} = 2\%\ per\ year$$

Using formula (9-2) to calculate the required number of compounding periods, we obtain

$$n = \frac{\ln\left(\dfrac{FV}{PV}\right)}{\ln(1+i)}$$

$$= \frac{\ln\left(\dfrac{100,000}{75,000}\right)}{\ln(1.02)}$$

$$= \frac{0.28768}{0.019803}$$

$$= 14.527$$

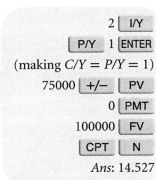

2 │ I/Y

│ P/Y │ 1 │ENTER

(making $C/Y = P/Y = 1$)

75000 │ +/− │ │ PV

0 │ PMT

100000 │ FV

│ CPT │ │ N

Ans: 14.527

It requires 14.527 compounding periods for the population to grow from 75,000 to 100,000. Since a compounding period equals one year,

$$14.527 \text{ compounding periods} = 14 \text{ years} + 0.527 \times 12 \text{ months}$$
$$= 14 \text{ years} + 6.32 \text{ months}$$

Rounded to the nearest month, it will take 14 years and 6 months for the city's population to reach 100,000.

EXAMPLE 9.2C   **CALCULATING AN INVESTMENT'S DOUBLING TIME**

How long will it take an investment to double in value if it earns:

a. 6% compounded annually?   **b.** 10% compounded annually?

Include accrued interest and round the answer to the nearest month.

SOLUTION

We require the maturity value of an investment to be twice the initial investment. Therefore, we can simply set $PV = \$1$ and $FV = \$2$.

In Part (a), $i = \frac{j}{m} = \frac{6\%}{1} = 6\%$ per year. In Part (b), $i = \frac{j}{m} = \frac{10\%}{1} = 10\%$ per year.

a. Substituting in formula (9-2),

$$n = \frac{\ln\left(\frac{FV}{PV}\right)}{\ln(1+i)}$$
$$= \frac{\ln(2)}{\ln(1.06)}$$
$$= 11.896$$

> 6 | I/Y
> P/Y 1 ENTER
> (making $C/Y = P/Y = 1$)
> 1 +/− PV
> 0 PMT
> 2 FV
> CPT N
> *Ans:* 11.896

The doubling time is

11.896 years = 11 years + 0.896 × 12 months = 11 years + 10.75 months

An investment earning 6% compounded annually will double in 11 years and 11 months (rounded to the nearest month).

b. Substituting in formula (9-2),

$$n = \frac{\ln\left(\frac{FV}{PV}\right)}{\ln(1+i)} = \frac{\ln(2)}{\ln(1.10)} = 7.2725$$

> Same *P/Y, C/Y*
> Same *PV, PMT, FV*
> 10 | I/Y
> CPT N
> *Ans:* 7.2725

The doubling time is

7.2725 years = 7 years + 0.2725 × 12 months = 7 years + 3.27 months

An investment earning 10% compounded annually will double in 7 years and 3 months (rounded to the nearest month).

Rule of 72 Investors have a rule-of-thumb to quickly *estimate* the number of years it will take an investment to double.[2] Known as the **Rule of 72**, it says:

$$\text{Doubling time (in years)} \approx \frac{72}{\text{Percent annual rate of return}}$$

---

[2] The approximation is very good for annual interest rates between 5% and 11%; the value estimated for the doubling time is within 2% of its true value.

For example, an investment earning 9% compounded annually will double in approximately $\frac{72}{9} = 8$ years. If the investment earns 12% compounded annually, it will double in about $\frac{72}{12} = 6$ years.

The answers in the preceding Example 9.2C provide an indication of the accuracy of the Rule of 72. At an annually compounded rate of 6%, we calculated a doubling time of 11.90 years (vs. 12.0 years using the Rule of 72). At 10% compounded annually, we calculated a doubling time of 7.27 years (vs. 7.2 years using the Rule of 72). In both cases, the estimate is within 1% of the correct value.

Valuing Strip Bonds and Other Single-Payment Investments Most loans and investments are structured so that the full term equals an integer multiple of the compounding period. However, an existing loan or investment contract may be sold and transferred to a new investor on a date that does not coincide with an interest-conversion date. The time remaining until maturity includes a partial compounding interval which must be taken into account in the price calculation. Consequently, n is not an integer in such cases.

In Table 9.1, consider the Province of Newfoundland strip bond maturing on April 17, 2023. Let us see how the market's required rate of return (5.275% in the Yield column) on June 1, 2009, determines the $48.55 market price quoted on that date. (Recall that bond prices are quoted in the media as the price per $100 of face value, and that yields are understood to be annual rates with semiannual compounding.)

TABLE 9.1 Strip Bond Price and Yield Quotations (June 1, 2009)

Issuer	Maturity Date	Price ($)	Yield (%)
Province of Quebec	April 1, 2015	80.49	3.755
Province of British Columbia	February 19, 2018	68.95	4.311
Province of Ontario	March 8, 2021	55.40	5.081
Province of Newfoundland	April 17, 2023	48.55	5.275
Bell Canada	November 15, 2025	40.67	5.544
Bell Canada	May 15, 2032	26.40	5.887

As indicated on the following timeline, the quoted price should be the present value of the $100 face value discounted at 5.275% compounded semiannually all the way back from the maturity date (April 17, 2023) to June 1, 2009. For the present value calculation, we need to know the number of compounding periods in this interval. In general, this number will not be an integer. Determine the integer and fractional components of the number separately. Working back from the maturity date, there are $13\frac{1}{2}$ years (27 compounding periods) from April 17, 2023, back to October 17, 2009. Then there are an additional 138 days from October 17, 2009, back to June 1, 2009. This 138-day interval is the fraction $\frac{138}{183}$ of the full 183-day compounding period from April 17, 2009, to October 17, 2009.

Therefore, $n = 27\frac{138}{183} = 27.7541$ compounding periods, $i = \frac{5.275\%}{2} = 2.6375\%$, and

$$\text{Price, } PV = FV(1 + i)^{-n} = \$100(1.026375)^{-27.7541} = \$48.55$$

This equals the quoted price accurate to the cent. (In general, a yield rounded to four figures guarantees only three-figure accuracy in the price.)

EXAMPLE 9.2D **CALCULATING THE TIME UNTIL MATURITY OF A STRIP BOND**

A $10,000 face value strip bond was purchased for $4188.77. At this price, the bond provided the investor with a return of 5.938% compounded semiannually until the maturity date. To the nearest day, how long before the maturity date was the bond purchased? Assume that each half year is exactly 182 days long.

SOLUTION

The purchase price of a strip bond equals the present value, on the date of purchase, of the bond's face value. The prevailing market rate of return should be used as the discount rate. In this example, $4188.77 is the present value of $10,000 discounted at 5.938% compounded semiannually. To determine the time interval used in the present value calculation, we must first calculate the number of compounding periods. We are given:

$$PV = \$4188.77, FV = \$10,000, \text{ and } i = \frac{j}{m} = \frac{5.938\%}{2} = 2.969\%$$

Substituting in formula (9-2),

$$n = \frac{\ln\left(\frac{FV}{PV}\right)}{\ln(1+i)}$$
$$= \frac{\ln\left(\frac{\$10,000}{\$4188.77}\right)}{\ln(1.02969)}$$
$$= 29.74176$$

5.938	I/Y
P/Y	2 ENTER

(making C/Y = P/Y = 2)

4188.77 +/−	PV
0	PMT
10000	FV
CPT	N

Ans: 29.74176

Since each compounding period is 0.5 year, the time remaining to maturity is

$$(0.50 \times 29) \text{ years} + (0.74176 \times 182) \text{ days} = 14.5 \text{ years} + 135.00 \text{ days}$$

Hence, the bond was purchased with 14 years, 6 months, and 135 days remaining until its maturity date.

EXAMPLE 9.2E **SOLVING FOR A NONINTEGER "n" IN A DISCOUNTING PROBLEM**

A loan contract requires the payment of $4000 plus interest two years after the contract's date of issue. The interest rate on the $4000 face value is 9.6% compounded quarterly. Before the maturity date, the original lender sold the contract to an investor for $4327.70. The sale price was based on a discount rate of 8.5% compounded semiannually from the date of sale. How many months before the maturity date did the sale take place?

SOLUTION

The selling price represents the present value (on the date of sale) of the loan's maturity value. In other words, $4327.70 was the present value of the maturity value, discounted at 8.5% compounded semiannually. Therefore, the solution requires two steps as indicated in the following time diagram.

1. Calculate the maturity value of the debt.

2. Determine the length of time over which the maturity value was discounted to give a present value of $4327.70.

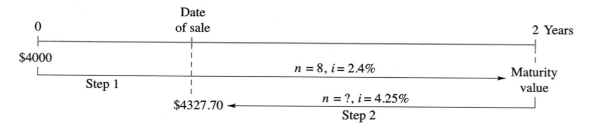

Step 1:   For the maturity value calculation,

$$n = m(\text{Term}) = 4(2) = 8 \text{ and } i = \frac{j}{m} = \frac{9.6\%}{4} = 2.4\%.$$

The maturity value of the contract is

$$\left.\begin{array}{l} FV = PV(1 + i)^n \\ \quad = \$4000(1.024)^8 \\ \quad = \$4835.70 \end{array}\right\}$$

9.6	I/Y
P/Y	4 ENTER

(making $C/Y = P/Y = 4$)

8	N
4000 +/−	PV
0	PMT
CPT	FV

Ans: 4835.70

Step 2:   For discounting the maturity value,

$$i = \frac{j}{m} = \frac{8.5\%}{2} = 4.25\%.$$

The number of compounding periods between the date of sale and the maturity date is

$$\left.\begin{array}{l} n = \dfrac{\ln\left(\dfrac{FV}{PV}\right)}{\ln(1 + i)} \\[3ex] \quad = \dfrac{\ln\left(\dfrac{\$4835.70}{\$4327.70}\right)}{\ln(1.0425)} \\[3ex] \quad = 2.6666 \end{array}\right\}$$

Same *PMT, FV*

8.5	I/Y
P/Y	2 ENTER

(making $C/Y = P/Y = 2$)

4327.70 +/−	PV
CPT	N

Ans: 2.6666

Each compounding period is six months long. Therefore, the date of sale was

2.6666 × 6 months = 16.00 months before the maturity date.

SPREADSHEET STRATEGIES   Number of Compounding Periods

Connect provides a partially completed template for calculating *n*, the number of compounding periods. Go to the Student Edition of Connect and find "NPER Function." The "Introduction" page of the workbook describes Excel's built-in NPER function.

The main features of a completed "NPER Function" template are presented below. The formula programmed into

cell C9 is displayed in cell C10. Here data are entered to solve Example 9.2A. In this example, $4000 invested in a GIC earning 5.5% compounded annually grew to a maturity value of $5227.84. We are asked to determine the term of the GIC. After entering the known values into the input cells, the computed number of compounding periods appears immediately in the output cell.

	A	B	C	D
1				
2	Using a spreadsheet to calculate the number of compounding periods.			
3	Example 9.2A:			
4				
5		Future value, *FV*	5,227.84	
6		Present value, *PV*	-4,000.00	
7		Periodic rate of interest, *i* (%)	5.500%	
8				
9		No. of cmpding periods, NPER	5.00000	
10		Formula in cell C9:	=NPER(C7,0,C6,C5,0)	
11				

Since each compounding period equals one year, the term of the GIC was five years.

CONCEPT QUESTIONS

1. Under what circumstance does the value calculated for n equal the number of years in the term of the loan or investment?

2. Which investment scenario requires more time: "$1 growing to $2" or "$3 growing to $5?" Both investments earn the same rate of return. Justify your choice.

EXERCISE 9.2

■ connect·

Spreadsheet template: A partially completed Excel template for calculating the number of compounding periods is provided in Connect. Go to the Student Edition of Connect and find "NPER Function." The completed template may be used wherever you need to calculate n in Exercise 9.2.

Answers to the odd-numbered problems are at the end of the book.

1. An $1100 investment earning 6.3% compounded annually grew to $4483.92. What was the term of the investment?

2. How long did it take $4625 earning 7.875% compounded annually to grow to $8481.61?

3. $5000 invested in a GIC earning 3.7% compounded semiannually matured at $5789.73. What was the term of the GIC?

4. The current balance on a loan is $3837.30. If the interest rate on the loan is 10% compounded monthly, how long ago was the $2870 loan made?

5. Marilyn was supposed to pay $1450 to Bernice on March 1. Some time later Marilyn paid Bernice an equivalent payment of $1528.01, allowing for a time value of money of 4.5% compounded monthly. When did Marilyn make the payment?

6. What is the remaining time until the maturity date of a $10,000 strip bond if it is purchased for $4011.33 to yield 6.4% compounded semiannually until maturity?

7. A number of years ago, your client invested $6000 at a rate of return of 9% compounded annually. If the investment is currently worth $10,968.25, for how long has she held the investment? (Taken from CIFP course materials.)

8. A few years ago Avtar invested $6000 in a compound-interest GIC that earned 4.5% compounded semiannually. He recently received the maturity value of $7168.99. What was the term of the GIC?

9. Rounded to the nearest month, how long will it take a town's population to:
   a. Grow from 32,500 to 40,000 if the annual growth rate is 3%?
   b. Shrink from 40,000 to 32,500 if the annual rate of decline is 3%?

10. Rounded to the nearest month, how long will it take an investment to double if it earns:
   a. 8.4% compounded annually? b. 10.5% compounded semiannually?

11. Rounded to the nearest month, how long will it take an investment to triple if it earns:
   a. 9% compounded annually? b. 8% compounded quarterly?

12. Rounded to the nearest quarter year, how long will it take an investment to quadruple if it earns:
   a. 8% compounded annually? b. 9% compounded semiannually?

13. Rounded to the nearest month, how long before a scheduled payment of $10,000 would a payment of $5000 be an economically equivalent alternative? Assume money is worth 5% compounded annually.

14. How long before a future payment of $1000 would a payment of just $100 (only 10% of the nominal amount of the future payment) be an economically equivalent alternative? Round your answer to the nearest month. Assume money can earn 4.8% compounded semiannually.

15. Your client wants to invest a $250,000 inheritance and grow it to $325,000. Rounded to the nearest month, how long will this take if the investment earns 7% compounded annually? (Taken from CIFP course materials.)

16. Your client invests $10,000 today at a rate of return of 7.7% compounded quarterly. Rounded to the nearest month, how long will it take the investment to grow to $22,000? (Taken from CIFP course materials.)

○17. Rounded to the nearest month, how long will it take money to lose half of its purchasing power if the annual inflation rate is:

   a. 2.5%?   **b.** 3.5%?

○18. Rounded to the nearest month, how long will it take money to lose 25% of its purchasing power if the annual rate of inflation is:

   a. 2%?   **b.** 4%?

○19. When discounted to yield 10.5% compounded monthly, a $2600 three-year promissory note bearing interest at 12.25% compounded annually was priced at $3283.57. How many months after the issue date did the discounting take place?

○20. The proceeds from the sale of a $4500 five-year promissory note bearing interest at 9% compounded quarterly were $6055.62. How many months before its maturity date was the note sold if it was discounted to yield 10.5% compounded monthly?

○21. A $4000 loan at 7.5% compounded monthly was settled by a single payment of $5000 including accrued interest. Rounded to the nearest day, how long after the initial loan was the $5000 payment made? For the purpose of determining the number of days in a partial month, assume that a full month has 30 days.

○22. If money is worth 8% compounded quarterly, how long (to the nearest day) before a scheduled payment of $6000 will $5000 be an equivalent payment? For the purpose of determining the number of days in a partial calendar quarter, assume that a full quarter has 91 days.

○23. Wilf paid $557.05 for a $1000 face value strip bond. At this price the investment will yield a return of 5.22% compounded semiannually. How long (to the nearest day) before its maturity date did Wilf purchase the bond? Assume that each half-year has exactly 182 days.

○24. A $5000 face value strip bond may be purchased today for $1073.36 yielding the purchaser 7.27% compounded semiannually. How much time (to the nearest day) remains until the maturity date? Assume that each half-year has exactly 182 days.

○25. $7500 was borrowed for a four-year term at 9% compounded quarterly. The terms of the loan allow prepayment of the loan based on discounting the loan's maturity value at 7% compounded quarterly. How long (to the nearest day) before the maturity date was the loan prepaid if the payout amount was $9380.24 including accrued interest? For the purpose of determining the number of days in a partial calendar quarter, assume that a full quarter has 91 days.

○26. Consider the Province of British Columbia strip bond in Table 9.1.

   a. Calculate the bond's market price on June 1, 2009, based on the quoted yield of 4.311% compounded semiannually.

   b. What would the price be one year later if the bond's yield remains the same?

◦**27.** Consider the Province of Ontario strip bond in Table 9.1.

    a. Calculate the bond's market price on June 1, 2009, based on the quoted yield of 5.081% compounded semiannually.

    b. What would the price be on June 1, 2015, if the bond's yield remains the same?

◦**28.** Consider the Province of Newfoundland strip bond in Table 9.1.

    a. Calculate the bond's yield to four-figure accuracy on June 1, 2009, based on the quoted price of $48.55.

    b. What would the yield be one year later if the bond's price remains the same?

◦**29.** Consider the Bell Canada strip bond maturing on May 15, 2032, in Table 9.1.

    a. Calculate the bond's yield to four-figure accuracy on June 1, 2009, based on the quoted price of $26.40.

    b. What would the yield be one year later if the bond's price remains the same?

9.3 | EFFECTIVE INTEREST RATE

LO2 The future value of $100 invested for one year at 10% compounded semiannually is $110.25. The future value of $100 invested for one year at 10.25% compounded annually is also $110.25. Therefore, an interest rate of 10% compounded semiannually has the *same effect* as a rate of 10.25% compounded annually. The **effective interest rate,** *f,* is defined as the *annually* compounded rate[3] that produces the *same* future value after one year as the given nominal rate. In the present example, 10% compounded semiannually has an effective rate[4] of 10.25%.

> **TIP** | **Intuitive Approach for Calculating *f***
>
> Note in the preceding example that the effective interest rate (10.25%) is numerically equal to the actual amount of interest ($10.25) that $100 will earn in one year at the given nominal rate. This is a general result for all nominal interest rates. We can use this idea for our financial calculator method for determining *f*. That is, we can calculate the future value of $100 after one year at the given nominal rate. Then we can just inspect the future value to see the amount of interest earned (and thereby identify the value of *f*.)

We can readily derive a formula for *f*. Suppose you invest $100 for one year at the effective rate *f* (compounded annually) and another $100 for one year at the nominal rate $j = mi$. Their future values are calculated in parallel columns below.

The first $100 will undergo just one compounding of the effective rate *f*.

$$FV = PV(1 + i)^n$$
$$= \$100(1 + f)^1$$

The second $100 will undergo *m* compoundings of the periodic rate *i*.

$$FV = PV(1 + i)^n$$
$$= \$100(1 + i)^m$$

---

[3] There is a natural preference in business for discussing interest rates on the basis of annual compounding. This is because an *annually* compounded rate of return represents the *actual* percentage increase in a year. For example, at a return of 9% compounded annually, you can immediately say that $100 will grow by 9% ($9) in the next year. But at a return of 9% compounded monthly, you cannot say how much $100 will grow in a year without a short calculation. In the second case, the *actual* percentage increase will be more than 9%.

[4] When an effective interest rate is quoted or calculated, the compounding frequency does not need to be specified. Everyone understands from the definition of effective interest rate that "effective" implies "annual compounding."

For f to be equivalent to the nominal rate j, these future values must be equal. That is,

$$\$100(1 + f) = \$100(1 + i)^m$$
$$1 + f = (1 + i)^m$$

EFFECTIVE INTEREST RATE

$$f = (1 + i)^m - 1 \qquad\qquad (9\text{-}3)$$

> **TIP** **Comparing Nominal Rates of Interest**
>
> To compare two nominal rates of interest, convert each to its effective interest rate. Then you can directly compare the effective rates, and thereby rank the given nominal rates.

EXAMPLE 9.3A **CONVERTING A NOMINAL INTEREST RATE TO AN EFFECTIVE INTEREST RATE**

What is the effective rate of interest corresponding to 10.5% compounded monthly?

SOLUTION

Given: $j = 10.5\%$ and $m = 12$

For the financial calculator solution, we will use the intuitive approach described in the first TIP above.

Then $i = \frac{j}{m} = \frac{10.5\%}{12} = 0.875\%$ per month and

$$\left. \begin{aligned} f &= (1 + i)^m - 1 \\ &= (1.00875)^{12} - 1 \\ &= 1.11020 - 1 \\ &= 0.11020 \\ &= 11.02\% \end{aligned} \right\}$$

10.5 [I/Y]
[P/Y] 12 [ENTER]
(making $C/Y = P/Y = 12$)
12 [N]
100 [+/−] [PV]
0 [PMT]
[CPT] [FV]
Ans: 111.020
f

The effective interest rate is 11.02% (compounded annually).

EXAMPLE 9.3B **COMPARING ALTERNATIVE NOMINAL INTEREST RATES**

Which is the most attractive of the following interest rates offered on five-year GICs?
a. 5.70% compounded annually   **b.** 5.68% compounded semiannually
c. 5.66% compounded quarterly   **d.** 5.64% compounded monthly

SOLUTION

The preferred rate is the one having the highest effective rate. The algebraic calculations of the effective rates are presented in the table below.

j	m	i	$f = (1 + i)^m - 1$
a. 5.70%	1	0.057	$f = j$ when $m = 1; f = 5.700\%$
b. 5.68%	2	0.0284	$f = (1.0284)^2 - 1 = 0.05761 = 5.761\%$
c. 5.66%	4	0.01415	$f = (1.01415)^4 - 1 = 0.05781 = 5.781\%$
d. 5.64%	12	0.0047	$f = (1.0047)^{12} - 1 = 0.05788 = 5.788\%$

In Appendix 9A, we describe and demonstrate the use of the Texas Instruments BA II PLUS's Interest Conversion Worksheet (ICONV). Let us now use this worksheet to calculate the effective interest rates in Parts (b), (c), and (d).

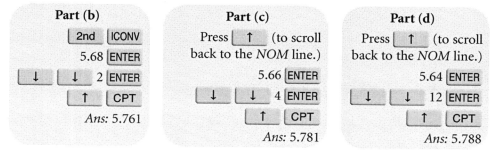

Part (b)	Part (c)	Part (d)
2nd ICONV	Press ↑ (to scroll back to the *NOM* line.)	Press ↑ (to scroll back to the *NOM* line.)
5.68 ENTER	5.66 ENTER	5.64 ENTER
↓ ↓ 2 ENTER	↓ ↓ 4 ENTER	↓ ↓ 12 ENTER
↑ CPT	↑ CPT	↑ CPT
Ans: 5.761	*Ans:* 5.781	*Ans:* 5.788

The most attractive rate is 5.64% compounded monthly since it has the highest effective rate. For the alternative rates in this example, the ranking in terms of effective rates is in the reverse order of the nominal rates.

POINT OF INTEREST

Not in Your Best Interest

The Canada Revenue Agency (CRA) charges interest on overdue income tax, Canada Pension Plan contributions, and Employment Insurance Premiums. The prescribed rate is adjusted by the CRA every 3 months based on changes in the Bank of Canada rate. For the third quarter of 2009, the prescribed nominal rate was 5%.

You now know that the compounding frequency matters. The more frequently a given nominal rate is compounded, the higher the effective rate of interest. Considering who is setting the rate in this case, you would probably guess that the prescribed rate is compounded monthly (the highest compounding frequency normally encountered in commerce). Not so! But before you think the CRA has some compassion after all, think again—the prescribed rate is compounded daily!

QUESTIONS

1. Calculate the effective rate of interest corresponding to 5% compounded daily.
2. How much more interest would accrue on a $1000 debt in a year at 5% compounded daily than at 5% compounded monthly?

EXAMPLE 9.3C   **FINDING THE EFFECTIVE RATE GIVEN THE PRINCIPAL AND MATURITY VALUE**

Calculate the effective rate of interest if $100 grew to $150 in $3\frac{1}{2}$ years with quarterly compounding.

SOLUTION

The problem can be solved by first finding the quarterly compounded nominal rate that produces the given maturity value. Then the corresponding effective rate may be calculated. But this two-step solution is unnecessarily long.

The essential question (which may be answered in one step) is: At what annually compounded rate will $100 grow to $150 after $3\frac{1}{2}$ years?

With $PV = \$100$, $FV = \$150$, $m = 1$, and $n = 3.5$, formula (9-1) gives

$$
\begin{aligned}
i &= \left(\frac{FV}{PV}\right)^{1/n} - 1 \\
&= \left(\frac{\$150}{\$100}\right)^{1/3.5} - 1 \\
&= 1.5^{0.28571} - 1 \\
&= 0.1228
\end{aligned}
$$

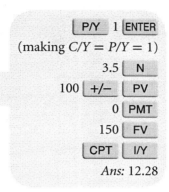

P/Y 1 ENTER
(making $C/Y = P/Y = 1$)
3.5 N
100 +/− PV
0 PMT
150 FV
CPT I/Y
Ans: 12.28

Since $100 will grow to $150 in $3\frac{1}{2}$ years at 12.28% compounded annually, the effective interest rate is 12.28%.

TIP   Clarification of Terminology

Be clear on the distinction between the descriptions "compounded semiannually" and "per half year." The former refers to the compounding *frequency*. The latter refers to the compounding *period*. For example, if you hear or read "6% compounded semiannually," you are being given the value for "*j*." Then $i = j/m = 6\%/2 = 3\%$ (per half year). On the other hand, if an interest rate is described as "6% per half year," you are being given the value for "*i*" and the period to which it applies. Then $j = mi = 2i = 12\%$ compounded semiannually.

EXAMPLE 9.3D   **CALCULATING THE EFFECTIVE INTEREST RATE ON A CHARGE CARD**

A department store credit card quotes a rate of 1.75% per month on the unpaid balance. Calculate the effective rate of interest being charged.

SOLUTION

Since accrued interest is paid or converted to principal each month, we have monthly compounding with $i = 1.75\%$ per month, $m = 12$, and $j = mi = 12(1.75\%) = 21\%$ compounded monthly.

Therefore,

$$
\begin{aligned}
f &= (1 + i)^m - 1 \\
&= (1.0175)^{12} - 1 \\
&= 0.23144 \\
&= 23.14\%
\end{aligned}
$$

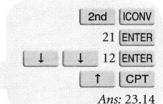

2nd ICONV
21 ENTER
↓ ↓ 12 ENTER
↑ CPT
Ans: 23.14

The effective rate on the credit card is 23.14%.

EXAMPLE 9.3E **CONVERTING AN EFFECTIVE INTEREST RATE TO A NOMINAL INTEREST RATE**

What monthly compounded (nominal) rate of interest has an effective rate of 10%?

SOLUTION

Given: $f = 10\%$ $m = 12$

Substitute these values into formula (9-3) and solve for i.

$$f = (1 + i)^m - 1$$
$$0.10 = (1 + i)^{12} - 1$$
$$1.10 = (1 + i)^{12}$$

Now use the rule that

If $x^m = a$, then $x = a^{1/m}$

Therefore,

$$1.1^{1/12} = 1 + i$$
$$1 + i = 1.1^{0.08\overline{3}}$$
$$i = 1.007974 - 1$$
$$= 0.007974$$
$$= 0.7974\%$$

Then $j = mi = 12(0.7974\%) = 9.57\%$ compounded monthly.

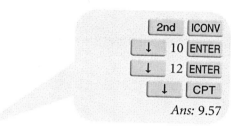

Ans: 9.57

EXAMPLE 9.3F **CONVERTING AN INTEREST RATE FROM NOMINAL TO EFFECTIVE AND BACK TO NOMINAL**

The department store mentioned in Example 9.3D has been charging 1.75% per month on its credit card. In response to lower prevailing interest rates, the Board of Directors has agreed to reduce the card's effective interest rate by 4%. To the nearest 0.01%, what will be the new periodic rate (per month)?

SOLUTION

To solve this problem, we must first calculate the effective rate corresponding to $i = 1.75\%$ per month. Then we must calculate the new monthly compounded rate whose effective rate is 4% lower.

Step 1: See the solution to Example 9.3D for this calculation. We obtained $f = 23.14\%$.

Step 2: The new effective rate must be 23.14% − 4% = 19.14%.

Substitute $f = 19.14\%$ and $m = 12$ into formula (9-3).

$$f = (1 + i)^m - 1$$
$$0.1914 = (1 + i)^{12} - 1$$
$$1.1914 = (1 + i)^{12}$$
$$1 + i = 1.1914^{1/12}$$
$$i = 1.1914^{0.08\overline{3}} - 1$$
$$= 1.01470 - 1$$
$$= 0.01470$$
$$= 1.47\%$$

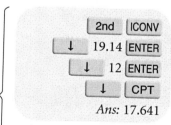

Ans: 17.641

The new periodic rate will be

$$i = \frac{j}{m} = \frac{17.641\%}{12} = 1.47\%$$

The new periodic interest rate on the credit card will be 1.47% per month.

POINT OF INTEREST

Payday-Loan Operations Return from Near-Death Experience

In the 1990s and early 2000s, storefront cheque-cashing and payday-loan businesses proliferated in Canada. There are several franchise operations with names like Money Mart, Stop 'N' Cash, Premier Cash Advance Inc., The Cash Store, and A OK Payday Loans. The Financial Consumer Agency of Canada estimates that over two million Canadians have used a cheque-cashing or payday-loan company. The typical loan is a $300 amount for a 14-day period.

In a typical payday-loan transaction, the amount of the loan can be up to 30% of the borrower's *net* pay, which must be verified by a recent pay stub. Payday lenders do not require credit checks or collateral. The loan may be advanced on the spot if the borrower provides proof of:

- Identification (by a suitable photo ID)
- Residence (by a recent utility bill)
- An active chequing account (by a bank statement for the preceding month)

At the time of receiving a loan, the borrower provides a cheque (post-dated to the next payday) for the amount needed to repay the loan.

The interest rate charged on payday loans is high but less than the 60% effective rate established as a "criminal rate of interest" by Section 347 of the Criminal Code. Payday lenders also apply other service charges or processing fees in addition to interest on the loan.

From 2003 to 2007, most payday-loan operations became defendants in class-action lawsuits. The Statements of Claim typically argued that the effective rates of interest charged on payday loans exceeded the 60% limit set by the Criminal Code. "Interest" has a broad definition in the Criminal Code—it includes other charges and fees associated with a loan. Although many cases still remained before the courts in 2008, there was an evolving pattern of judges ruling in favour of the plaintiff and awarding settlements in the millions of dollars.

For example, in August of 2006, the Supreme Court of British Columbia issued its decision in a class-action lawsuit against A OK Payday Loans. A OK charged a 21% annual rate of interest *plus* a "processing fee" of $9.50 for every $50 borrowed! If a customer wished to extend or "roll over" a loan when it came due on payday, A OK charged a "deferral fee" of $25 for every $100 extended. The judge ruled that the processing and deferral fees were interest under the definition of the Criminal Code. Consequently, A OK was charging its customers a criminal rate of interest. The ultimate payout as a result of this decision is expected to be several million dollars.

QUESTIONS

1. Under A OK's former lending practice (described above), what would be the total interest and other charges for a two-week loan of $300? (The processing fee of $9.50 per $50 loaned does not depend on the duration of the loan. Apply the 21% interest rate as simple interest.)

2. Treating all charges as interest, what overall effective rate of interest do they represent? Assume that a year is exactly 52 weeks long.

3. In August of 2006, Justice Brenda Brown of the BC Supreme Court ordered A OK Payday Loans to pay back everything it had charged customers in excess of an effective rate of 60%. Under the judge's ruling, how much must A OK refund on the loan described in Question 1?

The legal environment threatening the viability of payday-loan operations started to change in 2007. The federal government amended the Criminal Code to exempt payday lenders from the Code's criminal interest provisions in situations of short-term loans made in "designated provinces". A province can become designated by establishing legislation and regulations to license lenders and protect borrowers (including measures to set limits on the total cost of borrowing.)

During 2008 and 2009, most provinces took the necessary steps to become designated. The limit on borrowing costs was usually set in terms of a maximum dollar amount (including all fees and interest) per $100 of short-term loan. Specific examples are $31 (per $100) in Nova Scotia, $21 in Ontario, $17 in Manitoba, $23 in Alberta, and $23 in British Columbia. These amounts do not depend on the duration of the loan.

QUESTION

4. Using the new provincial maximum lending charges, calculate the effective interest rate on a $300 payday loan for two weeks in:
   a. Ontario.
   b. Alberta and British Columbia.
   c. Nova Scotia.

SPREADSHEET STRATEGIES · Interest Rate Conversion

Connect provides a partially completed template for (1) converting a nominal rate of interest to an effective rate and (2) converting an effective rate to a nominal rate. Go to the Student Edition of Connect and find "Interest Rate Conversion." The "Introduction" page of the workbook describes Excel's built-in EFFECT and NOMINAL functions.

The main features of a completed Interest Rate Conversion template are presented below. The formulas programmed into cells C9 and C16 are displayed in cells C10 and C17, respectively. Data are entered to solve Example 9.3F. In this example, a department store has been charging 1.75% per month on its credit card. The Board of Directors have decided to reduce the effective annual rate on the card by 4%. The question asks us to determine the new periodic interest rate (per month).

Enter the values for $j = 12(1.75\%) = 21.0\%$ and $m = 12$ into cells C6 and C7. The effective rate immediately appears in C9. Next we reduce the effective rate to $23.144\% - 4\% = 19.144\%$ and enter this new rate into C13. Also enter $m = 12$ in C14. The new nominal rate appears in C16.

	A	B	C	D
1				
2	Using a spreadsheet for interest rate conversions.			
3	Example 9.3F:			
4				
5	**Converting a Nominal Rate to an Effective Rate:**			
6		Nominal rate of interest, *j* (%)	21.000%	
7		# compounding periods per year, *m*	12.00	
8				
9		Effective rate of interest, *f*	23.1439%	
10		Formula in cell C9:	=EFFECT(C6,C7)	
11				
12	**Converting an Effective Rate to a Nominal Rate:**			
13		Effective rate of interest, *f* (%)	19.144%	
14		# compounding periods per year, *m*	12.00	
15				
16		Nominal rate of interest, *j*	17.6446%	
17		Formula in cell C16:	=NOMINAL(C13,C14)	
18				

It remains only to calculate the new periodic rate: $i = \frac{j}{m} = \frac{17.6446\%}{12} = 1.47\%$ per month.

CONCEPT QUESTIONS

1. What is meant by the effective rate of interest?
2. Is the effective rate of interest ever numerically smaller than the nominal interest rate? Explain.
3. Is the effective rate of interest ever equal to the nominal interest rate? Explain.
4. A semiannually compounded nominal rate and a monthly compounded nominal rate have the same effective rate. Which has the larger nominal rate? Explain.
5. From a lender's point of view, would you rather disclose to borrowers the nominal interest rate or the effective interest rate?

EXERCISE 9.3

Spreadsheet template: A partially completed Excel template for converting interest rates is provided in Connect. Go to the Student Edition of Connect and find "Interest Rate Conversion." The completed template may be used throughout Exercise 9.3.

Answers to the odd-numbered problems are at the end of the book.

Calculate interest rates and growth rates accurate to the nearest 0.01%.

1. What is the effective interest rate corresponding to a nominal annual rate of:
   a. 6% compounded semiannually?
   b. 6% compounded quarterly?
   c. 6% compounded monthly?
2. What is the effective interest rate corresponding to a nominal annual rate of:
   a. 7.5% compounded semiannually?
   b. 7.5% compounded quarterly?
   c. 7.5% compounded monthly?
3. What is the effective interest rate corresponding to a nominal annual rate of:
   a. 9% compounded semiannually?
   b. 9% compounded quarterly?
   c. 9% compounded monthly?
4. What is the effective interest rate corresponding to a nominal annual rate of:
   a. 4% compounded monthly?
   b. 8% compounded monthly?
   c. 12% compounded monthly?
5. To have an effective rate of 10%, what must be the corresponding nominal interest rate with:
   a. Annual compounding?
   b. Semiannual compounding?
   c. Quarterly compounding?
   d. Monthly compounding?
6. For the effective rate to be 7%, what must be the corresponding nominal interest rate with:
   a. Annual compounding?
   b. Semiannual compounding?
   c. Quarterly compounding?
   d. Monthly compounding?
7. Which of the following nominal interest rates has the highest effective rate: 12% compounded annually, 11.9% compounded semiannually, 11.8% compounded quarterly, or 11.7% compounded monthly?

8. Which interest rate would you prefer to earn on a three-year GIC: 6% compounded monthly, 6.1% compounded quarterly, 6.2% compounded semiannually, or 6.3% compounded annually?

9. Which interest rate would you prefer to pay on a loan: 9% compounded monthly, 9.1% compounded quarterly, 9.2% compounded semiannually, or 9.3% compounded annually?

10. What is the effective rate of interest on a credit card that calculates interest at the rate of 1.8% per month?

11. If an invoice indicates that interest at the rate of 2% per month will be charged on overdue amounts, what effective rate of interest will be charged?

12. If the nominal rate of interest paid on a savings account is 2% compounded monthly, what is the effective rate of interest?

13. A company reports that its sales have grown 3% per quarter for the last eight fiscal quarters. What annual growth rate has the company been experiencing for the last two years?

14. If a $5000 investment grew to $6450 in 30 months of monthly compounding, what effective rate of return was the investment earning?

15. After 27 months of quarterly compounding, a $3000 debt had grown to $3810. What effective rate of interest was being charged on the debt?

16. Lisa is offered a loan from a bank at 7.2% compounded monthly. A credit union offers similar terms, but at a rate of 7.4% compounded semiannually. Which loan should she accept? Present calculations that support your answer.

17. Craig can buy a three-year compound-interest GIC paying 4.6% compounded semiannually or 4.5% compounded monthly. Which option should he choose? Present calculations that support your answer.

18. Camille can obtain a residential mortgage loan from a bank at 6.5% compounded semiannually, or from an independent mortgage broker at 6.4% compounded monthly. Which source should she pick if other terms and conditions of the loan are the same? Present calculations that support your answer.

19. ABC Ltd. reports that its sales are growing at the rate of 1.3% per month. DEF Inc. reports sales increasing by 4% each quarter. What is each company's effective annual rate of sales growth?

20. Columbia Trust wants its annually, semiannually, and monthly compounded five-year GICs all to have an effective interest rate of 5.75%. What nominal annual rates should it quote for the three compounding options?

21. Belleville Credit Union has established interest rates on its three-year GICs so that the effective rate of interest is 7% on all three compounding options. What are the monthly, semiannually, and annually compounded rates?

○22. A department store chain currently charges 18% compounded monthly on its credit card. To what amount should it set the monthly compounded annual rate if it wants to add 2% to the effective interest rate?

○23. An oil company wants to drop the effective rate of interest on its credit card by 3%. If it currently charges a periodic rate of 1.7% per month, at what amount should it set the periodic rate?

9.4   EQUIVALENT INTEREST RATES

Preamble The main purpose of this section is to prepare you for a routine calculation you will carry out for a broad category of annuities in Chapters 10, 11, 12, and 14. The concept behind the calculation is developed here because it is an extension of ideas from Section 9.3.

LO3   **Equivalent interest rates** are interest rates that produce the *same* future value after one year. For example, 8% compounded quarterly and 8.08% compounded semiannually are equivalent *nominal* interest rates. If you calculate the future value of $100 invested at either rate for one year, you will obtain $108.24. You can see that equivalent interest rates have *different numerical values* but produce the *same effect*.

If *nominal* rates are equivalent, so also are their respective *periodic* rates. From the preceding example, we can conclude that:

$$i = \frac{8\%}{4} = 2\% \text{ per quarter is equivalent to } i = \frac{8.08\%}{2} = 4.04\% \text{ per half } year$$

They will both produce the same future value when compounded over a one-year term.

We want to be able to answer questions such as:

"What periodic rate per half year is equivalent to 2.5% per quarter?"

To answer this and similar questions, we will derive a formula that answers the general question:

"What i_2 with a specified m_2 is equivalent to a given i_1 with a given m_1?"

For equivalence, $100 invested at each rate for one year must have the same future value. The two investments are shown in the following diagrams. Both future values are obtained using $FV = PV(1 + i)^n$.

We want to solve for the value of i_2 that makes the two future values equal. That is, solve for i_2 in

$$\$100(1 + i_2)^{m_2} = \$100(1 + i_1)^{m_1}$$
$$(1 + i_2)^{m_2} = (1 + i_1)^{m_1}$$

Divide both exponents by m_2, giving

$$1 + i_2 = (1 + i_1)^{m_1/m_2}$$

Hence,

EQUIVALENT PERIODIC RATE

$$i_2 = (1 + i_1)^{m_1/m_2} - 1 \qquad\qquad \textbf{(9-4)}$$

To answer the question: "What periodic rate per half year is equivalent to 2.5% per quarter?" substitute $m_2 = 2$, $i_1 = 2.5\% = 0.025$, and $m_1 = 4$ into formula (9-4).

$$i_2 = (1 + i_1)^{m_1/m_2} - 1 = (1.025)^{4/2} - 1 = 1.025^2 - 1 = 0.050625 = 5.0625\% \text{ per half year}$$

EXAMPLE 9.4A **CALCULATION OF THREE EQUIVALENT INTEREST RATES**

For a given interest rate of 10% compounded quarterly, what is the equivalent nominal rate of interest with:

a. Annual compounding?   **b.** Semiannual compounding?   **c.** Monthly compounding?

SOLUTION

The given rate is $j_1 = 10\%$ with $m_1 = 4$. Therefore, $i_1 = 2.5\%$ per quarter.

In the following columns, we substitute the given values for m_1, m_2, and i_1 into formula (9-4).

a. $m_2 = 1$
$i_2 = (1.025)^{4/1} - 1$
$\quad = 0.10381$
$\quad = 10.381\%$ per year

$j_2 = m_2 \times i_2$
$\quad = 1 \times 10.381\%$
$\quad = 10.381\%$ compounded annually

b. $m_2 = 2$
$i_2 = (1.025)^{4/2} - 1$
$\quad = 0.050625$
$\quad = 5.0625\%$ per half-year

$j_2 = m_2 \times i_2$
$\quad = 2 \times 5.0625\%$
$\quad = 10.125\%$ compounded semiannually

c. $m_2 = 12$
$i_2 = (1.025)^{4/12} - 1$
$\quad = 0.0082648$
$\quad = 0.82648\%$ per month

$j_2 = m_2 \times i_2$
$\quad = 12 \times 0.82648\%$
$\quad = 9.918\%$ compounded monthly

To use the ICONV worksheet, first compute the effective rate corresponding to the given nominal interest rate. Then compute the requested nominal rates that are equivalent to this effective rate.

Part (a)	Part (b)	Part (c)
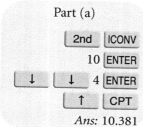	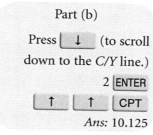	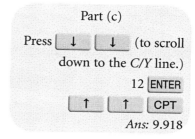

a. $j = f = 10.381\%$ compounded annually

b. $j = 10.125\%$ compounded semiannually

c. $j = 9.918\%$ compounded monthly

CONCEPT QUESTIONS

1. What is the significance of two nominal interest rates being equivalent?

2. Suppose the periodic rate for six months is 4%. Is the equivalent periodic rate for three months (pick one):
   (i) equal to $4\% \times \frac{3}{6} = 2\%$?
   (ii) less than 2%?
   (iii) greater than 2%?
   Answer the question without doing any calculations. Explain your choice.

3. Suppose the periodic rate for one month is 0.5%. Is the equivalent periodic rate for six months (pick one):
   (i) equal to $6(0.5\%) = 3\%$?
   (ii) less than 3%?
   (iii) greater than 3%?
   Answer the question without doing calculations. Explain your choice.

EXERCISE 9.4   *Answers to the odd-numbered problems are at the end of the book.*

Throughout this Exercise, calculate interest rates accurate to the nearest 0.01%.

1. To be equivalent to 10% compounded annually, what must be the nominal rate with:
   a. Semiannual compounding?   b. Quarterly compounding?
   c. Monthly compounding?

2. To be equivalent to 10% compounded semiannually, what must be the nominal rate with:
   a. Annual compounding?   b. Quarterly compounding?
   c. Monthly compounding?

3. To be equivalent to 10% compounded quarterly, what must be the nominal rate with:
   a. Annual compounding?   b. Semiannual compounding?
   c. Monthly compounding?

4. To be equivalent to 10% compounded monthly, what must be the nominal rate with:
   a. Annual compounding?   b. Semiannual compounding?
   c. Quarterly compounding?

5. What annually compounded interest rate is equivalent to 6% compounded:
   a. Semiannually?   b. Quarterly?   c. Monthly?

6. What semiannually compounded rate is equivalent to 6% compounded:
   a. Annually?   b. Quarterly?   c. Monthly?

7. What quarterly compounded rate is equivalent to 6% compounded:
   a. Annually?   b. Semiannually?   c. Monthly?

8. What monthly compounded interest rate is equivalent to 6% compounded:
   a. Annually?   b. Semiannually?   c. Quarterly?

9. What semiannually compounded rate is equivalent to 4% compounded monthly?

10. What quarterly compounded rate is equivalent to 7.5% compounded semiannually?

11. What monthly compounded rate is equivalent to 6% compounded quarterly?

12. What semiannually compounded rate is equivalent to 8.5% compounded quarterly?

13. What quarterly compounded rate is equivalent to 10.5% compounded monthly?

14. For a three-year GIC investment, what nominal rate compounded monthly would put you in the same financial position as 5.5% compounded semiannually?

15. A trust company pays 5.5% compounded semiannually on its three-year GIC. For you to prefer an annually compounded GIC of the same maturity, what value must its nominal interest rate exceed?

16. You are offered a loan at a rate of 9% compounded monthly. Below what nominal rate of interest would you choose semiannual compounding instead?

17. Banks usually quote residential mortgage interest rates on the basis of semiannual compounding. An independent mortgage broker is quoting rates with monthly compounding. What rate would the broker have to give to match 6.5% compounded semiannually available from a bank?

18. A credit union pays 5.25% compounded annually on five-year compound-interest GICs. It wants to set the rates on its semiannually and monthly compounded GICs of the same maturity so that investors will earn the same total interest. What should the rates be on the GICs with the higher compounding frequencies?

19. A bank offers a rate of 5.0% compounded semiannually on its four-year GIC. What monthly compounded rate should the bank offer on four-year GICs to make investors indifferent between the alternatives?

20. A life insurance company pays investors 5% compounded annually on its five-year GICs. For you to be indifferent as to which compounding option you choose, what would the nominal rates have to be on GICs with:

   a. Semiannual compounding?

   b. Quarterly compounding?

   c. Monthly compounding?

21. In your search for the best rate on a new-car loan, you note that various lenders quote rates with differing compounding frequencies. Your car dealer offers financing at 7.5% compounded monthly. For you to be indifferent as to which lending rate to choose, what would the nominal rate be on a loan from another lender with interest compounded

   a. Annually?   b. Semiannually?   c. Quarterly?

9.5 INVESTMENT RETURNS FROM STOCKS AND MUTUAL FUNDS

LO4   There are two ways you can benefit from an investment. The first is by receiving **income**—money you receive without selling any part of the investment. Aside from any income it generates, an investment may grow in value. The increase in value of the investment is called the **capital gain**. The forms taken by the income and capital gain from various types of investments are presented in Table 9.2.

TABLE 9.2   Forms of Income and Capital Gain From Various Types of Investments

Investment	Income	Capital gain
Stocks (or shares)	Dividends	Change in share price
Canada Savings Bonds (Sec. 8.5)	Interest	None (Redeemable at purchase price)
Marketable bonds (Chapter 15)	Interest	Change in bond price
Mutual fund units	Distributions	Change in unit value
Gold bullion	None	Change in market price of gold
GICs (Sec. 8.5)	Interest	None (Redeemable at purchase price)

A typical investment scenario is represented in Figure 9.1. The initial value (or beginning value) of the investment is V_i. In finance, the term **holding period** is used for the time interval over which we are calculating the income and capital gain. Income may be received from the investment at one or more points during the holding period. The final value of the investment at the end of the holding period is V_f. The capital gain is the increase in value, $V_f - V_i$. (If the value of an investment declines during the holding period, the capital gain will be negative, indicating a **capital loss**.) The sum of the income and capital gain from the investment is called the **total return**. In summary,

$$\text{Capital gain} = \text{Final value } (V_f) - \text{Initial value } (V_i)$$

$$\text{Total return} = \text{Income} + \text{Capital gain}$$

FIGURE 9.1   The Components of Investment Returns

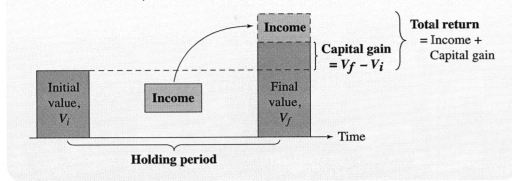

The distinction between the "income" and "capital gain" components of the "total return" is important for two reasons. One is that "income" represents actual cash inflow that can be used by the investor to cover living expenses. To convert the "capital gain" component into a usable cash inflow, the investor must first sell the investment. When the investment is sold, we say that "the capital gain is realized." (Up to that point it was an "unrealized capital gain," sometimes described in everyday language as a "paper gain.") The second reason for separating the "income" and "capital gain" components of "total return" is that capital gains are subject to a lower rate of income tax than investment income.

The income, capital gain, and total return amounts are all in terms of dollars. When discussing the performance of investments, investors prefer to express these amounts as a percentage of the initial value, V_i. Accordingly, we define:

INVESTMENT YIELDS AND RATE OF TOTAL RETURN

$$\text{Income yield} = \frac{\text{Income}}{V_i} \times 100\%$$

$$\text{Capital gain yield} = \frac{\text{Capital gain}}{V_i} \times 100\% = \frac{V_f - V_i}{V_i} \times 100\%$$

$$\text{Rate of total return} = \text{Income yield} + \text{Capital gain yield}$$
$$= \frac{\text{Income} + \text{Capital gain}}{V_i} \times 100\%$$

(9-5)

In their advertising, mutual funds emphasize the rates of total return, but give little or no information about the income and capital gain components. They do so because (1) the rate of total return is the figure of greatest importance to investors, and (2) most investors in mutual funds do not understand how the income (distribution) and capital gain components of total return are determined for a mutual fund. When we used the term "rate of return" in connection with mutual funds in Section 9.1, we were really referring to "rate of *total* return." To get information about the income and capital gain components of a mutual fund's total return, you need to go to the mutual fund's annual financial report or to a mutual fund database such as globefund.com.

TIP   Watch for Key Words

The words "yield" and "rate" indicate amounts calculated as a percentage of the initial investment. Particular names may be used for specific types of income yield. For example, shareholders refer to a stock's "dividend yield," but bond investors speak of a bond's "current yield."

In everyday life, terms are sometimes used with less precision than in an academic environment. For example, "yield" may be dropped from "capital gain yield" when investors discuss capital gains.

Tables 9.3 and 9.4 provide price and income data for selected stocks and mutual funds. These data are used in Example 9.5A and Exercise 9.5.

TABLE 9.3 Income and Price Data for Selected Stocks

Company name	Share price ($) at the end of: 2007	2008	2009	Dividends ($) paid in: 2008	2009
TD Bank	69.50	43.45	65.96	2.36	2.44
Potash Corporation	143.49	89.54	114.39	0.42	0.42
Cameco Corporation	39.57	21.05	33.93	0.24	0.24
Suncor Energy	53.96	23.72	37.21	0.20	0.40
Research in Motion Ltd.	112.56	49.50	71.03	0.00	0.00

TABLE 9.4 Income and Price Data for Selected Mutual Funds

Name of mutual fund	Unit price ($) at the end of: 2007	2008	2009	Distribution ($) in: 2008	2009
PH&N Canadian Equity Fund (Series D)	91.39	57.42	76.23	1.38	1.20
Mawer New Canada Fund	42.65	23.63	34.77	2.41	0.93
Sprott Canadian Equity Fund	43.82	24.67	33.54	0.00	0.00
RBC Canadian Dividend Fund	47.44	34.21	42.81	0.47	0.66
PH&N Bond Fund (Series D)	9.81	9.69	10.08	0.43	0.53

EXAMPLE 9.5A **CALCULATING INVESTMENT RETURNS FROM SECURITIES**

To the nearest 0.01%, calculate the income yield, capital gain yield, and rate of total return in each of 2008 and 2009 for TD Bank shares and for PH&N Canadian Equity Fund units. Use the data in Tables 9.3 and 9.4.

SOLUTION

Security	Income yield $\left(\dfrac{Income}{V_i} \times 100\% \right)$	Capital gain yield $\left(\dfrac{V_f - V_i}{V_i} \times 100\% \right)$	Rate of total return (Income yield + Capital gain yield)
TD Bank shares (2008)	$\dfrac{\$2.36}{\$69.50} \times 100\%$ $= 3.40\%$	$\dfrac{\$43.45 - \$69.50}{\$69.50} \times 100\%$ $= -37.48\%$	$3.40\% + (-37.48\%)$ $= -34.08\%$
TD Bank shares (2009)	$\dfrac{\$2.44}{\$43.45} \times 100\%$ $= 5.62\%$	$\dfrac{\$65.96 - \$43.45}{\$43.45} \times 100\%$ $= 51.81\%$	$5.62\% + 51.81\%$ $= 57.43\%$
PH&N Cdn. Equity (2008)	$\dfrac{\$1.38}{\$91.39} \times 100\%$ $= 1.51\%$	$\dfrac{\$57.42 - \$91.39}{\$91.39} \times 100\%$ $= -37.17\%$	$1.51\% + (-37.17\%)$ $= -35.66\%$
PH&N Cdn. Equity (2009)	$\dfrac{\$1.20}{57.42} \times 100\%$ $= 2.09\%$	$\dfrac{\$76.23 - \$57.42}{\$57.42} \times 100\%$ $= 32.76\%$	$2.09\% + 32.76\%$ $= 34.85\%$

EXAMPLE 9.5B   **CALCULATING V_f GIVEN V_i, INCOME, AND RATE OF TOTAL RETURN**

An investor is prepared to buy common shares of Eagle Brewing Ltd. at the current share price of $11.50 if he can expect at least a 15% rate of total return over the next year. Assuming that the company repeats last year's $0.40 per share dividend, what will the minimum share price have to be one year from now for the investment objective to be achieved?

SOLUTION

Given: V_i = $11.50   Rate of total return = 15%   Income = $0.40

We want to determine what V_f must be one year from now for the rate of total return to be 15%. If the annual dividend is $0.40 per share,

$$\text{Income yield} = \frac{\$0.40}{\$11.50} \times 100\% = 3.478\%$$

The rest of the 15% rate of total return must come from capital gain. That is,

$$\text{Capital gain yield} = 15\% - 3.478\% = 11.522\%$$

Hence,

$$\text{Capital gain} = 0.11522 \times V_i = 0.11522 \times \$11.50 = \$1.33 \text{ per share}$$

and

$$V_f = V_i + \text{Capital gain} = \$11.50 + \$1.33 = \$12.83$$

The share price must be at least $12.83 one year from now for the investor to achieve the minimum desired rate of total return (15%).

POINT OF INTEREST

False Profits and Bull Marketing

The following tale reveals how little scrutiny is given to claims of investment performance. It also exposes our tendency to suspend critical analysis in the face of a good story.

In 1994 Hyperion published *The Beardstown Ladies' Common-Sense Investment Guide.* The book describes the homespun stock-picking methods of an investment club of sixteen women living in Beardstown, Illinois (population 6000). We are told they range in age from 41 to 87. According to the book's introduction, "their hand-picked portfolio of fewer than 20 stocks earned an average annual return of 23.4%" over the preceding 10 years (1984–1993). This return was almost twice the rate of return earned by the benchmark Standard & Poor's 500 (S&P 500) portfolio, and more than twice the average annual return achieved

by professional mutual fund managers! Naturally the story found great appeal among the general public — here was a group of savvy septuagenarians emerging from the Illinois cornfields to trounce Wall Street's overpaid MBAs. (The book also contained the ladies' favourite recipes, such as Ann's Kentucky Cream Cake and Helen's Springtime Pie.)

The Beardstown Ladies became celebrities almost overnight. The book was at the top of the *New York Times* bestseller list for three months and eventually sold over 800,000 copies in seven languages. The Beardstown Ladies were the subject of articles in scores of publications and appeared as guests on several television talk shows. Four more books followed in rapid succession. Along the way, the geriatric gurus produced their own home video titled *Cookin' up Profits on Wall Street.* After reviewing the video, the late great movie critic Gene Siskel wrote what proved to be a prescient one-liner: "Wait till you see what these ladies are up to!"

In early 1998, Shane Tristch, a managing editor at *Chicago Magazine,* started to write yet another warm fuzzy story about the lovable ladies from Beardstown. However, he was troubled by the following disclaimer which appeared in the front material of the Beardstown Ladies' first book.

> *"Investment clubs commonly compute their annual 'return' by calculating the increase in their total club balance over a period of time. Since this increase includes the dues that the members pay regularly, this 'return' may be different from the return that might be calculated for a mutual fund or a bank. Since the regular contributions are an important part of the club philosophy, the Ladies' returns described in this book are based on this common calculation."*

The "dues" refer to regular contributions of new money that most investment clubs require from each member. In the case of the Beardstown Ladies, each member contributed $25 per month right from the start in 1984. Anyone with a basic knowledge of investing should have an "Excuse me?" moment upon reading the disclaimer. It is preposterous to treat new injections of investment capital as part of the total return from a portfolio! Frankly, it is highly doubtful that this method of calculating returns is "commonly" used by investment clubs.

Tristch wrote an article for the March 1998 issue of *Chicago Magazine* exposing the flaw and challenging the claim of a 23.4% average annual return. The Beardstown Ladies allowed the international accounting firm Price Waterhouse to audit their records. Instead of the 23.4% average annual return, Price Waterhouse determined that the average annual rate of return was a modest 9.1%. This was far short of the publicized 23.4% return and well short of the 14.9% annual return on the unmanaged S&P 500 portfolio. The Beardstown Ladies and their publisher had built an empire based on a profoundly flawed calculation that went unchallenged by over 800,000 readers for four years!

LO5 **Compounding Rates of Return** Suppose you read that a stock's price rose by 10% in Year 1 and 20% in Year 2. Does this mean that the overall price increase for the two-year period was 10% + 20% = 30%? No—the understanding is that, in Year 2, the price rose 20% from its value at the *end* of Year 1. In other words, the understanding is that you should *compound* the returns given for successive periods. This corresponds to what you did in Section 8.4 with the interest rates earned in successive periods by GICs and Canada Savings Bonds. (For these investments, the interest rate equals the rate of *total* return each year because GICs and CSBs do not experience capital gains or losses.) We can use

$$FV = PV(1 + i_1)(1 + i_2)(1 + i_3)...(1 + i_n) \qquad \text{(8-4)}$$

for compounding rates of total return. Simply view $i_1, i_2, i_3, ..., i_n$ as the rates of total return in each of the n successive periods.

EXAMPLE 9.5C   **COMPOUNDING RATES OF TOTAL RETURN ON AN INVESTMENT**

The China Fund is a mutual fund that can be purchased on the New York Stock Exchange (trading symbol CHN). As its name suggests, the fund invests in the stocks of companies in China. The investment research firm Morningstar Inc. reports that the rates of total return provided by the fund for individual years 2004 to 2008 were −9.3%, −21.6%, 66.5%, 49.3%, and −40.7%, respectively. (As these rates of return indicate, Chinese stocks are notoriously volatile.)

a. If you had invested $1000 in the fund at the beginning of 2004, what was your investment worth at the end of 2008?

b. What would have been the dollar amount of your total return in 2006?

SOLUTION

a. We can directly substitute the given values into formula (8-4).

$$FV = PV(1 + i_1)(1 + i_2)(1 + i_3)(1 + i_4)(1 + i_5)$$
$$= \$1000[1 + (-0.093)][1 + (-0.216)](1 + 0.665)(1 + 0.493)[1 + (-0.407)]$$
$$= \$1000(0.907)(0.784)(1.665)(1.493)(0.593)$$
$$= \$1048.22$$

b. In 2006 the rate of total return was 66.5%. The dollar amount of the total return was

$$0.665 \times (\text{Value of the investment at the end of 2005})$$
$$= 0.665 \times \$1000(0.907)(0.784)$$
$$= \$472.87$$

The total return in 2006 was $472.87.

EXAMPLE 9.5D   COMPARING THE PERFORMANCE OF A MUTUAL FUND TO A BENCHMARK

The following table presents the rates of total return on the Phillips Hager & North (PH&N) Dividend Income mutual fund for each year from 2004 to 2008 inclusive. Corresponding figures are also given for the Toronto Stock Exchange's S&P/TSX Composite Total Return Index. (This Index measures the performance of a portfolio of the common shares of over 200 of the largest Canadian companies trading on the Toronto Stock Exchange. The index is often used as the benchmark for evaluating the performance of other portfolios of Canadian stocks.)

What is the difference between the overall rate of total return on the mutual fund and on the benchmark portfolio represented by the S&P/TSX Index?

	Rate of total return (%)				
Fund name	2004	2005	2006	2007	2008
PH&N Dividend Income Fund (Series A)	14.5	13.6	16.5	−3.9	−32.5
S&P/TSX Composite Total Return Index	14.5	24.1	17.3	9.8	−33.0

SOLUTION

Suppose you invested an amount PV in the PH&N Dividend Income Fund at the beginning of 2004. By the end of 2008, the investment would have grown to

$$FV = PV(1 + i_1)(1 + i_2)(1 + i_3)(1 + i_4)(1 + i_5)$$
$$= PV(1 + 0.145)(1 + 0.136)(1 + 0.165)(1 - 0.039)(1 - 0.325)$$
$$= PV(0.983)$$

Since the final value is 0.983 times the initial value, the investment in the mutual fund declined by 1.7%

For the same initial investment in the portfolio represented by the S&P/TSX Composite Index,

$$FV = PV(1 + i_1)(1 + i_2)(1 + i_3)(1 + i_4)(1 + i_5)$$
$$= PV(1 + 0.145)(1 + 0.241)(1 + 0.173)(1 + 0.098)(1 - 0.330)$$
$$= PV(1.226)$$

This portfolio grew by 22.6%. Therefore, the PH&N Dividend Income Fund grew by

$$22.6\% - (-1.7\%) = 24.3\%$$

less than the unmanaged S&P/TSX Index portfolio.

> **EXAMPLE 9.5E**   **CALCULATING ONE OF A SERIES OF PERCENT CHANGES**
>
> Hanako invested in a stock that doubled in the first year and rose another 50% in the second year. Now at the end of the third year, Hanako is surprised to discover that the stock's price is up only 80% from her purchase price. By what percentage did the stock's price change in the third year?
>
> **SOLUTION**
>
> The stock's price is up 80% over the entire three-year period. Therefore,
>
> $$FV = 1.80PV$$
>
> In terms of the capital gain yield in individual years,
>
> $$\begin{aligned} FV &= PV(1 + i_1)(1 + i_2)(1 + i_3) \\ &= PV(1 + 1.00)(1 + 0.50)(1 + i_3) \\ &= PV(3.0)(1 + i_3) \end{aligned}$$
>
> For the same final value in both cases, we require
>
> $$\begin{aligned} PV(1.80) &= PV(3.0)(1 + i_3) \\ 1.80 &= 3.0(1 + i_3) \\ \frac{1.80}{3.0} &= 1 + i_3 \\ i_3 &= 0.60 - 1 = -0.40 = -40\% \end{aligned}$$
>
> The stock's price declined 40% in Year 3.

POINT OF INTEREST

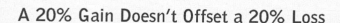

A 20% Gain Doesn't Offset a 20% Loss

Equal positive and negative rates of return in successive years have a curious lack of symmetry in their effects on the overall return from an investment. A 20% gain in Year 2 will not recoup a 20% loss in Year 1—you need a 25% gain to break even after a 20% loss!

Conversely, a 20% gain followed by a 20% loss also leaves you in a net loss position. A 20% loss will, in fact, erase an earlier 25% gain!

The *Globe and Mail's* Personal Finance writer Rob Carrick pointed out effects of this sort in an October 4, 2001 article titled *"In denial about your stocks? It's time to get real."* Quoting from the article:

> *"Lose half your money and you need a 100% rise (to recover your losses.) Lose 60% and you need a 150% gain. To get back to even, a stock down 80% would have to surge 400%. A stock down 90%—hello Nortel—would have to rise 900% to get back to where you bought it."*

QUESTION 1

Verify Rob Carrick's numbers. That is, show the calculation of the percent gains required to break even after losses of 50%, 60%, 80%, and 90%.

When a series of annual returns are given for an investment, you may be tempted to calculate the average of the annual returns to obtain a measure of the overall long-term performance of the investment. At best, this average is only an approximation of the investment's annual rate of growth. At worst, it can give a very misleading result. We can dramatically illustrate this point using the rather extreme example of a 100% gain followed by a 50% loss in successive years. The simple average of a 100% gain and a 50% loss is [100% + (−50%)] / 2 = 25% per year. But if a $1000 investment doubles to $2000 (a 100% gain) and then loses half its value (50% loss), the investment will be right back at its beginning value of $1000. The actual two-year gain was 0%!

The average (25%) of the individual rates of return for the two years is meaningless!

You must, therefore, be very cautious about drawing conclusions based on a simple average of a series of annual rates of return. It will always *overstate* the actual performance. The more volatile the year-to-year rates of return, the greater will be the degree of overstatement.

QUESTION 2

For the ten years 1997 to 2006 inclusive, the AIM Global Technology Fund had rates of return of 37.9%, 34.5%, 200.3%, −27.9%, −43.8%, −48.9%, 16.2%, −5.2%, −4.2%, and 7.4%, respectively.

a. What was the average annual rate of return for the ten years?

b. If a $1000 investment earned this average rate of return each and every year for ten years, what was its final value?

c. If $1000 was invested in the AIM Global Technology Fund at the beginning of 1997, what was the actual value of the investment at the end of 2006?

SPREADSHEET STRATEGIES — Calculating Investment Returns

Connect presents a partially completed template for calculating the income yield, capital gain yield, and rate of total return for each of several investments, given their initial value, final value, and income for the holding period. Go to the Student Edition of Connect and find "Investment Returns."

The main features of the completed template are presented below. The formulas programmed into cells E7, F7, G7, and H7 are displayed in Row 13. Data are entered for answering Example 9.5A. In this example, we are to determine the income yield, capital gain yield, and rate of total return in both 2008 and 2009 for TD Bank shares and the PH&N Canadian Equity Fund based on data provided in Tables 9.3 and 9.4. After entering the given information for each investment in the yellow input cells, the answers appear in the blue output cells.

	A	B	C	D	E	F	G	H
1								
2	Using a spreadsheet to calculate investment returns.							
3	Example 9.5A:							
4								
5		Initial	Final		Capital	Income	Capital	Rate of
6	Security	value, V_i	value, V_f	Income	gain	yield	gain yield	total return
7	TD Bank shares (2008)	$69.50	$43.45	$2.36	-$26.05	3.40%	-37.48%	-34.08%
8	TD Bank shares (2009)	$43.95	$65.96	$2.44	$22.01	5.62%	51.81%	57.43%
9	PH&N Cdn. Equity (2008)	$91.39	$57.42	$1.38	-$33.97	1.51%	-37.17%	-35.66%
10	PH&N Cdn. Equity (2009)	$57.42	$76.23	$1.20	$18.81	2.09%	32.76%	34.85%
11								
12								
13				Formulas in Row 7:	=C7-B7	=D7/B7	=E7/B7	=F7+G7
14								

CONCEPT QUESTIONS

1. What is meant by a "capital loss?"

2. What is meant by the "total return" from an investment?

3. Can the income yield from an investment be negative? Explain or give an example.

4. Is it possible for the capital gain yield to exceed 100%? Explain or give an example.

5. Is it possible for a capital loss to be worse than −100%? Explain or give an example.

6. Does the combined effect of a 20% increase followed by a 20% decrease differ from the combined effect of a 20% decrease followed by a 20% increase? Justify your answer.

7. How much will an investment of $100 be worth after 20 years if it increases in value by 25% in each of 10 years, but declines by 20% in each of the other 10 years?

8. If a series of compound percent changes are all positive, is the overall percent increase larger or smaller than the sum of the individual percent changes? Justify your answer.

9. If a series of compound percent changes are all negative, is the overall percent decrease larger or smaller (in magnitude) than the sum of the individual percent changes? Justify your answer.

EXERCISE 9.5

connect

Spreadsheet templates: The "Investment Returns" template provided in Connect may be used in Problems 1–14. The "Formula (8-4) Calculator" template in Connect is helpful in answering Problems 17 and 30-33.

Answers to the odd-numbered problems are at the end of the book.

Determine yields and rates of return to the nearest 0.01%. Calculate dollar amounts accurate to the cent.

1. A $100 investment purchased one year ago is now worth $110. It also earned $10 of income during the year. Determine the investment's:

   a. Income yield. **b.** Capital gain yield. **c.** Rate of total return.

2. A $100 investment purchased one year ago is now worth $90. It also generated $10 of income during the year. Determine the investment's:

   a. Income yield. **b.** Capital gain yield. **c.** Rate of total return.

3. Shares purchased one year ago for $8790 are now worth $15,390. During the year, the shares paid dividends totalling $280. Calculate the shares':

   a. Income yield. **b.** Capital gain yield. **c.** Rate of total return.

4. One year ago, $13,000 was invested in units of a mutual fund. The units paid a distribution of $260 during the year, but the mutual fund units are now worth only $11,400. What has been the:

   a. Income yield? **b.** Capital gain yield? **c.** Rate of total return?

5. Calculate the income yield, capital gain yield, and rate of total return in each of 2008 and 2009 for Potash Corporation's shares and Mawer New Canada Fund units. Use the data in Tables 9.3 and 9.4.

6. Calculate the income yield, capital gain yield, and rate of total return in each of 2008 and 2009 for Cameco Corporation shares and Sprott Canadian Equity Fund units. Use the data in Tables 9.3 and 9.4.

7. Calculate the income yield, capital gain yield, and rate of total return in each of 2008 and 2009 for Research in Motion shares and PH&N Bond Fund units. Use the data in Tables 9.3 and 9.4.

8. One year ago, Art Vandelay bought Norwood Industries shares for $37 per share. Today they are worth $40 per share. During the year, Art received dividends of $0.60 per share. What was his income yield, capital gain yield, and rate of total return for the year?

9. Rose purchased units of the Trimark Fund one year ago at $24.10 per unit. Today they are valued at $25.50. On the intervening December 31, there was a distribution of $0.83 per unit. ("Distribution" is the term used by most mutual funds for income paid to unitholders.) Calculate Rose's income yield, capital gain yield, and rate of total return for the year.

10. The market value of Stephanie's bonds has declined from $1053.25 to $1021.75 per bond during the past year. In the meantime she has received two semiannual interest payments of $35 per bond. Calculate Stephanie's income yield, capital gain yield, and rate of total return for the year.

11. Vitaly's shares of Dominion Petroleum have dropped in value from $36.75 to $32.25 during the past year. The shares paid a $0.50 per share dividend six months ago. Calculate Vitaly's income yield, capital gain yield, and rate of total return for the year.

12. Jeff purchased some Mitel preferred shares on the Toronto Stock Exchange for $13.50. The shares pay a quarterly dividend of $0.50. Twelve months later the shares were trading at $15.25. What was Jeff's rate of total return for the year?

∘13. Assume that the TD Bank shares in Table 9.3 will pay a $2.54 per share dividend in 2010. What must the share price be at the end of 2010 for a total rate of return in 2010 of 10%?

∘14. Assume that the Potash Corporation shares in Table 9.3 will pay a $0.48 per share dividend in 2010. What must the share price be at the end of 2010 for a total rate of return in 2010 of 7%?

∘15. One year ago, Morgan invested $5000 to purchase 400 units of a mutual fund. He has just noted in the *Financial Post* that the fund's rate of return on investment for the year was 22% and that the current price of a unit is $13.75. What amount did the fund distribute as income per unit during the year?

•16. The *Globe and Mail* Report on Business noted that shares of Compact Computers produced a 55% rate of total return in the past year. The shares paid a dividend of $0.72 per share during the year, and they currently trade at $37.50. What was the price of the shares one year ago?

17. Adjusted for stock splits, the price of Microsoft shares rose 88.3%, 56.4%, 114.6%, and 68.4% in the years 1996 to 1999 respectively. In 2000, the share prices fell 62.8%.
    a. What was the overall five-year percent change in the price of Microsoft shares?
    b. If the share price at the end of 2000 was $43.38, what was the price at the beginning of 1996?

18. The federal government cut transfer payments to the provinces by a total of 20% over a five-year period. In the next budget speech, the Minister of Finance announced "the level of transfer payments will be restored to their former level by a 20% increase to be phased in over the next two years." Is this an accurate statement? Explain briefly.

19. The price of Bionex Inc. shares rose by 25% in each of two successive years. If they began the two-year period at $12 per share, what was the percent increase in price over the entire two years?

20. The price of Biomed Corp. shares also began the same two-year period (as in Problem 19) at $12, but fell 25% in each year. What was their overall percent decline in price?

21. What rate of return in the second year of an investment will wipe out a 50% gain in the first year?

22. What rate of return in the second year of an investment will nullify a 25% return on investment in the first year?

23. What rate of return in the second year of an investment is required to break even after a 50% loss in the first year?

24. What rate of return in the second year of an investment is required to break even after a rate of return of −20% in the first year?

25. After two consecutive years of 10% rates of return, what rate of return in the third year will produce a cumulative gain of 30%?

26. After two consecutive years of 10% losses, what rate of return in the third year will produce a cumulative loss of 30%?

○27. Victor cannot find the original record of his purchase four years ago of units of the Imperial Global Fund. The current statement from the fund shows that the total current value of the units is $47,567. From a mutual fund database, Victor found that the fund's rates of return for Years 1 to 4 have been 15.4%, 24.3%, 32.1%, and −3.3%, respectively.

    a What was Victor's original investment in the fund?

    b. What was the dollar increase in the value of his investment in Year 3?

○28. The S&P/TSX Composite Index rose 3.4%, dropped 1.4%, and then rose 2.1% in three successive months. The Index ended the three-month period at 9539.

    a. What was the Index at the beginning of the three-month period?

    b. How many points did the Index drop in the second month?

○29. In three successive years the price of the common shares of Abysmal Resources Ltd. fell 35%, 55%, and 80%, ending the third year at 75 cents.

    a. What was the share price at the beginning of the three-year skid?

    b. How much (in dollars and cents) did the share price drop in the third year?

30. The following table shows the rates of total return in successive years from 2004 to 2008 for the AGF Canadian Stock Fund and for the benchmark Toronto Stock Exchange S&P/TSX Composite Index. By how much did the mutual fund's overall percentage return exceed or fall short of the Index's growth?

Fund name	Rate of total return (%)				
	2004	2005	2006	2007	2008
AGF Canadian Stock Fund	12.2	20.3	18.6	5.2	−31.0
S&P/TSX Composite Total Return Index	14.5	24.1	17.3	9.8	−33.0

31. The following table shows the rates of total return in successive years from 2004 to 2008 for the Ethical Growth Fund and for the benchmark Toronto Stock Exchange S&P/TSX Composite Index. By how much did the mutual fund's overall percentage return exceed or fall short of the Index's growth?

Fund name	Rate of total return (%)				
	2004	2005	2006	2007	2008
Ethical Growth Fund	8.2	15.7	19.6	2.4	−31.2
S&P/TSX Composite Total Return Index	14.5	24.1	17.3	9.8	−33.0

32. The following table shows the rates of total return in successive years from 2004 to 2008 for the Sceptre Canadian Equity Fund and for the benchmark Toronto Stock Exchange S&P/TSX Composite Index. By how much did the mutual fund's overall percentage return exceed or fall short of the Index's growth?

Fund name	Rate of total return (%)				
	2004	2005	2006	2007	2008
Sceptre Canadian Equity Fund	16.2	21.5	29.8	10.5	−36.0
S&P/TSX Composite Total Return Index	14.5	24.1	17.3	9.8	−33.0

33. The following table shows the rates of total return in successive years from 2004 to 2008 for the Sprott Canadian Equity Fund and for the benchmark Toronto Stock Exchange S&P/TSX Composite Index. By how much did the mutual fund's overall percentage return exceed or fall short of the Index's growth?

Fund name	Rate of total return (%)				
	2004	2005	2006	2007	2008
Sprott Canadian Equity Fund	37.9	13.2	39.6	13.8	−43.7
S&P/TSX Composite Total Return Index	14.5	24.1	17.3	9.8	−33.0

KEY TERMS

Capital gain **p. 358**	Equivalent interest rate **p. 355**	Rate of total return **p. 359**
Capital gain yield **p. 359**	Holding period **p. 358**	Rule of 72 **p. 340**
Capital loss **p. 358**	Income **p. 358**	Total return **p. 358**
Effective interest rate **p. 346**	Income yield **p. 359**	

SUMMARY OF NOTATION AND KEY FORMULAS

f = Effective rate of interest

FORMULA (9-1) $i = \sqrt[n]{\dfrac{FV}{PV}} - 1 = \left(\dfrac{FV}{PV}\right)^{1/n} - 1$ Finding the periodic interest rate (or periodic rate of return)

FORMULA (9-2) $n = \dfrac{\ln\left(\dfrac{FV}{PV}\right)}{\ln(1+i)}$ Finding the number of compounding periods

FORMULA (9-3) $f = (1+i)^m - 1$ Finding the effective rate of interest (or effective rate of return)

FORMULA (9-4) $i_2 = (1+i_1)^{m_1/m_2} - 1$ Finding an equivalent periodic interest rate

FORMULA (9-5)
$$\text{Income yield} = \frac{Income}{V_i} \times 100\%$$
$$\text{Capital gain yield} = \frac{Capital\ gain}{V_i} \times 100\% = \frac{V_f - V_i}{V_i} \times 100\%$$
$$\text{Rate of total return} = \text{Income yield} + \text{Capital gain yield}$$
$$= \frac{Income + Capital\ gain}{V_i} \times 100\%$$
Finding investment yields and rate of total return

REVIEW PROBLEMS

Answers to the odd-numbered review problems are at the end of the book.

Calculate percentages accurate to the nearest 0.01%.

1. **(LO1)** The home the Bensons purchased 13 years ago for $85,000 is now appraised at $215,000. What has been the annual rate of appreciation of the value of their home during the 13-year period?

2. **(LO1)** If the Consumer Price Index rose from 109.6 to 133.8 over an $8\frac{1}{2}$-year period, what was the equivalent compound annual inflation rate during the period?

3. **(LO2)** Which of the following rates would you prefer for a loan: 7.6% compounded quarterly, 7.5% compounded monthly, or 7.7% compounded semiannually?

4. **(LO1)** A $10,000 investment grew to $12,000 after 39 months of semiannual compounding. What effective rate of return did the investment earn?

5. **(LO5)** One thousand shares of Frontier Mining were purchased at $6.50 per share. The share price rose 110% in the first year after purchase, declined 55% in the second year, and then dropped another 55% in the third year.

    a. What was the percent change in share price over the entire three years?

    b. How much (in dollars and cents) did the share price drop in the second year?

6. **(LO1)** Maxine found an old pay statement from nine years ago. Her hourly wage at the time was $13.50 versus her current wage of $20.80 per hour. At what equivalent (compound) annual rate has her wage grown over the period?

7. **(LO1)** If a company's annual sales grew from $165,000 to $485,000 in a period of eight years, what has been the compound annual rate of growth of sales during the period?

8. **(LO3)** What monthly compounded nominal rate would put you in the same financial position as 5.5% compounded semiannually?

9. **(LO3)** You are offered a loan at a rate of 10.5% compounded monthly. Below what figure must a semiannually compounded nominal rate be to make it more attractive?

10. **(LO3)** A bank offers a rate of 5.3% compounded semiannually on its four-year GICs. What monthly and annually compounded rates should it quote in order to have the same effective interest rate at all three nominal rates?

11. **(LO2)** If an invoice indicates that interest at the rate of 1.2% per month will be charged on overdue amounts, what effective rate of interest will be charged?

12. **(LO2)** If the nominal rate of interest paid on a savings account is 3% compounded monthly, what is the effective rate of interest paid?

13. **(LO2)** If an interest rate of 6.9% compounded semiannually is charged on a car loan, what effective rate of interest should be disclosed to the borrower?

14. **(LO4)** One year ago, Christos bought 1000 units of the Dominion Aggressive Growth Fund at $20.35 per unit. Today a unit's value is $19.10. During the year, the fund made a distribution of $0.40 per unit. On this investment, what is Christos's:

    a. Income yield?

    b. Capital gain yield?

    c. Total return in dollars?

    d. Rate of total return?

15. **(LO5)** A company's annual report states that its common shares had price gains of 23%, 10%, −15%, and 5% during the preceding four fiscal years. The share price stood at $30.50 after last year's 5% gain.

    a. What was the price of the shares at the beginning of the four-year period?

    b. How much (in dollars and cents) did the share price decline in the third year?

16. **(LO1)** If a $15,000 investment grew to $21,805 in $4\frac{1}{2}$ years of quarterly compounding, what effective rate of return was the investment earning?

17. **(LO2)** Camille can obtain a residential mortgage loan from a bank at 8.75% compounded semiannually or from an independent mortgage broker at 8.6% compounded monthly. Which source should she pick if other terms and conditions of the loan are the same? Present calculations that support your answer.

18. **(LO3)** A trust company pays 5.375% compounded annually on its five-year GICs. What semiannually compounded interest rate would produce the same maturity value?

19. **(LO5)** One of the more volatile mutual funds in recent years has been the AGF China Focus Fund. The fund's annual returns in successive years from 2003 to 2008 inclusive were 63.4%, −9.3%, 8.6%, 67.6%, 30.5%, and −41.7%, respectively. What was the fund's equivalent compound annual return for the six years ended December 31, 2008?

20. **(LO1)** To the nearest month, how long will it take an investment to increase in value by 200% if it earns 7.5% compounded semiannually?

∘21. **(LO1)** Rounded to the nearest month, how long will it take money to lose one-third of its purchasing power if the annual inflation rate is 3%?

∘22. **(LO1)** An investor paid $4271.17 to purchase a $10,000 face value strip bond for her RRSP. At this price the investment will provide a return of 6.47% compounded semiannually. How long (to the nearest day) after the date of purchase will the bond mature? Assume that each half-year is exactly 182 days long.

∘23. **(LO1)** An investor's portfolio increased in value by 53% over a five-year period while the Consumer Price Index rose from 121.6 to 135.3. What was the annually compounded real rate of return on the portfolio for the five years?

∘24. **(LO5)** A portfolio earned −13%, 18%, 5%, 24%, and −5% in five successive years. What was the portfolio's five-year compound annual return?

∘25. **(LO5)** The Fidelity Latin America Sr B fund (managed by Fidelity Investments Canada) was one of the top-performing mutual funds for the five years ending December 31, 2008. As of December 31, 2008, what three-year and five-year compound annual returns did the fund report if its annual returns in successive years from 2004 to 2008 inclusive were 28.8%, 48.7%, 44.2%, 18.2%, and −41.8%, respectively?

∘26. **(LO1)** Terry was supposed to pay $800 to Becky on March 1. At a later date, Terry paid Becky an equivalent payment in the amount of $895.67. If they provided for a time value of money of 8% compounded monthly, on what date did Terry make the payment?

27. **(LO1)** What is the time remaining until the maturity date of a $50,000 strip bond if it has just been purchased for $20,822.89 to yield 5.38% compounded semiannually until maturity?

∘28. **(LO1)** When discounted to yield 9.5% compounded quarterly, a $4500 four-year promissory note bearing interest at 11.5% compounded semiannually was priced at $5697.84. How long after the issue date did the discounting take place?

∘29. **(LO1)** The population of a mining town declined from 17,500 to 14,500 in a five-year period. If the population continues to decrease at the same compound annual rate, how long, to the nearest month, will it take for the population to drop by another 3000?

∘30. **(LO1)** To the nearest day, how long will it take a $20,000 investment to grow to $22,000 (including accrued interest) if it earns 7% compounded quarterly? Assume that a quarter year has 91 days.

∘31. **(LO1)** A company's sales dropped 10% per year for five years.

   a. What annual rate of sales growth for the subsequent five years would return the sales to the original level?

   b. To the nearest month, how long would it take for sales to return to the original level if they increased at 10% per year?

∘32. **(LO1)** An investor's portfolio increased in value from $35,645 to $54,230 over a six-year period. At the same time, the Consumer Price Index rose by 26.5%. What was the portfolio's annually compounded real rate of return?

∘33. **(LO4)** Gabriel received $200 of income from an investment during the past year. This represents an income yield of 4%. If the capital gain yield for the year was 10%, what was the value of the investment (not including income) at the end of the year?

∘34. **(LO4)** An $8600 investment was worth only $7900 one year later. If the rate of total return for the year was −5%, how much income was received from the investment during the year?

CASE Mountains of Money

One of the oldest mutual funds in Canada is the Templeton Growth Fund Ltd. Shares in the fund were first sold at the end of November 1954. A common graphic for dramatically illustrating the long-term performance of a mutual fund is known as a "mountain chart." The vertical scale of the chart is a logarithmic scale. On a logarithmic scale, each doubling of the investment produces the same interval on the vertical scale. An investment that grows by the same percentage every year will plot as an upward sloping straight line on this type of chart.

The time axis covers 54 years and 9 months (from November 29, 1954, to August 31, 2009). The chart indicates that an investment of $10,000 on November 29, 1954, was worth $4,999,179 on August 31, 2009. (This outcome assumes that all dividends paid on shares of the fund were reinvested in additional shares.)

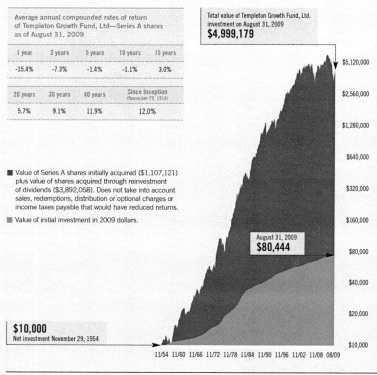

Average annual compounded rates of return of Templeton Growth Fund, Ltd—Series A shares as of August 31, 2009

1 year	3 years	5 years	10 years	15 years
-15.4%	-7.3%	-1.4%	-1.1%	3.0%

20 years	30 years	40 years	Since Inception (November 29, 1954)
5.7%	9.1%	11.9%	12.0%

Total value of Templeton Growth Fund, Ltd. investment on August 31, 2009
$4,999,179

■ Value of Series A shares initially acquired ($1,107,121) plus value of shares acquired through reinvestment of dividends ($3,892,058). Does not take into account sales, redemptions, distribution or optional charges or income taxes payable that would have reduced returns.

▓ Value of initial investment in 2009 dollars.

August 31, 2009
$80,444

$10,000
Net investment November 29, 1954

11/54 11/60 11/66 11/72 11/78 11/84 11/90 11/96 11/02 11/08 08/09

SOURCE: Reproduced with permission of Franklin Templeton Investments.

Based on increases in the Consumer Price Index, the chart also indicates that you needed $80,444 in August of 2009 to have the same purchasing power as $10,000 in November of 1954.

QUESTIONS

1. Calculate the fund's equivalent compound annual rate of return over the entire $54\frac{9}{12}$ years.
2. What was the equivalent compound annual rate of inflation during the entire period?
3. What was the fund's *real* compound annual rate of return over the entire period?
4. From the chart, we can estimate that the original $10,000 investment was worth about $400,000 in November of 1984. Compare the fund's performance before this date to its performance after this date. That is, compare the fund's compound annual rates of return before and after November 30, 1984.

APPENDIX 9A

THE TEXAS INSTRUMENTS BA II PLUS INTEREST CONVERSION WORKSHEET

Notice the letters **ICONV** above the [2] key. This means that the Interest Conversion Worksheet is the second function of the [2] key. You can access the worksheet by pressing [2nd] [2] in sequence. Hereafter, we will represent these keystrokes as [2nd] [ICONV]. The calculator's display then shows:

$NOM =$	n.nn

where the n's represent numerical digits. (Your display may show more or fewer digits.)

You should think of a worksheet as a single column of items that you can view one-at-a-time in the display. The Interest Conversion Worksheet's column consists of the following three items:

$NOM =$	n.nn
$EFF =$	n.nn
$C/Y =$	n

The solid line around the first item indicates that the calculator's display currently provides a "window" to the first item in the column. You can use the scroll keys [↓] and [↑] to move down or up the list. The three worksheet symbols are defined as follows:

$NOM =$ Nominal annual interest rate, j
$EFF =$ Effective interest rate, f
$C/Y =$ Number of compoundings per year, m

The Interest Conversion Worksheet allows you to enter values for any two of these three variables and then compute the value of the remaining third variable. Close the worksheet by pressing [2nd] [QUIT]. (By the [QUIT] key, we mean the key showing **QUIT** as its second function.)

Let us use the worksheet to answer Example 9.3A which asks us to calculate the effective interest rate corresponding to 10.5% compounded monthly.

[2nd] [ICONV]	⇒ Open the Interest Conversion Worksheet.
10.5 [ENTER]	⇒ Key in and save the value for *NOM*.
[↓] [↓] 12 [ENTER]	⇒ Scroll down to *C/Y*. Key in and save its value.
[↑] [CPT]	⇒ Scroll back up to *EFF*. Compute its value.

The effective interest rate appearing in the display is 11.02%.

CHAPTER 10

Ordinary Annuities:
Future Value and Present Value

CHAPTER OUTLINE

LEARNING OBJECTIVES

After completing this chapter, you will be able to:

LO1 Define and distinguish between ordinary simple annuities and ordinary general annuities

LO2 Calculate the future value and present value of both ordinary simple annuities and ordinary general annuities

LO3 Calculate the fair market value of a cash flow stream that includes an annuity

LO4 Calculate the principal balance owed on a loan immediately after any payment

LO5 Calculate the present value and period of deferral of a deferred annuity

LO6 Calculate the interest rate per payment interval in a general annuity

A LARGE NUMBER OF PERSONAL and business transactions involve an annuity—a series of equal regular payments. Examples are loan payments, wages, pensions, rent, instalment savings plans, insurance premiums, mortgage payments, leases, bond interest, and preferred share dividends.

Many circumstances require the calculation of the future value or the present value of an annuity. For example, how much (future value) will you accumulate after 20 years if you invest $100 per month? What is the balance (present value) you owe on a loan that has 23 remaining monthly payments of $227?

In this chapter, you will learn the language of annuities and how to answer these questions. This chapter is also the foundation we will build upon throughout Chapters 11 to 15. If you master the content of Chapter 10, you will be in an excellent position to comfortably handle the later chapters.

10.1 TERMINOLOGY

An **annuity** is a series of equal payments at regular intervals. We will use the symbols

$$PMT = \text{Periodic payment in an annuity}$$
$$n = \text{Number of payments in the annuity}$$

In Figure 10.1, the n payments are shown on a time line. The time between successive payments is called the **payment interval**. Chapters 10 and 11 are concerned with **ordinary annuities** in which payments are made at the *end* of each payment interval.[1] The total time from the *beginning* of the first payment interval to the *end* of the last payment interval is the **term of the annuity**. To illustrate the use of these new terms, imagine you have obtained a personal loan to be repaid by 48 equal monthly payments. The *payment interval* is one month and the *term of the annuity* is 48 months, or four years. The first payment will be due one month after you receive the loan—that is, at the *end* of the first payment interval. Therefore, the payments form an *ordinary annuity*.

FIGURE 10.1   Time Diagram for an *n*-Payment Ordinary Annuity

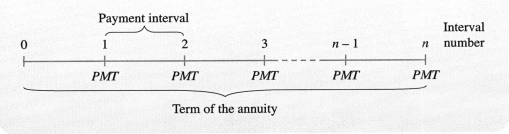

---

[1] Chapter 12 will cover **annuities due** in which payments are made at the *beginning* of each payment interval.

> ## TRAP   "Where Do We Begin?"
>
> Don't confuse the *beginning of an annuity* with the "beginning of payments" or with the "date of the first payment." The "beginning of an annuity" means the "beginning of the annuity's term" or the "beginning of the first payment interval." The beginning of an annuity occurs one payment interval *before* the first payment in an *ordinary annuity*.
>
> Similarly, the *end of an annuity* refers to the "end of the annuity's term" or the "end of the last payment interval." It does coincide with the last payment in an ordinary annuity.

Let's use an example to illustrate how we attach specific dates to the start and end points of individual payment intervals. Suppose an ordinary annuity with monthly payments begins at 11:00 A.M. on November 1. The first payment interval ends one month later. Therefore, it ends at 11:00 A.M. on December 1, and the first payment is due at that point. The second payment interval begins at the same moment. Although both the end of the first payment interval and the beginning of the second interval fall on December 1, we do not end up "double-counting" that day in the payment *intervals*. The first interval is from 11:00 A.M. November 1 to 11:00 A.M. December 1. The second interval is from 11:00 A.M. December 1 to 11:00 A.M. January 1, and so on. In the financial world, calculations of annuity payments and payments on *term* loans assume that all months have the same length.

The following diagram presents the defining characteristics for two types of ordinary annuities. For example, if the interest rate on a monthly-payment loan is compounded monthly, then the payment interval (one month) equals the compounding interval (one month). Therefore, the payments form an ordinary simple annuity. But if the interest rate is compounded semiannually or compounded annually, the payments constitute an ordinary general annuity. In Sections 10.2, 10.3, and 10.4, we shall be concerned with ordinary simple annuities. Then, in Section 10.5, we shall learn the extra step needed to handle ordinary general annuities.

Ordinary Annuities

Ordinary Simple Annuities:
The payment interval equals
the compounding interval.

Ordinary General Annuities:
The payment interval differs
from the compounding interval.

 ## CONCEPT QUESTIONS

1. What distinguishes an ordinary simple annuity from an ordinary general annuity?

2. What is meant by the "term" of an annuity?

3. If you pay automobile insurance premiums by monthly pre-authorized chequing, do the payments form an ordinary annuity?

4. If an ordinary annuity with quarterly payments and a $5\frac{1}{2}$-year term began June 1, 2005, what are the dates of the first and last payments?

10.2 FUTURE VALUE OF AN ORDINARY SIMPLE ANNUITY

LO2   The **future value of an annuity** is the sum of the future values of all the payments (evaluated at the end of the last payment interval). We introduce the techniques for calculating an annuity's future value by considering a specific case.

FUTURE VALUE USING THE ALGEBRAIC METHOD

Figure 10.2 is a time diagram showing the investment of $1000 at the *end* of every six months for two years. Suppose the invested money earns 8% compounded semiannually. Since we have semiannual payments and semiannual compounding, the four $1000 payments form an ordinary *simple* annuity. The only way we can calculate the annuity's future value at this stage is to use $FV = PV(1 + i)^n$ to calculate the future value of each payment, one at a time. Then, as indicated in the time diagram, we add these future values to obtain the future value of the annuity.

FIGURE 10.2   The Future Value of a Four-Payment Ordinary Simple Annuity

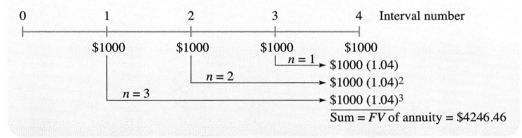

$$FV \text{ of annuity} = \$1000 + \$1000(1.04) + \$1000(1.04)^2 + \$1000(1.04)^3$$
$$= \$1000 + \$1040 + \$1081.60 + \$1124.86$$
$$= \$4246.46$$

The investments, including earnings, will amount to $4246.46 by the end of the annuity.

If an annuity consists of many payments, this "brute force" approach to the future value calculation can become very time-consuming and laborious. Fortunately, there is a relatively compact formula for the future value of an ordinary simple annuity.

FUTURE VALUE OF AN ORDINARY SIMPLE ANNUITY

$$FV = PMT\left[\frac{(1 + i)^n - 1}{i}\right] \tag{10-1}$$

Let us now use formula (10-1) to determine the future value of the annuity shown in Figure 10.2. We are given $PMT = \$1000$, $i = 4\% = 0.04$ per half year, and $n = 4$. Substituting these values into formula (10-1), we have

$$FV = \$1000\left[\frac{(1 + 0.04)^4 - 1}{0.04}\right] = \$1000\left(\frac{1.16985856 - 1}{0.04}\right) = \$4246.46$$

This is the same result obtained previously by the "brute force" approach. As the number of payments in an annuity increases, the time saved by employing formula (10-1) increases proportionately.

FUTURE VALUE USING THE FINANCIAL CALCULATOR FUNCTIONS

Save the known values for n, j (the nominal annual interest rate), and PMT in the N , I/Y , and PMT memories. Remember to use the cash-flow sign convention for the dollar amount entered in PMT . Except for the cases mentioned in the following "TIP," zero should be entered in the PV memory. Open the *P/Y* worksheet and enter the number of payments per year. Remember that the calculator then *automatically* assigns the same value to *C/Y*, the number of compoundings per year. (This automatic feature is a convenience with *simple* annuities where, by definition, $C/Y = P/Y$.) After quitting the *P/Y* worksheet, the keystrokes CPT FV instruct the calculator to compute the annuity's future value.

> **TIP**   **Use of the [PV] Memory with Annuities**
>
> If you do not have zero in the [PV] memory when you perform a future value calculation, the calculator interprets the amount in [PV] as an *additional single* cash flow occurring at the *beginning* of the annuity. At the [CPT] [FV] command, the calculator will compute the *combined* future value of the annuity and the amount in [PV]. This feature is useful in cases where, in a single calculation, we actually do want the combined future value of an annuity and a single beginning amount.

To calculate the future value of the annuity represented in Figure 10.2, the keystrokes are:

4 [N] 8 [I/Y] 0 [PV] 1000 [+/−] [PMT]

[2nd] [P/Y] 2 [ENTER] [2nd] [QUIT] [CPT] [FV]   *Answer:* 4246.46

In Example problems, we will present the keystroke sequence in a call-out box as shown at the right. For a reason that will become clear in Section 10.5, first we enter all of the information concerning the interest rate. To conserve space, we *represent* the actual keystroke sequence

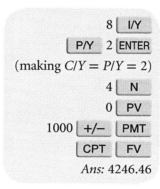

8 [I/Y]
[P/Y] 2 [ENTER]
(making *C/Y = P/Y = 2*)
4 [N]
0 [PV]
1000 [+/−] [PMT]
[CPT] [FV]
Ans: 4246.46

[2nd] [P/Y] 2 [ENTER] [2nd] [QUIT]

by the abbreviated sequence

[P/Y] 2 [ENTER]

You must supply the missing keystrokes.

CONTRIBUTION OF EACH PAYMENT TO AN ANNUITY'S FUTURE VALUE

When you use formula (10-1) or a calculator's financial functions to calculate an annuity's future value, the amount each payment contributes to the future value is not apparent. Figure 10.3 helps us see the pattern. Five $10 investments are represented by columns at one-year payment intervals along the time axis. Assuming the investments earn 10% compounded annually, each payment's contribution to the $61.05 future value is indicated at the right side of the diagram. It is no surprise that an early payment contributes more to future value than any subsequent payment. The interesting feature is that the difference between the contributions from successive payments does not stay the same. The first payment contributes $1.33 more than the second payment, the second payment contributes $1.21 more than the third payment, and so on. Putting it another way, each payment's contribution to future value increases in an *accelerating* manner as we look at earlier payments. This reinforces the point made in Chapter 8 concerning the advantages of starting a savings plan as early in life as possible. Consider the following remarkable illustration of the relative effect of earlier versus later payments. Suppose you construct Figure 10.3 to include 30 annual investments of $10.00. You would find that the first seven payments (in combination) contribute *more* to the future value than the remaining 23 payments (in combination)! Can you think of a way to verify this outcome?

FIGURE 10.3   Contribution of Each Payment to an Annuity's Future Value

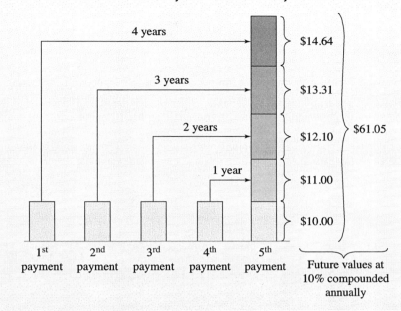

APPLICATIONS OF THE FUTURE VALUE OF AN ANNUITY

Most applications of the future-value calculation fall into two categories (with the first being much more common):

- Determining the total amount of principal plus interest that will be accumulated at the end of a series of equal regular investments.

- Determining the single payment at the end of an annuity that is economically equivalent to the annuity. The interest rate that should be used in this case is the rate of return that can be earned on a low-risk investment. (A suitable value is the rate of return currently available on Government of Canada bonds whose time remaining until maturity is similar to the term of the annuity.)

NET @ssets

An interactive Future Value Chart is available on the textbook's Web site. In Chapter 10 of the Student Edition, find the "Future Value Chart."

Any initial investment or accumulated amount should be entered in the box for "Starting amount." If you have a pure annuity problem, enter "0" in this box.

Enter the amount of each annuity payment in the "Annuity payments" box and select the payment frequency in the drop-down list on the right.

For terms up to 15 years, you will get a bar chart. The bar for each year represents the future value at the end of the year. If you move the cursor over a bar, the numerical amount of the future value will appear.

For terms exceeding 15 years, the chart presents the future value as a continuous curve. You can view a table listing the interest earned each year and the future value at the end of each year by clicking on the "View Report" button.

Try to get a "feel" for the influence of each variable by changing its value while leaving the other variables unchanged.

EXAMPLE 10.2A **THE FUTURE VALUE OF PERIODIC INVESTMENTS**

Heinz has been contributing $300 at the end of each month for the past 15 months to a savings plan that earns 6% compounded monthly. What amount will he have one year from now if he continues with the plan?

SOLUTION

The total amount will be the future value of $n = 15 + 12 = 27$ contributions of $PMT = \$300$ each. Payments and compounding both occur at one-month intervals. Therefore, the payments form an ordinary simple annuity having $i = \frac{6\%}{12} = 0.5\%$ per month.

$$
\begin{aligned}
FV &= PMT\left[\frac{(1+i)^n - 1}{i}\right] \\
&= \$300\left[\frac{(1.005)^{27} - 1}{0.005}\right] \\
&= \$300\left(\frac{1.14415185 - 1}{0.005}\right) \\
&= \$8649.11
\end{aligned}
$$

6 | I/Y

P/Y 12 ENTER

(making $C/Y = P/Y = 12$)

27 | N

0 | PV

300 | +/- | PMT

CPT | FV

Ans: 8649.11

One year from now, Heinz will have $8649.11 in the plan.

EXAMPLE 10.2B **CALCULATING THE FUTURE VALUE WHEN THE RATE OF RETURN CHANGES DURING THE TERM OF THE ANNUITY**

Calculate the future value of an ordinary annuity with payments of $600 every six months for 16 years. The rate of return will be 8% compounded semiannually for the first $5\frac{1}{2}$ years and 9% compounded semiannually for the subsequent $10\frac{1}{2}$ years.

SOLUTION

Because the compounding interval and the payment interval are both six months, we have an ordinary *simple* annuity with

$i = \frac{j}{m} = \frac{8\%}{2} = 4\%$ and $n = 2(5.5) = 11$ for the first $5\frac{1}{2}$ years, and

$i = \frac{9\%}{2} = 4.5\%$ and $n = 2(10.5) = 21$ for the subsequent $10\frac{1}{2}$ years.

Since the rate of return changes during the term of the annuity, we must consider the first $5\frac{1}{2}$ years separately from the subsequent $10\frac{1}{2}$ years. The algebraic solution has three steps, as indicated in the following time diagram.

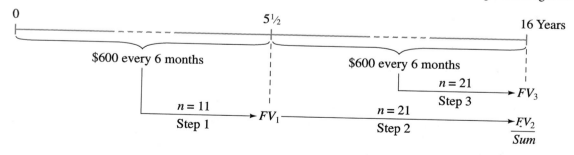

Step 1:   Calculate the future value, FV_1, of the first 11 payments.

$$FV_1 = PMT\left[\frac{(1 + i)^n - 1}{i}\right]$$

$$= \$600\left[\frac{(1.04)^{11} - 1}{0.04}\right]$$

$$= \$600\left[\frac{1.539454 - 1}{0.04}\right]$$

$$= \$8091.81$$

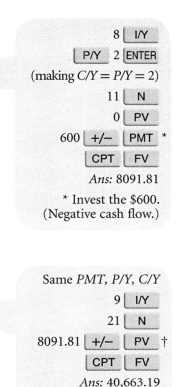

8   I/Y

P/Y   2 ENTER

(making $C/Y = P/Y = 2$)

11   N

0   PV

600   +/−   PMT *

CPT   FV

Ans: 8091.81

* Invest the $600.
(Negative cash flow.)

Step 2:   Determine the future value, FV_2, of $8091.81
after an *additional* $10\frac{1}{2}$ years.

$$FV_2 = PV(1 + i)^n$$

$$= \$8091.81(1.045)^{21}$$

$$= \$20,393.31$$

Step 3:   Calculate the future value, FV_3, of the last
21 annuity payments. Then add FV_2 and FV_3.

$$FV_3 = \$600\left[\frac{(1.045)^{21} - 1}{0.045}\right]$$

$$= \$600\left[\frac{2.5202412 - 1}{0.045}\right]$$

$$= \$20,269.88$$

$$FV_2 + FV_3 = \$40,663.19$$

Same *PMT, P/Y, C/Y*

9   I/Y

21   N

8091.81   +/−   PV †

CPT   FV

Ans: 40,663.19

† Re-invest the $8091.81.
(Negative cash flow.)

The future value of the annuity is $40,663.19.

EXAMPLE 10.2C   **CALCULATING THE FUTURE VALUE AFTER AN INTERRUPTION OF PAYMENTS**

Mr. Cloutier, just turned 43, has already accumulated $34,500 in his Registered Retirement Savings Plan. He makes monthly contributions of $300 to the plan and intends to do so until age 60. He plans to retire then and cease further contributions. The RRSP will be allowed to continue to accumulate earnings until he reaches age 65. If the RRSP earns 8% compounded monthly for the next 22 years, what amount will his RRSP contain when he reaches age 65?

SOLUTION

The amount in the RRSP will be the combined future value of the $34,500 already accumulated and future contributions. The number of additional $300 contributions that Mr. Cloutier will make to his RRSP is

$$n = m\,(\text{Years of contributions}) = 12(17) = 204$$

The periodic rate is $i = \frac{j}{m} = \frac{8\%}{12} = 0.\overline{6}\%$ per month. The time diagram below illustrates the three steps in the solution.

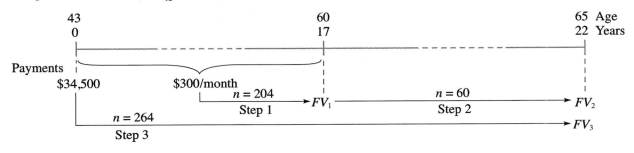

Step 1:   Calculate FV_1, the future value at age 60 of the $300 per month annuity.

$$FV_1 = PMT\left[\frac{(1+i)^n - 1}{i}\right]$$

$$= \$300\left[\frac{(1.00\overline{6})^{204} - 1}{0.00\overline{6}}\right]$$

$$= \$300\left[\frac{3.87864829 - 1}{0.00\overline{6}}\right]$$

$$= \$129,539.17$$

8	I/Y
P/Y	12 ENTER

(making $C/Y = P/Y = 12$)

204	N
0	PV
300 +/−	PMT
CPT	FV

Ans: 129,539.17

Step 2:   Calculate FV_2, the future value at age 65 of $129,539.17.

$$FV_2 = PV(1+i)^n$$
$$= \$129,539.17(1.00\overline{6})^{60}$$
$$= \$192,993.38$$

Same *I/Y, P/Y, C/Y*

60	N
129539.17 +/−	PV
0	PMT
CPT	FV

Ans: 192,993.38

Step 3:   Calculate FV_3, the future value at age 65 of the initial $34,500.

$$FV_3 = \$34,500(1.00\overline{6})^{264}$$
$$= \$199,361.27$$

Same *I/Y, P/Y, C/Y, PMT*

264	N
34500 +/−	PV
CPT	FV

Ans: 199,361.27

The total amount in the RRSP when Mr. Cloutier reaches age 65 will be

$$FV_2 + FV_3 = \$192,993.38 + \$199,361.27 = \$392,354.65$$

POINT OF INTEREST

Your Potential to Become a Millionaire!

One of the favourite themes of personal finance writers is to show you that, if you will only give up one or two of your wasteful habits and invest the money saved, you can become a millionaire. You can kick a filthy habit and become filthy rich! Attain better health and more wealth! Live longer and die richer!

Smoking is the primary target in these health-and-wealth scenarios. Suppose you give up a pack-a-day habit. At $10 per pack, that will save you about $30 \times \$10 = \$300$ per month.

QUESTIONS

1. If you invest the saving at the end of each month and earn 9% compounded monthly, how much (rounded to the nearest dollar) will you accumulate after:
   a. 20 years?   **b.** 30 years?   **c.** 40 years?

9% compounded monthly is a realistic long-run rate of return. It is close to historical long-term rates of return achieved by diversified stock portfolios and equity mutual funds. (See, for example, the chart for the Templeton Growth Fund in the Case at the end of Chapter 9.)

2. How much will your investment portfolio be worth after 40 years if it earns:
   a. 8% compounded monthly?
   b. 10% compounded monthly?

Note the large difference an extra 1% rate of return over a long time frame makes to the value of a portfolio. But will you *feel* like a millionaire in Question 1.c.? Note that we have ignored inflation.

3. If the rate of inflation averages 2.4% compounded monthly, how many dollars will you need 40 years from now to have the same purchasing power as $1,000,000 today?

We have also ignored the fact that the price of a pack of cigarettes will also rise in the future. Consequently, the amount you save each month will rise from time to time over the years. (In Chapter 13, we will show

you how to handle the case of a steadily growing payment.) These increases in the monthly saving rate will largely offset (or even more than offset) the effect of inflation on the purchasing power of your investment portfolio. Consequently, the answers in Question 1 can be viewed as reasonable estimates of the purchasing power in today's dollars of your portfolio.

If you are not a smoker, consider some other luxury you can forgo—a daily latte, two of the four beers you drink each weekend, lunches you buy (instead of getting out of bed five minutes earlier to pack a bag-lunch at half the cost), etc.

SPREADSHEET STRATEGIES Future Value of an Ordinary Simple Annuity

Connect provides a partially completed template for calculating the future value of an ordinary simple annuity. Go to the Student Edition of Connect and find "FV of Ord. Simple Annuity."

The Future Value template employs two methods—one based on the algebraic formula (10-1) and the other based on Excel's built-in Future Value (*FV*) function. The first page of the "FV of Ord. Simple Annuity" workbook discusses Excel's *FV* function.

The main features of a completed Future Value template are presented below. The formulas programmed into cells

C13 and C15 are displayed in cells C14 and C16, respectively. (After programming a spreadsheet that has broad application, you should save it in a directory to make it available for other applications.)

Data are entered to solve Example 10.2A. In this example, we are asked to determine the future value of $300 invested every month for 27 months if the investment earns 6% compounded monthly. After entering these known values in the yellow input cells, the computed future value immediately appears in the output cells C13 and C15.

	A	B	C	D
1				
2	Using a spreadsheet to calculate the future value of an ordinary simple annuity.			
3	Example 10.2A:			
4				
5		Nominal annual interest rate, *j*	6.000%	
6		Compoundings per year, *m*	12	
7		Periodic rate of interest, *i* or *rate*	0.5000%	
8		Number of payments, *n* or *nper*	27.00	
9		Regular annuity payment, *PMT* or *pmt*	-$300.00	
10		One-time initial payment, *pv*	$0.00	
11		Annuity *type*	0	
12				
13		Formula (10-1), *FV* (assumes *pv* = 0)	$8,649.11	
14		Formula in cell C13:	=-C9*((1+C7)^C8-1)/C7	
15		*FV(rate, nper, pmt, pv, type)*	$8,649.11	
16		Formula in cell C15:	=FV(C7,C8,C9,C10,C11)	

The accumulated amount will be $8649.11.

CONCEPT QUESTIONS

1. How would you determine how much of an annuity's future value is interest earned over the term of the annuity?

2. Annuity A has the same *n* and *i* as Annuity B. A's *PMT* is double B's *PMT*. Will A's future value be (pick one): (**i**) double, (**ii**) more than double, or (**iii**) less than double the amount of B's future value? Give the reason for your choice.

3. Annuity G has the same *i* and *PMT* as Annuity H. G has twice as many payments as H. Will G's future value be (pick one): (**i**) double, (**ii**) more than double, or (**iii**) less than double the amount of H's future value? Give the reason for your choice.

EXERCISE 10.2

▣ connect

Spreadsheet template: A partially completed Excel template for calculating the future value of an ordinary simple annuity is provided in Connect. You can use this template for many of the problems in Exercise 10.2. Go to the Student Edition of Connect and find "FV of Ord. Simple Annuity."

Answers to the odd-numbered problems are at the end of the book.

1. This problem demonstrates the dependence of an annuity's future value on the size of the periodic payment. Suppose a fixed amount will be invested at the end of each year and that the invested funds will earn 8% compounded annually. What will be the future value of the investments after 25 years if the periodic investment is:

   a. $1000 per year?   **b.** $2000 per year?   **c.** $3000 per year?

   Note that the future value of an annuity is proportional to the size of the periodic payment.

2. This problem demonstrates the dependence of the future value of an annuity on the number of payments. Suppose $1000 is invested at the end of each year. Assume the investments earn 10% compounded annually. Calculate the future value of the investments after each of the following numbers of payments:

   a. 5.   **b.** 10.   **c.** 15.   **d.** 20.   **e.** 25.   **f.** 30.

   Note that the future value increases proportionately *more* than *n* as *n* is increased.

3. This problem demonstrates the dependence of the future value of an annuity on the interest rate. Suppose $1000 is invested at the end of each year for 20 years. Calculate the future value if the investments earn an annually compounded rate of return of:

   a. 9%.   **b.** 10%.   **c.** 11%.   **d.** 12%.

   Note that the future value increases proportionately *more* than the interest rate.

4. Calculate the future value after 25 years in each of the following scenarios:

   a. $6000 invested at end of each year earning 9% compounded annually.

   b. $3000 invested at end of each half-year earning 9% compounded semiannually.

   c. $1500 invested at end of each quarter earning 9% compounded quarterly?

   d. $500 invested at end of each month earning 9% compounded monthly?

   Note that the same total amount ($6000) is invested every year at nominally equal rates of return (9%). The combined beneficial effects of (i) smaller but earlier and more frequent payments, and (ii) more frequent compounding are quite significant.

5. What is the future value after $5\frac{1}{2}$ years of $100 invested at the end of every quarter if the funds earn 10% compounded quarterly?

6. $75 was invested at the end of every month for $2\frac{1}{2}$ years. Calculate the future value if the funds earned 8% compounded monthly.

7. Aaron contributed $2000 to his RRSP at the end of every half-year. What was the value of his RRSP after $12\frac{1}{2}$ years if the RRSP grew at 7.5% compounded semiannually?

8. Elga plans to invest $175 every month by purchasing units of a diversified equity mutual fund. If the fund generates an overall rate of return of 6% compounded monthly, what will her holdings be worth after $8\frac{1}{4}$ years?

9. Danica has purchased $700 worth of units in a Global Equity Fund every calendar quarter for the past 7 years and 9 months. On average, the fund has earned 9% compounded quarterly. What were Danica's holdings worth immediately after her last purchase?

10. What will be the future value after 6 years and 7 months of regular month-end investments of $435 earning 8.5% compounded monthly?

11. Assume that your client invests $1000 at the end of each of the next three years. The investments earn 8% compounded annually. What is the future value at the end of the three years? (Taken from CIFP course materials.)

12. Your client plans to invest $2000 at the end of each year. The rate of return on the investment is 7.5% compounded annually. What will be the value of the investment at the end of the 12 years? (Taken from CIFP course materials.)

13. Your client has systematically invested $1000 at the end of each half-year for the past 17 years. The invested funds have earned 6.4% compounded semiannually. What is the value of your client's investments today? (Taken from CIFP course materials.)

14. Markus spends $60 per month on cigarettes. Suppose he quits smoking and invests the same amount at the end of each month for 20 years. If the invested money earns 7.5% compounded monthly, how much will Markus accumulate after 20 years?

15. Pascal has just agreed with his financial planner to begin a voluntary accumulation plan. He will invest $500 at the end of every three months in a balanced mutual fund. How much will the plan be worth after 20 years if the mutual fund earns:

    a. 8% compounded quarterly?   **b.** 10% compounded quarterly?

○16. Calculate and rank the equivalent values eight years from now of the following cash flow streams:

    (i) A single payment of $5000 today.
    (ii) An ordinary annuity starting today with eight annual payments of $910.
    (iii) An ordinary annuity starting in three years with five annual payments of $1675.

    Do the calculations and ranking for each of the following two cases:

    a. Money can earn 8% compounded annually for the next eight years.

    b. Money can earn 10% compounded annually for the next eight years.

17. Dave Bidini has saved $20,000 for a down payment on a home and plans to save another $5000 at the end of each year for the next five years. He expects to earn 7.25% compounded annually on his savings. How much will he have in five years' time? (Taken from CIFP course materials.)

○18. Dakota intends to save for occasional major travel holidays by contributing $275 at the end of each month to an investment plan. At the end of every three years, she will withdraw $10,000 for a major trip abroad. If the plan earns 6% compounded monthly, what will be the plan's balance after seven years?

○19. Calculate the future value of an ordinary annuity consisting of quarterly payments of $1200 for five years if the payments earn 10% compounded quarterly for the first two years and 9% compounded quarterly for the last three years.

○**20.** Herb has made contributions of $2000 to his RRSP at the end of every six months for the past eight years. The plan has earned 9.5% compounded semiannually. He has just moved the funds to another plan that earns 8% compounded quarterly. He will now contribute $1500 at the end of every three months. What total amount will Herb have in the plan seven years from now?

○**21.** Marika has already accumulated $18,000 in her RRSP. If she contributes $2000 at the end of every six months for the next 10 years, and $300 per month for the subsequent five years, what amount will she have in her plan at the end of the 15 years? Assume that her plan will earn 9% compounded semiannually for the first 10 years, and 9% compounded monthly for the next five years.

○**22.** Rajeev's new financial plan calls for end-of-quarter contributions of $2000 to his RRSP. In addition, at each year-end, he intends to contribute another $5000 out of the annual bonus he receives from his employer. What will be the amount in his RRSP after four years if it earns 7% compounded quarterly?

23. **Using the Future Value Chart** The NET @ssets feature earlier in this section describes how to access and use the Future Value Chart available on this textbook's Web site. Use this chart to answer the following problems (rounded to the nearest dollar).

   a. Exercise 10.2, Problem 2   **b.** Exercise 10.2, Problem 11

   c. Exercise 10.2, Problem 13   **d.** Exercise 10.2, Problem 17

24. **Stop Smoking and Save Calculator** Go to the Student Edition on this textbook's Web site. In Chapter 10, find "Stop Smoking and Save." This calculator allows you to estimate how much you will accumulate over several years if you stop smoking and invest the savings. The calculator assumes the compounding frequency equals the investing frequency. Based on a half-pack per day consumption and the price of cigarettes where you live, how much would you accumulate after 30 years if your savings earn 9%?

The strong dependence of an annuity's future value on n *(as demonstrated in Problem 2) means that it is important to start a savings plan as early as possible in order to accumulate a substantial retirement fund. Problems 25 to 28 reinforce this point in different ways. Round to the nearest dollar.*

25. How much more will you have in your RRSP 30 years from now if you start to contribute $1000 per year at the end of this year, instead of waiting five years to begin contributing $1000 at each year-end? Assume that the funds earn 8% compounded annually in the RRSP.

26. How much more will you have in your RRSP at age 65 if you begin annual $1000 contributions to your plan on your twenty-sixth birthday instead of on your twenty-seventh birthday? Assume that the RRSP earns 8% compounded annually, and that the last contribution is on your sixty-fifth birthday.

27. How much more will you have in your RRSP 30 years from now if you make fixed contributions of $3000 at the end of each of the next 30 years, instead of waiting 15 years and making annual contributions that are twice as large for half as many years? Assume that the RRSP earns 8% compounded annually.

○**28.** Leona contributed $3000 per year to her RRSP on every birthday from age 21 to age 30 inclusive. She stopped employment to raise a family and made no further contributions. Her husband, John, started to make annual contributions of $3000 to his RRSP on his thirty-first birthday and plans to continue up to and including his sixty-fifth birthday. Assuming that both plans earn 8% compounded annually over the years, calculate and compare the amounts in their RRSPs at age 65.

10.3 | PRESENT VALUE OF AN ORDINARY SIMPLE ANNUITY

LO2   The **present value of an annuity** is the sum of the present values of all of the payments (evaluated at the beginning of the first payment interval). To illustrate the techniques for calculating an annuity's present value, we will consider a specific case.

PRESENT VALUE USING THE ALGEBRAIC METHOD

Figure 10.4 shows an ordinary annuity consisting of four semiannual payments of $1000. Suppose we want to find the present value of the annuity using a discount rate of 8% compounded semiannually. Since we have semiannual payments and semiannual compounding, the payments form an ordinary *simple* annuity. A "brute force" approach for determining the annuity's present value is shown in the diagram. In this approach, we calculate the present value of each payment using $PV = FV(1 + i)^{-n}$. Then we add the four present values to obtain the present value of the annuity.

FIGURE 10.4   The Present Value of a Four-Payment Ordinary Simple Annuity

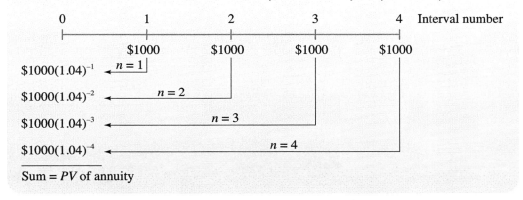

The present value of the annuity is

$$PV = \$1000(1.04)^{-1} + \$1000(1.04)^{-2} + \$1000(1.04)^{-3} + \$1000(1.04)^{-4}$$
$$= \$961.54 + \$924.56 + \$889.00 + \$854.80$$
$$= \$3629.90$$

As in the case of the future-value calculation, there is a formula that makes the present-value calculation more efficient.

PRESENT VALUE OF AN ORDINARY SIMPLE ANNUITY

$$PV = PMT\left[\frac{1 - (1 + i)^{-n}}{i}\right] \qquad \text{(10-2)}$$

Substitute $PMT = \$1000$, $n = 4$, and $i = 0.04$ into formula (10-2) to obtain the present value of the preceding four-payment annuity.

$$PV = \$1000\left[\frac{1 - (1 + 0.04)^{-4}}{0.04}\right]$$
$$= \$1000\left(\frac{1 - 0.8548042}{0.04}\right)$$
$$= \$3629.90$$

This is the same result we obtained previously by the "brute force" approach. As the number of payments in an annuity increases, the time saved by employing formula (10-2) increases proportionally.

PRESENT VALUE USING THE FINANCIAL CALCULATOR FUNCTIONS

Save the known values for *n, j* (the nominal annual interest rate), and *PMT* in the $\boxed{\text{N}}$, $\boxed{\text{I/Y}}$, and $\boxed{\text{PMT}}$ memories. Remember to use the cash-flow sign convention for the dollar amount entered in $\boxed{\text{PMT}}$. Except for the cases mentioned in the following "TIP," zero should be entered into the $\boxed{\text{FV}}$ memory. Open the *P/Y* worksheet and enter the number of payments per year. Remember that the calculator then *automatically* assigns the same value to *C/Y*, the number of compoundings per year. (This automatic feature is a convenience with *simple* annuities where, by definition, *C/Y = P/Y.*) After quitting the *P/Y* worksheet, the keystrokes $\boxed{\text{CPT}}$ $\boxed{\text{PV}}$ instruct the calculator to compute the annuity's present value.

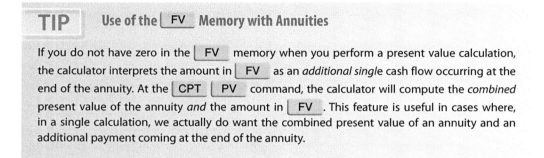

TIP   Use of the $\boxed{\text{FV}}$ Memory with Annuities

If you do not have zero in the $\boxed{\text{FV}}$ memory when you perform a present value calculation, the calculator interprets the amount in $\boxed{\text{FV}}$ as an *additional single* cash flow occurring at the end of the annuity. At the $\boxed{\text{CPT}}$ $\boxed{\text{PV}}$ command, the calculator will compute the *combined* present value of the annuity *and* the amount in $\boxed{\text{FV}}$. This feature is useful in cases where, in a single calculation, we actually do want the combined present value of an annuity and an additional payment coming at the end of the annuity.

To calculate the present value of the annuity represented in Figure 10.4, the keystrokes are:

4 $\boxed{\text{N}}$ 8 $\boxed{\text{I/Y}}$ 1000 $\boxed{\text{PMT}}$ 0 $\boxed{\text{FV}}$

$\boxed{\text{2nd}}$ $\boxed{\text{P/Y}}$ 2 $\boxed{\text{ENTER}}$ $\boxed{\text{2nd}}$ $\boxed{\text{QUIT}}$ $\boxed{\text{CPT}}$ $\boxed{\text{PV}}$ *Answer:* −3629.90

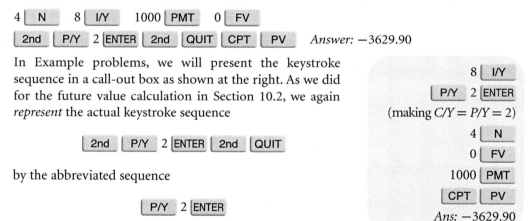

In Example problems, we will present the keystroke sequence in a call-out box as shown at the right. As we did for the future value calculation in Section 10.2, we again *represent* the actual keystroke sequence

$\boxed{\text{2nd}}$ $\boxed{\text{P/Y}}$ 2 $\boxed{\text{ENTER}}$ $\boxed{\text{2nd}}$ $\boxed{\text{QUIT}}$

by the abbreviated sequence

$\boxed{\text{P/Y}}$ 2 $\boxed{\text{ENTER}}$

You must supply the missing keystrokes.

Interpretation: The present value ($3629.90) represents the initial investment required to generate the four $1000 payments. The computed value is negative because the initial investment is a cash outflow (negative) from the investor's point of view. The difference between the payments received and the initial investment is

$$4(\$1000) - \$3629.90 = \$370.10$$

This difference represents the earnings (at the rate of 8% compounded semiannually) on the balance that remains invested from time to time.

EXAMPLE 10.3A   **THE PRESENT VALUE OF AN ORDINARY SIMPLE ANNUITY**

Determine the present value of $500 paid at the end of each calendar quarter for $6\frac{1}{2}$ years. Use a discount rate of 6% compounded quarterly.

SOLUTION

Given: $PMT = \$500$, Term $= 6\frac{1}{2}$ years, $j = 6\%$ compounded quarterly
Therefore,

$$i = \frac{6\%}{4} = 1.5\% \quad \text{and} \quad n = 4(6.5) = 26$$

$$PV = PMT\left[\frac{1 - (1 + i)^{-n}}{i}\right]$$

$$= \$500\left(\frac{1 - (1.015)^{-26}}{0.015}\right)$$

$$= \$500\left(\frac{1 - 0.67902052}{0.015}\right)$$

$$= \$10,699.32$$

Assume *PMTs* are inflows.

6 [I/Y]

[P/Y] 4 [ENTER]

(making $C/Y = P/Y = 4$)

26 [N]

500 [PMT]

0 [FV]

[CPT] [PV]

Ans: −10,699.32

Note that we keep 8-figure accuracy in "0.67902052 to get 7-figure accuracy in the answer. The present value of the annuity is $10,699.32.

CONTRIBUTION OF EACH PAYMENT TO AN ANNUITY'S PRESENT VALUE

When you use formula (10-2) or a calculator's financial functions to calculate an annuity's present value, the amount each payment contributes to the present value is not apparent. Figure 10.5 helps us see the pattern. Five $10 payments are represented by columns at one-year intervals along the time axis. Using a discount rate of 10% compounded annually, each payment's contribution to the $37.91 present value is indicated at the left side of the diagram. Not surprisingly, each successive payment contributes a smaller amount to the present value. But notice that the *difference* between the contributions from two successive payments gets smaller as you look at later payments. For example, the second payment contributes

FIGURE 10.5 Contribution of Each Payment to an Annuity's Present Value

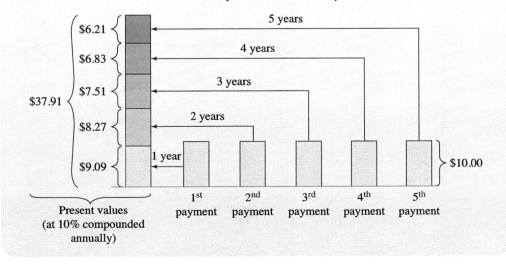

$0.83 less than the first payment, the third payment contributes $0.75 less than the second payment, and so on. Eventually, distant payments contribute an insignificant amount to the present value. As an indication, suppose the annuity in Figure 10.5 is extended to 30 years. The total present value is $94.27, to which the thirtieth payment contributes only $0.57 (0.6%). If a further 20 payments are added (in Years 31 to 50), they will add only a combined $4.88 or 5.2% to the present value.

APPLICATIONS OF THE PRESENT VALUE OF AN ANNUITY

There are more applications of the present-value calculation than of the future-value calculation. Fundamentally, all present value applications are some form of *valuation*—placing a price tag on the "package" of annuity payments that are about to start. Three categories of applications are discussed in this section. A key issue in each category is how to choose the discount rate for the present-value calculation.

1. The Market Value of an Annuity Clearly, the right to receive a series of future payments has value today. The *market* value of an annuity is the price at which it could be bought or sold among investors who are fully aware of investment alternatives. We look to the Valuation Principle (Section 7.2) for guidance in calculating the fair market value of any series of cash flows. It instructs us to calculate the present value of the cash flows, discounting them at the prevailing market rate of return (on investments of similar risk and duration). That is,

LO3

$$\begin{pmatrix} \text{Fair market value} \\ \text{of an annuity} \end{pmatrix} = \begin{pmatrix} \text{Present value of the annuity payments} \\ \text{(discounted at the } \textit{market rate of return}) \end{pmatrix}$$

Current market rates offered by insurance companies to purchasers of annuities are periodically reported in the major financial newspapers. Market rates on annuities of various terms may also be obtained from annuity brokers.

The present-value calculation also allows you to estimate the amount you must accumulate by the time you retire in order to purchase, for example, a 25-year annuity paying $3000 per month. (You would have to make an assumption about the market rate of return at the date of the annuity purchase.)

The cash flows from some investments include an annuity component. For example, some types of bonds pay a fixed dollar amount of interest every six months until the face value of the bond is repaid at maturity. Some preferred shares pay fixed quarterly dividends until the "par value" of the share is repaid on the redemption date. These two types of investments may be bought or sold in the financial markets on any business day. Consequently, valuation at *prevailing market* rates of return is important on a day-by-day basis. The fair market value is the present value of *all* remaining payments. The annuity *component* can be valued separately and added to the present value of the *other* expected payments.

NET @ssets

Most annuities are now sold to retirees. They use money accumulated in their RRSPs to purchase Registered Retirement Income Funds (RRIFs) that provide a steady stream of income.

Go to the textbook's Web site. In Chapter 10 of the Student Edition, find "RRIF Annuities." The resulting Web page presents the rates of return offered by various banks and insurance companies on 10-, 15-, and 20-year RRIF annuities.

EXAMPLE 10.3B **CALCULATING THE PURCHASE PRICE OF AN ANNUITY**

Suppose the funds used to purchase an annuity will earn 6% compounded monthly. What amount is needed to purchase an annuity paying $1000 at the end of each month for 20 years?

SOLUTION

The annuity is an ordinary simple annuity with $PMT = \$1000$ and $n = 12(20) = 240$ payments. The amount required to purchase the annuity is the present value of the payments discounted at $i = \frac{6\%}{12} = 0.5\%$ per month.

$$PV = PMT\left[\frac{1-(1+i)^{-n}}{i}\right]$$

$$= \$1000\left[\frac{1-(1.005)^{-240}}{0.005}\right]$$

$$= \$1000\left[\frac{1-0.302096142}{0.005}\right]$$

$$= \$139,580.77$$

6	I/Y
P/Y 12	ENTER

(making $C/Y = P/Y = 12$)

240	N
1000	PMT
0	FV
CPT	PV

Note that we keep 9-figure accuracy in 0.302096142 to get 8-figure accuracy in the answer.

The purchase price of the annuity is $139,580.77.

Ans: $-139,580.77$

EXAMPLE 10.3C **THE PRESENT VALUE OF AN ANNUITY AND A TERMINAL "LUMP" PAYMENT**

A certain investment will pay you $50 at the end of every six months for 17 years. At the end of the 17 years, the investment will pay you an additional $1000 along with the last regular $50 payment. What is the fair market value of the investment if the prevailing rate of return on similar investments is 8.5% compounded semiannually?

SOLUTION

The fair market value of the investment is the present value of *all* of the payments discounted at the prevailing rate of return. The semiannual payments form an ordinary simple annuity having

$$PMT = \$50 \quad n = 2(17) = 34 \text{ payments} \quad i = \frac{8.5\%}{2} = 4.25\%$$

The combined present value of the annuity and the terminal lump payment is

Formula (10-2)   Formula (8-2)

$$PV = PMT\left[\frac{1-(1+i)^{-n}}{i}\right] + FV(1+i)^{-n}$$

$$= \$50\left[\frac{1-(1.0425)^{-34}}{0.0425}\right] + \$1000(1.0425)^{-34}$$

$$= \$50\left(\frac{1-0.24289235}{0.0425}\right) + \$1000(0.2428923)$$

$$= \$890.715 + \$242.892$$

$$= \$1133.61$$

8.5	I/Y
P/Y 2	ENTER

(making $C/Y = P/Y = 2$)

34	N
50	PMT
1000	FV
CPT	PV

Ans: -1133.61

The fair market value of the investment is $1133.61.

EXAMPLE 10.3D   **THE PRESENT VALUE OF TWO ANNUITIES IN SERIES**

How much will it cost to purchase a two-level retirement annuity that will pay $2000 at the end of each month for the first 10 years, and $3000 per month for the next 15 years? Assume that the payments represent a rate of return to the annuitant (the person receiving the payments) of 7.5% compounded monthly.

SOLUTION

The purchase price will be the present value of all of the payments. Since we have month-end payments and monthly compounding, the payments form two ordinary simple annuities in sequence. The given information and a three-step solution strategy are presented in the time diagram.

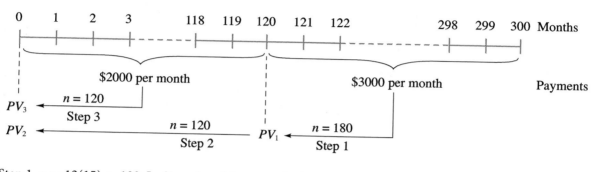

In Step 1, $n = 12(15) = 180$. In Steps 2 and 3, $n = 12(10) = 120$. In every step, $i = \frac{7.5\%}{12} = 0.625\%$.

Step 1:   Calculate the present value, PV_1, of the $3000 annuity at its beginning.

$$PV_1 = PMT\left[\frac{1 - (1 + i)^{-n}}{i}\right]$$

$$= \$3000\left(\frac{1 - 1.00625^{-180}}{0.00625}\right)$$

$$= \$323,620.28$$

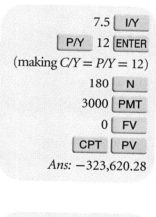

7.5 ⌊ I/Y
⌊ P/Y   12 ⌊ENTER
(making $C/Y = P/Y = 12$)
180 ⌊ N
3000 ⌊ PMT
0 ⌊ FV
⌊ CPT   ⌊ PV
Ans: −323,620.28

Step 2:   Calculate the present value, PV_2, of the Step 1 result at time 0.

$$PV_2 = FV(1 + i)^{-n}$$

$$= \$323,620.28(1.00625)^{-120}$$

$$= \$153,224.61$$

Step 3:   Calculate the present value, PV_3, of the $2000 annuity at time 0.

$$PV_3 = \$2000\left[\frac{1 - (1.00625)^{-120}}{0.00625}\right]$$

$$= \$168,489.49$$

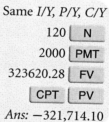

Same *I/Y, P/Y, C/Y*
120 ⌊ N
2000 ⌊ PMT
323620.28 ⌊ FV
⌊ CPT   ⌊ PV
Ans: −321,714.10

The total present value will be

$$PV_2 + PV_3 = \$153,224.61 + \$168,489.49 = \$321,714.10$$

The purchase price of the two-level retirement annuity will be $321,714.10.

EXAMPLE 10.3E   **PRICING AN ANNUITY TO PROVIDE A REQUIRED RATE OF RETURN**

Crazy Ed's Furniture Mart is holding a "nothing-down-and-no-interest-to-pay" promotion on purchases exceeding $1000. Customers can pay six equal month-end payments with no interest charged. On such instalment sales, the customer signs a conditional sale contract.[2] Crazy Ed's immediately sells the conditional sale contract to Consumers Finance Company. The finance company purchases the contract at a discounted price that builds in a rate of return (on its purchase price) of 15% compounded monthly. What will Consumers Finance pay for a $1200 contract (consisting of six payments of $200)?

SOLUTION

The six instalment payments form an ordinary simple annuity. To build the required rate of return into the purchase price, the payments must be discounted at the required rate of return. So we need to calculate the present value of $n = 6$ payments of $PMT = \$200$, discounting at $i = \frac{15\%}{12} = 1.25\%$ per month.

$$PV = PMT\left[\frac{1 - (1 + i)^{-n}}{i}\right]$$
$$= \$200\left[\frac{1 - (1 + 0.0125)^{-6}}{0.0125}\right]$$
$$= \$1149.20$$

| 15 | I/Y |
| P/Y | 12 ENTER |

(making $C/Y = P/Y = 12$)

6	N
200	PMT
0	FV
CPT	PV

Ans: -1149.20

The finance company will pay $1149.20 for the contract.

LO4   2. Loan Balance and Market Value of a Loan Contract In Section 8.3 we established the general principle that

> Original loan = [Present value of *all* payments (discounted at the *contractual rate of interest* on the loan)]

The original loan is also the initial balance on the loan. The balance at any later time is the present value of the *remaining* payments.

> Principal balance = [Present value of the *remaining* payments (discounted at the *contractual rate of interest* on the loan)]

Both principles apply to any pattern of loan payments. However, most loans require equal periodic payments.[3] In these cases, we use formula (10-2) for the present value calculation.

Most loan contracts permit the lender to sell the contract to another investor at any time during the term of the loan. The investor/buyer is then entitled to receive subsequent loan payments from the borrower. To determine a price for the loan contract, the buyer and seller first agree upon the rate of return the buyer should earn. (Current interest rates offered by financial institutions on *new* loans provide a reference point for negotiating the buyer's rate of return.) Then this rate of return is "built in" or "locked in" by using it as the discount rate for calculating the present value of the remaining loan payments.

> Selling price of a loan contract = (Present value of the remaining payments (discounted at the *negotiated rate of return*))

[2] It is common for furniture retailers to sell such conditional sale contracts to a finance company. The retailer gets immediate cash and avoids having to set up a credit department.

[3] As a technical point, the last payment in so-called equal-payment loans usually differs slightly from the others. In Section 14.1 you will learn how to calculate the exact amount of the final payment. Until then, we will make the assumption that the final payment is the same as the others. When you assume the final payment equals the others in the present value calculation for the "Original loan" or "Loan balance," your answer will have a small immaterial error. To obtain strictly correct present values, you must use the strictly correct value for the final payment.

EXAMPLE 10.3F   **CALCULATING THE ORIGINAL LOAN AND A SUBSEQUENT BALANCE**

The required monthly payment on a five-year loan bearing interest at 9% compounded monthly is $249.10.

a. What was the original principal amount of the loan?

b. What is the balance owed just after the seventeenth payment?

SOLUTION

The loan payments form an ordinary simple annuity having $PMT = \$249.10$, $n = 12(5) = 60$, and $i = \frac{9\%}{12} = 0.75\%$ per month.

a. Original principal = Present value of all 60 payments

$$\text{Original principal} = PMT\left[\frac{1 - (1 + i)^{-n}}{i}\right]$$

$$= \$249.10\left(\frac{1 - 1.0075^{-60}}{0.0075}\right)$$

$$= \$249.10\left(\frac{1 - 0.63869970}{0.0075}\right)$$

$$= \$11{,}999.99$$

Take borrower's viewpoint for the sign convention.

9 I/Y
P/Y 12 ENTER
(making $C/Y = P/Y = 12$)
60 N
249.10 +/− PMT
0 FV
CPT PV
Ans: 11,999.99

b. Balance after 17 payments = Present value of the remaining 43 payments

$$\text{Balance} = \$249.10\left(\frac{1 - 1.0075^{-43}}{0.0075}\right)$$

$$= \$249.10\left(\frac{1 - 0.72520810}{0.0075}\right)$$

$$= \$9126.76$$

Same I/Y, PMT, FV
Same P/Y, C/Y
43 N
CPT PV
Ans: 9126.76

The original loan was $12,000 and the balance after 17 payments is $9126.76.

EXAMPLE 10.3G   **CALCULATING THE SELLING PRICE OF A LOAN CONTRACT**

Suppose the original lender in Example 10.3F wishes to sell the loan just after the seventeenth payment. What is the selling price if the negotiated rate of return to the buyer is to be:

a. 7.5% compounded monthly?

b. 9% compounded monthly (the same as the interest rate on the loan)?

c. 10.5% compounded monthly?

SOLUTION

In each case,

$$\text{Selling price} = \binom{\text{Present value of the remaining 43 payments}}{\text{(discounted at the negotiated rate of return)}}$$

a. The periodic rate is $i = \frac{7.5\%}{12} = 0.625\%$

$$\text{Selling price} = PMT\left[\frac{1 - (1 + i)^{-n}}{i}\right]$$

$$= \$249.10\left(\frac{1 - 1.00625^{-43}}{0.00625}\right)$$

$$= \$9367.20$$

Take buyer's viewpoint for the sign convention.

7.5 I/Y
P/Y 12 ENTER
(making $C/Y = P/Y = 12$)
43 N
249.10 PMT
0 FV
CPT PV
Ans: −9367.20

b. The periodic rate is $i = \frac{9\%}{12} = 0.75\%$

$$\text{Selling price} = \$249.10\left(\frac{1 - 1.0075^{-43}}{0.0075}\right)$$

$$= \$9126.76$$

Same *P/Y, C/Y, N,*
PMT, FV

9 ⎿ I/Y ⏌

⎿ CPT ⏌ ⎿ PV ⏌

Ans: −9126.76

c. The periodic rate is $i = \frac{10.5\%}{12} = 0.875\%$

$$\text{Selling price} = \$249.10\left(\frac{1 - 1.00875^{-43}}{0.00875}\right)$$

$$= \$8894.86$$

Same *P/Y, C/Y, N,*
PMT, FV

10.5 ⎿ I/Y ⏌

⎿ CPT ⏌ ⎿ PV ⏌

Ans: −8894.86

Postscript: Note that the answer in Part (b) equals the actual loan balance (which we calculated in Part (b) of Example 10.3F). The current Example 10.3G illustrates three scenarios summarized below.

Part	Rate of return vs. Interest rate on loan	Selling price vs. Balance on loan
a.	Rate of return < Interest rate on loan	Selling price > Balance on loan
b.	Rate of return = Interest rate on loan	Selling price = Balance on loan
c.	Rate of return > Interest rate on loan	Selling price < Balance on loan

Expressing the same relationships in another way,

- If the price you pay to purchase a loan is *equal* to the balance on the loan, the rate of return on your investment will be the *same* as the interest rate on the loan.

- Consequently, if you pay *more* than the loan balance, your rate of return will be *less* than the interest rate on the loan.

- Conversely, if you pay *less* than the loan balance, your rate of return will be *more* than the interest rate on the loan.

3. The Economic Value of an Annuity The *economic* value of a payment stream on a particular date (focal date) refers to a *single* amount that is an economic substitute for the payment stream. You will end up in the same financial position if you accept the economic value (on its focal date) instead of the scheduled payment stream.

The economic value of an annuity at the beginning of the annuity is just its present value. An appropriate value for the discount rate is the rate of return currently available on Government of Canada bonds (whose time until maturity is similar to the term of the annuity).

EXAMPLE 10.3H **COMPARING THE ECONOMIC VALUES OF TWO ANNUITIES**

An eligible individual may elect to start collecting the Canada Pension Plan monthly retirement pension at any time between the ages of 60 and 65. The payments are then reduced by 0.5% for each month the pension is collected before age 65. For example, if the pension starts five years early, at age 60, the monthly payment will be decreased by (5 × 12 months) × (0.5%) = 30%. The reduction is permanent, extending to payments after age 65 as well.

The average life expectancy of a woman aged 60 is another 25 years. If a retired woman aged 60 lives just the expected 25 years, compare the economic values at age 60 of the following two alternatives:

- Collect a 100% pension from age 65.
- Collect a 70% pension from age 60.

Assume that money is worth 6% compounded monthly.

SOLUTION

The economic value at age 60 of a stream of pension payments will be the present value of the payments discounted at $i = \frac{6\%}{12} = 0.5\%$ per month.

The *relative* economic values of the pension alternatives will not depend on whether a 100% pension represents $500, $1000, or $1500 per month. Let's work on the basis of $1000 per month. Then the woman can choose either a full pension after age 65 of $1000 per month or a reduced pension after age 60 of $700 per month. The alternative pension payments are illustrated in the following time diagrams. In the first diagram, PV_1 represents the present value at age 60 of the reduced pension payments.

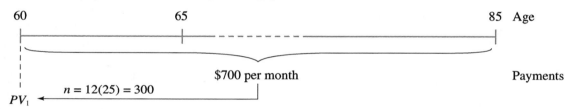

In the next diagram, PV_2 is the present value at age 65 of the full pension payments. PV_3 is the present value at age 60 of PV_2.

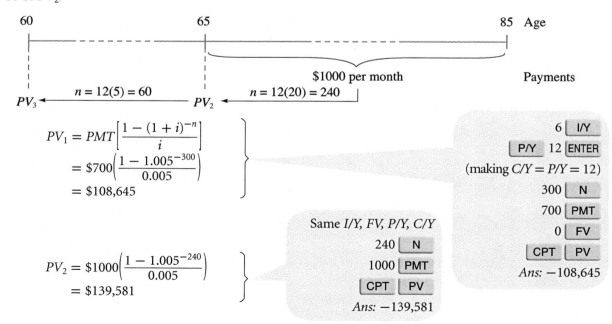

$$PV_1 = PMT\left[\frac{1 - (1 + i)^{-n}}{i}\right]$$
$$= \$700\left(\frac{1 - 1.005^{-300}}{0.005}\right)$$
$$= \$108,645$$

$$PV_2 = \$1000\left(\frac{1 - 1.005^{-240}}{0.005}\right)$$
$$= \$139,581$$

6 **I/Y**
P/Y 12 **ENTER**
(making *C/Y = P/Y =* 12)
300 **N**
700 **PMT**
0 **FV**
CPT **PV**
Ans: −108,645

Same *I/Y, FV, P/Y, C/Y*
240 **N**
1000 **PMT**
CPT **PV**
Ans: −139,581

$$PV_3 = FV(1 + i)^{-n}$$
$$= \$139{,}581(1.005)^{-60}$$
$$= \$103{,}481$$

Same *I/Y, P/Y, C/Y*

60	N
0	PMT
139581	FV
CPT	PV

Ans: −103,481

The economic value at age 60 of the early pension option is $108,645. The economic value, also at age 60, of the full pension option is $103,481. Based on our assumptions for life expectancy and the time value of money, the early pension option is worth

$$\frac{\$108{,}645 - \$103{,}481}{\$103{,}481} \times 100\% = 4.99\%$$

more than the age 65 option. (We would get the same 4.99% advantage of the early pension alternative for any dollar amount of the full 100% monthly pension.)

POINT OF INTEREST

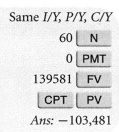

"Instant Millionaire?"

No doubt you have seen it on TV—a Publishers Clearing House (PCH) Prize Patrol van pulls up to a neat little bungalow in suburbia. Then with cameras rolling, a guy in an expensive suit knocks on the door, waits for the occupant to appear, and then bellows something about "winner of the Publishers Clearing House $1,000,000 Grand Prize." We watch the winner go through the usual stages of denial and shock before going "bananas". Finally, we see the "instant millionaire" being presented with a billboard-size certificate with the figure "$1 Million" prominently displayed.

However, there's a little detail we don't pick up from the TV commercial—the winner does not receive a *cash* prize of $1,000,000. The Official Rules for the various PCH sweepstakes and prizes state that the winner of a $1 million Grand Prize or the $10 million Super Prize will receive annual payments distributed over future years—many future years. Furthermore, in recent years PCH has restructured the payment schedules in ways that reduce the economic value of the prizes.

In 2000, the rules specified that the winner of a $1 million prize would be paid $50,000 in the first year, $25,000 per year for the next 18 years, and a final "balloon" payment of $500,000 in the 20th year. In 2004, a $1 million prize would be paid as follows: $25,000 per year for 29 years plus $275,000 in the 30th year. The winner of a PCH $1 million prize in 2007 would receive 40 annual payments of $25,000.

Clearly, the pattern has been to stretch out the payments over longer periods of time and/or to "back-end load" the payments (with a large balloon payment at the end). This tactic reached a rather absurd point in the 2007 Official New Member PCH Lotto Sweepstakes. The winner of the $5 million Grand Prize would receive $25,000 per year for 39 years plus a balloon payment of $4,025,000 in the 40th year!

QUESTIONS

Assume that all payments are made at the end of each year.

1. On the day a $1 million prize was won, what was its economic value under each of the payment schedules for Year 2000, 2004, and 2007? Use 7% compounded annually for the discount rate.

2. **a.** On the day the $5 million PCH Lotto Sweepstakes Grand Prize was won, what was its economic value? Use 7% compounded annually for the discount rate.

   b. How much does the final payment of $4,025,000 contribute to that economic value?

3. Repeat Question 1 using 8% compounded annually as the discount rate. The changes from the previous answers indicate how sensitive the economic value calculations are to the discount rate used.

SPREADSHEET STRATEGIES   Present Value of an Ordinary Simple Annuity

Connect provides a partially completed template for calculating the present value of an ordinary simple annuity. Go to the Student Edition of Connect and find "PV of Ord. Simple Annuity."

The Present Value template employs two methods—one based on the algebraic formula (10-2) and the other based on Excel's built-in Present Value (*PV*) function. The first page of the "PV of Ord. Simple Annuity" workbook discusses Excel's *PV* function.

The main features of a completed Present Value template are presented below. The formulas programmed into cells C13 and C15 are displayed in cells C14 and C16, respectively. Here data are entered to solve Example 10.3A. In this example, we are asked to determine the present value of $500 paid at the end of each calendar quarter for $6\frac{1}{2}$ years. The discount rate is 6% compounded quarterly. After entering these known values into the input cells, the computed present value immediately appears in the output cells C13 and C15.

	A	B	C	D
1				
2		Using a spreadsheet to calculate the present value of an ordinary simple annuity.		
3	Example 10.3A:			
4				
5		Nominal annual interest rate, *j*	6.000%	
6		Compoundings per year, *m*	4	
7		Periodic rate of interest, *i* or *rate*	1.5000%	
8		Number of payments, *n* or *nper*	26.00	
9		Regular annuity payment, *PMT* or *pmt*	-$500.00	
10		One-time final payment, *fv*	$0.00	
11		Annuity *type*	0	
12				
13		Formula (10-2), *PV* (assumes *fv* = 0)	$10,699.32	
14		Formula in cell C13:	=-C9*(1-(1+C7)^-C8)/C7	
15		*PV(rate, nper, pmt, pv, type)*	$10,699.32	
16		Formula in cell C15:	=PV(C7,C8,C9,C10,C11)	

The present value of the annuity is $10,699.32.

CONCEPT QUESTIONS

1. Annuity A has the same *n* and *i* as Annuity B. A's *PMT* is double B's *PMT*. Will A's present value be (pick one): (i) double, (ii) more than double, or (iii) less than double the amount of B's present value? Give a reason for your choice.

2. Suppose the discount rate used to calculate the present value of an annuity is increased (leaving *n* and *PMT* unchanged). Will the annuity's present value be (pick one): (i) larger or (ii) smaller than before? Give a reason for your choice.

3. Annuity G has the same *i* and *PMT* as Annuity H. G has twice as many payments as H. Is G's present value (pick one): (i) double, (ii) more than double, or (iii) less than double the amount of H's present value? Give a reason for your choice.

4. Think of a 20-year annuity paying $2000 per month. If prevailing market rates decline over the next year, will the price to purchase a 20-year annuity increase or decrease? Explain.

EXERCISE 10.3

connect

Spreadsheet template: *A partially completed Excel template for calculating the present value of an ordinary simple annuity is provided in Connect. You can use this template for many of the problems in Exercise 10.3. Go to the Student Edition of Connect and find "PV of Ord. Simple Annuity."*

Answers to the odd-numbered problems are at the end of the book.

1. This problem demonstrates the dependence of an annuity's present value on the size of the periodic payment. Calculate the present value of 25 end-of-year payments of:

   a. $1000.   **b.** $2000.   **c.** $3000.

   Use a discount rate of 8% compounded annually. After completing the calculations, note that the present value is proportional to the size of the periodic payment.

2. This problem demonstrates the dependence of the present value of an annuity on the number of payments. Using 7% compounded annually as the discount rate, calculate the present value of an ordinary annuity paying $1000 per year for:

   a. 5 years.   **b.** 10 years.   **c.** 20 years.

   d. 30 years.   **e.** 100 years.   **f.** 1000 years.

   Observe that the present value increases with increasing *n*, but at a diminishing rate. In this case, the 970 payments from Year 30 to Year 1000 cause the present value to increase by just 15%.

3. This problem demonstrates the dependence of the present value of an annuity on the discount rate. For an ordinary annuity consisting of 20 annual payments of $1000, calculate the present value using an annually compounded discount rate of:

   a. 5%.   **b.** 10%.   **c.** 11%.   **d.** 15%.

   Observe that the present value decreases as you increase the discount rate. However, the present value decreases proportionately *less* than the increase in the discount rate.

4. An ordinary annuity consists of quarterly payments of $100 for $5\frac{1}{2}$ years. What is the annuity's present value, discounting at 10% compounded quarterly?

5. Determine the present value of end-of-month payments of $75 continuing for $2\frac{1}{2}$ years. Use 8% compounded monthly as the discount rate.

6. How much will it cost to purchase an ordinary annuity delivering semiannual payments of $2000 for $12\frac{1}{2}$ years if the money used to purchase the annuity can earn 7.5% compounded semiannually?

7. A contract requires end-of-month payments of $175 for another $8\frac{1}{4}$ years. What would an investor pay to purchase this contract if she requires a rate of return of 6% compounded monthly?

8. A new loan at 9% compounded quarterly requires quarterly payments of $727.88 for seven years. Rounded to the nearest dollar, what amount was borrowed?

9. Semiannual payments of $1240 will pay off the balance owed on a loan in $9\frac{1}{2}$ years. If the interest rate on the loan is 9.9% compounded semiannually, what is the current balance on the loan?

10. The original lender wishes to sell a loan contract delivering month-end payments of $350 for another 11 years and 5 months. At what price would an investor be prepared to buy the contract in order to "build in" a rate of return of 8.75% compounded monthly?

11. Your client is scheduled to receive $2000 at the end of each year for the next 10 years. If money is currently worth 7% compounded annually, what is the present value of the annuity? (Taken from CIFP course materials.)

12. Determine the present value of payments of $100 at the end of each month for 20 years. Use a discount rate (interest rate) of 6% compounded monthly.

13. What is the present value of end-of-quarter payments of $2500 for seven years? Use a discount rate of 6% compounded quarterly.

14. Imperial Life Inc. is quoting a rate of return of 5.2% compounded quarterly on 15-year annuities. How much will you have to pay for a 15-year annuity that pays $5000 (at the end of) every three months?

15. The rate of return offered by Reliance Insurance Co. on its 20-year annuities is 4.8% compounded monthly. What amount is required to purchase a 20-year annuity with month-end payments of $1000?

16. Mr. and Mrs. Dafoe are doing some estimates of the amount of funds they will need in their RRSP to purchase an annuity paying $5000 at the end of each month. For each combination of term and monthly compounded interest rate in the following table, calculate the initial amount required to purchase the annuity.

| | Interest rate | |
Term of annuity	6%	7%
20 years	?	?
25 years	?	?

17. If money can earn 6% compounded monthly, how much more money is required to fund an ordinary annuity paying $200 per month for 30 years than to fund the same monthly payment for 20 years?

18. Isaac wishes to purchase a 25-year annuity providing monthly payments of $1000 for the first 15 years and $1500 for the remaining 10 years. An insurance company has quoted him a rate of return of 4.8% compounded monthly for such an annuity. How much will he pay for the annuity?

○19. François and Pat wish to structure the payments from a 20-year annuity so that the end-of-quarter payments increase by $500 every five years. Maritime Insurance Co. will pay 5% compounded quarterly on funds received to purchase such an annuity. How much must François and Pat pay for an annuity in which the quarterly payments increase from $2000 to $2500 to $3000 to $3500 in successive five-year periods?

○20. A Government of Canada bond will pay $50 at the end of every six months for the next 15 years, and an additional $1000 lump payment at the end of the 15 years. What is the appropriate price to pay if you require a rate of return of 6.5% compounded semiannually?

21. Harold and Patricia Abernathy made a loan to their son, Jason. To repay the loan, Jason will make payments of $2000 at the end of each year for 10 years. If the interest rate on the loan is 7% compounded annually, what was the amount of the original loan? (Taken from CIFP course materials.)

22. Gabriela's monthly payments of $567.89 will pay off her mortgage loan in 7 years and 5 months. The interest rate on her mortgage is 6.6% compounded monthly. What is the current balance on the loan?

23. A 20-year loan requires semiannual payments of $1037.33 including interest at 6.8% compounded semiannually.
   a. What was the original amount of the loan?
   b. What is the loan's balance $8\frac{1}{2}$ years later (just after the scheduled payment)?

24. The monthly payments on a five-year loan at 7.5% compounded monthly are $200.38.
   a. What was the original amount of the loan?
   b. What is the balance after the thirtieth payment?

25. Kent sold his car to Carolynn for $2000 down and monthly payments of $295.88 for $3\frac{1}{2}$ years, including interest at 7.5% compounded monthly. What was the selling price of the car?

26. Manuel purchased a boat for $2000 down with the balance to be paid by 36 monthly payments of $224.58 including interest at 10% compounded monthly.
    a. What was the purchase price of the boat?
    b. What is the balance owed just after the ninth payment?

27. A conditional sale contract between Classic Furniture and the purchaser of a dining room set requires month-end payments of $250 for 15 months. Classic Furniture sold the contract to Household Finance Co. at a discount to yield 19.5% compounded monthly. What price did Household pay Classic Furniture?

28. Osgood Appliance Centre is advertising refrigerators for six monthly payments of $199, including a payment on the date of purchase. What cash price should Osgood accept if it would otherwise sell the conditional sale agreement to a finance company to yield 18% compounded monthly?

○29. A mortgage broker offers to sell you a mortgage loan contract that will pay $800 at the end of each month for the next $3\frac{1}{2}$ years, at which time the principal balance of $45,572 is due and receivable. What is the highest price you should pay for the contract if you require a return of at least 7.5% compounded monthly?

○30. What is the maximum price you should pay for a contract guaranteeing month-end payments of $500 for the next 12 years if you require a rate of return of at least 8% compounded monthly for the first five years and at least 9% compounded monthly for the next seven years?

31. The Ottawa Senators fired their coach two years into his five-year contract, which paid him $90,000 at the end of each month. If the team owners buy out the remaining term of the coach's contract for its economic value at the time of firing, what will be the settlement amount? Assume that money can earn 7.5% compounded monthly.

32. The Montreal Canadiens have just announced the signing of Finnish hockey sensation Gunnar Skoroften to a 10-year contract at $3 million per year. The media are reporting the deal as being worth $30 million to the young Finn. Rounded to the dollar, what current economic value would you place on the contract if Skoroften will be paid $250,000 at each month-end, and money can earn 6% compounded monthly?

33. Your client has the following choices for an insurance benefit: She can receive $2000 at the end of each year for the next five years or one "lump" sum today. If the current interest rate is 4.5% compounded annually, what lump payment today is equivalent to the five payments? (Taken from CIFP course materials.)

34. You can purchase a residential building lot for $90,000 cash, or for $20,000 down and quarterly payments of $5000 for four years. The first payment would be due three months after the purchase date. If the money you would use for a cash purchase can earn 8% compounded quarterly during the next four years, which option should you choose? What is the economic advantage in current dollars of the preferred alternative?

35. You have received two offers on the used car you wish to sell. Mr. Lindberg is offering $9500 cash, and Mrs. Martel's offer is five semiannual payments of $2000, including one on the purchase date. Which offer has the greater economic value using a discount rate of 6% compounded semiannually? What is the economic advantage in current dollars of the preferred alternative?

○36. A lottery offers the winner the choice between a $150,000 cash prize or month-end payments of $1000 for $12\frac{1}{2}$ years, increasing to $1500 per month for the next $12\frac{1}{2}$ years. Which alternative would you choose if money can earn 8.25% compounded monthly over the 25-year period?

○**37.** For its "No Interest for One Year Sale," Flemming's Furniture advertises that customers pay only a 10% down payment. The balance may be paid by 12 equal monthly payments with no interest charges. Flemming's has an operating loan on which it pays interest at 8.4% compounded monthly. If Flemming's sells furniture in a cash transaction rather than on the 10%-down-and-no-interest promotion, Flemming's can use the extra cash proceeds to reduce the balance on its loan, and thereby save on interest costs. What percentage discount for cash could Flemming's give and still be no worse off than receiving the full price under the terms of the sale?

•**38.** An individual qualifying for Canada Pension Plan benefits may elect to start collecting the CPP monthly retirement benefit at any time between the ages of 60 and 70. If the retirement benefit starts after age 65, the pension payments are increased (from the amount that would otherwise be paid at age 65) by 0.5% for each month after age 65. For example, if the retiree chooses to begin receiving the benefit after turning 68, the CPP payments will be increased by (36 months) × (0.5%) = 18%.

   The average life expectancy of a man aged 65 is another 15 years. If a man aged 65 lives just the expected 15 years, compare the economic values at age 65 of the two alternatives of collecting a 100% pension from age 65 versus a 118% pension from age 68. Assume that money is worth 7.5% compounded monthly.

•**39.** The British Columbia Teachers' Pension Plan allows a teacher to begin collecting a retirement pension before age 60, but the pension is reduced by 3% for each year the retiring teacher's age is under 60. For example, a teacher retiring at age 56 would receive 100% − 4(3%) = 88% of the monthly pension that she would receive at age 60 (with the same number of years of service). The reduction is permanent, extending to payments beyond age 60.

   Suppose that a female teacher will live the average life expectancy of 28 additional years for a woman aged 55. Compare the economic values at age 55 of the two alternatives of collecting an 85% pension from age 55 versus collecting a 100% pension from age 60. Assume that money is worth 7.5% compounded monthly.

40. **Current Amounts Needed to Purchase an Annuity** Go to the Student Edition of the textbook's Web site. In Chapter 10, find "RRIF Annuities." Obtain high, low, and mid-range interest rate quotes from three financial institutions for a 20-year RRIF annuity. Assuming the interest rates are compounded monthly, calculate the amount required in each case to purchase a 20-year annuity paying $3000 at the end of each month.

○**41.** **Influence of Annuity Variables** Go to the Student Edition of the textbook's Web site. In Chapter 10, find "Influence of Annuity Variables." This interactive chart enables you to observe and compare the effects of changes in the variables *PMT*, *n*, and *i* on both the future value and present value of an annuity.

   a. Enter *PMT* = $100 and *i* = 8% for both Annuity A and Annuity B. Set *n* = 20 for Annuity A and *n* = 40 for Annuity B. This means that B contains twice as many payments as A. In percentage terms,
   (i) How much larger is the present value of B than the present value of A?
   (ii) How much larger is the future value of B than the future value of A?

b. Enter $PMT = \$100$ and $n = 30$ for both annuities. Set $i = 8\%$ for Annuity A and $i = 9\%$ for Annuity B. In relative terms, the interest rate for B is

$$\frac{9\% - 8\%}{8\%} \times 100\% = 12.5\%$$

larger than the rate for A. In percentage terms,

  (i) How much *smaller* is the present value of B than the present value of A?

  (ii) How much *larger* is the future value of B than the future value of A?

10.4 DEFERRED ANNUITIES

A **deferred annuity** may be viewed as an *ordinary* annuity that does not begin until a time interval (named the **period of deferral**) has passed. Figure 10.6 shows a deferred annuity on a time line. In the figure,

$$d = \text{Equivalent number of payment intervals in the period of deferral}$$

Note that the period of deferral ends one payment interval *before* the first payment. Viewed from the *end* of the period of deferral, the payments then form an ordinary annuity.

FIGURE 10.6   Time Diagram for a Deferred Annuity

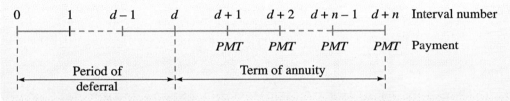

The future value of a deferred annuity is the future value of all of the payments at the end of the last payment interval. Can you see what needs to be done to determine the future value? Looking back from the end of the final payment interval, the payments appear as they would for an ordinary annuity. So it is a simple matter of doing the same future value calculation you learned in Section 10.2 for ordinary annuities.

LO2   The present value of a deferred annuity is the present value of all of the payments at the *beginning* of the period of deferral. How can the present value be calculated, using ideas you have already learned? The two regions identified in Figure 10.6 suggest a two-step procedure indicated in Figure 10-7.

1. Calculate the present value, PV_1, of the payments at the *end* of the period of deferral—this is just the present value of an ordinary annuity.
2. Calculate the present value, PV_2, of the Step 1 amount at the *beginning* of the period of deferral.

FIGURE 10.7   The Present Value of a Deferred Annuity

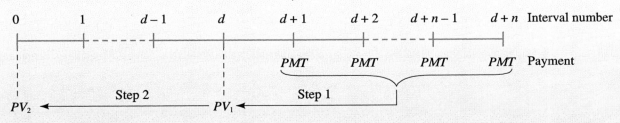

EXAMPLE 10.4A **CALCULATING THE PRESENT VALUE OF A DEFERRED ANNUITY**

Mr. and Mrs. Templeton are setting up a fund to help finance their granddaughter's college education. They want her to be able to withdraw $3000 every three months for three years after she starts college. Her first withdrawal will be $5\frac{1}{2}$ years from now. If the fund can earn 7.2% compounded quarterly, what single amount contributed today will provide for the withdrawals?

SOLUTION

The money the Templetons invest now will have $5\frac{1}{2}$ years to grow before withdrawals start. Thereafter, further earnings of money still in the fund will help support the periodic withdrawals. The one-time "up front" contribution is the present value of the withdrawals.

The time diagram is presented below. Viewed from today, the withdrawals form a deferred annuity. In order to have an *ordinary* annuity following the period of deferral, the period of deferral must end three months before the first payment. This makes the period of deferral only $5\frac{1}{4}$ years.

Since payments and compounding both occur quarterly, we have a deferred *simple* annuity with

$$PMT = \$3000 \quad n = 4(3) = 12 \quad d = 4(5.25) = 21 \quad \text{and} \quad i = \frac{7.2\%}{4} = 1.8\%$$

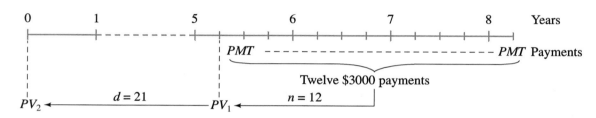

The present value of the payments $5\frac{1}{4}$ years from now is

$$PV_1 = PMT\left[\frac{1 - (1 + i)^{-n}}{i}\right]$$
$$= \$3000\left(\frac{1 - 1.018^{-12}}{0.018}\right)$$
$$= \$32,119.23$$

7.2 | I/Y |
| P/Y | 4 | ENTER |
(making $C/Y = P/Y = 4$)
12 | N |
3000 | PMT |
0 | FV |
| CPT | PV |
Ans: −32,119.23

The present value of the payments today is

$$PV_2 = FV(1 + i)^{-n}$$
$$= \$32,119.23(1.018)^{-21}$$
$$= \$22,083.19$$

Same *I/Y, P/Y, C/Y*
21 | N |
0 | PMT |
32119.23 | FV |
| CPT | PV |
Ans: −22,083.19

The Templetons can provide the desired financial support for their granddaughter by putting $22,083.19 into the fund today.

EXAMPLE 10.4B   CALCULATING THE LENGTH OF THE DEFERRAL PERIOD

Mrs. Sevard purchased a deferred annuity from an insurance company for $10,971. The money used to purchase the annuity will earn 6% compounded quarterly. The annuity will provide sixteen quarterly payments of $1000. If the first payment is to be received on October 1, 2015, when did Mrs. Sevard purchase the deferred annuity?

SOLUTION

The key idea on which we base the solution is that the purchase price is the present value, on the date of purchase, of all sixteen annuity payments. The payments form a deferred simple annuity with $PMT = \$1000$, $n = 16$, and $i = \frac{6\%}{4} = 1.5\%$. The data and solution steps are presented in the diagram below.

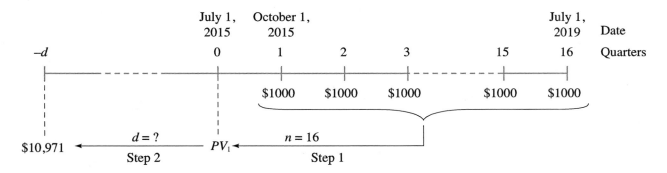

For the payments to be treated as an *ordinary* annuity, the period of deferral must end on July 1, 2015 (one payment interval before the first payment).

The present value of the payments on July 1, 2015 is

$$PV_1 = PMT\left[\frac{1-(1+i)^{-n}}{i}\right]$$
$$= \$1000\left(\frac{1-1.015^{-16}}{0.015}\right)$$
$$= \$14,131.26$$

> 6 [I/Y]
> [P/Y] 4 [ENTER]
> (making $C/Y = P/Y = 4$)
> 16 [N]
> 1000 [PMT]
> 0 [FV]
> [CPT] [PV]
> *Ans:* −14,131.26

This amount is the future value, at the end of the period of deferral, of the $10,971 purchase price. We must now use formula (9-2) to calculate the number of compounding periods required for $10,971 to grow to $14,131.26.

$$d = \frac{\ln\left(\frac{FV}{PV}\right)}{\ln(1+i)} = \frac{\ln\left(\frac{\$14,131.26}{\$10,971}\right)}{\ln 1.015} = 17.00$$

> Same *I/Y, P/Y, C/Y*
> 10971 [+/−] [PV]
> 0 [PMT]
> 14131.26 [FV]
> [CPT] [N]
> *Ans:* 17.00

Therefore, the period of deferral is 17 calendar quarters (4 years, 3 months) before July 1, 2015. That places the purchase date of the deferred annuity at April 1, 2011.

POINT OF INTEREST

Card Tricks, Part 3—The "No-Interest, No-Payments-for-a-Year" Trap

No-interest-and-nothing-to-pay for a six-month or one-year grace period is a common type of promotion offered by furniture and appliance stores, and by department stores on the sale of furniture, major appliances, big-screen TVs, etc. In most cases, you must put the purchase on the store's own credit card in order to qualify for the deferral of payment.

But here's the catch. If you don't pay the purchase price *before* the no-interest grace period ends, you are likely to be charged interest for the *entire* grace period at the credit card's full rate (typically 28.8%). Since this circumstance proves highly profitable for the retailer, you can't expect to receive a reminder from the retailer as you approach the end of your "interest-free" period.

Suppose you try to argue that "no interest" ought to mean "no interest payable for the grace period

regardless of whether you pay during the grace period." You are then likely to be referred to the fine print in the purchase or credit card agreement where it indicates that interest actually accrues during the grace period, but this interest will be cancelled if you pay the principal within the grace period. So technically it's not an "interest-free" period, but rather a grace period during which the retailer will cancel or rebate the interest if the principal is paid on time.

QUESTION

On a $5000 purchase (including sales taxes) under a "no-interest and nothing-to-pay-for-one-year" promotion, how much interest will you be charged for the grace period if you are one day late on your payment of the principal? Use an interest rate of 28.8% compounded monthly.

CONCEPT QUESTIONS

1. What is meant by a deferred annuity?
2. How long is the period of deferral if the first quarterly payment of a deferred annuity will be paid $3\frac{1}{2}$ years from today?
3. Why do we terminate the period of deferral one payment interval before the first payment?
4. For the same n, PMT, and i, is the present value of a deferred annuity larger or smaller than the present value of an ordinary annuity? Explain.
5. For the same n, PMT, and i, compare the future value of a deferred annuity to the future value of an ordinary annuity.
6. For the same n, PMT, and i, would it cost more or less to purchase a deferred annuity than an ordinary annuity? Explain.

EXERCISE 10.4   *Answers to the odd-numbered problems are at the end of the book.*

1. The first of ten semiannual payments of $2000 will be made $5\frac{1}{2}$ years from today. What is the present value of this deferred annuity using a discount rate of 7% compounded semiannually?

2. A life insurance company can invest funds to earn (after expenses) 8% compounded quarterly. A client wishes to purchase a five-year ordinary annuity that will commence $3\frac{1}{2}$ years from now. What will the insurance company charge for the annuity, if the quarterly payments are $750?

3. What minimum initial amount of money, invested to earn 9% compounded monthly, will support a monthly payout of $500 for $3\frac{1}{2}$ years, if the first payment occurs 2 years and 10 months from now?

4. What amount of money invested now will provide monthly payments of $200 for five years, if the ordinary annuity is deferred for $3\frac{1}{2}$ years and the money earns 7.5% compounded monthly?

5. A deferred ordinary annuity is comprised of eight annual payments of $1500. What is the period of deferral if the present value of the payments, discounted at 7.9% compounded annually, is $6383.65

6. For $30,000, Manny purchased a deferred ordinary annuity from an insurance company that will pay him quarterly payments of $1076.71 for $12\frac{1}{2}$ years. The payments are based upon the purchase amount earning 7% compounded quarterly. When will Manny receive the first payment?

7. Ronelda has accumulated $33,173.03 in her RRSP. If she makes no further contributions and her RRSP continues to earn 9.75% compounded monthly, for how long a period of deferral must she wait before her RRSP can sustain month-end withdrawals of $400 for 15 years?

8. Mr. Haddit plans to retire eight years from today. He projects that he will need $30,000 per year in his retirement, which he assumes will be for 15 years. The first payment will be nine years from today. To fund his retirement, Mr. Haddit will invest a lump amount today and later use it to sustain the 15 withdrawals. If his investment earns 6% compounded annually, how much must he invest today?

9. Marion's grandfather's will established a trust that will pay her $1500 every three months for 11 years. The first payment will be made six years from now, when she turns 19. If money is worth 6.5% compounded quarterly, what is today's economic value of the bequest?

10. Using an inheritance he recently received, Sam wants to purchase a deferred annuity that will pay $5000 every three months between age 60 (when he plans to retire) and age 65 (when his permanent pension will begin). The first payment is to be three months after he reaches 60, and the last is to be on his sixty-fifth birthday. If Sam's current age is 50 years and 6 months, and the invested funds will earn 6% compounded quarterly, what amount must he invest in the deferred annuity?

∘11. If money can earn 6.5% compounded annually for the next 20 years, which of the following annuities has the greater economic value today: $1000 paid at the end of each of the next 10 years, or 10 annual payments of $2000 with the first payment occurring 11 years from today?

12. A conditional sale contract requires the debtor to make six quarterly payments of $569, with the first payment due in six months. What amount will a finance company pay to purchase the contract on the date of sale if the finance company requires a rate of return of 16% compounded quarterly?

13. What price will a finance company pay to a merchant for a conditional sale contract that requires 15 monthly payments of $231 beginning in six months? The finance company requires a rate of return of 18% compounded monthly.

∘14. Negotiations between Delco Manufacturing and the union representing its employees are at an impasse. The union is seeking a 4.5% wage increase. Delco's offer is 2%. The employees have passed a vote authorizing job action. Suppose the union succeeds in winning the 4.5% increase after a two-month strike. For an employee 10 years from retirement, will there be any economic gain? Compare the current economic values of (1) 10 years' end-of-month wages at the employer's offer (102% of last year's wages) vs. (2) wages including a 4.5% increase to the same time horizon but after a two-month strike. Assume money is worth 6% compounded monthly.

○**15.** A $35,000 loan bearing interest at 10% compounded quarterly was repaid, after a period of deferral, by quarterly payments of $1573.83 over 12 years. What was the time interval between the date of the loan and the first payment?

○**16.** A finance company paid a merchant $3975 for a conditional sale contract after discounting it to yield 18% compounded monthly. If the contract is for 20 monthly payments of $256.96 following a payment-free period, what is the time interval between the date of sale and the first payment?

○**17.** A $10,000 investment will be allowed to grow at 8.5% compounded semiannually until it can support semiannual withdrawals of $1000 for 20 years. Rounded to the nearest month, how long before the first withdrawal must the investment be allowed to grow?

○**18.** Mrs. Corriveau has just retired at age 58 with $160,360 in her RRSP. She plans to live off other savings for a few years and allow her RRSP to continue to grow on a tax-deferred basis until there is an amount sufficient to purchase a 25-year annuity paying $2000 at the end of each month. If her RRSP and the annuity each earn 7.5% compounded monthly, how much longer must she let her RRSP grow (before she buys the annuity)?

10.5 FUTURE VALUE AND PRESENT VALUE OF ORDINARY GENERAL ANNUITIES

To this point, we have considered only ordinary *simple* annuities (in which the payment interval *equals* the compounding interval). We will now learn how to handle ordinary *general* annuities (in which the payment interval *differs* from the compounding interval). Actually, we have already covered all you need to know to calculate the future value and present value of an ordinary general annuity. We need only "link" two topics whose connection is not obvious.

Let us begin with formula (10-1) for the future value of an ordinary simple annuity.

$$FV = PMT\left[\frac{(1+i)^n - 1}{i}\right] \qquad \text{(10-1)}$$

LO6 Keep in mind that this formula can be used *only* in cases where the compounding interval equals (or "matches") the payment interval. But if we can find a way to *transform* a general annuity into a simple annuity, then we can still use formula (10-1).

Sometimes an insight comes more easily if we consider a specific numerical example. Suppose we wish to find the future value of an ordinary annuity consisting of 12 semiannual payments of $100 that earn 8% compounded quarterly. We are given:

$$PMT = \$100 \text{ every six months} \quad i = \frac{8\%}{4} = 2\% \text{ per quarter} \quad n = 12$$

Since the payment interval is six months but the compounding interval is three months, the payments form an ordinary *general* annuity. In order to use formula (10-1), we need the periodic rate for six months (the payment interval) that is *equivalent* to the given periodic rate of 2% per quarter. This is precisely the type of calculation for which formula (9-4) was derived in Section 9.4.

$$i_2 = (1 + i_1)^{m_1/m_2} - 1 \qquad \text{(9-4)}$$

For the case at hand,

i_1 = The *given* periodic rate ($i = 2\%$)
m_1 = Number of compoundings per year (4) at the *given* interest rate
m_2 = Number of compoundings per year at the *equivalent* interest rate
    [This will equal the number of payments per year (2).]
i_2 = Periodic interest rate for a payment interval

In this case, the exponent m_1/m_2 in formula (9-4) is

$$\frac{m_1}{m_2} = \frac{\text{Number of compoundings per year (at the given interest rate)}}{\text{Number of payments per year}} = \frac{4}{2} = 2$$

Substituting in formula (9-4), the periodic rate per payment interval (six months) is

$$i_2 = (1 + i_1)^{m_1/m_2} - 1 = 1.02^{4/2} - 1 = 1.02^2 - 1 = 0.0404 = 4.04\%$$

Now substitute this value of i_2 for i in formula (10-1).

$$FV = PMT\left[\frac{(1+i)^n - 1}{i}\right] = \$100\left[\frac{(1.0404)^{12} - 1}{0.0404}\right] = \$1506.03$$

The future value of the general annuity is $1506.03.

Let us streamline formula (9-4) for use in general annuity problems. As noted in the preceding analysis,

$$i_1 = i \quad \text{and} \quad \frac{m_1}{m_2} = \frac{\text{Number of compoundings per year}}{\text{Number of payments per year}}$$

Since $\frac{m_1}{m_2}$ is a commonly occurring ratio in general annuities, we can simplify the appearance of formula (9-4) if we define a new symbol:

NUMBER OF COMPOUNDINGS PER PAYMENT INTERVAL

$$c = \frac{\text{Number of compoundings per year}}{\text{Number of payments per year}} \qquad (10\text{-}3)$$

Then we can write formula (9-4) as

EQUIVALENT PERIODIC RATE FOR GENERAL ANNUITIES

$$i_2 = (1 + i)^c - 1 \qquad (9\text{-}4c)$$

 TIP   Some Things Just Have to Be Memorized

You need to commit the definition of *c* to memory. The symbol "*c*" reminds us that "compoundings per year" comes first (in the numerator).

LO2   We have used the future value calculation to introduce the mathematics of general annuities. The same approach works in all types of general annuity calculations. It is summarized below.

Approach for Solving a General Annuity Problem
Transform the general annuity problem into a simple annuity problem by:
1. Using $i_2 = (1 + i)^c - 1$ to calculate the equivalent periodic rate that matches the payment interval.
2. Using this equivalent periodic rate as the value for *i* in the appropriate simple annuity formula.

Using the Texas Instruments BA II PLUS for General Annuities Recall that, when you enter a value for P/Y, C/Y is automatically given the same value. This is appropriate for simple annuities. But for general annuities, after entering the value for P/Y you must scroll down to C/Y and enter its different value. Then close the worksheet. The keystrokes for obtaining the future value of 12 semiannual payments of $100 earning 8% compounded quarterly are shown at right.

8	I/Y
P/Y	2 ENTER
C/Y	4 ENTER
12	N
0	PV
100 +/–	PMT
CPT	FV

Ans: 1506.03

TIP   **Be Intentional About Identifying the Type of Annuity**

A common error students make beyond this point in the course is to forget to make the necessary adjustments to calculations when the annuity is *not* an *ordinary simple* annuity. To avoid this omission, immediately after your initial reading of the question, you should note the type of annuity at hand. (By the time you are part way into Chapter 12, there will be *four* possible types.) If you intend to use your calculator's financial functions for the computation, you should also enter values for *I/Y*, *P/Y*, and *C/Y* at this early point. This is why we have been showing these values as being entered *first* in the call-out boxes for the financial calculator solutions (even though we have been dealing only with ordinary simple annuities up to Section 10.5).

EXAMPLE 10.5A   **CALCULATING THE EQUIVALENT PERIODIC INTEREST RATE**

To five-figure accuracy, calculate the periodic interest rate that matches the payment interval for:

a. Semiannual payments earning 5% compounded annually.

b. Monthly payments discounted at 6% compounded quarterly.

SOLUTION

a. $i = \dfrac{5\%}{1} = 5\%$ per *year*   and $c = \dfrac{1 \text{ compounding per year}}{2 \text{ payments per year}} = 0.5$

Thus,

$$i_2 = (1 + i)^c - 1 = 1.05^{0.5} - 1 = 0.024695 = 2.4695\% \text{ per half year}$$

TIP   **Estimating i_2**

You can easily *estimate* the value of i_2, the periodic rate for a payment interval. It is a good idea to do this to check the "reasonableness" of the value you calculate for i_2. In Part (a), the interest rate for six months (the payment interval) will be *about* half the nominal annual rate of 5%; that is, $i_2 \approx 2.5\%$. (This number is only an approximation because it ignores compounding.) If formula (9-4) does not give you a value close to 2.5%, you have made an error in your calculations. To estimate i_2 in general, simply divide the given nominal rate by the number of payments per year.

---

b. $i = \dfrac{6\%}{4} = 1.5\%$ per quarter   and $c = \dfrac{4 \text{ compoundings per year}}{12 \text{ payments per year}} = 0.\overline{3}$

Thus,

$$i_2 = (1 + i)^c - 1 = 1.015^{0.\overline{3}} - 1 = 0.0049752 = 0.49752\% \text{ per month}$$

> **TIP**   **Improving the Accuracy of Calculated Results**
>
> Sometimes the value for c is a *repeating* decimal. This happened in Part (b) of the preceding example, where we obtained $c = 0.\overline{3}$. In such cases, use your calculator in a way that optimizes the accuracy of the value you obtain for i_2. For example, immediately after dividing 4 by 12 in the preceding Part (b), save the quotient to memory. The calculator then retains at least two more digits than you see in the display. Later, when you need the exponent for the $\boxed{y^x}$ function, recall the value for c from the memory.
>
> Typically, the value you calculate for i_2 will be used in further calculations. Again, to optimize accuracy, i_2's value should be saved in memory immediately after you calculate it. The value in memory will have two or three more digits than you see in the display. Whenever i_2 is needed in a subsequent calculation, recall it from the memory. This procedure will improve both your efficiency in using the calculator and the accuracy of your results.

EXAMPLE 10.5B   **CALCULATING THE FUTURE VALUE OF AN ORDINARY GENERAL ANNUITY**

If $1000 is invested at the end of every year at 8% compounded semiannually, what will be the total value of the periodic investments after 25 years?

SOLUTION

Since the compounding period (six months) differs from the payment interval (one year), the regular investments form a general annuity having

$$PMT = \$1000 \quad n = 1(25) = 25 \quad \text{and} \quad i = \tfrac{8\%}{2} = 4\%$$

The total value of the investments will be their combined future value.

Before we can calculate this future value, we must determine the periodic interest rate for the one-year payment interval. (It will be *about* 8%.) Since

$$c = \frac{2 \text{ compoundings per year}}{1 \text{ payment per year}} = 2$$

then

$$
\begin{aligned}
i_2 &= (1 + i)^c - 1 \\
&= 1.04^2 - 1 \\
&= 0.0816 \text{ per year}
\end{aligned}
$$

Substitute this value for i in formula (10-1).

$$
\begin{aligned}
FV &= PMT\left[\frac{(1 + i)^n - 1}{i}\right] \\
&= \$1000\left[\frac{(1.0816)^{25} - 1}{0.0816}\right] \\
&= \$74{,}836.81
\end{aligned}
$$

The total value after 25 years will be $74,836.81.

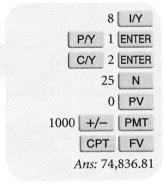

8 I/Y
P/Y 1 ENTER
C/Y 2 ENTER
25 N
0 PV
1000 +/− PMT
CPT FV
Ans: 74,836.81

EXAMPLE 10.5C   **CALCULATING THE PRESENT VALUE OF A DEFERRED GENERAL ANNUITY**

Maureen has just had her fifty-fifth birthday and plans to retire from teaching at age 60. While reviewing Maureen's personal net worth statement, her financial adviser points out that she has overlooked a significant asset—the current economic value of her future pension. The adviser calculates that the 25 years of service Maureen has already accumulated entitle her to a pension of $3500 at each month's end starting at age 60.

Based on a 22-year life expectancy from age 60 and money worth 8% compounded semiannually, estimate, to the nearest dollar, the current economic value of Maureen's pension.

SOLUTION

The current economic value of the pension can be estimated by calculating the present value of the expected pension payments discounted at 8% compounded semiannually. With monthly payments and semiannual compounding, the pension (viewed from her fifty-fifth birthday) constitutes a *deferred* ordinary *general* annuity. The period of deferral is five years. We are given

$$PMT = \$3500 \quad n = 12(22) = 264 \quad d = 12(5) = 60 \quad i = \frac{8\%}{2} = 4\%$$

The diagram below indicates the two main steps in the solution.

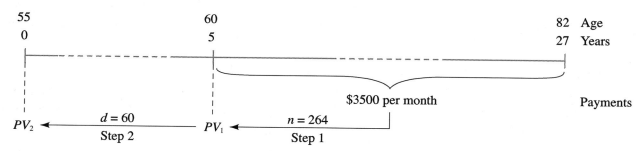

But first we must calculate the periodic rate that matches the one-month payment interval. (It will be about $\frac{8\%}{12} = 0.67\%$.)

$$c = \frac{2 \text{ compoundings per year}}{12 \text{ payments per year}} = 0.1\overline{6}$$

Using formula (9-4c),

$$i_2 = (1 + i)^c - 1 = 1.04^{01\overline{6}} - 1 = 0.00655819692 \text{ per month}$$

Substitute this value for i in formula (10-2) to obtain the present value of the pension at age 60.

$$PV_1 = PMT\left[\frac{1 - (1 + i)^{-n}}{i}\right]$$

$$= \$3500\left[\frac{1 - (1.00655819692)^{-264}}{0.00655819692}\right]$$

$$= \$438,662.91$$

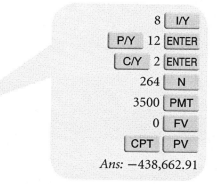

Using formula (8-2) in the form $PV = FV(1 + i)^{-n}$, the present value of \$438,662.91 five years earlier is

$$PV_2 = \$438{,}662.91(1 + i_2)^{-d}$$
$$= \$438{,}662.91(1.00655819692)^{-60}$$
$$= \$296{,}344.94$$

Same I/Y, P/Y, C/Y	
60	N
0	PMT
438662.91	FV
CPT	PV

Ans: $-296{,}344.94$

The current economic value of Maureen's pension is \$296,345. The significance of this number is that, if Maureen did not belong to the pension plan, she would need current savings of \$296,345 in a personal RRSP earning 8% compounded semiannually in order to duplicate the future pension benefits to age 82.

EXAMPLE 10.5D   CALCULATING THE FAIR MARKET VALUE OF A PREFERRED SHARE

The preferred shares of Dominion Trust Co. will pay a \$0.75 per share dividend at the end of every calendar quarter until they are redeemed (that is, bought back by Dominion Trust) $8\frac{1}{2}$ years from now. On the redemption date, a shareholder will receive the \$40 par value of each share in addition to the last regular dividend. What is the fair market value of a share if preferred shares of similar risk are currently generating a total rate of return of 6.5% compounded semiannually?

SOLUTION

This is a valuation application of present value. The fair market value of a share will be the combined present value of the dividends and the \$40 payment of the par value. The dividend stream constitutes an *ordinary general annuity* having

$$PMT = \$0.75 \quad n = 4(8.5) = 34 \quad \text{and} \quad i = \tfrac{6.5\%}{2} = 3.25\%$$

Then

$$c = \frac{2 \text{ compoundings per year}}{4 \text{ payments per year}} = 0.5$$

and

$$i_2 = (1 + i)^c - 1 = 1.0325^{0.5} - 1 = 0.0161201 \text{ per quarter}$$

Fair market value = Present value of dividends + Present value of par value

$$= PMT\left[\frac{1 - (1 + i)^{-n}}{i}\right] + FV(1 + i)^{-n}$$

$$= \$0.75\left(\frac{1 - 1.0161201^{-34}}{0.0161201}\right) + \$40(1.0161201)^{-34}$$

$$= \$19.513 + \$23.224$$

$$= \$42.74$$

6.5	I/Y
P/Y 4	ENTER
C/Y 2	ENTER
34	N
0.75	PMT
40	FV
CPT	PV

Ans: -42.74

The fair market value of a preferred share is \$42.74.

POINT OF INTEREST

The Alphabet Soup of Tax-Favoured Investing

To encourage people to save for retirement and their children's post-secondary education, the federal government has created programs under which investment contributions and/or the earnings thereon receive favourable income tax treatment. These programs usually have "Registered" in their name because every individual's plan is set up under a Declaration of Trust which is administered by a financial institution. The financial institution registers the "plan" with the Canada Revenue Agency (CRA), and reports to the CRA all contributions to and withdrawals from the plan.

The oldest (introduced in 1957) and best-known of these programs is the Registered Retirement Savings Plan (RRSP). The major features of RRSPs were described in the Point of Interest in Section 8.5.

In 1974, Registered Education Savings Plans (RESP) were created to encourage parents and grand-parents to save for their children's and grand-children's post-secondary education. Unlike contributions to an RRSP, contributions to an RESP *may not* be deducted from the contributor's taxable income. Consequently, there is no initial tax "break" or tax "sheltering" of money contributed to an RESP. However, the federal government's Canadian Education Savings Grant (CESG) provides a 20% "jump-start" for the growth of the RESP. For every $100 contributed per child per year to an RESP, the RESP receives a $20 grant (up to a maximum grant of $500 per child per year.)

As with RRSPs, income and capital gains on investments held in an RESP are not taxed until they are withdrawn from the RESP. The income, capital gains, and CESG portions of RESP withdrawals must normally be paid to the beneficiary children for costs related to their post-secondary education. These portions (but not the portion representing original contributions) are subject to income tax *in the hands* of the beneficiary/student. However, a student normally qualifies for enough tax credits that he or she can receive at least $15,000 in a calendar year from employment income and RESP withdrawals before he pays any income tax. In most cases, therefore, investment returns earned within RESPs are ultimately received tax-free by the beneficiary.

The newest addition (in 2009) to the "alphabet soup" of tax-favoured investment plans is the Tax-Free Savings Account (TFSA). Any individual, age 18 or older, may contribute up to $5000 per year[4] to a TFSA. Contributions are *not* deductible from taxable income. Investment returns within the plan are not subject to tax, and withdrawals of *both* contributions and earnings are *not subject to income tax*! Unused contribution "room" from one year can be carried forward and accumulated with new contribution room in subsequent years. For example, if you contributed nothing in 2009 and only $2000 in 2010, then in 2011 you may contribute

$5000 (for 2009) + $3000 (for 2010)
+ $5000 (for 2011) = $13,000

(ignoring inflation adjustments to the $5000 annual maximum contribution.)

On the withdrawal side, a TFSA is the most flexible of all the tax-favoured savings plans. If money is needed for an emergency or a major expenditure, funds may be withdrawn at any time *without* tax consequences. The amount withdrawn is added to the cumulative amount eligible for future contributions to the TFSA.

The Case at the end of this chapter will examine and compare the tax-reducing benefits of investing within RRSPs, RESPs, and TFSAs vs. conventional investing outside such plans.

SPREADSHEET STRATEGIES   FV and PV of an Ordinary General Annuity

Connect provides two Excel workbooks ("FV of Any Annuity" and "PV of Any Annuity") that may be used to compute the future value and the present value of both *simple* and *general* annuities. We will use the future value spreadsheet to determine the future value of an ordinary *general* annuity. Go to the Student Edition of Connect and find "FV of Any Annuity." The first page of this workbook discusses how to adapt Excel's *FV* and *PV* functions (designed for *simple* annuities) to ordinary *general* annuities.

The main features of a completed future value template are presented below. The formulas programmed into cells C11 and C18 are displayed in cells C12 and C19, respectively. Data are entered to solve Example 10.5B. In this example, we are asked to determine the value after 25 years of $1000 invested at the end of every year for 25 years, if the investment earns 8% compounded semiannually. After entering these known values into the yellow input cells, the computed future value immediately appears in the output cell C18.

	A	B	C	D
1				
2	Using a spreadsheet to calculate the future value of an ordinary general annuity.			
3	Example 10.5B:			
4				
5		Nominal annual interest rate, *j*	8.000%	
6		Compoundings per year, *m*	2	
7		Given periodic rate of interest, *i*	4.0000%	
8				
9		Payments per year	1	
10		Compoundings per payment interval, *c*	2.0000000000	
11		Periodic rate of interest, i_2 or *rate*	8.160000000%	
12		Formula in cell C11:	=(1+C7)^C10-1	
13		Number of payments, *n* or *nper*	25.00	
14		Regular annuity payment, *PMT* or *pmt*	-$1,000.00	
15		One time initial payment, *pv*	$0.00	
16		Annuity *type*	0	
17				
18		FV(rate, nper, pmt, pv, type)	$74,836.81	
19		Formula in cell C18:	= FV(C11,C13,C14,C15,C16)	
20				

The total value after 25 years will be $74,836.81.

Note: After you have correctly programmed each of the *FV* and *PV* templates for the first time, you should save the programmed templates in permanent files on your computer. You will be able to use them (without having to re-program the output cells) in many applications in future chapters.

CONCEPT QUESTIONS

1. What are the distinguishing characteristics of an ordinary general annuity?

2. An income annuity with quarterly payments earns 6% compounded monthly. What is the value of *c*? What is the approximate value of the periodic rate of return for one payment interval? Will the correct value be larger or smaller than your estimate? Explain.

3. A loan at 6% compounded semiannually requires equal monthly payments. What is the value of *c*? What is the approximate value of the periodic interest rate for one payment interval? Will the correct value be larger or smaller than your estimate? Explain.

EXERCISE 10.5

≣ connect

Spreadsheet templates: Partially completed Excel templates for calculating the future value and present value of an ordinary general annuity are provided in Connect. You can use these templates for many of the problems in Exercise 10.5. Go to the Student Edition of Connect to find "FV of Any Annuity" or "PV of Any Annuity."

Answers to the odd-numbered problems are at the end of the book.

1. The nominal interest rate associated with an ordinary general annuity is 7% compounded annually. Rounded to the nearest 0.001%, what is the corresponding periodic rate of interest that matches the payment interval for:

   a. Semiannual payments?

   b. Quarterly payments?

   c. Monthly payments?

2. The nominal interest rate associated with an ordinary general annuity is 7% compounded semiannually. Rounded to the nearest 0.001%, what is the corresponding periodic rate of interest that matches the payment interval for:

   a. Annual payments?

   b. Quarterly payments?

   c. Monthly payments?

3. The nominal interest rate associated with an ordinary general annuity is 8% compounded quarterly. Rounded to the nearest 0.001%, what is the corresponding periodic rate of interest that matches the payment interval for:

   a. Annual payments?

   b. Semiannual payments?

   c. Monthly payments?

4. The nominal interest rate associated with an ordinary general annuity is 8% compounded monthly. Rounded to the nearest 0.001%, what is the corresponding periodic rate of interest that matches the payment interval for:

   a. Annual payments?

   b. Semiannual payments?

   c. Quarterly payments?

5. This problem demonstrates the dependence of an annuity's future value on the compounding frequency. Suppose $1000 is invested at the end of each year for 25 years. Calculate the future value if the invested funds earn:

   a. 6% compounded annually.　　　　b. 6% compounded semiannually.

   c. 6% compounded quarterly.　　　　d. 6% compounded monthly.

6. This problem demonstrates the dependence of an annuity's present value on the compounding frequency. What minimum initial amount will sustain a 25-year annuity paying $1000 at the end of each year if the initial amount can be invested to earn:

   a. 6% compounded annually?　　　　b. 6% compounded semiannually?

   c. 6% compounded quarterly?　　　　d. 6% compounded monthly?

7. An ordinary annuity consists of quarterly payments of $400 for 11 years. Based on a nominal rate of 6.5% compounded annually, calculate the annuity's:

   a. Present value.　　　　　　　　　b. Future value.

8. An annuity consists of end-of-month payments of $150 continuing for $6\frac{1}{2}$ years. Based on a nominal rate of 10% compounded quarterly, calculate the annuity's:

   a. Present value.   b. Future value.

9. An ordinary annuity consists of semiannual payments of $2750 for a $3\frac{1}{2}$-year term. Using a nominal rate of 8% compounded monthly, calculate the annuity's:

   a. Present value.   b. Future value.

10. Payments of $1500 will be made at the end of every quarter for $13\frac{1}{2}$ years. Using a nominal rate of 7.5% compounded semiannually, calculate the annuity's:

    a. Present value.   b. Future value.

11. Payments of $3500 will be made at the end of every year for 17 years. Using a nominal rate of 5.25% compounded monthly, calculate the annuity's:

    a. Present value.   b. Future value.

12. An annuity consists of semiannual payments of $950 for a term of $8\frac{1}{2}$ years. Using a nominal rate of 9% compounded quarterly, calculate the ordinary annuity's:

    a. Present value.   b. Future value.

13. A deferred annuity consists of an ordinary annuity paying $2000 semiannually for a 10-year term after a 5-year period of deferral. Calculate the deferred annuity's present value using a discount rate of 7% compounded quarterly.

14. The first quarterly payment of $750 in a five-year annuity will be paid $3\frac{3}{4}$ years from now. Based on a discount rate of 8.25% compounded monthly, what is present value of the payments today?

15. A loan granted today will be repaid by payments of $500 per month running for $3\frac{1}{2}$ years. The first payment is due 2 years and 10 months from today. What amount was borrowed if the interest rate on the loan is 9% compounded quarterly?

16. Mr. and Mrs. Krenz are contributing to a Registered Education Savings Plan (RESP) they have set up for their children. What amount will they have in the RESP after eight years of contributing $500 at the end of every calendar quarter if the plan earns 6% compounded monthly? How much of the total amount is interest?

17. What is the future value eight years from now of each of the following cash-flow streams if money can earn 9% compounded semiannually?

    a. A single payment of $5000 today.

    b. An ordinary annuity starting today with eight annual payments of $900.

    c. An ordinary annuity starting in three years with 20 quarterly payments of $400.

18. How much larger will the value of an RRSP be at the end of 25 years if the RRSP earns 9% compounded monthly instead of 9% compounded annually? In both cases a contribution of $1000 is made at the end of every three months.

19. What amount will be required to purchase a 20-year annuity paying $2500 at the end of each month, if the annuity provides a return of 6.75% compounded annually?

20. An Agreement for Sale contract on a house requires payments of $4000 at the end of every six months. The contract has seven years to run. The payee wants to sell her interest in the contract. What will an investor pay in order to realize an annually compounded rate of return on the purchase price of:

    a. 8%?

    b. 10%?

21. Kent sold his car to Carolynn for $2000 down and monthly payments of $259.50 for $3\frac{1}{2}$ years, including interest at 7.5% compounded annually. What was the selling price of the car?

22. LeVero's monthly payments of $567.89 will pay off his mortgage loan in 4 years and 7 months. The interest rate on his mortgage is 6.6% compounded semiannully. What is the current balance on the loan?

23. **Advantage of Early Investing** Go to the Student Edition on this textbook's Web site. In Chapter 10, find "Advantage of Early Investing." You can enter data to compare three investment plans. For each plan, enter your regular end-of-period investment contribution, the frequency of contribution, the age range over which you will contribute, any initial amount already accumulated, and the projected rate of return. Compare the outcomes at age 65 for the following three alternatives:
    (i) Plan A: Invest $100/month starting at age 25.
    (ii) Plan B: Invest $200/month starting at age 35.
    (iii) Plan C: Invest $400/month starting at age 45.

    Enter 9% for the growth rate. The calculations will assume annual compounding. After completing the data entry, click on "Submit." A new window opens presenting a table of future values at various ages for each investment plan. Scroll down the window to view an attractive graphic comparing the growth of the three plans.

    a. Calculate the total of the *nominal* contributions under each plan. Compare them using a ratio A:B:C with terms reduced to small integers.

    b. Compare the future values at age 65 in a ratio A:B:C. Reduce the ratio so that the smallest term is "1."

○24. How much larger will the value of an TFSA be at the end of 25 years if the contributor makes month-end contributions of $300 instead of year-end contributions of $3600? In both cases the TFSA earns 8.5% compounded semiannually.

○25. Mr. Eusanio contributed $1500 to his RRSP on March 1 and on September 1 of each year for 25 years. The funds earned 6% compounded monthly for the first 10 years and 7% compounded annually for the next 15 years. What was the value of his RRSP after his contribution on September 1 of the 25th year?

○26. A savings plan requires end-of-month contributions of $100 for 25 years. What will be the future value of the plan if it earns 7% compounded quarterly for the first half of the annuity's term, and 8% compounded semiannually for the last half of the term?

○27. Year-end contributions of $1000 will be made to a TFSA for 25 years. What will be the future value of the account if it earns $7\frac{1}{2}$% compounded monthly for the first 10 years and 8% compounded semiannually thereafter?

○28. Monty expects to contribute $300 to his TFSA at the end of every month for the next five years. For the subsequent 10 years, he plans to contribute $2000 at the end of each calendar quarter. How much will be in his TFSA at the end of the 15 years if the funds earn 8% compounded semiannually?

○29. Gloria has just made her ninth annual $2000 contribution to her RRSP. She now plans to make semiannual contributions of $2000. The first contribution will be made six months from now. How much will she have in her RRSP 15 years from now if the plan has earned and will continue to earn 8% compounded quarterly?

○**30.** The Toronto Raptors announce the signing of one of their players to a "seven-year deal worth $43.2 million." The player will earn $400,000 at the end of each month for the first three years, and $600,000 at the end of each month for the subsequent four years. How do the Raptors get the $43.2 million figure? To the nearest $1000, what is the current economic value of the deal if money can earn 7% compounded annually?

○**31.** Micheline wishes to purchase a 25-year annuity providing payments of $1000 per month for the first 15 years and $1500 per month for the remaining 10 years. Sovereign Insurance Co. has quoted her a rate of return of 5% compounded annually for such an annuity. How much will it cost Micheline to purchase the annuity from Sovereign?

○**32.** Joshua wants to structure a 20-year annuity so that its end-of-quarter payments are $2000 for the first 10 years and $2500 for the next 10 years. Pacific Life Insurance Co. offers to sell this annuity with a 4.8% compounded monthly rate of return to the annuitant. What amount must Joshua pay to Pacific for the annuity?

○**33.** What is the value of a contract that will pay $500 at the end of each month for $2\frac{1}{2}$ years and $2000 at the end of each quarter for the subsequent $3\frac{1}{2}$ years? Use a discount rate of 6% compounded semiannually.

○**34.** What amount must be invested today to provide for quarterly payments of $2500 at the end of every quarter for 15 years after a six-year deferral period? Assume that the funds will earn 5% compounded semiannually.

○**35.** What is the current economic value of an inheritance that will pay $2000 to the beneficiary at the beginning of every three months for 20 years, starting when the beneficiary reaches 20 years of age, $4\frac{1}{2}$ years from now? Assume that money is worth 6% compounded monthly. (Round to the nearest dollar.)

○**36.** To sell a farm that it had acquired in a foreclosure action, the RBC Royal Bank agreed to monthly payments of $2700 for 20 years, with the first payment due 15 months from the date of sale. If the purchaser paid 15% down and the interest rate on the balance is 9% compounded annually, what was the purchase price? (Round to the nearest $100.)

○**37.** Sabrina borrowed $30,000 at an interest rate of 7% compounded quarterly. Monthly payments of $356.83 will commence after a period of deferral and will pay off the loan over the subsequent $12\frac{1}{2}$ years. What is the length of the period of deferral?

○**38.** An investor purchased a deferred annuity contract for $4608.07, a price calculated to provide a rate of return on investment of 9.75% compounded monthly. The semiannual payments of $400, once started, continue for a term of 15 years. How long is the period of deferral?

○**39.** How long (before the first withdrawal) must a $19,665 investment earning 9.5% compounded semiannually be allowed to grow before it can provide 60 quarterly withdrawals of $1000?

○**40.** Duncan retired recently and plans to utilize other savings for a few years while his RRSP continues to grow on a tax-deferred basis. The RRSP is currently worth $142,470. How long will it be until the amount in the RRSP is large enough to purchase a 25-year annuity paying $1700 at the end of each month? Assume that the RRSP and the annuity will earn 8.75% compounded semiannually.

•**41.** What will be the amount in an RRSP after 25 years if contributions of $3000 are made at each year-end for the first seven years and month-end contributions of $500 are made for the subsequent 18 years? Assume that the plan earns 8% compounded quarterly for the first 12 years, and 7% compounded semiannually for the subsequent 13 years.

KEY TERMS

Annuity **p. 375**

Annuity due **p. 375**

Deferred annuity **p. 403**

Future value of an annuity **p. 376**

Ordinary annuity **p. 375**

Ordinary general annuity **p. 376**

Ordinary simple annuity **p. 376**

Payment interval **p. 375**

Period of deferral **p. 403**

Present value of an annuity **p. 387**

Term of an annuity **p. 375**

SUMMARY OF NOTATION AND KEY FORMULAS

PMT = Periodic payment in an annuity

n = Number of payments in the annuity

FV = Future value of an ordinary annuity

PV = Present value of an ordinary annuity

i = (Given) periodic interest rate

i_2 = Equivalent periodic interest rate (per payment interval for a general annuity)

$c = \dfrac{\text{Number of compoundings per year}}{\text{Number of payments per year}}$

d = Equivalent number of payment intervals in the period of deferral

FORMULA (10-1) $FV = PMT\left[\dfrac{(1 + i)^n - 1}{i}\right]$ Finding the future value of an ordinary simple annuity

FORMULA (10-2) $PV = PMT\left[\dfrac{1 - (1 + i)^{-n}}{i}\right]$ Finding the present value of an ordinary simple annuity

FORMULA (10-3) $c = \dfrac{\text{Number of compoundings per year}}{\text{Number of payments per year}}$ Finding the number of compoundings per payment interval

FORMULA (9-4c) $i_2 = (1 + i)^c - 1$ Finding the periodic interest rate that matches the payment interval in a general annuity

Original loan = [Present value of *all* payments (discounted at the *contractual rate of interest* on the loan)]

Principal balance = [Present value of the *remaining* payments (discounted at the *contractual rate of interest* on the loan)]

Approach for Solving a General Annuity Problem

Transform the general annuity problem into a simple annuity problem by:

1. Using $i_2 = (1 + i)^c - 1$ to calculate the equivalent periodic rate that matches the payment interval.
2. Using this equivalent periodic rate as the value for i in the appropriate simple annuity formula.

REVIEW PROBLEMS

Answers to the odd-numbered review problems are at the end of the book.

1. **(LO2)** Calculate the amounts that will be accumulated after 20 years if:

    a. $1000 is invested at the end of every six months at 8.5% compounded semiannually.

    b. $2000 is invested at the end of every year at 8.5% compounded annually.

2. **(LO3)** Louiselle purchased a motor home for $9000 down, with the balance to be paid by 60 monthly payments of $1176.40 including interest at 6% compounded monthly.

    a. What was the purchase price of the motor home?

    b. If the principal balance may be prepaid at any time, what is the payout amount two years after the purchase date (not including the scheduled payment on that date)?

3. **(LO3)** What price will a finance company pay for a conditional sale contract requiring 15 monthly payments of $180.50, if the company requires a rate of return of 21% compounded semiannually? The first payment is due one month from now.

4. **(LO3)** You can purchase a residential building lot for $60,000 cash, or for $10,000 down and month-end payments of $1000 for five years. If money is worth 7.5% compounded monthly, which option should you choose?

5. **(LO2)** A victim of a car accident won a judgment for wages lost over a two-year period that ended nine months before the date of the judgment. In addition, the court awarded interest at 6% compounded monthly on the lost wages from the date they would otherwise have been received to the date of the judgment. If the monthly salary was $5500, what was the total amount of the award (on the date of the judgment)?

6. **(LO3)** Dr. Wilson is buying a 50% ownership in a veterinary practice by end-of-month payments of $714.60, including interest at 7% compounded semiannually for 15 years. Rounded to the nearest dollar,

    a. What valuation was placed on the partnership at the beginning of the payments?

    b. What total amount of interest will she pay over the 15 years?

7. **(LO2)** What minimum amount of money earning 7% compounded semiannually will sustain withdrawals of $1000 at the end of every month for 12 years?

8. **(LO4)** A 15-year loan requires month-end payments of $587.33 including interest at 8.4% compounded monthly.

    a. What was the original amount of the loan?

    b. What is the balance on the loan after half of the payments have been made?

9. **(LO2)** What amount of money invested now will provide payments of $500 at the end of every month for five years following a four-year period of deferral? The money will earn 7.2% compounded monthly.

10. **(LO2)** What price will a finance company pay to a merchant for a conditional sale contract that requires 12 monthly payments of $249, with the first payment due six months from now? The finance company requires a return of 16.5% compounded monthly.

11. **(LO2)** Calculate the future value of an ordinary annuity consisting of monthly payments of $300 for five years. The rate of return was 9% compounded monthly for the first two years, and will be 7.5% compounded monthly for the last three years.

12. **(LO2)** How much larger will the value of an RRSP be at the end of 20 years if the contributor makes month-end contributions of $500, instead of year-end contributions of $6000? In both cases the RRSP earns 7.5% compounded semiannually.

13. **(LO2)** Dr. Krawchuk made deposits of $2000 to his RRSP at the end of each calendar quarter for six years. He then left general practice for specialist training and did not make further contributions for $2\frac{1}{2}$ years. What amount was in his RRSP at the end of this period, if the plan earned 10% compounded quarterly over the entire $8\frac{1}{2}$ years?

14. **(LO3)** A Province of Ontario bond has $14\frac{1}{2}$ years remaining until it matures. The bond pays $231.25 interest at the end of every six months. At maturity, the bond repays its $5000 face value in addition to the final interest payment. What is the fair market value of the bond, if similar provincial bonds are currently providing investors with a return of 7.8% compounded semiannually?

∘15. **(LO2)** A court-ordered award for family support calls for payments of $800 per month for five years, followed by payments of $1000 per month for 10 more years. If money is worth 6% compounded monthly, what is the economic value of the award one month before the first payment?

∘16. **(LO2)** Calculate the future value of investments of $800 at the end of each calendar quarter for seven years. The rate of return will be 10% compounded quarterly for the first 30 months and 9% compounded semiannually for the remainder of the annuity's term.

∘17. **(LO5)** C&D Stereo sold a stereo system on a plan that required no down payment and nothing to pay until January 1 (four months away). Then the first of 12 monthly payments of $226.51 must be made. The payments were calculated to provide C&D Stereo with a return on the account receivable of 16.5% compounded monthly. What was the selling price of the stereo system?

∘18. **(LO2)** Charlene has made contributions of $3000 to her RRSP at the end of every half year for the past seven years. The plan has earned 9% compounded semiannually. She has just moved the funds to another plan earning 7.5% compounded quarterly, and will now contribute $2000 at the end of every three months. What total amount will she have in the plan five years from now?

∘19. **(LO2)** What percentage more funds will you have in your RRSP 20 years from now if you make fixed contributions of $3000 at the end of every six months for the next 20 years, instead of waiting 10 years and making semiannual contributions that are twice as large for half as many years? Assume that the RRSP earns 8% compounded semiannually.

∘20. **(LO3)** A mortgage broker offers to sell you a mortgage loan contract delivering month-end payments of $900 for the next $2\frac{3}{4}$ years. At that point, the principal balance of $37,886 is due and payable. What should you pay for the contract, if you require a return of 7.2% compounded monthly?

∘21. **(LO3)** What is the appropriate price to pay for a contract guaranteeing payments of $1500 at the end of each quarter for the next 12 years? You require a rate of return of 6% compounded quarterly for the first five years, and 7% compounded quarterly for the next seven years.

∘22. **(LO2)** Suppose Evan contributes $2000 to his RRSP at the end of every quarter for the next 15 years, and then contributes $1000 at each month's end for the subsequent 10 years. How much will he have in his RRSP at the end of the 25 years? Assume that the RRSP earns 8% compounded semiannually.

∘23. **(LO5)** What is the current economic value of an inheritance that will pay $2500 to the beneficiary at the beginning of every three months for 20 years starting when the beneficiary reaches 21 years of age, $5\frac{1}{4}$ years from now? Assume that money can earn 6% compounded monthly.

•24. **(LO5)** A $30,000 loan bearing interest at 9% compounded monthly was repaid, after a period of deferral, by monthly payments of $425.10 for 10 years. What was the time interval between the date of the loan and the first payment?

CASE Sheltering Investments from Taxes

The Points of Interest in Sections 8.5 and 10.5 have described the main features of three plans (RRSPs, RESPs, and TFSAs) that Canadians can use to enhance their ability to save for retirement or for the post-secondary education of their children. As we have seen in those Points of Interest, the enhancement is achieved through favourable income tax treatment of the contributions to these plans or the earnings of investments held within the plans (or both).

In this Case, we will create a "fair comparison" scenario and calculate the growth of savings within each of these plans. Then we will compare the ultimate after-tax pay-outs from the plans. In addition, we will compare the outcomes from the tax-favoured plans with the result achieved by investing outside such plans, fully exposed to income tax. For a fair comparison, in each situation we will assume that:

- The same *pre-tax* amount of $1500 is available for contribution/investment each year.
- The investor's marginal tax rate is $33\frac{1}{3}$%.
- The same annual end-of-year contribution will be made for 20 years.
- The investments will earn a pre-tax rate of return of 7.5% compounded annually. (These earnings are not taxed within an RRSP, RESP, or TFSA.)
- After 20 years, the accumulated funds (continuing to earn 7.5% compounded annually) will be withdrawn in eight equal end-of-year payments. (For an RESP, a plausible circumstance would be three beneficiary children receiving, in succession, payments for three years, three years, and two years.)

QUESTIONS

1. **RRSP:** What will be the annual after-tax withdrawal from the RRSP? [Remember that the entire withdrawal each year will be subject to income tax at the contributor's marginal tax rate. Assume that the contributor retired just before withdrawals start, and that her marginal tax rate (at her reduced income level) is 25%.]

2. **RESP:** Unlike contributions to an RRSP, contributions to an RESP (or to a TFSA in Question 3) are not deductible from taxable income. Consequently, of the pre-tax $1500 available for investing, 0.33333 × $1500 = $500 must be used to pay income tax. That leaves only $1000 each year to contribute to an RESP or a TFSA, or to invest outside of a tax-favoured plan. Recall that the federal government will provide a CESG grant of 20% of the annual $1000 RESP contribution. Therefore, the combined annual contribution to the RESP is $1200.

   What will be the annual after-tax withdrawal from the RESP? (Remember that only the portion of a withdrawal representing investment growth and CESG grants is taxable, and then only at the student's marginal tax rate. After tax credits, this rate is effectively 0% for income below $15,000.)

3. **TFSA:** As with the RESP, only $1000 of the pre-tax $1500 is left after tax to invest. What will be the annual withdrawal from the TFSA? (Remember that withdrawals from a TFSA are not taxable.)

4. **Unsheltered Investing:** As with the RESP and TFSA, only $1000 of the pre-tax $1500 is available after tax to invest. What annual after-tax withdrawal will the unsheltered portfolio sustain? [Remember that each year's investment returns will be taxed at the investor's marginal tax rate. For the first 20 years, this rate is $33\frac{1}{3}$%. Therefore, the after-tax rate of return during these 20 years will be 7.5% × (1 − 0.3333) = 5.0% compounded annually. During the final eight years, the retired investor's marginal tax rate is only 25%.]

5. Rank the four scenarios in the order of their annual payout. Express each payout as a percentage of the lowest annual payout.

6. Identify the main one or two factors that give:
   a. The top-ranked plan or outcome its advantage over the second-ranked plan or outcome;
   b. The second-ranked plan its advantage over the third-ranked plan;
   c. The third-ranked plan its advantage over the fourth-ranked plan.

CHAPTER

11

Ordinary Annuities: Periodic Payment, Number of Payments, and Interest Rate

CHAPTER OUTLINE

LEARNING OBJECTIVES

After completing this chapter, you will be able to:

LO1 Calculate the periodic payment in ordinary and deferred annuities

LO2 Calculate the number of payments in ordinary and deferred annuities

LO3 Calculate the interest rate in ordinary annuities

IN CHAPTER 10, OUR DISCUSSION of ordinary annuities was restricted to applications of future value and present value calculations. But there are many circumstances in which one of the other variables must be determined. Consider the following questions:

- What is the monthly payment required to repay a $10,000 loan at 9% compounded monthly in four years?
- At a forecast rate of return, how long will it take to accumulate $500,000 in an RRSP if you contribute $300 per month?
- What rate of return is required for RRSP contributions of $400 per month to grow to $600,000 in 25 years?
- What interest rate are you being charged when you purchase equipment, furniture, insurance, memberships, magazine subscriptions, etc., on an instalment plan instead of paying cash?

Clearly, the ability to answer such questions is important both in business and in your personal financial affairs.

In this chapter, you will learn how to answer these questions if the payments form an ordinary annuity. (Chapter 12 will examine cases in which the payments are at the beginning of each payment interval.) The introduction to Chapter 10 stated that its contents would be "the foundation we will build upon throughout Chapters 11 to 15." As you will soon discover, you already have the fundamentals in place for the topics in this chapter. You need only adapt familiar concepts and formulas to new situations.

11.1 CALCULATING THE PERIODIC PAYMENT

Some circumstances in which the periodic payment, *PMT*, must be calculated are:

- Determining the monthly payments on a loan.

- Determining the amount that must be saved on a regular basis to reach a savings goal.

- Determining the periodic payment from an annuity purchased with accumulated savings.

LO1   In order to calculate *PMT*, you need to know the number of payments, *n*, and the periodic interest rate, *i*, (or be able to readily determine them from the given information). In addition, you must know *either* the present value, *PV*, or the future value, *FV*, of the annuity.

Algebraic Method The calculation of *PMT* may require up to four steps.

Step 1: If the payments form a *simple* annuity, go directly to Step 2.
If the payments form a *general* annuity, use $i_2 = (1 + i)^c - 1$ to calculate the periodic interest rate that matches the payment interval. Use i_2 as the value for *i* in Step 2.

Step 2: If the annuity's *FV* is known, substitute values of *FV*, *n*, and *i* into

$$FV = PMT\left[\frac{(1 + i)^n - 1}{i}\right] \quad (10\text{-}1)$$

Step 2: If the annuity's *PV* is known, substitute values of *PV*, *n*, and *i* into

$$PV = PMT\left[\frac{1 - (1 + i)^{-n}}{i}\right] \quad (10\text{-}2)$$

Step 3: Calculate the quantity within the square brackets.

Step 4: Rearrange the equation to solve for *PMT*.

Financial Calculator Method (Texas Instruments BA II PLUS) Enter the known values for $\boxed{N}$, $\boxed{I/Y}$, $\boxed{PV}$, $\boxed{FV}$, $\boxed{P/Y}$, and $\boxed{C/Y}$. Remember to use the cash-flow sign convention for amounts entered in $\boxed{PV}$ and $\boxed{FV}$. Then press $\boxed{CPT}$ $\boxed{PMT}$ to execute the computation.

EXAMPLE 11.1A   **CALCULATING THE PERIODIC INVESTMENT NEEDED TO REACH A SAVINGS TARGET**

Markham Auto Body wishes to accumulate a fund of $300,000 during the next 18 months in order to open at a second location. At the end of each month, a fixed amount will be invested in a money market savings account with an investment dealer. What should the monthly investment be in order to reach the savings objective? The planning assumption is that the account will earn 3.6% compounded monthly.

SOLUTION

The savings target of $300,000 represents the future value of the fixed *monthly* investments. Since earnings are compounded *monthly,* the *end-of-month* investments form an *ordinary simple* annuity. We are given:

Step 1: $FV = \$300,000$ $n = 18$ and $i = \frac{3.6\%}{12} = 0.3\%$ per month

Step 2:   Substitute the given values into formula (10-1).

$$FV = PMT\left[\frac{(1 + i)^n - 1}{i}\right]$$

$$\$300,000 = PMT\left[\frac{1.003^{18} - 1}{0.003}\right]$$

Step 3: $\$300,000 = PMT(18.4664273)$

Step 4: $PMT = \dfrac{\$300,000}{18.4664273} = \$16,245.70$

3.6 $\boxed{I/Y}$
$\boxed{P/Y}$ 12 $\boxed{ENTER}$
(making $C/Y = P/Y = 12$)
18 $\boxed{N}$
0 $\boxed{PV}$
300,000 $\boxed{FV}$
$\boxed{CPT}$ $\boxed{PMT}$
Ans: $-16,245.70$

Markham Auto Body should make monthly investments of $16,245.70 in order to accumulate $300,000 after 18 months.

EXAMPLE 11.1B   **CALCULATING THE PERIODIC LOAN PAYMENTS THAT FORM AN ORDINARY GENERAL ANNUITY**

A $5000 loan requires payments at the end of each quarter for four years. If the interest rate on the loan is 9% compounded monthly, what is the size of each payment?

SOLUTION

The original loan equals the present value of all payments discounted at the loan's interest rate. Since interest is compounded *monthly* and payments are made at the *end* of each *quarter,* we have an *ordinary general* annuity with

$$PV = \$5000 \quad n = 4(4) = 16 \quad \text{and} \quad i = \frac{9\%}{12} = 0.75\% \text{ per month}$$

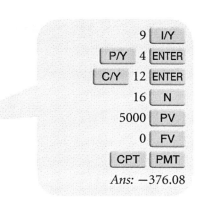

Step 1:   Then, $c = \dfrac{12 \text{ compoundings per year}}{4 \text{ payments per year}} = 3$

and $i_2 = (1 + i)^c - 1$

$= (1.0075)^3 - 1$

$= 0.02266917 \text{ per quarter}$

Step 2:   Substitute the preceding values into formula (10-2).

$$PV = PMT\left[\dfrac{1 - (1 + i)^{-n}}{i}\right]$$

$$\$5000 = PMT\left[\dfrac{1 - 1.02266917^{-16}}{0.02266917}\right]$$

Step 3: $\$5000 = PMT(13.29497)$

Step 4: $PMT = \dfrac{\$5000}{13.29497} = \$376.08$

The size of each quarterly payment is $376.08.

EXAMPLE 11.1C   **CALCULATING THE PERIODIC LOAN PAYMENT REQUIRED TO REACH A TARGET BALANCE**

Simon owns a mobile welding business. Every three years, he trades in his old pickup truck and buys a new one. In each cycle, he finances the full purchase price with a loan structured so that the balance owed after three years will be the truck's anticipated trade-in value. Simon is about to purchase a new truck for $37,000, including taxes. The interest rate on the $37,000 loan will be 7.2% compounded monthly. What monthly payment will reduce the balance on the loan after three years to the expected trade-in value of $16,500?

SOLUTION

Again we will use the fundamental principle that

Original principal = Present value of all payments

This principle applies whether or not all payments are equal. (The $16,500 balance after three years can be viewed as the amount which, along with the last monthly payment, will pay off the loan.)

$$\$37,000 = \left(\begin{array}{c}\text{Present value of the}\\\text{loan payment annuity}\end{array}\right) + \left(\begin{array}{c}\text{Present value of}\\\text{the \$16,500 balance}\end{array}\right) \quad ①$$

Since we have *end-of-month* payments and *monthly* compounding, the payments form an *ordinary simple* annuity. For both the annuity and the terminal payment,

$n = 12(3) = 36$ and $i = \frac{7.2\%}{12} = 0.6\%$

Using formulas (10-2) and (8-2) on the right side of equation ①, we obtain

$$PV = PMT\left[\dfrac{1 - (1 + i)^{-n}}{i}\right] + FV(1 + i)^{-n}$$

$$\$37,000 = PMT\left(\dfrac{1 - 1.006^{-36}}{0.006}\right) + \$16,500(1.006)^{-36}$$

$$\$37,000 = PMT(32.290749) + \$13,303.22$$

Solving for *PMT*,

$32.290749PMT = \$37,000 - \$13,303.22 = \$23,696.78$

$PMT = \dfrac{\$23,696.78}{32.290749} = \$733.86$

Monthly payments of $733.86 will reduce the balance to $16,500 after three years.

EXAMPLE 11.1D   **CALCULATING THE PERIODIC INVESTMENT REQUIRED TO PURCHASE A SPECIFIED ANNUITY ON A FUTURE DATE**

Douglas and Margaret Kuramoto want to retire in 15 years with enough funds in their RRSPs to purchase a 25-year annuity that will pay $5000 at the end of each month. They have already accumulated $125,000 in their RRSPs. In order to fulfil the plan, what RRSP contribution should they make at the end of each of the next 15 years? For the financial projections, they are assuming returns of 8% compounded annually on their RRSPs and 6% compounded monthly on the annuity purchased with their RRSP funds.

SOLUTION

The given information and the steps in the solution are presented in the time diagram shown on the right.

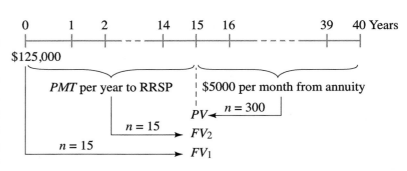

The total amount in the RRSPs 15 years from now will be the future value, FV_1, of the $125,000 already in the RRSPs *plus* the future value, FV_2, of 15 more annual contributions of size *PMT*. The amount needed to purchase the annuity paying $5000 per month will be the present value, *PV*, of the $12(25) = 300$ payments discounted at $i = \frac{6\%}{12} = 0.5\%$. Each series of payments forms an ordinary simple annuity.

In order to have enough money in their RRSPs 15 years from now to purchase the desired annuity, the Kuramotos require

$$FV_1 + FV_2 = PV \quad ①$$

The amount that will be needed to purchase the annuity is

$$PV = PMT\left[\frac{1 - (1 + i)^{-n}}{i}\right]$$

$$= \$5000\left(\frac{1 - 1.005^{-300}}{0.005}\right)$$

$$= \$776,034.32$$

6 | I/Y
P/Y 12 ENTER
(making $C/Y = P/Y = 12$)
300 | N
5000 | PMT
0 | FV
CPT | PV
Ans: −776,034.32

The future value of the $125,000 already saved is

$$FV_1 = PV(1 + i)^n$$
$$= \$125,000(1.08)^{15}$$
$$= \$396,521.14$$

The future value of the 15 annual contributions of *PMT* is

$$FV_2 = PMT\left[\frac{(1 + i)^n - 1}{i}\right]$$

$$= PMT\left(\frac{1.08^{15} - 1}{0.08}\right)$$

$$= 27.152114PMT$$

8 | I/Y
P/Y 1 ENTER
(making $C/Y = P/Y = 1$)
15 | N
125000 | +/− | PV
776034.32 | FV
CPT | PMT
Ans: −13,977.30

Substituting these values into equation ①, we obtain

$$\$396,521.14 + 27.152114PMT = \$776,034.32$$
$$27.152114PMT = \$379,513.18$$
$$PMT = \$13,977.30$$

The Kuramotos must make annual RRSP contributions of $13,977.30.

EXAMPLE 11.1E   **CALCULATING THE PERIODIC PAYMENT IN A DEFERRED ANNUITY**

Budget Appliances has a promotion on a washer-dryer combination selling for $1750. Buyers will pay "no money down and no payments for six months." The first of 12 equal monthly payments is required six months from the purchase date. What should the monthly payments be if Budget Appliances is to earn 15% compounded monthly on its account receivable during both the deferral period and the repayment period?

SOLUTION

Viewed from the date of the sale, the payments form a deferred simple annuity—a 12-payment ordinary simple annuity following a five-month period of deferral. That is,

$$n = 12 \quad d = 5 \quad \text{and} \quad i = \frac{15\%}{12} = 1.25\%$$

In effect, Budget Appliances makes a $1750 loan to the customer on the date of the sale. As indicated on the timeline below, the balance owed on the loan will increase to FV over the next five months as interest accrues. Then the 12 monthly payments will pay off this balance. Hence,

$$\begin{pmatrix} \text{Future value of \$1750} \\ \text{at the end of Month 5} \end{pmatrix} = \begin{pmatrix} \text{Present value of the payments} \\ \text{at the end of Month 5} \end{pmatrix}$$

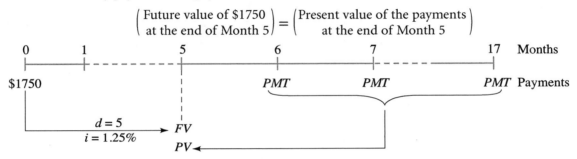

The amount owed after five months will be

$$FV = PV(1 + i)^n$$
$$= \$1750(1.0125)^5$$
$$= \$1862.14$$

This amount is the present value of the 12-payment simple annuity. Substituting in formula (10-2),

$$PV = PMT\left[\frac{1 - (1 + i)^{-n}}{i}\right]$$

$$\$1862.14 = PMT\left[\frac{1 - (1.0125)^{-12}}{0.0125}\right]$$

$$\$1862.14 = PMT(11.07931)$$

Hence,

$$PMT = \frac{\$1862.14}{11.07931} = \$168.07$$

15	I/Y
P/Y 12	ENTER
(making C/Y = P/Y = 12)	
5	N
1750 +/−	PV
0	PMT
CPT	FV
Ans: 1862.14	

Same I/Y, P/Y, C/Y	
12	N
1862.14 +/−	PV
0	FV
CPT	PMT
Ans: 168.07	

Monthly payments of $168.07 will provide Budget Appliances with a return of 15% compounded monthly on its account receivable.

POINT OF INTEREST

Reality Check

The cover story in the September 29, 1997 issue of *Maclean's* magazine was "Getting Ready for Retirement." One of the key points made in the article was the mismatch between Canadians' financial dreams and the reality of their financial affairs. For example, a poll conducted for Maclean's found that 49% of respondents hoped to retire before age 60. However, only 7% of Canadian households in the 45–54 age group had savings in excess of $250,000 (exclusive of real estate). As pollster Dan Richards bluntly put it: "Clearly, Canadians are living in a state of mass delusion. There is no way on God's green earth that the average person is going to be able to retire in comfort at age 58, given what we know about the savings rate."

A survey by Environics Research for TD Wealth Management in 2001 found that 80% of Canadians are confident they will have enough money to retire comfortably.

When asked what accumulated savings will be needed for a comfortable retirement, 16% indicated that $100,000 or less will be sufficient, and another 24% thought savings between $100,000 and $500,000 would be required.

The results of Desjardins Financial Security's annual survey released in February 2004 indicated that early retirement was becoming a more elusive goal for Canadians. Even on a matter given to over-optimism, half of respondents aged 40 to 54 believed they would not be able to retire at or before age 58. Taylor Train, Director of Business Development for Desjardins, suggested that workers should build massive RRSPs to retire in style. Fifty-year-olds should aim for at least $500,000 in an RRSP plus $250,000 more in non-registered savings.

More recently, the recession of 2008–2009 and the vicious "bear" market (which took the S&P/TSX Composite Index down from above 15,000 in June,

2008, to below 7500 in March, 2009) caused many middle-aged workers to postpone their planned retirement dates. The average age at retirement has now started to rise after a 30-year decline.

In a side box to its 1997 article, *Maclean's* presented its estimates of the savings required to retire comfortably at age 65. It is presented verbatim below.

BUILDING A GOLDEN NEST EGG

How much do you need to put aside for retirement? The answer depends partly on when you start. The following figures show how much someone would have to save every year to generate a retirement income (excluding government and company pension benefits) equal to $50,000 in today's dollars, assuming the individual stops work at age 65 and lives to 90. The calculations are based on 3% annual inflation and an 8% return on investments. Experts say that, in general, a person needs 70% of his or her pre-retirement income to maintain a similar standard of living after retirement.

Starting at age	Savings required at age 65	Annual savings
20	$2,018,387	$5222
35	$1,295,523	$17,154
50	$831,544	$45,938

SOURCE: *Maclean's*, September 29, 1997. Reprinted with permission.

QUESTIONS

1. For the starting-at-age-20 case, what income at age 65 will have the same purchasing power as $50,000 at age 20?

2. For the starting-at-age-20 case, show how the amounts for the "Savings required" and "Annual savings" are obtained.

3. The annual savings figures given by *Maclean's* for age 35 and age 50 are, in fact, incorrect. What are the correct values?

SPREADSHEET STRATEGIES   Calculating the Payment in an Annuity

Connect provides a partially completed template for calculating the amount of an annuity's payment. Go to the Student Edition of Connect and find "*PMT* for Any Annuity." The first page of this workbook discusses Excel's *PMT* function.

The main features of a completed *PMT* template are presented below. The formulas programmed into cells C11 and C18 are displayed in cells C12 and C19, respectively.

Data are entered to solve Example 11.1B. In this example, we are asked to determine the quarterly payment on a $5000 four-year loan carrying an interest rate of 9% compounded monthly. After entering the known values in the yellow input cells, the computed payment appears immediately in the output cell C18.

	A	B	C	D
1				
2	Using a spreadsheet to calculate the payment for an annuity.			
3	Example 11.1B:			
4				
5		Nominal annual interest rate, *j*	9.000%	
6		Compoundings per year, *m*	12	
7		Given periodic rate of interest, *i*	0.7500%	
8				
9		Payments per year	4	
10		Compoundings per payment interval, *c*	3.0000000000	
11		Periodic rate of interest, i_2 or *rate*	2.266917188%	
12		Formula in cell C11:	=(1+C7)^C10-1	
13		Number of payments, *n* or *nper*	16.00	
14		Present value, *pv*	$5,000.00	
15		Future value, *fv*	$0.00	
16		Annuity *type*	0	
17				
18		PMT(rate, nper, pv, fv, type)	-$376.08	
19		Formula in cell C18:	=PMT(C11,C13,C14,C15,C16)	
20				

The quarterly payment on the loan is $376.08.

Note: After you have correctly programmed the *PMT* template for the first time, you should save it in a permanent file on your computer. You will be able to use it (without having to re-program the output cells) in many other applications in Chapters 11 to 14.

CONCEPT QUESTIONS

1. Suppose you choose to pay off a loan over 10 years instead of 5 years. The principal and interest rate are the same in both cases. Will the payment for the 10-year term be: **(i)** Half the payment for the 5-year term? **(ii)** More than half the payment? **(iii)** Less than half the payment? Give the reasoning for your choice.

2. You intend to accumulate $100,000 in 10 years instead of 20 years by making equal monthly investment contributions. Will the monthly contribution for a 10-year plan be: **(i)** Twice the monthly contribution for a 20-year plan? **(ii)** Less than twice the monthly contribution? **(iii)** More than twice the monthly contribution? Assume the same rate of return in both cases. Give the reasoning for your choice.

Spreadsheet template: *A partially completed Excel template for calculating the payment in an annuity is provided in Connect. You can use this template for many of the problems in Exercise 11.1. Go to the Student Edition of Connect and find "PMT for Any Annuity."*

Answers to the odd-numbered problems are at the end of the book.

1. Calculate the amount that must be invested at the end of each year at 9% compounded annually in order to accumulate $500,000 after:

   a. 25 years.   **b.** 30 years.

   In each case, also determine what portion of the $500,000 represents earnings on the annual investments.

2. In order to accumulate $500,000 after 25 years, calculate the amounts that must be invested at the end of each year, if the invested funds earn:

   a. 6% compounded annually.   **b.** 7% compounded annually.

   c. 8% compounded annually.   **d.** 9% compounded annually.

   In each case, also calculate the total earnings.

3. A 20-year annuity is purchased for $400,000. What payment will it deliver at the end of each quarter, if the undistributed funds earn:

   a. 4% compounded quarterly?   **b.** 5% compounded quarterly?

   c. 6% compounded quarterly?   **d.** 7% compounded quarterly?

   In each case, also calculate the total earnings distributed over the life of the annuity.

4. The interest rate on a $100,000 loan is 7.5% compounded monthly. What must be the monthly payment for the loan to be repaid in:

   a. 5 years?   **b.** 10 years?   **c.** 15 years?   **d.** 20 years?

   In each case, also calculate the total interest paid. (Note that a doubling of the term more than doubles the total interest paid over the life of the loan.)

5. Assume that the investments within an RRSP will earn 7% compounded annually. What monthly contribution must be made to the RRSP for it to grow to $750,000 in:

   a. 15 years?   **b.** 20 years?   **c.** 25 years?   **d.** 30 years?

   In each case, also calculate the total earnings within the RRSP. (Note that the total earnings increase proportionately more than the duration of contributions.)

6. Marissa intends to make contributions to a TFSA such that the account will accumulate $150,000 after 20 years. What end-of-quarter contributions must be made, if the TFSA earns 6% compounded:

   a. Annually?   **b.** Semiannually?   **c.** Quarterly?   **d.** Monthly?

7. What monthly payment is required to pay off a $50,000 loan in seven years, if the interest rate on the loan is 7.5% compounded:

   a. Annually?   **b.** Semiannually?   **c.** Quarterly?   **d.** Monthly?

8. The first of 80 quarterly payments on a $50,000 loan at 6.4% compounded quarterly will be made 30 months after the date the loan was granted. What will be the amount of each payment?

9. Noel has $300,000 with which to purchase an ordinary annuity delivering monthly payments for 20 years after a 10-year period of deferral. What monthly payment will he receive, if the undistributed funds earn 5% compounded semiannually?

10. Your client will retire this year. Currently she has $560,000 in accumulated capital. She wants to invest this capital to provide equal payments at the end of each year for 20 years, at which time the capital will be fully depleted. If her capital earns 7.5% compounded annually, what annual payment will she receive? (Taken from CIFP course materials.)

11. Karen obtained a $20,000 loan at 8% compounded semiannually. What monthly payment will repay the loan in $7\frac{1}{2}$ years? How much interest will Karen pay over the life of the loan?

12. Brenda and Tom want to save $30,000 over the next four years for a down payment on a house. What amount must they regularly save from their month-end pay cheques if their savings can earn 5.5% compounded semiannually?

13. Henry can buy a farm for $700,000 with terms of $100,000 down and the balance payable over 20 years by quarterly payments including interest at 8% compounded annually. What will be the size of the payments? How much interest will Henry pay over the life of the loan?

14. RBC Royal Bank approved a four-year $20,000 Royal Buy-Back Car Loan to Zaman at 7.5% compounded monthly. The monthly payments are to reduce the balance on the loan to the Royal Bank's guaranteed buy-back value of $7250. Calculate the monthly payment.

15. Ardith is scheduled to make a lump payment of $25,000, 11 months from now, to complete a real estate transaction. What end-of-month payments for the next 11 months should the vendor be willing to accept instead of the lump payment if he can invest the funds at 5.4% compounded monthly?

◦16. In order to purchase another truck, Beatty Transport recently obtained a $50,000 loan for five years at 7.8% compounded semiannually.

   a. What are the monthly payments on the loan?

   b. What will be the loan's balance at the end of the second year?

   c. How much interest will Beatty pay in the first two years?

◦17. Mr. Bean wants to borrow $7500 for three years. The interest rate is 9% compounded monthly.

   a. What quarterly payments are required on the loan?

   b. What will be the balance owed on the loan at the start of the third year?

◦18. The interest rate on a $200,000 loan is 8% compounded quarterly.

   a. What payments at the end of every quarter will reduce the balance to $150,000 after $3\frac{1}{2}$ years?

   b. If the same payments continue, what will be the balance seven years after the date that the loan was received?

   c. How much interest will be paid during the first seven years?

◦19. As of Betty's fifty-sixth birthday, she has accumulated $195,000 in her RRSP. She has ceased contributions but will allow the RRSP to grow at an expected 8.4% compounded monthly until she reaches age 65. Then she will use the funds in the RRSP to purchase a 20-year annuity. What will her end-of-month annuity payments be if the money used to purchase the annuity earns 7.2% compounded monthly?

◦20. On the date of his granddaughter's birth, Mr. Parry deposited $5000 in a trust fund earning 6.2% compounded annually. After the granddaughter's nineteenth birthday, the trust account will make end-of-month payments to her for four years to assist with the costs of post-secondary education. If the trust account earns 4.8% compounded monthly during these four years, what will be the size of the monthly payments?

○**21.** Elizabeth has been able to transfer a $25,000 retiring allowance into an RRSP. She plans to let the RRSP accumulate earnings at the rate of 7% compounded annually for 10 years, and then purchase a 15-year annuity making payments at the end of each quarter. What size of payment can she expect if the funds in the annuity earn 5.2% compounded quarterly?

○**22.** Ken and Barbara have two children, aged three and six. At the end of every six months for the next $12\frac{1}{2}$ years, they wish to contribute equal amounts to a Registered Education Savings Plan (RESP). Six months after the last RESP contribution, the first of 12 semiannual withdrawals of $5000 will be made. If the RESP earns 8.5% compounded semiannually, what must be the size of their regular RESP contributions?

○**23.** Four years from now, Tim and Justine plan to take a year's leave of absence from their jobs and travel through Asia, Europe, and Africa. They want to accumulate enough savings during the next four years so they can withdraw $3000 at each month-end for the entire year of leave. What amount must they pay into the fund at the end of every calendar quarter for the next four years to reach their goal? The planning assumptions are that their savings will earn 6% compounded quarterly for the next four years and 4.2% compounded monthly during the fifth year.

○**24.** Beth and Nelson want to accumulate a combined total of $600,000 in their RRSPs by the time Beth reaches age 60, which will be 30 years from now. They plan to make equal contributions at the end of every six months for the next 25 years, and then no further contributions for the subsequent five years of semiretirement. For planning purposes, assume that their RRSPs will earn 7% compounded semiannually for the next 30 years.

  a. What should be their combined semiannual RRSP contributions?

  b. What monthly amount can they expect to receive if they use the $600,000 in their RRSPs 30 years from now to purchase a 25-year ordinary annuity? Assume that the funds used to purchase the annuity will earn 7.2% compounded monthly.

○**25.** Dr. Collins wants the value of her RRSP 30 years from now to have the purchasing power of $500,000 in current dollars.

  a. Assuming an inflation rate of 2% per year, what nominal dollar amount should Dr. Collins have in her RRSP after 30 years?

  b. Assuming her RRSP will earn 8.5% compounded semiannually, what contributions should she make at the end of every three months to achieve the goal?

○**26.** Harold, just turned 27, wants to accumulate an amount in his RRSP at age 60 that will have the purchasing power of $300,000 in current dollars. What annual contributions on his twenty-eighth through sixtieth birthdays are required to meet this goal if the RRSP earns 8.5% compounded annually and the rate of inflation is 2.5% per year?

○**27.** As of Brice's fifty-fourth birthday, he has accumulated $154,000 in his Registered Retirement Savings Plan (RRSP). What size of end-of-month payments in a 20-year annuity will these funds purchase at age 65 if he makes no further contributions? Assume that his RRSP and the investment in the annuity will earn 8.25% compounded monthly.

○**28.** Leslie received a settlement when her employer declared her job redundant. Under special provisions of the Income Tax Act, she was eligible to place $22,000 of the settlement in an RRSP. Fifteen years from now, she intends to transfer the money from the RRSP to a Registered Retirement Income Fund (RRIF). Thereafter, Leslie will make equal withdrawals at the end of each quarter for 20 years. If both the RRSP and the RRIF earn 8.5% compounded quarterly, what will be the amount of each withdrawal?

○**29.** A firm obtained a $3 million low-interest loan from a government agency to build a factory in an economically depressed region. The loan is to be repaid in semiannual payments over 15 years, and the first payment is due three years from today, when the firm's operations are expected to be well established.

    a. What will the payments be if the interest rate on the loan is 6% compounded semiannually?

    b. What is the nominal amount of interest that will be paid over the lifetime of the loan?

○**30.** During a one-week promotion, Al's Appliance Warehouse is planning to offer terms of "nothing down and nothing to pay for four months" on major appliances priced above $500. Four months after the date of sale, the first of eight equal monthly payments is due. If the customer is to pay interest at the rate of 12% compounded monthly on the outstanding balance from the date of sale, what will be the monthly payments on an automatic dishwasher priced at $995?

○**31.** Mr. Donatelli moved from Toronto to Winnipeg to take a job promotion. After selling their Toronto home and buying a home in Winnipeg, the Donatellis have $85,000 in cash on hand. If the funds are used to purchase a deferred annuity from a life insurance company providing a rate of return of 5.5% compounded annually, what payments will they receive at the end of every six months for 20 years after a 9-year deferral period?

○**32.** Fred asked two life insurance companies to give quotes on a 20-year deferred annuity (after a 5-year deferral period) that can be purchased for $100,000. Northwest Mutual quoted payments of $875 payable at the end of each month. Liberty Standard stated that all their annuity options provide a rate of return equal to 5.5% compounded annually. Which company should Fred choose?

•**33.** Jack Groman's financial plan is designed to accumulate sufficient funds in his RRSP over the next 28 years to purchase an annuity paying $6000 at the end of each month for 25 years. He will be able to contribute $7000 to his RRSP at the end of each year for the next 10 years. What year-end contribution must he make for the subsequent 18 years to achieve his objective? For these projections, assume that Jack's RRSP will earn 7.5% compounded annually, and that the annuity payments are based on a return of 7.5% compounded monthly.

•**34.** Cynthia currently has $31,000 in her RRSP. She plans to contribute $5000 at the end of each year for the next 17 years, and then use the accumulated funds to purchase a 20-year annuity making month-end payments.

    a. If her RRSP earns 8.75% compounded annually for the next 17 years, and the fund from which the annuity is paid will earn 5.4% compounded monthly, what monthly payments will she receive?

    b. If the rate of inflation for the next 17 years is 2%, what will be the purchasing power (in today's dollars) of the monthly payments at the start of the annuity?

•**35.** Mr. Parmar wants to retire in 20 years and purchase a 25-year annuity that will make equal payments at the end of every quarter. The first payment should have the purchasing power of $6000 in today's dollars. If he already has $54,000 in his RRSP, what contributions must he make at the end of every half-year for the next 20 years to achieve his retirement goal? Assume that the rate of inflation for the next 20 years will be 2.5%, the RRSP will earn 8% compounded semiannually, and the rate of return on the fund from which the annuity is paid will be 5.5% compounded quarterly.

■ connect

36. **Using the "Cool Million" Chart** An interactive "Cool Million" chart in the textbook's Web site enables you to visualize the growth of your retirement savings over several years. Another feature allows you to determine what changes you would need to make to your investment plan for you to attain nominal "millionaire" status on your 65th birthday.

Go to the Student Edition on this textbook's Web site. In Chapter 11, find "Cool Million."

Enter data for an investment plan that will be reasonable for you after you gain full-time employment. Note that the "Expected rate of return" and the "Expected inflation rate" are both *annually* compounded rates. Click on the "Calculate" button to generate a new chart. The series of blue bars show the growth of your investments. If you move your cursor over any bar, the numerical value (in $000s) will be displayed.

The series of purple bars represent the inflation-adjusted value, or purchasing power, of the investments in terms of dollars at the very beginning—the "Your age" date.

If you click on the "View Report" button, a window containing a bulleted list of three suggested changes will appear. *Any one* of these changes to your savings plan will enable you to accumulate (a nominal) $1,000,000 at your target retirement age. Adjust one or more items in your input data to arrive at a plan that represents your best chance of entering retirement as a millionaire. What will be the purchasing power of your nominal $1,000,000 in beginning dollars?

11.2 CALCULATING THE NUMBER OF PAYMENTS

Circumstances in which the number of payments, n, must be calculated include:

- Determining the time required for periodic payments to pay off a loan.

- Determining the time required for a periodic savings plan to reach a savings target.

- Determining how long a single investment can sustain periodic withdrawals.

LO2 In order to calculate the number of annuity payments, you need to know *PMT* and i (or be able to determine them from the given information). In addition, you must know either the *PV* or the *FV* of the annuity.

Suppose you substitute known values for *FV*, *PMT*, and i in formula (10-1) for the future value of an annuity, and then proceed to solve for n. The procedure is more complex than it was in Section 11.1 for isolating *PMT*—it requires some familiarity with manipulating logarithms. Similar comments apply to formula (10-2) for the present value of an annuity. For these reasons, we present the following versions of formulas (10-1) and (10-2) rearranged to calculate n.

$$n = \frac{\ln\left(1 + \dfrac{i \times FV}{PMT}\right)}{\ln(1 + i)} \qquad \text{(10-1}n\text{)}$$

$$n = -\frac{\ln\left(1 - \dfrac{i \times PV}{PMT}\right)}{\ln(1 + i)} \qquad \text{(10-2}n\text{)}$$

Since these are merely new versions of formulas (10-1) and (10-2), we will refer to them as (10-1n)[1] and (10-2n). If the payments form a general annuity, the periodic interest rate that matches the payment interval (that is, i_2) must be substituted for i.

---

[1] The derivation of formula (10-1n) from formula (10-1) is presented in Chapter 11 of the textbook's Web site; see "Appendix 11A" there.

> ### TIP   Interpretation of "*n*" When it is Not an Integer
>
> The value obtained for *n* will not necessarily be an integer. To illustrate the interpretation of a non-integer value, suppose *n* = 21.3 in a particular case. This means that there are 22 payments, but the last payment is smaller than the others. Prevailing business practice is to allow a full payment interval for the final reduced payment. Even though the fractional part of *n* in this case is 0.3, it is only an approximation to say that the last payment is 30% of the size of the others. The method for calculating the exact size of the final payment will be presented in Chapter 14.

> ### TIP   Obtaining the Term of an Annuity from the Value of "*n*"
>
> A problem may ask for the *term* of the annuity rather that the number of payments. Let's consider a specific numerical example before addressing the general case. Suppose a question has asked you to determine the term of an annuity in which there are four payments per year. Suppose you obtained *n* = 34.5 payments. This means the annuity consists of 35 payments. (Remember the preceding "Tip.") Since there are four payments per year, the annuity's term in years is
>
> $$\frac{35 \text{ payments}}{4 \text{ payments per year}} = 8.75 \text{ years.}$$
>
> In general,
>
> $$\text{Term of annuity (in years)} = \frac{n \text{ (rounded upward)}}{\text{Number of payments per year}}$$
>
> The common practice is to convert the fractional part of a year to months. Since
>
> $$0.75 \text{ years} = 0.75(12 \text{ months}) = 9 \text{ months}$$
>
> the term in our numerical example would normally be expressed as "8 years and 9 months."

EXAMPLE 11.2A   CALCULATING *n* GIVEN THE FUTURE VALUE OF AN ORDINARY GENERAL ANNUITY

One month from now, Maurice will make his first monthly contribution of $250 to a TFSA. Over the long run, he expects to earn 8% compounded annually. How long will it take for the contributions and accrued earnings to reach $100,000? (Round *n* to the next larger integer.)

SOLUTION

Since compounding occurs *annually* but the contributions are made *monthly*, the payments form a *general* annuity having

$$FV = \$100,000 \quad PMT = \$250 \quad \text{and} \quad i = \tfrac{8\%}{1} = 8\%$$

To obtain the periodic rate matching the monthly payment interval, first calculate

$$c = \frac{1 \text{ compounding per year}}{12 \text{ payments per year}} = 0.08\overline{3}$$

Then

$$i_2 = (1 + i)^c - 1 = 1.08^{0.08\overline{3}} - 1 = 0.00643403 \text{ per month}$$

Substitute these values into formula (10-1n).

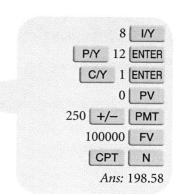

$$n = \frac{\ln\left(1 + \frac{i \times FV}{PMT}\right)}{\ln(1 + i)}$$

$$= \frac{\ln\left[1 + \frac{0.00643403(\$100,000)}{\$250}\right]}{\ln(1.00643403)}$$

$$= \frac{1.27358}{0.0064134}$$

$$= 198.58$$

8 | I/Y

P/Y 12 | ENTER

C/Y 1 | ENTER

0 | PV

250 | +/− | PMT

100000 | FV

CPT | N

Ans: 198.58

The annuity has 199 payments taking 199 months. We need to express the time required in years and months.

$$199 \text{ months} = \frac{199}{12} \text{ years} = 16.583 \text{ years} = 16 \text{ years} + (0.5833 \times 12 \text{ months}) = 16 \text{ years}, 7 \text{ months}$$

It will take 16 years and 7 months for Maurice to accumulate $100,000 in the TFSA.

EXAMPLE 11.2B   **CALCULATING THE TIME REQUIRED TO PAY OFF A LOAN**

Roy and Lynn are discussing the terms of a $28,000 home improvement loan with their bank's lending officer. The interest rate on the loan is 7.5% compounded monthly.

a. How long will it take to repay the loan if the monthly payments are $220?

b. How long will it take to repay the loan if they pay an extra $20 per month?

c. Calculate the approximate total nominal interest savings over the life of the loan as a result of making payments of $240 instead of $220 per month.

SOLUTION

The original loan equals the present value of all the payments. The payments form an ordinary simple annuity with $PV = \$28,000$ and $i = \frac{7.5\%}{12} = 0.625\%$. In Part (a), $PMT = \$220$, and in Part (b), $PMT = \$240$.

a. Substitute $PV = \$28,000$, $i = 0.625\%$, and $PMT = \$220$ into formula (10-2n).

$$n = -\frac{\ln\left(1 - \frac{i \times PV}{PMT}\right)}{\ln(1 + i)}$$

$$= -\frac{\ln\left[1 - \frac{0.00625(\$28,000)}{\$220}\right]}{\ln(1.00625)}$$

$$= 254.71$$

7.5 | I/Y

P/Y 12 | ENTER

(making $C/Y = P/Y = 12$)

28000 | PV

220 | +/− | PMT

0 | FV

CPT | N

Ans: 254.71

It will take 255 payments, requiring 255 months to pay off the loan.

$$255 \text{ months} = \frac{255}{12} \text{ years} = 21.25 \text{ years} = 21 \text{ years} + (0.25 \times 12) \text{ months} = 21 \text{ years}, 3 \text{ months}$$

Therefore, it will take 21 years and 3 months to pay off the loan. (The last payment will be *approximately* $0.71 \times \$220 \approx \$156$.)

b. Again, we can substitute $PV = \$28,000$, $i = 0.625\%$, and $PMT = \$240$ into formula (10-2n). For those who prefer to work from first principles (and reduce the number of formulas with which they work), we will give one demonstration of calculating n from the basic PV formula (10-2). Substituting the above values into formula (10-2), we obtain

$$PV = PMT\left[\frac{1 - (1 + i)^{-n}}{i}\right]$$

$$\$28,000 = \$240\left(\frac{1 - 1.00625^{-n}}{0.00625}\right)$$

Multiplying both sides by $\frac{0.00625}{\$240}$ yields

$$\frac{0.00625}{\$240}(\$28,000) = 1 - 1.00625^{-n}$$

Rearrange the equation to isolate 1.00625^{-n} on the left-hand side.

$$1.00625^{-n} = 1 - 0.72916\overline{6} = 0.27083\overline{3}$$

Taking logarithms of both sides,

$$-n\ln(1.00625) = \ln(0.27083\overline{3})$$

Hence,

$$n = -\frac{\ln(0.270833)}{\ln(1.00625)} = -\frac{-1.30625}{0.00623055} = 209.65$$

> Same *I/Y, P/Y, C/Y*
> Same *PV, FV*
> 240 [+/−] [PMT]
> [CPT] [N]
> *Ans:* 209.65

It will take 210 months (17 years and 6 months) to pay off the loan. The last payment will be *approximately* $0.65(\$240) \approx \$156$.

c. With monthly payments of $220, the total of all payments is approximately

$$254.71(\$220) \approx \$56,036$$

With monthly payments of $240, the total of all payments is approximately

$$209.65(\$240) \approx \$50,316$$

Ignoring the time value of money, the saving of interest is approximately

$$\$56,036 - \$50,316 \approx \$5720$$

Postscript: By increasing their monthly payments by less than 10%, Roy and Lynn will pay off the loan in about 18% less time ($17\frac{1}{2}$ years instead of $21\frac{1}{4}$ years). Their total interest costs on the $28,000 loan will be reduced by over 20% (from $28,036 to $22,316). This outcome is typical of long-term debt. It is one of the main reasons why financial planners encourage us to make even slightly larger payments on long-term debt.

EXAMPLE 11.2C   **CALCULATING THE TIME REQUIRED TO REACH A SAVINGS GOAL AND THE LENGTH OF TIME A FUND WILL SUSTAIN REGULAR WITHDRAWALS**

a. Annual contributions of $5000 will be made at every year-end to an RRSP. Rounding n upwards, how long will it take for the funds in the RRSP to grow to $500,000 if they earn 7.5% compounded annually?

b. If the $500,000 will be used to purchase an annuity earning 6% compounded quarterly and paying $12,000 at the end of each quarter, how long after the purchase date will the annuity payments continue?

SOLUTION

In Part (a), the future value of the contributions is to be $500,000. The contributions form an ordinary simple annuity with $PMT = \$5000$ and $i = \frac{7.5\%}{1} = 7.5\%$.

In Part (b), the accumulated $500,000 becomes the present value of an ordinary simple annuity having $PMT = \$12,000$ and $i = \frac{6\%}{4} = 1.5\%$.

a. Substitute the known values into formula (10-1*n*).

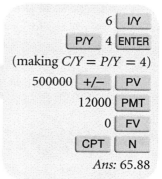

$$n = \frac{\ln\left(1 + \dfrac{i \times FV}{PMT}\right)}{\ln(1 + i)}$$

$$= \frac{\ln\left[1 + \dfrac{0.075(\$500,000)}{\$5000}\right]}{\ln(1.075)}$$

$$= 29.59135$$

Rounding n upwards, it will take 30 years for the RRSP to accumulate $500,000. (In this particular case, the interest earned during the thirtieth year will allow the RRSP to reach $500,000 before[2] the thirtieth contribution is actually made.)

b. Substitute the known values into formula (10-2*n*).

$$n = -\frac{\ln\left(1 - \dfrac{i \times PV}{PMT}\right)}{\ln(1 + i)}$$

$$= -\frac{\ln\left[1 - \dfrac{0.015(\$500,000)}{\$12,000}\right]}{\ln(1.015)}$$

$$= 65.88$$

There will be 66 quarterly payments, with the last payment being about 12% smaller than the others. Therefore, the annuity payments will run for

$$\frac{66 \text{ quarters}}{4 \text{ quarters per year}} = 16.5 \text{ years} = 16 \text{ years and 6 months}$$

Calculator panel (a):
7.5 I/Y
P/Y 1 ENTER
(making C/Y = P/Y = 1)
0 PV
5000 +/– PMT
500000 FV
CPT N
Ans: 29.59

Calculator panel (b):
6 I/Y
P/Y 4 ENTER
(making C/Y = P/Y = 4)
500000 +/– PV
12000 PMT
0 FV
CPT N
Ans: 65.88

---

[2]   The calculation is actually telling us that the RRSP will reach $500,000 after 29.59135 years if a 30th payment of (essentially) 0.59135 × $5000 is paid into the plan after only 0.59135 of the 30th year. This is not what actually happens—no contribution will be made before the end of the 30th year. To calculate precisely when the RRSP will reach $500,000 (including accrued interest),
   • Calculate the amount in the RRSP after 29 contributions (years).
   • Use formula (9-2) to calculate the fraction of a year required for the preceding amount to grow to $500,000 through the accrual of interest.

EXAMPLE 11.2D   **CALCULATING THE NUMBER OF PAYMENTS IN A DEFERRED ANNUITY**

$10,000 is invested in a fund earning 9.25% compounded semiannually. Five years later, the first semiannual withdrawal of $1000 will be taken from the fund. After how many withdrawals will the fund be depleted? (The final payment that extinguishes the fund will be smaller than $1000. Include it in the count.)

SOLUTION

Viewed from the date of the investment, the withdrawals form a deferred simple annuity. The period of deferral is $4\frac{1}{2}$ years long. We have

$$PMT = \$1000 \quad d = 2(4.5) = 9 \quad \text{and} \quad i = \frac{9.25\%}{2} = 4.625\%$$

In effect, the accumulated funds after 4.5 years purchase a "home-made" annuity. As indicated in the following diagram,

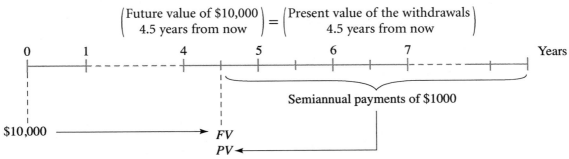

The future value of $10,000 after $4\frac{1}{2}$ years will be

$$\begin{aligned} FV &= PV(1 + i)^n \\ &= \$10,000(1.04625)^9 \\ &= \$15,021.71 \end{aligned}$$

9.25	I/Y
P/Y	2 ENTER
(making $C/Y = P/Y = 2$)	
9	N
10000 +/−	PV
0	PMT
CPT	FV
Ans: 15,021.71	

Now use formula (10-2n) to obtain n.

$$\begin{aligned} n &= -\frac{\ln\left[1 - \dfrac{i \times PV}{PMT}\right]}{\ln(1 + i)} \\ &= -\frac{\ln\left[1 - \dfrac{0.04625 \times \$15,021.71}{\$1000}\right]}{\ln(1.04625)} \\ &= 26.25 \end{aligned}$$

Same I/Y, P/Y, C/Y	
15021.71 +/−	PV
1000	PMT
0	FV
CPT	N
Ans: 26.25	

The fund will be depleted after 27 withdrawals. (The last withdrawal will be *approximately* $0.25 \times \$1000 = \$250$).

POINT OF INTEREST

How the Rich Got Rich

Two American professors, Thomas Stanley and William Danko, have studied and written about wealthy Americans for over 25 years. Their book, *The Millionaire Next Door: The Surprising Secrets of America's Wealthy*, was on the New York Times bestseller list for more than one year. In the book, Stanley and Danko present their findings on who the wealthy are and how they became wealthy. They define "wealthy" as having a *household* net worth (assets minus debts) of at least $1,000,000.

According to Statistics Canada, 1.1 million Canadian households (about 9% of all Canadian households) had a net worth of at least C$1 million in 2005. This net worth figure includes savings, investments, RRSPs, RRIFs, homes and other real estate, and employer-sponsored pension plans.

Most surveys of household wealth are conducted by financial institutions that are primarily interested in a household's "investable financial assets." These are assets other than real estate and group pension plans—in other words, the assets that financial institutions would like to help manage. Merrill Lynch estimated that 232,000 Canadians had financial assets of at least $1 million at the end of 2005.

As the title of Stanley and Danko's book suggests, typical millionaires do not flaunt the trappings of wealth. Their lifestyles are surprisingly modest. In the words of Stanley and Danko:

"Many people who live in expensive homes and drive luxury cars do not have much wealth. Many people who have a great deal of wealth do not live in upscale neighbourhoods.... They buy cars that are, on average, only slightly more expensive than the cars less wealthy Americans buy."

Who are the wealthy? According to Stanley and Danko,

- The average age of American millionaires is 57.
- Their average college GPA was 2.92.

- About 80% are first-generation affluent.
- More than 50% never received a single dollar of inheritance. Only 20% got wealthy through inheritance.
- Two-thirds are self-employed.

How did they become wealthy?
- Most live well below their means. They believe financial independence is more important than displaying high economic status. Most drive domestic cars and own rather than lease their vehicles. They wear inexpensive clothing.
- They plan and budget. Two-thirds of millionaires set short-term and long-term goals. Sixty-two percent know how much their family spends on food, clothing and shelter.
- Most invest at least 15% of household income.
- 95% of millionaires own stocks but most are not active traders. In any year, almost half of them make no trades.

Saving 15% of household income seems a daunting prospect. But many Canadians contribute about 5% off the top of their income to a pension plan. This is usually matched by their employers. In such cases, employees are already saving 10% of their income before they begin a personal savings plan.

Many people overlook the economic value of accrued pension benefits when they calculate their net worth. An individual retiring at age 60 on an indexed pension of $25,000 per year owns, in effect, an asset worth over $300,000. [You will be able to confirm this in Chapter 13 using formula (13-3). Calculate the present value of a 22-payment annuity starting at $25,000 per year and growing at 2.5% per year with money worth 7% compounded annually.] There are many millionaires who do not realize they are millionaires!

SPREADSHEET STRATEGIES   Calculating the Number of Payments in an Annuity

Connect provides a partially completed template for calculating the number of payments in an annuity. Go to the Student Edition of Connect and find "NPER for Any Annuity." The first page of this workbook discusses Excel's *NPER* function.

The main features of a completed *NPER* template are presented below. The formulas programmed into cells C11 and C18 are displayed in cells C12 and C19, respectively.

Data are entered to solve Example 11.2A. In this example, we are asked to determine how long it will take for monthly RRSP contributions of $250 earning 8% compounded annually to grow to $100,000. After entering the known values in the yellow input cells, the computed number of payments immediately appears in the output cell C18.

	A	B	C	D
1				
2		Using a spreadsheet to calculate the number of annuity payments.		
3		Example 11.2A:		
4				
5		Nominal annual interest rate, *j*	8.000%	
6		Compoundings per year, *m*	1	
7		Given periodic rate of interest, *i*	8.0000%	
8				
9		Payments per year	12	
10		Compoundings per payment interval, *c*	0.0833333333	
11		Periodic rate of interest, i_2 or *rate*	0.643403011%	
12		Formula in cell C11:	=(1+C7)^C10-1	
13		Regular annuity payment, *PMT* or *pmt*	-$250.00	
14		Present value, *PV* or *pv*	$0.00	
15		Future value, *FV* or *fv*	$100,000.00	
16		Annuity *type*	0	
17				
18		NPER (rate, pmt, pv, fv, type)	198.5800	
19		Formula in cell C18:	=NPER(C11,C13,C14,C15,C16)	
20				

The future value of the RRSP will pass $100,000 with the 199th monthly contribution. The total time required is 199 months, or 16 years and 7 months.

Note: After you have correctly programmed the NPER template for the first time, you should save it in a permanent file on your computer. You will be able to use it (without having to re-program the output cells) in many other applications in Chapters 11 to 14.

CONCEPT QUESTIONS

1. If you double the size of the monthly payment you make on a loan, will you pay it off in (pick one): **(i)** half the time? **(ii)** less than half the time? **(iii)** more than half the time? Give the reason for your choice.

2. If you contribute $250 per month to an RRSP instead of $500 per month, will the time required to reach a particular savings target be (pick one): **(i)** twice as long? **(ii)** less than twice as long? **(iii)** more than twice as long? Give the reason for your choice.

EXERCISE 11.2

■connect

Spreadsheet template: A partially completed Excel template for calculating the number of payments in an annuity is provided in Connect. You can use this template for many of the problems in Exercise 11.2. Go to the Student Edition of Connect and find "NPER for Any Annuity."

Answers to the odd-numbered problems are at the end of the book.

1. Semiannual payments of $3874.48 are made on a $50,000 loan at 6.5% compounded semiannually. How long will it take to pay off the loan?

2. The future value of an annuity consisting of end-of-year investments of $1658.87 earning 5.2% compounded annually is $100,000. How many annual investments were made?

3. For $200,000, Jamal purchased an annuity that delivers end-of-quarter payments of $3341.74. If the undistributed funds earn 4.5% compounded quarterly, what is the term of the annuity?

4. If money in a new TFSA earns 8.25% compounded monthly, how long will it take for the plan to reach $30,000 in value based on end-of-month contributions of $209.59?

5. An endowment fund is set up with a donation of $100,000. If it earns 9% compounded monthly, for how long will it sustain end-of-month withdrawals of $1000? (Include the final smaller withdrawal.)

6. Rounding up the number of contributions to the next integer, how long will it take an RRSP to surpass $100,000, if it takes in end-of-quarter contributions of $3000 and earns 6% compounded quarterly?

7. For how long has William been making end-of-quarter contributions of $1200 to his RRSP, if the RRSP has earned 8.75% compounded annually and is currently worth $74,385?

8. Monthly payments of $315.49 are required on a $20,000 loan at 5.5% compounded quarterly. What is the term of the loan?

9. How long will it take an RRSP to grow to $700,000, if it takes in month-end contributions of $1000 and it earns:
   a. 6% compounded monthly?   b. 7% compounded monthly?
   c. 8% compounded monthly?   d. 9% compounded monthly?
   Round up the number of contributions to the next integer.

10. How long will it take for monthly payments of $800 to repay a $100,000 loan, if the interest rate on the loan is:
   a. 6% compounded monthly?   b. 7% compounded monthly?
   c. 8% compounded monthly?   d. 9% compounded monthly?

11. How long will it take for monthly payments of $740 to repay a $100,000 loan, if the interest rate on the loan is:
   a. 7.5% compounded annually?   b. 7.5% compounded semiannually?
   c. 7.5% compounded quarterly?   d. 7.5% compounded monthly?

12. How long will it take an RESP to grow to $200,000, if the plan owner contributes $250 at the end of each month and the plan earns:
   a. 8% compounded monthly?   b. 8% compounded quarterly?
   c. 8% compounded semiannually?   d. 8% compounded annually?
   Round up the number of contributions to the next integer before calculating the total time.

13. Rounded to the next higher month, how long will it take end-of-month deposits of $500 to accumulate $100,000 in an investment account that earns 5.25% compounded monthly?

14. Silas is about to begin regular month-end contributions of $500 to a bond fund. The fund's long-term rate of return is expected to be 6% compounded semiannually. Rounded to the next higher month, how long will it take Silas to accumulate $300,000?

15. How long will $500,000, in an investment account that earns 5.25% compounded monthly, sustain month-end withdrawals of $3000?

16. Farah has $600,000 in her RRSP and wishes to retire. She is thinking of using the funds to purchase an annuity that earns 5% compounded annually and pays her $3500 at the end of each month. If she buys the annuity, for how long will she receive payments?

17. If $300,000 is used to purchase an annuity earning 7.5% compounded monthly and paying $2500 at the end of each month, what will be the term of the annuity?

○18. Rashid wants to use $500,000 from his RRSP to purchase an annuity that pays him $2000 at the end of each month for the first 10 years and $3000 per month thereafter. Global Insurance Co. will sell Rashid an annuity of this sort with a rate of return of 4.8% compounded monthly. For how long will the annuity run?

19. How much longer will it take month-end RRSP contributions of $500 to accumulate $500,000 than month-end contributions of $550? Assume that the RRSP earns 7.5% compounded monthly. Round the time required in each case to the next higher month.

20. Suppose that you contribute $400 per month to your RRSP. Rounding up to the nearest month, how much longer will it take for the RRSP's value to reach $500,000 if it earns 7.5% compounded annually than if it earns 7.5% compounded monthly?

21. How much longer will it take to pay off a $100,000 loan with monthly payments of $1000 than with monthly payments of $1100? The interest rate on the loan is 10.5% compounded monthly.

22. How much longer will it take monthly payments of $1000 to pay off a $100,000 loan if the monthly compounded rate of interest on the loan is 10.5% instead of 9.75%?

23. What duration of annuity paying $5000 at the end of every quarter can be purchased with $200,000 if the invested funds earn 5.5% compounded semiannually?

24. Bonnie and Clyde want to take a six-month leave of absence from their jobs to travel extensively in South America. Rounded to the next higher month, how long will it take them to save $40,000 for the leave if they make month-end contributions of $700 to their employer's salary deferral plan? The salary deferral plan earns 7.5% compounded semiannually.

25. Finest Furniture sells a colour television set priced at $1395 for $50 down and payments of $50 per month, including interest at 13.5% compounded monthly. How long after the date of purchase will the final payment be made?

○26. **a.** How long will it take monthly payments of $400 to repay a $50,000 loan if the interest rate on the loan is 8% compounded semiannually?

   b. How much will the time to repay the loan be reduced if the payments are $40 per month larger?

○27. A 65-year-old male can purchase either of the following annuities from a life insurance company for $50,000. A 25-year term annuity will pay $307 at the end of each month. A life annuity will pay $408 at the end of every month until the death of the annuitant. To what age must the man survive for the life annuity to have the greater economic value? Assume that money can earn 6% compounded monthly.

○**28.** A 60-year-old woman can purchase either of the following annuities from a life insurance company for $50,000. A 30-year term annuity will pay $367 at the end of each month. A life annuity will pay $405 at the end of every month until the death of the annuitant. To what age must the woman survive for the life annuity to have the greater economic value? Assume that money can earn 8% compounded monthly.

○**29.** $10,000 was invested in a fund earning 7.5% compounded monthly. How many monthly withdrawals of $300 can be made if the first occurs $3\frac{1}{2}$ years after the date of the initial investment? Count the final smaller withdrawal.

○**30.** Nancy borrowed $8000 from her grandfather to buy a car when she started college. The interest rate being charged is only 4.5% compounded monthly. Nancy is to make the first $200 monthly payment on the loan three years after the date of the loan. How long after the date of the initial loan will she make the final payment?

○**31.** Twelve years ago, Mr. Lawton rolled a $17,000 retiring allowance into an RRSP that subsequently earned 10% compounded semiannually. Three years ago he transferred the funds to an RRIF. Since then, he has been withdrawing $1000 at the end of each quarter. If the RRIF earns 8% compounded quarterly, how much longer can the withdrawals continue?

○**32.** Novell Electronics recently bought a patent that will allow it to bring a new product to market in $2\frac{1}{2}$ years. Sales forecasts indicate that the product will increase the quarterly profits by $28,000. If the patent cost $150,000, how long after the date of the patent purchase will it take for the additional profits to repay the original investment along with a return on investment of 15% compounded quarterly? Assume that the additional profits are received at the end of each quarter.

○**33.** Helen and Morley borrowed $20,000 from Helen's father to make a down payment on a house. The interest rate on the loan is 8% compounded annually, but no payments are required for two years. The first monthly payment of $300 is due on the second anniversary of the loan. How long after the date of the original loan will the last payment be made?

○**34.** A property development company obtained a $2.5 million loan to construct a commercial building. The interest rate on the loan is 10% compounded semiannually. The lender granted a period of deferral until rental revenues become established. The first quarterly payment of $100,000 is required 21 months after the date of the loan. How long after the date of the original loan will the last payment be made?

○**35.** Bernice is about to retire with $139,000 in her RRSP. She will make no further contributions to the plan, but will allow it to accumulate earnings for another six years. Then she will purchase an annuity providing payments of $5000 at the end of each quarter. Assume that the RRSP will earn 8.5% compounded annually and the funds invested in the annuity will earn 7.5% compounded monthly. How long after the purchase of the annuity will its payments continue?

•**36.** Harold's RRSP is already worth $56,000. Rounding n to the next higher integer, how long will it take the RRSP to reach $250,000 if additional contributions of $2000 are made at the end of every six months? Assume the RRSP earns 9.75% compounded monthly.

11.3 CALCULATING THE INTEREST RATE

Circumstances in which you need to calculate the interest rate include:

- Determining the rate of return required for periodic savings to reach a goal in a particular length of time.

- Determining the rate of return earned on money used to purchase an annuity.

- Determining the interest rate implied by specified loan payments.

- Determining the interest rate being charged when an instalment payment plan is offered as an alternative to a "cash" payment.

- Determining the interest rate built into the payments on a vehicle or equipment lease.

LO3   The interest rate most readily calculated is the periodic interest rate, i. To determine i, you must know the values for PMT, n, and either FV or PV.

Problems requiring the calculation of i pose some special difficulties for an algebraic approach. Formulas (10-1) for FV and (10-2) for PV cannot be rearranged through algebraic manipulations to isolate i. Consequently, no formulas can be given for i (corresponding to those for n in Section 11.2).

Appendix 11B in the textbook's Web site presents an approximation technique called the "trial-and-error method." The "trial-and-error method" is a systematic but time-consuming procedure for *improving an estimate* of an equation's solution. With each repetition or *iteration* of the procedure, the approximation gets closer to the correct solution. We illustrate the trial-and-error method in Appendix 11B by using it to solve Example 11.3A a second time.

In this section, we will show only the financial calculator method for the solutions to example problems. For the interest rate computation, the financial calculator also uses a repetitive iterative procedure when you press [CPT] [I/Y]. But the only evidence you may notice of this happening is that it takes the calculator slightly longer to compute I/Y than it takes to compute one of the other financial variables.

EXAMPLE 11.3A   **FINDING THE RATE OF RETURN ON FUNDS USED TO PURCHASE AN ANNUITY**

A life insurance company advertises that $50,000 will purchase a 20-year annuity paying $341.13 at the end of each month. What nominal rate of return and effective rate of return does the annuity investment earn?

SOLUTION

The purchase price of an annuity equals the present value of all payments. Hence, the rate of return on the $50,000 purchase price is the discount rate that makes the present value of the payments equal to $50,000. The payments form an ordinary annuity with

$$PV = \$50,000 \quad PMT = \$341.13 \quad m = 12 \quad \text{and} \quad n = 12(20) = 240$$

Enter these values in your calculator as indicated in the box at upper right. The nominal rate of return we obtain is 5.40% compounded monthly. Then $i = \frac{j}{m} = \frac{5.4\%}{12} = 0.450\%$ and the corresponding effective interest rate is

$$f = (1 + i)^m - 1 = 1.00450^{12} - 1 = 0.05536 = 5.54\%$$

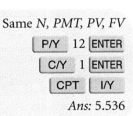

P/Y 12 [ENTER]
(making $C/Y = P/Y = 12$)
240 [N]
50000 [+/−] [PV]
341.13 [PMT]
0 [FV]
[CPT] [I/Y]
Ans: 5.400

Same N, PMT, PV, FV
P/Y 12 [ENTER]
C/Y 1 [ENTER]
[CPT] [I/Y]
Ans: 5.536

EXAMPLE 11.3B   **CALCULATING THE RATE OF RETURN REQUIRED TO REACH A SAVINGS GOAL IN A SPECIFIED TIME PERIOD**

What annually compounded rate of return must Rachel earn in her RRSP in order for month-end contributions of $500 to accumulate $600,000 after 25 years?

SOLUTION

The contributions form an ordinary annuity whose future value after 25 years is to be $600,000. That is,

$$FV = \$600,000 \quad PMT = \$500 \quad m = C/Y = 1 \quad P/Y = 12 \quad \text{and}$$
$$n = 12(25) = 300$$

Enter these values in your calculator as indicated in the box at right. The nominal rate of return we obtain is 9.82% compounded annually.

Rachel's RRSP must earn 9.82% compounded annually to reach her savings goal.

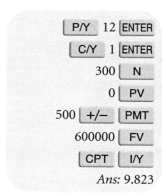

Ans: 9.823

EXAMPLE 11.3C   **CALCULATING THE IMPLIED INTEREST RATE FOR AN INSTALMENT PAYMENT OPTION**

Rolling Meadows Golf and Country Club allows members to pay the annual membership fee by a single payment of $2400 at the beginning of the year, or by payments of $220 at the beginning of each month. What effective rate of interest is paid by members who choose to pay by the month?

SOLUTION

The first monthly payment is due on the same date as the full annual fee. In effect, the golf club initially lends $2400 − $220 = $2180 to a member choosing the monthly payment option. The member then repays the "loan" by 11 month-end payments of $220.

Again we use the fundamental principle that the original "loan" equals the present value of all payments. We need to calculate the discount rate that makes $2180 the present value of 11 payments of $220. We have

$$PV = \$2180 \quad PMT = \$220 \quad P/Y = 12 \quad \text{and} \quad n = 11$$

Since we are asked for the effective rate, set $C/Y = m = 1$. Enter these values in your calculator as indicated in the box at right to obtain

$$I/Y = 23.62\% \text{ compounded annually}$$

Hence, members on the monthly payment plan are paying an effective rate of 23.62%.

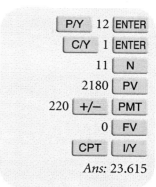

Ans: 23.615

EXAMPLE 11.3D   CALCULATING THE INTEREST RATE EQUIVALENT OF A FOREGONE CASH REBATE

An automobile manufacturer's advertisement announces: "1.8% factory financing over 48 months or $1000 cash back." Suppose a car buyer finances $15,000 of a car's purchase price at the low interest rate instead of paying a further $14,000 in cash (net of the $1000 cash-back rebate). If we include the foregone rebate as part of the cost of borrowing, what nominal rate of interest is the buyer paying?

SOLUTION

An additional front-end cost of the "cheap" 1.8% financing is the foregone $1000 rebate. To determine the true cost of the 1.8% financing, we will consider the following alternatives.

• Borrow $15,000 from the manufacturer at 1.8% (compounded monthly) for four years.
• Obtain a four-year loan for $14,000 elsewhere at the prevailing market interest rate. Use the $14,000 to complete a "full cash" purchase net of the $1000 rebate.

The alternatives are equivalent if the monthly loan payments are equal. Therefore, we will determine the interest rate in the second case that results in the same monthly payment as for the factory-financed loan. If we can find outside financing at a *lower* rate, we should borrow $14,000 from that source and choose the "$1000 cash-back" option.

Step 1:   Calculate the monthly payment on a factory-financed $15,000 four-year loan. The payments form an ordinary annuity having

$$PV = \$15,000 \quad j = 1.8\% \quad m = 12 \quad n = 12(4) = 48$$

Enter these values in your calculator as indicated in the box at right to obtain $PMT = \$324.12$.

| 1.8 | I/Y |
| P/Y 12 | ENTER |

(making $C/Y = P/Y = 12$)

48	N
15000	PV
0	FV
CPT	PMT

Ans: −324.12

Step 2:   Determine the interest rate on a four-year $14,000 loan that would result in the *same* monthly payment. For this loan,

$$PV = \$14,000 \quad PMT = \$324.12 \quad n = 48 \quad m = 12$$

Enter these values as indicated in the second box at right to obtain

$$j = 5.27\% \text{ compounded monthly}$$

Same P/Y, C/Y
Same N, PMT, FV

| 14000 | PV |
| CPT | I/Y |

Ans: 5.269

This result means that you will make the same monthly payment ($324.12) on either of the following loans:

• $15,000 for four years at 1.8% compounded monthly
• $14,000 for four years at 5.27% compounded monthly

Therefore, foregoing the cash rebate and financing at 1.8% compounded monthly has the same effect as external financing at 5.27% compounded monthly. (The buyer should arrange external financing if it can be obtained at any rate below 5.27% compounded monthly.)

POINT OF INTEREST

Should You Choose a Cash-Discount Incentive or Low-Interest-Rate Financing?

To promote vehicle sales, it is common for automobile manufacturers to offer the purchaser of a new vehicle the choice between:

- A discount (or incentive) on a "cash" purchase; or
- Financing at a lower interest rate than may be available from conventional lenders.

For example, in mid-2009, Nissan Canada offered buyers of a new Nissan Maxima 3.5 SV (MSRP $38,625) the choice of a $4000 cash incentive (deducted from the MSRP) or financing at 2.9% compounded monthly on a 48-month loan from Nissan Canada Finance. How do you decide which alternative to choose?

Your initial reaction may be that your personal financial condition will determine your choice. That is, if you have sufficient financial resources on hand, you will pay cash and take the discount. On the other hand, if you need financing, you will choose the below-market interest rate.

Let's think more carefully about the second scenario, and assume that you will need to finance $35,000 of the purchase price, including taxes. There is likely another option open to you. Instead of borrowing $35,000 at 2.9% compounded monthly through Nissan Canada Finance, you can approach a bank or credit union for a loan of only

$$\$35,000 - \$4000 = \$31,000$$

With the down payment you already have, this loan will give you enough to pay cash and qualify for the $4000 cash incentive. Now it is apparent that you must regard forgoing the $4000 incentive as an *additional* cost of the "cheap" 2.9% financing.

The following questions lead you through an analysis of the two financing alternatives. For the easiest comparison, let us assume the $31,000 bank loan has a four-year term.

QUESTIONS

1. What will the monthly payment be if you borrow $35,000 for 48 months through Nissan Canada Finance at 2.9% compounded monthly?

2. If, by a remarkable coincidence, the monthly payment on the $31,000 bank loan is exactly the same amount, what interest rate is the bank charging?

3. What, then, should be your decision rule for whether to choose the bank loan and take the cash discount incentive, or to choose the 2.9% financing?

4. Now consider the other scenario, in which you have sufficient financial resources to pay cash without borrowing. Suppose you have investments that you could sell and use the proceeds to purchase the vehicle. Nevertheless, you may still choose to borrow at the below-market rate of 2.9% because your investments are generating a high rate of return. What should be your rule for deciding whether to liquidate investments or to use the Nissan financing to purchase the vehicle?

SPREADSHEET STRATEGIES   Calculating the Interest Rate for an Annuity

Connect provides a partially completed template for calculating the interest rates (periodic, nominal, and effective) for an annuity. Go to the Student Edition of Connect and find "RATE for Any Annuity." The first page of the workbook discusses Excel's *RATE* function.

The main features of a completed *RATE* template are presented below. The formulas programmed into cells C10 and C14 are displayed in cells C11 and C15, respectively. Data are

entered to solve Example 11.3A. In this example, a 20-year annuity that pays $341.13 at the end of every month may be purchased for $50,000. We are asked to determine the nominal and effective rates of return on the purchase price. After entering the known values in the yellow input cells, the periodic rate, nominal rate, and effective rate immediately appear in output cells C10, C13, and C14, respectively.

	A	B	C	D
1				
2		A spreadsheet for calculating the periodic, nominal, & effective interest rates in an annuity.		
3	Example 11.3A:			
4				
5		Number of payments, *n* or *nper*	240	
6		Regular annuity payment, *PMT* or *pmt*	$341.13	
7		Present value, *PV* or *pv*	-$50,000.00	
8		Future value, *FV* or *fv*	$0.00	
9		Annuity *type*	0	
10		RATE (nper, pmt, pv, fv, type)	0.4500%	
11		Formula in cell C10:	=RATE (C5,C6,C7,C8,C9)	
12		Payments (& compoundings) per year	12	
13		Nominal annual rate, *j*	5.400%	
14		Effective rate of interest, *f*	5.5358%	
15		Formula in cell C14:	=EFFECT(C13, C12)	
16				
17				

The nominal rate of return is 5.40% compounded monthly and the effective rate is 5.54%.

Note: After you have correctly programmed the *RATE* template for the first time, you should save it in a permanent file on your computer. You will be able to use it (without having to re-program the output cells) in many other applications in Chapters 11 to 14.

EXERCISE 11.3

Spreadsheet template: A partially completed Excel template for calculating the interest rates for an annuity is provided in Connect. You can use this template for many of the problems in Exercise 11.3. Go to the Student Edition of Connect and find "RATE for Any Annuity."

Answers to the odd-numbered problems are at the end of the book.

Calculate all interest rates accurate to the nearest 0.01%.

1. An annuity purchased for $50,000 sustained quarterly withdrawals of $1941.01 for 7 years and 9 months. What nominal rate of return and effective rate of return were the retained funds earning?

2. The present value of an ordinary annuity of $500 per month for $8\frac{3}{4}$ years is $35,820. Calculate the nominal and effective values for the discount rate.

3. If RRSP contributions of $3030.02 at the end of every six months are projected to generate a plan worth $500,000 in 25 years, what nominal and effective rates of return were assumed in the forecast?

4. With end-of-month contributions of $251.33, a TFSA is expected to pass $100,000 in value after 15 years and 5 months. Determine the nominal and effective rates of return used in the projection.

5. Monty is checking potential outcomes for the growth of his RRSP. He plans to make contributions of $500 at the end of each month. What nominal rate of return must his RRSP earn for its future value after 25 years to be:

   a. $400,000?

   b. $500,000?

   c. $600,000?

   (Note that a modest increase in the rate of return over a long period produces substantially larger future values.)

6. Morgan has $500,000 accumulated in her RRSP and intends to use the amount to purchase a 20-year annuity. She is investigating the size of annuity payment she can expect to receive, depending on the rate of return earned by the undistributed funds. What nominal rate of return must the funds earn for the monthly payment to be:

   a. $3000?

   b. $3500?

   c. $4000?

7. If $100,000 will purchase a 20-year annuity paying $830 at the end of each month, what monthly compounded nominal rate and effective rate of interest will the invested funds earn?

8. If regular month-end deposits of $200 in an investment account amounted to $7727.62 after three years, what monthly compounded nominal rate and effective rate of interest were earned on the account?

9. After $10\frac{1}{2}$ years of contributions of $2000 at the end of every six months to an RRSP, the accumulated amount stood at $65,727.82. What semiannually compounded nominal rate of return and effective annual rate of return were earned by the funds in the RRSP?

10. What quarterly compounded nominal rate and effective rate of interest are being charged on a $5000 loan if quarterly payments of $302.07 will repay the loan in $5\frac{1}{2}$ years?

11. A $9000, four-year term loan requires monthly payments of $220.77. What are the monthly compounded nominal rate and the effective rate of interest on the loan?

12. A finance company paid a furniture retailer $1050 for a conditional sale contract requiring 12 end-of-month payments of $100. What effective rate of return will the finance company realize on the purchase?

13. For $150,000, Continental Life Insurance Co. will sell a 20-year annuity paying $1200 at the end of each month. What effective rate of return does the annuitant earn?

14. In an insurance settlement for bodily injury, a court awarded Mr. Goodman $103,600 for two years' loss of wages of $4000 per month plus interest on the lost wages to the end of the two years. What effective rate of interest has the court allowed on the lost wages?

15. A major daily newspaper charges $260 (paid in advance) for an annual subscription, or $26 per month payable at the end of each month to the carrier. What is the effective interest rate being charged to the monthly payment subscribers?

∘16. Vijay purchased a Province of Nova Scotia bond for $1050. The bond will pay $35 interest to Vijay at the end of every six months until it matures in seven years. On the maturity date the bond will pay back its $1000 face value (as well as the interest payment due on that date.) What semiannually compounded rate of return will Vijay earn during the seven years?

∘17. Another type of sales promotion for vehicles is to advertise the choice between a "Cash Purchase Price" *or* "0% Purchase Financing." The tiny print at the bottom of a GM Canada full-page advertisement included the statement: "*The GMAC purchase finance rates are not available with and are not calculated on the 'Cash Purchase Price' shown. The difference between the price for the GMAC purchase finance offer and the 'Cash Purchase Price' offer is deemed under provincial laws to be a cost of financing.*" In other words, there are two prices for a vehicle—a lower price if you pay cash and a higher price if you want to take advantage of the "0% financing." An additional disconcerting aspect of this type of promotion is that the higher price for the 0% financing is usually not quoted in the advertisement. Rather, it must be negotiated with the dealer.

   Suppose the "Cash Purchase Price" of a car is $23,498, and the price that qualifies for full 0% financing (with 48 monthly payments) turns out to be $26,198. What effective interest rate will you be paying for the "0% financing?"

•18. An advertisement for Hyundai cars offered "2.9% 12-month financing or $1000 cash back." A car buyer financed $17,000 at the low interest rate instead of paying $16,000 cash (after the $1000 rebate). What was the effective rate of interest on the loan if the foregone cash rebate was treated as part of the cost of financing? (The 2.9% interest rate was a monthly compounded nominal rate.)

•19. A Ford advertisement offered "$1250 cash back or 1.9% factory financing over 48 months" to purchasers of new Ford vans. A customer financed $20,000 at the low interest rate instead of paying $18,750 cash (after the $1250 rebate). What was the effective rate of interest on the loan if the foregone cash rebate was treated as part of the cost of financing? (The 1.9% interest rate was a monthly compounded nominal rate.)

SUMMARY OF NOTATION AND KEY FORMULAS

FORMULA (10-1n) $n = \dfrac{\ln\left(1 + \dfrac{i \times FV}{PMT}\right)}{\ln(1 + i)}$ Finding the number of annuity payments given *FV*, *PMT* and *i*

FORMULA (10-2n) $n = -\dfrac{\ln\left(1 - \dfrac{i \times PV}{PMT}\right)}{\ln(1 + i)}$ Finding the number of annuity payments given *PV*, *PMT* and *i*

REVIEW PROBLEMS

Answers to the odd-numbered review problems are at the end of the book.

Interest rates should be calculated accurate to the nearest 0.01%.

1. **(LO1)** Calculate the amount that must be invested at the end of every six months at 7.75% compounded semiannually in order to accumulate $500,000 after 20 years.

2. **(LO1)** What monthly payment for 15 years will pay off a $50,000 loan at 8.25% compounded monthly?

3. **(LO3)** For $100,000, Royal Life Insurance Co. will sell a 20-year annuity paying $802.76 at the end of each month. What monthly compounded nominal rate and effective rate of return does the annuitant earn on the invested funds?

4. **(LO2)** If $400,000 accumulated in an RRSP is used to purchase an annuity earning 7.2% compounded monthly and paying $4500 at the end of each month, what will be the term of the annuity?

5. **(LO3)** After contributing $2000 at the end of each quarter for $13\frac{3}{4}$ years, Foster has accumulated $205,064 in his RRSP. What effective rate of return was earned by the RRSP over the entire period?

6. **(LO3)** What semiannually compounded rate and effective rate of interest are being charged on a $12,000 loan if semiannual payments of $1204.55 will repay the loan in seven years?

7. **(LO2)** The interest rate on a $100,000 loan is 9% compounded monthly. How much longer will it take to pay off the loan with monthly payments of $1000 than with monthly payments of $1050?

8. **(LO3)** If $100,000 will purchase a 20-year annuity paying $739 at each month's end, what monthly compounded nominal rate and effective rate of interest are earned by the funds?

9. **(LO2)** An annuity purchased for $175,000 pays $4000 at the end of every quarter. How long will the payments continue if the funds earn 7% compounded semiannually?

10. **(LO3)** A finance company paid a furniture retailer $1934 for a conditional sale contract requiring 12 end-of-month payments of $175. What effective rate of return does the finance company earn on the purchase?

11. **(LO1)** Howardson Electric obtained a $90,000 loan at 9.75% compounded monthly. What size of semiannual payments will repay the loan in 10 years?

12. **(LO1)** The interest rate on a $30,000 loan is 7.5% compounded monthly.

    a. What monthly payments are required to pay off the loan in eight years?

    b. What monthly payments would be required to reduce the balance to $10,000 after five years?

13. **(LO2)** How much sooner will a $65,000 loan at 7.2% compounded monthly be paid off if the monthly payments are $625 instead of $600? What will be the approximate saving in (nominal) interest costs over the life of the loan?

14. **(LO3)** $2000 will be contributed to an RRSP at the end of every six months for 20 years. What effective rate of return must the funds in the plan earn if it is to be worth $250,000 at the end of the 20 years?

15. **(LO1)** What payments must be made at the end of each quarter to an RRSP earning 7.5% compounded annually so that its value $8\frac{1}{2}$ years from now will be $15,000?

○**16. (LO1) (LO2)** The McGowans are arranging a $90,000 mortgage loan from their bank. The interest rate on the loan will be 7.9% compounded semiannually.

    a. What will the monthly payments be if the loan has a 20-year term?

    b. If the McGowans choose to pay $800 per month, how long will it take to pay off the loan?

○**17. (LO2)** A series of $500 contributions were made at three-month intervals to a fund earning 7.5% compounded quarterly. The accumulated amount continued to earn 7.5% compounded quarterly for three years after the last contribution, ending the period at $13,232.56. How many $500 contributions were made?

○**18. (LO2)** Weston Holdings Ltd. loaned $3.5 million to a subsidiary to build a plant in Winnipeg. No payments are required for two years, to allow the operations of the plant to become well established. The first monthly payment of $40,000 is due two years after the date the loan was received. If the interest rate charged on the intercompany loan is 9% compounded monthly, how long (measured from the date of the first payment) will it take the subsidiary to pay off the loan?

○**19. (LO1)** Mr. Sandstrom's will directed that $20,000 be placed in each of two investment trusts for his grandchildren, Lena and Axel. On each grandchild's eighteenth birthday, he or she is to receive the first of a series of equal quarterly payments running for 15 years. Lena has just turned 13, and Axel's age is eight years, six months. If the funds earn 9.25% compounded semiannually, what size of payment will each grandchild receive?

○**20. (LO1)** The interest rate on a $100,000 loan is 7.5% compounded quarterly.

    a. What quarterly payments will reduce the balance to $75,000 after five years?

    b. If the same payments continue, what will be the balance 10 years after the date that the loan was received?

○**21. (LO1)** Mr. Braun wants the value of his RRSP 25 years from now to have the purchasing power of $400,000 in current dollars.

    a. Assuming an inflation rate of 2.5% per year, what nominal dollar amount should Mr. Braun have in his RRSP after 25 years?

    b. What contributions should he make at the end of every three months to achieve the goal if his RRSP earns 7.5% compounded semiannually?

○**22. a. (LO2)** How long will it take monthly payments of $600 to repay a $65,000 loan if the interest rate on the loan is 9.5% compounded semiannually?

    b. (LO2) How much will the time to repay the loan be reduced if the payments are $50 more per month?

○**23. (LO2)** A 70-year-old man can purchase either of the following annuities for the same price from a life insurance company. A 20-year-term annuity will pay $394 at each month-end. A life annuity will pay $440 at the end of each month until the death of the annuitant. To what age must the man survive for the life annuity to have the greater economic value? Assume that money can earn 7.2% compounded monthly.

○**24. (LO1)** Noreen's RRSP is currently worth $125,000. She plans to contribute for 10 more years and then let the plan continue to grow through internal earnings for an additional 5 years. If the RRSP earns 8% compounded annually, how much must she contribute at the end of every six months during the 10-year period to have $500,000 in the RRSP 15 years from now?

○**25. (LO2)** $30,000 is placed in a fund earning 7% compounded quarterly. How many quarterly withdrawals of $2000 can be made if the first withdrawal occurs three years from today? Count the final withdrawal, which will be less than $2000.

○**26. (LO1)** A conditional sale contract for a $1450 transaction required a 10% down payment with the balance to be paid by 12 equal monthly payments. The first payment is due six months after the date of the purchase. The retailer charges an interest rate of 13% compounded semiannually on the unpaid balance. What is the monthly payment?

○**27. (LO1)** After selling their Vancouver home and buying another in Saskatoon, the Martels have $120,000 cash on hand. If the funds are used to purchase a deferred annuity providing a rate of return of 7.25% compounded annually, what payments will they receive at the end of every six months for a 25-year term starting eight years from now?

○28. **(LO2)** Georgina is about to retire with $188,000 in her RRSP. She will make no further contributions to the plan, but will allow it to accumulate earnings for another five years. Then she will purchase an annuity providing payments of $6000 at the end of each quarter. What will be the annuity's term if the RRSP earns 8% compounded annually and the funds invested in the annuity earn 7.5% compounded monthly?

○29. **(LO1)** By the time he turns 60, Justin (just turned age 31) wants the amount in his RRSP to have the purchasing power of $250,000 in current dollars. What annual contributions on his 32nd through 60th birthdays inclusive are required to meet this goal if the RRSP earns 8% compounded annually and the rate of inflation is 2% per year?

•30. **(LO3)** An advertisement for Ford trucks offered "2.9% financing (for 48 months) or $2000 cash back." A truck buyer financed $20,000 at the low interest rate instead of paying $18,000 cash (after the $2000 rebate). What was the effective rate of interest on the loan if the foregone cash rebate is treated as part of the cost of financing? (The 2.9% interest rate is a monthly compounded nominal rate.)

CASE Should You Borrow to Make an RRSP Contribution?

Answering this question occupies dozens of financial commentaries as the March 1 RRSP contribution deadline approaches each year. Many financial institutions and mutual fund companies promote the idea of arranging an "RRSP loan" to obtain money for an RRSP contribution. They sometimes present a scenario giving the impression that borrowing to contribute to an RRSP is so advantageous it is virtually a "no-brainer." The conventional wisdom among financial planners seems to be that it is a good idea with two qualifications—the tax refund from the RRSP contribution should be applied to paying down the loan, and the loan should be paid off within a year. However, as often happens in financial analyses of even moderate complexity, the thinking is usually muddled and flawed.

In this case study, we will identify the key variable(s) for answering the question in the heading. We will discover that the decision (based strictly on financial considerations) turns on a single criterion. Here is the scenario. Suppose your marginal tax rate is 40%. Consequently, if you contribute $1000 to an RRSP, your taxable income will be reduced by $1000 and your income tax will be reduced by $400 (40% of $1000). To obtain the money for a $1000 RRSP contribution, you borrow $1000 at 6% compounded monthly and immediately use the $400 tax saving to reduce the loan balance to $600.

QUESTIONS

1. What is the monthly loan payment required to pay off the $600 balance in one year?
2. To what amount will the single $1000 contribution grow over the next 20 years if your RRSP earns 6% compounded monthly?

Virtually all analyses of the issue fail to mention a logical alternative to borrowing money for an RRSP contribution. If your budget permits monthly payments on an RRSP loan over the next year, then an alternative to borrowing for an immediate lump RRSP contribution is to use the same budget "room" to start monthly contributions to an RRSP. A subtle but key point will now be developed. In the loan scenario, you immediately applied the tax saving to reduce the loan balance. In effect, you needed to borrow only $600 to make a $1000 RRSP contribution. The $1000 contribution cost you only $600. Similarly, if you make a monthly RRSP contribution of $100, it will really cost you only $60 because of the $40 tax saving. In other words, your after-tax cost is only 60% of your monthly contribution.

Let's turn the last point around and answer this question: How much can you contribute to an RRSP if the after-tax cost to you is to be, say, $50? In this case, the $50 cost represents 60% of your contribution. Therefore, the contribution is $\frac{\$50}{0.6} = \$83.33$.

QUESTIONS

3. What monthly RRSP contribution will have the same after-tax cost to you as the monthly loan payment calculated in Question 1?

4. Suppose you make these monthly RRSP contributions. What amount will you have in the RRSP just after the twelfth contribution?

5. To what future value will the Question 4 amount grow over the subsequent 19 years?

6. The future values calculated in Questions 2 and 5 are the amounts in your RRSP 20 years from now under *two alternatives that have the same cost to you.* Comment on the outcome. What is your response to the question in the case's title when the interest rate on an RRSP loan is the same as the rate of return earned by your RRSP investments?

7. Suppose the RRSP earns 9% compounded monthly instead of 6% compounded monthly. Answer Questions 2, 4, and 5 again. Should you borrow for the RRSP contribution in this case?

8. What will be the nature of the outcome if the rate of return earned by the RRSP is *less* than the interest rate on the loan?

9. Summarize your findings as a general decision criterion. (Under what circumstance should you borrow to make an RRSP contribution?)

CHAPTER **12**

Annuities Due

CHAPTER OUTLINE

LEARNING OBJECTIVES

After completing this chapter, you will be able to:

LO1 Calculate the future value and present value of annuities due

LO2 Calculate the payment size, number of payments, and interest rate for annuities due

IF YOU RENT RESIDENTIAL OR commercial real estate, the typical lease contract requires payments at the beginning of each month. The leasing of vehicles, aircraft, office equipment, and computers is widespread—about one-quarter of new vehicles are leased rather than purchased. Lease payments are normally made at the beginning of each month or quarter. Insurance premiums must be paid at the beginning of each period of coverage. Membership dues are usually paid in advance. These are all examples of annuities due for which the payments occur at the beginning of each payment interval. Clearly, it is important that you understand the mathematics of annuities due. As you will soon learn, you can handle annuities due by making only a small change to the mathematics of ordinary annuities.

12.1   FUTURE VALUE OF AN ANNUITY DUE

In an **annuity due**,[1] the payments are made at the *beginning* of each payment interval. Note that we now have two *independent* criteria for classifying annuities. Based on the *timing* of the payment within the payment interval, an annuity is classified as *either* an *ordinary* annuity *or* an annuity *due*. Based on whether or not the payment interval equals the compounding interval, an annuity is *either* a *simple* annuity *or* a *general* annuity. These two independent criteria result in four categories of annuities, which are summarized in Table 12.1.

TABLE 12.1   Distinguishing Characteristics of Annuity Categories

Annuity category	Is the payment at the end or at the beginning of each payment interval?	Compare the payment interval to the compounding interval.
Ordinary simple annuity	End	Equal
Ordinary general annuity	End	Not equal
Simple annuity due	Beginning	Equal
General annuity due	Beginning	Not equal

Figure 12.1 presents the time diagram for an annuity due consisting of n payments, each of size *PMT*. The serial number for each payment *interval* is placed above the tick mark at the *end* of the interval.

FIGURE 12.1   Time Diagram for an *n*-Payment Annuity Due

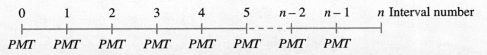

The future value of an annuity due is the sum of the future values of all of the payments (evaluated at the end of the annuity). We will use the symbol *FV*(due) for the future value of an annuity due. The symbols *PMT*, n, and i have the same meaning as for ordinary annuities.

---

[1] An annuity *due* is sometimes referred to as an annuity *in advance*. An *ordinary* annuity is then called an annuity *in arrears*.

> ### TRAP   What is Meant by the End of an Annuity?
>
> Don't confuse "the end of an annuity" with "the end of the payments" or "the date of the last payment." The end of an annuity means "the end of the annuity's *term*" or "the end of the last payment interval." It occurs one payment interval *after* the last payment in an annuity *due*.
>
> Similarly, the *beginning of an annuity* refers to "the start of the annuity's term" or "the start of the first payment interval." It does coincide with the first payment in an annuity due.

FUTURE VALUE USING THE ALGEBRAIC METHOD

LO1 The formula for the future value of an annuity *due* may be quickly derived from the formula for the future value of an *ordinary* annuity. Figure 12.2 helps us to see the connection between them. In the figure, n annuity payments of size PMT are shown on each of two time lines.

In the upper part of the figure, the payments are viewed as an annuity due. The focal date for its future value, FV(due), is at the end of the annuity (one payment interval after the last payment). In the lower part of the figure, the payments are viewed as an ordinary annuity. The focal date for its future value, FV, is at the end of the annuity (coincident with the last payment).

FIGURE 12.2   The Relationship between FV(due) and FV

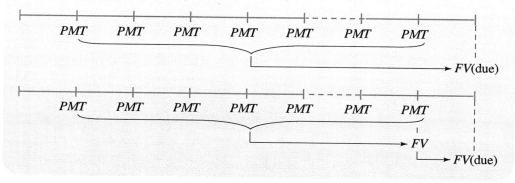

Each of these future values is economically equivalent to the *same* series of payments. The two future values are thus equivalent to each other, allowing for the time interval between them. Therefore, FV(due) equals the future value of FV, one payment interval later. That is,

$$FV(\text{due}) = FV \times (1 + i)$$

We see that the future value of an annuity due is simply $(1 + i)$ times the future value of an ordinary annuity. Substituting from formula (10-1) for FV, we obtain

FUTURE VALUE OF A SIMPLE ANNUITY DUE

$$FV(\text{due}) = FV \times (1 + i)$$
$$= PMT\left[\frac{(1 + i)^n - 1}{i}\right] \times (1 + i) \qquad (12\text{-}1)$$

If the payments form a general annuity due, use $i_2 = (1 + i)^c - 1$ to calculate the periodic interest rate that matches the payment interval. Then substitute this value for i in formula (12-1).

FUTURE VALUE USING THE FINANCIAL CALCULATOR FUNCTIONS

Since $FV(\text{due}) = FV \times (1 + i)$, the approach that probably occurs to you is to compute the annuity's future value as though it were an *ordinary* annuity, and then multiply the result by $(1 + i)$. The financial calculator will do this multiplication automatically if it is first "informed" that the annuity is an annuity *due*. Appendix 12A provides instructions for setting various financial calculator models in the annuity due mode. In example problems, "**BGN mode**" indicates that the calculator should be set to the annuity due mode.

> ### TIP   Clues to the Type of Annuity
>
> Information that helps you identify an annuity due may lie in subtle wording of a problem. Look for a key word or phrase that provides the clue. Some examples of wording that indicates an annuity due are:
> - "Payments at the beginning of each …"
> - "Payments … in advance"
> - "First payment … made today"
> - "Payments … starting now"

EXAMPLE 12.1A   **CALCULATING THE FUTURE VALUE OF A SIMPLE ANNUITY DUE**

To the nearest dollar, how much will Stan accumulate in his RRSP by age 60 if he makes semiannual contributions of $2000 starting on his twenty-seventh birthday? Assume that the RRSP earns 8% compounded semiannually and that no contribution is made on his sixtieth birthday.

SOLUTION

The accumulated amount will be the future value of the contributions on Stan's sixtieth birthday. Viewed from the future value's focal date at his sixtieth birthday, the RRSP contributions are made at the *beginning* of every six months. Therefore, they form an annuity *due*. Since the payment interval equals the compounding interval, we have a *simple* annuity due with:

$$PMT = \$2000 \quad i = \tfrac{8\%}{2} = 4\% \quad \text{and} \quad n = 2(33) = 66 \text{ payments}$$

Substitute the preceding values into formula (12-1)

$$FV(\text{due}) = PMT\left[\frac{(1 + i)^n - 1}{i}\right] \times (1 + i)$$

$$= \$2000\left(\frac{1.04^{66} - 1}{0.04}\right) \times (1.04)$$

$$= \$2000\left(\frac{13.310685 - 1}{0.04}\right)(1.04)$$

$$= \$640,156$$

Stan will have $640,156 in his RRSP at age 60.

BGN mode

8	I/Y
P/Y 2	ENTER

(making $C/Y = P/Y = 2$)

66	N
0	PV
2000 +/−	PMT
CPT	FV

Ans: 640,156

EXAMPLE 12.1B **CALCULATING THE FUTURE VALUE OF A GENERAL ANNUITY DUE**

Repeat Example 12.1A with the change that the RRSP earns 8% compounded annually instead of 8% compounded semiannually.

SOLUTION

We now have a general annuity since the compounding interval (one year) differs from the payment interval (six months). The value we must use for i in the FV formula is the periodic rate for the six-month payment interval. (It will be about $\frac{8\%}{2} = 4\%$.) Substitute

$$i = \frac{8\%}{1} = 8\% \quad \text{and} \quad c = \frac{\text{Number of compoundings per year}}{\text{Number of payments per year}} = \frac{1}{2} = 0.5$$

into formula (9-4c) giving

$$i_2 = (1 + i)^c - 1 = (1.08)^{0.5} - 1 = 0.039230485 \text{ per six months}$$

Use this value for i in formula (12-1) giving

$$FV(\text{due}) = PMT\left[\frac{(1 + i)^n - 1}{i}\right] \times (1 + i)$$

$$= \$2000\left(\frac{1.039230485^{66} - 1}{0.039230485}\right) \times (1.039230485)$$

$$= \$2000\left(\frac{12.676050 - 1}{0.039230485}\right)(1.039230485)$$

$$= \$618,606$$

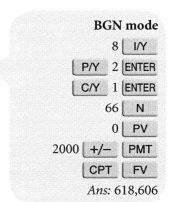

BGN mode

8 [I/Y]

[P/Y] 2 [ENTER]

[C/Y] 1 [ENTER]

66 [N]

0 [PV]

2000 [+/–] [PMT]

[CPT] [FV]

Ans: 618,606

Stan will have \$618,606 in his RRSP at age 60.

EXAMPLE 12.1C **CALCULATING THE FUTURE VALUE OF AN ANNUITY DUE WHERE AN INTEREST RATE CHANGE OCCURS DURING THE TERM OF THE ANNUITY**

Stephanie intends to contribute \$2500 to her RRSP at the beginning of every six months, starting today. If the RRSP earns 8% compounded semiannually for the first seven years and 7% compounded semiannually thereafter, what amount will she have in the plan after 20 years?

SOLUTION

The amount in the plan will be the future value of the contributions.

Note: The wording of this question means that you are to determine the amount in the RRSP after *20 years'* *contributions*. There will be 40 contributions in 20 years. The fortieth contribution will occur $19\frac{1}{2}$ years from now. The 40 contributions form an annuity due when viewed from the future value's focal date 20 years from now. (If Stephanie makes a forty-first contribution 20 years from today, that payment will not be included in FV(due) calculated for 40 payments at a focal date 20 years from today.)

The future value cannot be calculated in one step because the interest rate changes after seven years. The solution strategy is indicated in the following time diagram. Since the payment interval equals the compounding interval throughout, the payments form a simple annuity in both segments of the 20 years.

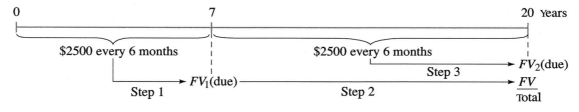

For the first 7 years, $i = \frac{8\%}{2} = 4\%$ and $n = 2(7) = 14$

For the next 13 years, $i = \frac{7\%}{2} = 3.5\%$ and $n = 2(13) = 26$

The future value, after seven years, of the first 14 contributions will be

$$FV_1(\text{due}) = PMT\left[\frac{(1 + i)^n - 1}{i}\right] \times (1 + i)$$

$$= \$2500\left(\frac{1.04^{14} - 1}{0.04}\right) \times (1.04)$$

$$= \$2500(18.291911)(1.04)$$

$$= \$47,558.97$$

BGN mode

8 [I/Y]

[P/Y] 2 [ENTER]

(making $C/Y = P/Y = 2$)

14 [N]

0 [PV]

2500 [+/−] [PMT]

[CPT] [FV]

Ans: 47,558.97

The future value of $47,558.97 an additional 13 years later will be

$$FV = PV(1 + i)^n = \$47,558.97(1.035)^{26} = \$116,327.27$$

The future value, 20 years from now, of the last 26 payments will be

$$FV_2(\text{due}) = \$2500\left[\frac{(1.035)^{26} - 1}{0.035}\right] \times (1.035)$$

$$= \$2500(41.3131017)(1.035)$$

$$= \$106,897.65$$

BGN mode

Same *PMT, P/Y, C/Y*

7 [I/Y]

26 [N]

47558.97 [+/−] [PV]

[CPT] [FV]

Ans: 223,224.92

The total amount in the RRSP after 20 years will be

$$FV + FV_2(\text{due}) = \$116,327.27 + \$106,897.65 = \$223,224.92$$

Stephanie will have $223,224.92 in her RRSP after 20 years.

POINT OF INTEREST

The Ten-Percent Solution for Achieving Financial Security

In 1989 *The Wealthy Barber* by David Chilton was first published by Stoddart Publishing Co. Ltd. Its engaging style and commonsense approach to personal financial planning made it one of the all-time Canadian best-sellers. In various editions over the years, it has sold over 3 million copies in Canada and the United States. In the book, the principles of financial planning and money management are revealed through conversations between an unlikely financial hero, barber shop proprietor Roy Miller, and his patrons.

In Chapter 4, titled "The Ten Percent Solution," Tom and Dave arrive for their haircut accompanied by Dave's sister Cathy. They are all in their late twenties and eager to hear Roy reveal his "golden secret" that "guarantees … someday you'll be rich."

To impress the wealth-building potential of compound interest upon Tom, Dave, and Cathy, Roy poses two questions. (The questions and their answers are underlined for later reference.) With your current knowledge of annuities, you should be able to obtain the answers that amaze Tom, Dave, and Cathy. Roy is speaking as we join the dialogue.

"Wealth beyond your wildest dreams is possible if you learn the golden secret: Invest ten percent of all you make for long-term growth. If you follow that one simple guideline, someday you'll be a very rich man."

"That's it?" asked Tom. "I could get that from a Scotiabank commercial!"

"Patience, Tom," replied Roy. "I'll tell you things that turn a seemingly simple sentence into an extremely powerful thought."

"Cathy, if you invested $2400 a year, say $200 a month, for the next 30 years, and averaged a 15% return per year, how much money do you think you'd end up with?" challenged Roy.

"Well, $2400 times 30 is $72,000 … plus growth … I don't know … I'd say $200,000. Maybe not quite that much," Cathy concluded.

"Wrong. The answer is $1,402,000." Roy declared.

"Get real!" was Tom's initial reaction. When he realized that Roy was serious, he paled. "What about inflation? And where am I going to get 15%? For that matter, where am I going to get $200 per month?" he stammered.

"All good questions, Tom, and we'll get to them in due course. Dave, you try one. If you had started putting $30 a month away, the equivalent of a dollar a day, at age 18 and you continued until age 65, averaging a 15% annual return, how much would you end up with?"

"I hate math, Roy, but I'll give it a shot," replied Dave. "Thirty dollars a month is $360 a year, times 47 years … Anybody have a calculator?"

"It's just under $17,000," injected Roy.

"Plus growth, I'll say about $70,000."

"Close," responded Roy. "The answer is $2,679,000."

"Bull," scoffed Tom.

"No, not bull … magic. The magic of compound interest—interest on principal and interest, not just simple interest on principal. The eighth wonder of the world. Thirty dollars a month, a dollar a day, will magically turn into over two and a half million. And do you know what's even more impressive? You know someone who has done it," Roy said proudly.

"Thirty-five years ago, I started my savings with $30 a month, which was approximately 10% of my earnings. I have achieved a 15% average annual return, actually a little higher. In addition, as my income rose, my 10% saving component rose accordingly. Thirty dollars a month became $60, then $100, and eventually hundreds of dollars a month. You three are looking at a very wealthy man!"

"Are you trying to tell us that by saving 10% of every pay cheque, you've turned yourself into a millionaire?" an intense Tom demanded.

"Precisely," was the incredulous response.

Roy Miller, a millionaire! Dave sat stunned. Roy was clearly deriving great pleasure from the disbelief on their faces.

"Compound interest … mind-boggling, isn't it?" he went on. "It's a real tragedy that most people don't understand compound interest and its wondrous powers."

QUESTIONS

1. Regarding Roy's first question (to Cathy), how does he arrive at the $1,402,000 figure? Does he use $2400 per year or $200 per month? Is the rate of return 15% compounded annually or 15% compounded monthly? Does he assume that the payments are at the beginning or at the end of each payment interval?

2. Regarding Roy's second question (to Dave), how does he arrive at the $2,679,000 figure? Does he assume that the $30 payments are at the beginning or at the end of each month?

3. Roy's advice is sound, but the assumption of a long-term compound annual rate of return of 15% is unrealistic. For the 20 years ended August 31, 2009, the compound annual return for the S&P/TSX Composite Total Return Index was 7.59%. The average compound annual return of Canadian Equity mutual funds was about 1% lower. (It is difficult to come up with a precise figure for the true long-term average performance of equity mutual funds because a poorly performing fund is typically wound up, or absorbed within a better performing fund in the family of funds run by the same investment manager. The poor performance of such a "disappeared" fund vanishes from published long-term average rates of return. Fewer than 10% of funds in the current list of Canadian Equity funds have a 20-year record.)

What would be the answers to Roy's two questions if we assume a more realistic rate of return of 8% compounded monthly?

SPREADSHEET STRATEGIES   Future Value of an Annuity Due

The Spreadsheet Strategies box in Section 10.5 described spreadsheet templates for calculating the future value and present value of an ordinary general annuity. At that time it was premature to point out that those same templates may, in fact, be employed to obtain the future value and present value of *any* of our four categories of annuity—ordinary simple, ordinary general, simple due, and general due. Use the "type" variable to distinguish between ordinary annuities and annuities due. For an *ordinary* annuity (whether simple or general) enter "0" for the "type;" for an annuity *due* (whether simple or general) enter "1" for the "type."

Below we employ the future value template to solve Example 12.1A from earlier in this section. The question requires us to calculate the future value of 66 RRSP contributions occurring at the beginning of every six months if they earn 8% compounded semiannually. Obtain the template from Chapter 10 of the textbook's Web site; look for "FV of Any Annuity." (If you saved your programmed FV template from Section 10.5, you can simply enter the new data from this problem in that template.)

The main features of the completed template are presented below. The formulas programmed into cells C11 and C18 are displayed in cells C12 and C19, respectively. After entering the given data in the yellow input cells, the computed future value immediately appears in the output cell C18. Note that cells C6 and C9 are equal (both "2" for this particular simple annuity). Whenever we have a *simple* annuity, the "any-annuity" templates from Sections 10.5, 11.1, 11.2, and 11.3 will obtain the same value for i_2 and i, and compute the value "1" for c.

	A	B	C	D
1				
2		Using a spreadsheet to calculate the future value of a simple annuity due.		
3	Example 12.1A:			
4				
5		Nominal annual interest rate, *j*	8.000%	
6		Compoundings per year, *m*	2	
7		Given periodic rate of interest, *i*	4.0000%	
8				
9		Payments per year	2	
10		Compoundings per payment interval, *c*	1.0000000000	
11		Periodic rate of interest, i_2 or *rate*	4.000000000%	
12		Formula in cell C11:	=(1+C7)^C10-1	
13		Number of payments, *n* or *nper*	66.00	
14		Regular annuity payment, *PMT* or *pmt*	-$2,000.00	
15		One-time initial payment, *pv*	$0.00	
16		Annuity *type*	1	
17				
18		FV(rate, nper, pmt, pv, type)	$640,155.60	
19		Formula in cell C18:	=FV(C11,C13,C14,C15,C16)	
20				

The future value of the RRSP (rounded to the nearest dollar) will be $640,156.

CONCEPT QUESTIONS

1. Give three examples of an annuity due.

2. For the future value of an annuity due, where is the focal date located relative to the final payment?

3. Other things being equal, why is the future value of an annuity due larger than the future value of an ordinary annuity?

EXERCISE 12.1

≣ connect

Spreadsheet template: The partially completed Excel template developed in Section 10.5 for calculating the future value of any annuity may be used for many of the problems in Exercise 12.1. Go to Chapter 10 of the Student Edition and find "FV of Any Annuity."

Answers to the odd-numbered problems are at the end of the book.

1. Annual contributions of $1000 will be made to a TFSA for 25 years. The contributor expects investments within the plan to earn 7% compounded annually. What will the TFSA be worth after 25 years if the contributions are made:

   a. At the end of each year?   **b.** At the beginning of each year?

   c. By what percentage does the answer to Part (b) exceed the answer to Part (a)?

2. Quarterly contributions of $1000 will be made to an RESP for 15 years. Assuming that the investments within the plan grow at 8% compounded quarterly, how much will the TFSA be worth after 15 years if the contributions are made:

   a. At the end of each quarter?   **b.** At the beginning of each quarter?

   c. By what percentage does the answer to Part (b) exceed the answer to Part (a)?

3. What is the future value of $100 invested at the beginning of every month for 25 years if the investments earn:

   a. 6% compounded monthly?   **b.** 8% compounded monthly?

4. Svetlana intends to invest $1000 at the beginning of every six months. If the investments earn 7% compounded semiannually, what will her investments be worth (rounded to the nearest dollar) after:

   a. 25 years?   **b.** 30 years?

5. Your client plans to invest $10,000 at the beginning of each year for the next 14 years. If the invested funds earn 9.1% compounded annually, what will be the total accumulated value after 14 years? (Taken from CIFP course materials.)

6. Your client has systematically contributed $3000 to her RRSP at the beginning of every three months for the past 17 years. If the RRSP has earned 8.8% compounded quarterly, what is its value today? (Taken from CIFP course materials.)

7. Today Gus is making his first annual contribution of $2500 to a TFSA. How much will the plan be worth 16 years from now if it earns 5.25% compounded monthly?

8. Astrid has just opened an RESP for her children with her first quarterly deposit of $1700. What will the RESP be worth $11\frac{1}{2}$ years from now if the investments within the plan earn 7.5% compounded semiannually?

9. Salvatore will contribute $500 to a mutual fund at the beginning of each calendar quarter.

   a. What will be the value of his mutual fund after $6\frac{1}{2}$ years if the fund earns 7.6% compounded annually?

   b. How much of this amount represents investment earnings?

10. Monarch Distributing Ltd. plans to accumulate funds for the purchase of a larger warehouse seven years from now. If Monarch contributes $10,000 at the beginning of each month to an investment account earning 4.5% compounded semiannually, what amount (rounded to the nearest dollar) will Monarch accumulate by the end of the seven years?

11. If Hans contributes $1500 to his RRSP on February 1, 1990, and every six months thereafter, up to and including February 1, 2017, what amount will he accumulate in the RRSP by August 1, 2017? Assume that the RRSP will earn 8.5% compounded semiannually. How much of the total will be earnings?

12. Many people make their annual RRSP contribution for a taxation year close to the end of the year. Financial advisers encourage clients to contribute as early in the year as possible. How much more will there be in an RRSP at the end of 25 years if annual contributions of $5000 are made at the beginning of each year instead of at the end? Assume that the RRSP will earn:

   a. 8% compounded annually.   **b.** 8% compounded monthly.

∘13. For the past 25 years, Giorgio has contributed $2000 to his RRSP at the beginning of every six months. The plan earned 8% compounded annually for the first 11 years and 7% compounded semiannually for the subsequent 14 years. What is the value of his RRSP today?

∘14. Keiko has already accumulated $150,000 in her RRSP. She intends to continue to grow her RRSP by making contributions of $500 at the beginning of every month. How much will her RRSP be worth 15 years from now if the RRSP earns 8% compounded annually?

∘15. Johan recently received his annual performance bonus from his employer. He has set up an investment savings plan to which he will contribute $2000 each year from his bonus and $400 per month from his regular salary. Johan will make his initial contributions of $2000 and $400 today. Rounded to the nearest dollar,

   a. What will the plan be worth after 25 years if it earns 7.5% compounded monthly?

   b. How much did Johan's contributions earn during the 25 years?

∘16. What will be the amount in an RRSP after 25 years if contributions of $2000 are made at the beginning of each year for the first 10 years, and contributions of $4000 are made at the beginning of each year for the subsequent 15 years? Assume that the RRSP will earn 8% compounded quarterly.

∘17. Fay contributed $3000 per year to her RRSP on every birthday from age 21 to 30 inclusive. She then ceased employment to raise a family and made no further contributions. Her husband Fred contributed $3000 per year to his RRSP on every birthday from age 31 to 64 inclusive. Assuming that both plans earn 8% compounded annually over the years, calculate and compare the amounts in their RRSPs at age 65.

🔲 connect   18. **Using the Future Value (Due) Chart** An interactive Future Value (Due) Chart is available on this textbook's Web site. In Chapter 12 of the Student Edition, find "Future Value (Due) Chart." Use this chart to solve the following problems (rounded to the nearest dollar).

   a. Exercise 12.1, Problem 5   **b.** Exercise 12.1, Problem 7

   c. Exercise 12.1, Problem 9   **d.** Exercise 12.1, Problem 14

🔲 connect   ∘19. **Components of the Future Value of an Annuity Due** We will use the Fidelity Investments' Growth Calculator referred to in the NET @ssets feature earlier in this section. Go to the Student Edition of this textbook's Web site. In Chapter 12, find "Growth Calculator."

   The bars in the Growth Calculator chart represent future values at the ends of successive years for the annuity specified by the data entered in cells below the chart. Values can be entered for "Years of Investing" (the annuity's term), the "Initial Balance" (initial lump investment), the "Annual Investment" (amount contributed at the beginning of each year), "Rate of Return" (compounded annually), "Inflation Rate" (compounded annually), and "Tax Rate" (applicable to each year's earnings).

   You can change a variable's value either by manually entering a new value or by dragging the slider located below the cell. The bar chart immediately adjusts to show the effect of the change.

Each bar in the chart shows three components of the future value. The chart refers to the three components as *Amount Invested*, *Simple Earnings*, and *Compound Earnings*. The *Amount Invested* is just the sum of the investments with no earnings. The *Simple Earnings* represents interest earned on invested capital on a simple-interest basis. *Compound Earnings* represents interest earned on previously converted interest. The values of these components at the end of the annuity appear in boxes near the bottom of the window.

The interactive chart and calculator will adjust for inflation in two respects. If you intend to increase your annual contributions to keep pace with the rate of inflation, check the "Increase annual investment with inflation" box located below the sliders. (This is the type of scenario we will discuss in Section 13.2). For *fixed* annual investments, delete the check mark from this box. The second optional inflation adjustment is to display the future value (and its components) in constant purchasing power dollars. You can activate this feature by selecting the "Real (Net of Inflation) Dollars" button.

The calculator will also display results on a before-income-tax basis (by setting *Tax Rate* = 0%) or on an after-tax basis. The number you enter for Tax Rate is the percentage of each year's investment earnings that will be paid in income tax. For example, if you enter 40% for *Tax Rate* and 10% for *Rate of Return*, the after-tax rate of growth will be only $10\% - 0.4(10\%) = 6\%$.

Answer the following questions for *Initial Balance* = $0, *Rate of Return* = 10%, and *Annual Investment* = $1000. Unless otherwise indicated, set *Tax Rate* = 0% (to simulate growth within an RRSP) and *Inflation Rate* = 0% (for fixed payments and nominal dollar outcomes).

a. How long does it take for the *Compound Earnings* component to exceed the *Simple Earnings* component?

b. After 10 years, what is each component's percentage of the future value?

c. After 25 years, what is each component's percentage of the future value?

d. If the annual rate of inflation is 2%, what is the future value after 25 years in constant purchasing power (real) dollars?

e. If the investments are held outside an RRSP and the annual earnings are taxed at 30%, how much less will you have (in nominal dollars) after 25 years than in Part (c)?

connect

20. **Using the Cool Million (Due) Chart** This chart is the annuity due version of the (ordinary annuity) Cool Million chart described in Problem 36 of Exercise 11.1. Go to the Student Edition on this textbook's Web site. In Chapter 12, find "Cool Million (Due)."

Return to Problem 36 in Exercise 11.1 to review the features of the chart. Use the same initial planning assumptions in both the Cool Million chart and the Cool Million (Due) chart. How much sooner will you become a millionaire if your regular savings are invested at the beginning of each month instead of at the end of each month?

12.2 PRESENT VALUE OF AN ANNUITY DUE

LO1   The present value of an annuity due is the sum of the present values, at the beginning of the annuity, of all payments. Since payments occur at the *beginning* of each payment interval, the beginning of the annuity coincides with the first payment. We will use the symbol *PV*(due) for the present value of an annuity due.

PRESENT VALUE USING THE ALGEBRAIC METHOD

The formula for PV(due) may be derived from the formula for the present value of an ordinary annuity. The line of reasoning is the same as used in Section 12.1 to derive the formula for FV(due). The outcome is that PV(due) is related to PV in the same way that FV(due) is related to FV. That is,

$$PV(\text{due}) = PV \times (1 + i)$$

Substituting from formula (10-2) for PV, we obtain

PRESENT VALUE OF A SIMPLE ANNUITY DUE

$$PV(\text{due}) = PV \times (1 + i)$$
$$= PMT\left[\frac{1 - (1 + i)^{-n}}{i}\right] \times (1 + i) \qquad \text{(12-2)}$$

If the payments form a *general* annuity due, use $i_2 = (1 + i)^c - 1$ to calculate the periodic interest rate that matches the payment interval. Then substitute this value for i in formula (12-2).

PRESENT VALUE USING THE FINANCIAL CALCULATOR FUNCTIONS

Set the calculator to the annuity due mode (so that "BGN" or "Begin" shows in the display). Then proceed as you would to compute the present value of an ordinary annuity.

APPLICATIONS OF THE PRESENT VALUE CALCULATION

As with ordinary annuities, most applications of the present value of an annuity due involve some aspect of valuation. Since the payments on most leases form an annuity due, we are now able to address an additional valuation topic.

The Book Value of a Lease When a business purchases equipment, its accountant records the acquisition of an asset (equipment). If instead, the business leases the equipment, you might think the accountant would just record the monthly lease payments as they are made. However, there is an additional issue.

Most leases for a fixed term are "non-cancellable." This means that the lessee is required to continue the lease payments for the full term of the lease, even if the leased equipment is no longer needed. Generally Accepted Accounting Principles (GAAP) require this commitment to be recorded as a liability.[2]

This raises the question: "What amount should we use for this lease liability?" Should we simply add up all the payments for the entire term of the lease? No—that would place the same value on a dollar paid at the end of the lease as a dollar paid at the beginning. Instead, we should record the current economic value (present value) of the future lease payments. The follow-up question arises: "What discount rate should be used in the present value calculation?"

To answer this second question, consider that the usual alternative to leasing equipment is purchasing the equipment using borrowed funds. For this reason, GAAP stipulates that the discount rate should be the interest rate the business would pay to finance the purchase of the equipment.[3]

As time passes, the decreasing number of remaining payments represents a declining lease liability. In accordance with GAAP, the value of the lease liability is regularly reduced.

---

[2] A leasehold asset is also recorded. The lease represents a long-term asset in the sense that the right to use the equipment will produce benefits over the term of the lease.

[3] This is consistent with a broader principle in accounting. The reported value of any long-term liability is the present value of future contractual payments discounted at the firm's borrowing rate (on the date the liability was incurred).

At any point during the term of the lease, the present value of the *remaining* lease payments is known as the **book value of the lease** liability.

$$\left(\begin{array}{c}\text{Book value of a} \\ \text{long-term lease liability}\end{array}\right) = \left(\begin{array}{c}\text{Present value of the remaining payments} \\ \text{(discounted at the interest rate on debt financing)}\end{array}\right)$$

EXAMPLE 12.2A **FINDING THE ECONOMIC VALUE OF A SIMPLE ANNUITY DUE**

The BC Lottery Corporation runs the "Millionaire Life" lottery. The winner of the Grand Prize can choose either $1,000,000 per year for 25 years or a single cash payment of $17,000,000. Which option should be chosen if the payments are made at the beginning of each year and, on low-risk investments, money can earn:

a. 3.2% compounded annually? **b.** 3.8% compounded annually?

SOLUTION

The annuity option should be chosen if its economic value on the prize date exceeds $17,000,000. Its economic value is the present value of the 25 payments discounted at the rate of return money can earn. Since the first payment is received immediately and the payment interval (one year) equals the compounding interval (one year), the payments form a simple annuity due having

$$PMT = \$1,000,000 \quad \text{and} \quad n = 25$$

a. $j = 3.2\%$ compounded annually and $i = \frac{3.2\%}{1} = 3.2\%$ per year

Substituting in formula (12-2), we obtain

$$PV(\text{due}) = PMT\left[\frac{1 - (1 + i)^{-n}}{i}\right] \times (1+i)$$

$$= \$1,000,000\left(\frac{1 - 1.032^{-25}}{0.032}\right)(1.032)$$

$$= \$1,000,000\left(\frac{1 - 0.45499599}{0.032}\right)(1.032)$$

$$= \$17,576,379 \text{ (rounded to the nearest dollar)}$$

Select the 25-year annuity because its current economic value is $576,379 more than the lump payment.

b. $j = 3.8\%$ compounded annually and $i = \frac{3.8\%}{1} = 3.8\%$ per year

$$PV(\text{due}) = \$1,000,000\left(\frac{1 - 1.038^{-25}}{0.038}\right)(1.038)$$

$$= \$16,564,021 \text{ (to the nearest dollar)}$$

Select the single lump payment option because it is worth

$$\$17,000,000 - \$16,564,021 = \$435,979$$

more than the economic value of the annuity.

BGN mode

3.2 I/Y

P/Y 1 ENTER

(making C/Y = P/Y = 1)

25 N

1000000 PMT

0 FV

CPT PV

Ans: −17,576,379

BGN mode

Same P/Y, C/Y

Same N, PMT, FV

3.8 I/Y

CPT PV

Ans: −16,564,021

EXAMPLE 12.2B   **THE BOOK VALUE OF A LEASE LIABILITY**

National Engineering Services (NES) acquired a machine under a capital lease agreement. NES pays the lessor $2400 at the beginning of every three months for five years. If National can obtain five-year financing at 10% compounded quarterly,

a. What long-term lease liability will NES initially record?

b. What liability will be reported two years later?

SOLUTION

The initial liability (book value) is the present value of all of the lease payments. At any later date, the liability reported in the financial statements is the present value of the remaining payments. In both cases, the discount rate should be the interest rate at which the firm could have borrowed at the time of signing the lease. When viewed from the dates in either Part (a) or Part (b), the lease payments form a simple annuity due having $PMT = \$2400$ and $i = \frac{10\%}{4} = 2.5\%$.

a. $n = m(\text{Term}) = 4(5) = 20$ payments

The initial lease liability is

$$PV(\text{due}) = PMT\left[\frac{1 - (1 + i)^{-n}}{i}\right] \times (1 + i)$$

$$= \$2400\left(\frac{1 - 1.025^{-20}}{0.025}\right)(1.025)$$

$$= \$38,349.34$$

b. After two years, $n = 4(3) = 12$ payments remain. The book value of the lease liability will be

$$PV(\text{due}) = \$2400\left(\frac{1 - 1.025^{-12}}{0.025}\right)(1.025)$$

$$= \$25,234.10$$

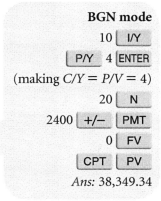

BGN mode

10   I/Y

P/Y   4 ENTER

(making $C/Y = P/V = 4$)

20   N

2400 +/– PMT

0   FV

CPT   PV

Ans: 38,349.34

BGN mode
Same *I/Y, P/Y, C/Y*
Same *PMT, FV*

12   N

CPT   PV

Ans: 25,234.10

EXAMPLE 12.2C   **PURCHASE OR LEASE A COMPUTER?**

Best-Buy Computers advertises a computer system for $2995. The same system may be leased for 24 months at $130 per month (at the beginning of each month). At the end of the lease, the system may be purchased for 10% of the retail price. Should you lease or purchase the computer if you can obtain a two-year loan at 12% compounded annually to purchase the computer?

SOLUTION

We cannot solve the problem by simply comparing the monthly loan payments to the monthly lease payments, for two reasons. Under the lease, you must pay an additional $299.50 two years from now to own the system. Also, lease payments are made at the beginning of each month but loan payments are made at the end of each month.

We will compare the present values of the two alternatives. Since we are paying out money instead of receiving it, we should choose the alternative with the *lower* present value.

From basic principles, we know that the present value of the loan payments, discounted at the interest rate on the loan, equals the initial loan ($2995). For a fair comparison, we should discount the lease payments (including the final payment to acquire ownership) using the same rate.

Since the payment interval (one month) differs from the compounding interval (one year), the lease payments form a *general* annuity due having

$$PMT = \$130 \text{ per month} \quad n = 24 \quad \text{and} \quad i = \frac{12\%}{1} = 12\% \text{ per year}$$

First calculate the periodic interest rate for the one-month payment interval. (It will be about $\frac{12\%}{12} = 1\%$.)

$$c = \frac{\text{Number of compoundings per year}}{\text{Number of payments per year}} = \frac{1}{12} = 0.08\overline{3}$$

$$i_2 = (1 + i)^c - 1 = 1.12^{0.08\overline{3}} - 1 = 0.009488793 \text{ per month}$$

Substitute this value for i in subsequent calculations.

The present value of the monthly lease payments is

$$PV(\text{due}) = PMT\left[\frac{1 - (1 + i)^{-n}}{i}\right] \times (1 + i)$$

$$= \$130\left[\frac{1 - 1.009488793^{-24}}{0.009488793}\right](1.009488793)$$

$$= \$2804.88$$

The present value of the end-of-lease purchase payment is

$$PV = FV(1 + i)^{-n} = \$299.50(1.009488793)^{-24} = \$238.76$$

The combined present value is $\$2804.88 + \$238.76 = \$3043.64$.

The economic cost (in current dollars) of the lease is

$$\$3043.64 - \$2995 = \$48.64$$

more than the economic cost of purchasing the computer using borrowed funds. Therefore, the computer system should be purchased.

BGN mode

12 | I/Y |
| P/Y | 12 | ENTER |
| C/Y | 1 | ENTER |
24 | N |
130 | +/− | PMT |
299.50 | +/− | FV |
| CPT | PV |

Ans: 3043.64

TIP   **Equivalent Views of a Deferred Annuity**

In Section 10.4, we viewed a deferred annuity as an *ordinary* annuity that followed a "period of deferral." The length of the period of deferral was chosen so that the first payment occurred one payment interval *after the end of* the period of deferral.

Now that we can handle annuities due, we can just as well view the same deferred annuity as an annuity *due* following a longer period of deferral. The period of deferral must end immediately before the first payment is made.

In Example 12.2D we demonstrate these alternative but equivalent viewpoints in the calculation of the present value of a deferred annuity. We show only the financial calculator solution in each approach.

EXAMPLE 12.2D   **THE PRESENT VALUE OF A DEFERRED ANNUITY**

Rico wants to buy a retirement annuity that will pay him the first of 50 semiannual payments of $10,000 ten years from now. How much must he pay to purchase the annuity today if the annuity issuer provides a return on investment of 4.8% compounded semiannually?

SOLUTION

The purchase price is today's present value of the 50 payments. We are given:

$$n = 50 \quad PMT = \$10,000 \quad j = 4.8\% \quad \text{and} \quad m = 2$$

In the left-hand column below, we view the deferred annuity as an *ordinary* simple annuity beginning after a $9\frac{1}{2}$-year period of deferral $[d = 2(9\frac{1}{2}) = 19$ compounding periods$]$. In the right-hand column, we regard the deferred annuity as a simple annuity *due* starting after a 10-year period of deferral $[d = 2(10) = 20]$. In each case, there are two steps:

Step 1:   Determine the present value of the annuity at the *end* of the period of deferral.

Step 2:   Calculate the present value of the Step 1 result at the *beginning* of the period of deferral.

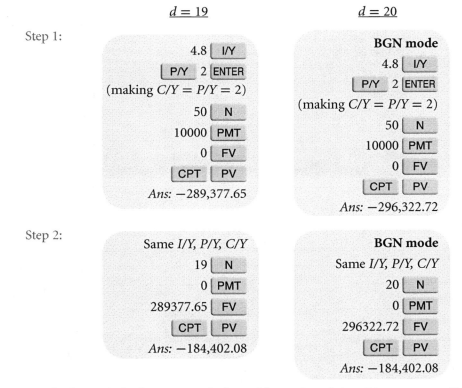

We obtain precisely the same result from either point of view. Rico must pay $184,402.08 for the deferred annuity.

SPREADSHEET STRATEGIES Present Value of an Annuity Due

The present value template introduced in Section 10.5 for ordinary general annuities may also be employed for simple annuities due and general annuities due. We simply enter "1" for the variable "type" when we have an annuity *due*.

Below we use this template to calculate the present value of the annuity in Part (a) of Example 12.2A. In Part (a), we need to compute the present value of 25 annual payments of $1,000,000 received at the beginning of each year. The

discount rate is 3.2% compounded annually. Obtain the template from Chapter 10 of the textbook's Web site; look for "PV of Any Annuity."

The main features of the completed template are presented below. The formulas programmed into cells C11 and C18 are displayed in cells C12 and C19, respectively. After entering the given data in the yellow input cells, the computed present value immediately appears in the output cell C18.

	A	B	C	D
1				
2		Using a spreadsheet to calculate the present value of a simple annuity due.		
3		Example 12.2A, Part a:		
4				
5		Nominal annual interest rate, j	3.200%	
6		Compoundings per year, m	1	
7		Given periodic rate of interest, i	3.2000%	
8				
9		Payments per year	1	
10		Compoundings per payment interval, c	1.0000000000	
11		Periodic rate of interest, i_2 or $rate$	3.200000000%	
12		Formula in cell C11:	=(1+C7)^C10-1	
13		Number of payments, n or $nper$	25.00	
14		Regular annuity payment, PMT or pmt	$1,000,000.00	
15		One-time final payment, fv	$0.00	
16		Annuity $type$	1	
17				
18		PV(rate, nper, pmt, fv, type)	-$17,576,379.37	
19		Formula in cell C18:	=PV(C11,C13,C14,C15,C16)	
20				

The present value of the annuity (rounded to the nearest dollar) is $17,576,379.

CONCEPT QUESTIONS

1. For the present value of an annuity due, where is the focal date located relative to the first payment?

2. Other things being equal, why is the present value of an annuity due larger than the present value of an ordinary annuity?

3. If the periodic interest rate for a payment interval is 3%, by what percentage will *PV*(due) exceed *PV*?

4. Other factors being equal, is the *PV* of an annuity due larger if the given nominal discount rate is compounded monthly instead of annually? Explain briefly.

Spreadsheet template: The partially completed Excel template developed in Section 10.5 for calculating the present value of an annuity may be used for many of the problems in Exercise 12.2. Go to Chapter 10 of the Student Edition and find "PV of Any Annuity."

Answers to the odd-numbered problems are at the end of the book.

1. An annuity consists of quarterly payments of $950 for 8 years and 9 months. Discounting at 8% compounded quarterly, determine the present value of the annuity if the payments are made:

    a. At the end of each quarter?

    b. At the beginning of each quarter?

    c. By what percentage does the answer to Part (b) exceed the answer to Part (a)?

2. Using a discount rate of 6% compounded monthly, calculate the present value of monthly payments of $325 for $7\frac{1}{4}$ years if the payments are made:

    a. At the end of each month?

    b. At the beginning of each month?

    c. By what percentage does the answer to Part (b) exceed the answer to Part (a)?

3. What is the present value of an annuity due consisting of semiannual payments of $1000 for 25 years, if money can earn:

    a. 6% compounded semiannually?   b. 8% compounded semiannually?

4. Money can earn 6% compounded monthly. What is the present value of beginning-of-month payments of $100 if the payments continue for:

    a. 25 years?   b. 30 years?

5. On the date of its financial statements, a company has $4\frac{1}{2}$ years remaining on the lease of a truck. The lease requires payments of $3000 at the beginning of every six months. What book value is reported for the lease liability if the company pays 8% compounded monthly on its medium-term debt?

6. If money can earn 5.25% compounded monthly, what is the value of an annuity consisting of annual payments of $2500 continuing for 16 years? The first payment will be received today.

7. Carmella purchased a refrigerator under a conditional sale contract that required 30 monthly payments of $60.26 with the first payment due on the purchase date. The interest rate on the outstanding balance was 18% compounded monthly.

    a. What was the purchase price of the refrigerator?

    b. How much interest did Carmella pay during the entire contract?

8. Rino has just purchased a five-year term life insurance policy. For his premium payments, Rino can choose either beginning-of-month payments of $38.50 or beginning-of-year payments of $455. In current dollars, how much will Rino save during the five years by choosing the lower-cost option? Assume that money can earn 4.8% compounded monthly.

∘9 Bram must choose between two alternatives for $1,000,000 of life insurance coverage for the next ten years. The premium quoted to him by Sun Life Insurance Co. is $51.75 per month. Atlantic Life will charge $44.25 per month for the first five years and $60.35 per month for the subsequent five years. In both cases, monthly premiums are payable at the beginning of each month. Which policy is "cheaper" if money can earn 4.8% compounded monthly? In current dollars, how much will Bram save by choosing the less costly policy?

10. Under the headline "Local Theatre Project Receives $1 Million!" a newspaper article explained that the Theatre Project had just received the first of ten annual grants of $100,000 from the Hinton Foundation. What is the current economic value of all of the grants if money is worth 7.5% compounded monthly?

11. You have received two offers on the used car you wish to sell. Mr. Lindberg is offering $8500 cash, and Rosie Senario's offer is five semiannual payments of $1900, including a payment on the purchase date. Which offer has the greater economic value at a discount rate of 10% compounded semiannually? What is the economic advantage (in current dollars) of the preferred alternative?

12. Osgood Appliance Centre is advertising refrigerators for six monthly payments of $199, including a payment on the date of purchase. What cash price should Osgood accept if it would otherwise sell the conditional sale agreement to a finance company to yield 18% compounded monthly?

13. The life expectancy of the average 65-year-old Canadian male is about 16 additional years. Karsten wants to have sufficient funds in his RRIF at age 65 to be able to withdraw $40,000 at the beginning of each year for the expected survival period of 16 years. If his RRIF earns 6% compounded annually, what amount must he have in the RRIF at the time he turns 65?

14. A rental agreement requires the payment of $900 at the beginning of each month.
    a. What single payment at the beginning of the rental year should the landlord accept instead of twelve monthly payments if money is worth 6% compounded monthly?
    b. Show that the landlord will be equally well off at the end of the year under either payment arrangement if rental payments are invested at 6% compounded monthly.

15. What minimum amount of money earning 9% compounded semiannually will sustain withdrawals of $1200 at the beginning of every month for 15 years?

16. The lease contract for a computer workstation requires quarterly payments of $2100 at the beginning of every three-month period for five years. The lessee would otherwise have to pay an interest rate of 10% compounded quarterly to borrow funds to purchase the workstation.
    a. What amount will the lessee initially report in its financial statements as the long-term lease liability?
    b. What will the liability be at the end of the fourth year?

17. Beaudoin Haulage has signed a five-year lease with GMAC on a new dump truck. Beaudoin intends to capitalize the lease and report it as a long-term liability. Lease payments of $2700 are made at the beginning of each month. To purchase the truck, Beaudoin would have had to borrow funds at 9% compounded monthly.
    a. What initial liability should Beaudoin report on its balance sheet?
    b. How much will the liability be reduced during the first year of the lease?

○18. What is the current economic value of an annuity due consisting of 22 quarterly payments of $700, if money is worth 6% compounded quarterly for the first three years, and 7% compounded quarterly thereafter?

○19. Calculate and rank the economic values of the following cash flow streams:
    (i) A single payment of $10,000 eight years from now.
    (ii) An annuity due starting today with eight annual payments of $850.
    (iii) An annuity due starting in eight years with eight annual payments of $1700.
    Do the calculations and ranking for each of two cases:
    a. Money can earn 8% compounded annually for the next 16 years.
    b. Money can earn 10% compounded annually for the next 16 years.

•**20.** Two insurance companies gave the following quotations on premiums for essentially the same long-term disability insurance coverage for a 25-year-old. Paul Revere Insurance Co. quoted monthly premiums of $54.83 from ages 26 to 30 inclusive, and $78.17 from ages 31 to 64 inclusive. The monthly premiums from Provident Insurance Co. are "flat" at $69.35 from ages 26 to 64 inclusive. All premiums are paid at the beginning of each month. The insurance broker recommended the Provident coverage because the aggregate lifetime premiums up to the client's sixty-fifth birthday are $32,455.80 versus $35,183.16 for the Paul Revere policy. Is the choice that simple? (*Hint:* Calculate and compare the economic value on the client's twenty-sixth birthday of each policy's stream of premiums assuming money can earn 9% compounded monthly.)

•**21.** The lease on the premises occupied by the accounting firm of Heath and Company will soon expire. The current landlord is offering to renew the lease for seven years at $2100 per month. The developers of a new building, a block away from Heath's present offices, are offering the first year of a seven-year lease rent-free. For the subsequent six years the rent would be $2500 per month. All rents are paid at the beginning of each month. Other things being equal, which lease should Heath accept if money is worth 7.5% compounded monthly?

12.3 CALCULATING THE PERIODIC PAYMENT, NUMBER OF PAYMENTS, AND INTEREST RATE

LO2 To calculate any one of these three quantities for an annuity due, follow the same procedure you would for an ordinary annuity, but with one change. You must use the annuity due formula that is the counterpart of the ordinary annuity formula. These counterparts are listed in the following table. Formulas (12-1n) and (12-2n) have not been presented before. They are versions of formulas (12-1) and (12-2), respectively, rearranged to isolate n.

Ordinary Annuity Formula		Annuity Due Formula	
$FV = PMT\left[\dfrac{(1+i)^n - 1}{i}\right]$	(10-1)	$FV(\text{due}) = PMT\left[\dfrac{(1+i)^n - 1}{i}\right] \times (1+i)$	(12-1)
$PV = PMT\left[\dfrac{1-(1+i)^{-n}}{i}\right]$	(10-2)	$PV(\text{due}) = PMT\left[\dfrac{1-(1+i)^{-n}}{i}\right] \times (1+i)$	(12-2)
$n = \dfrac{\ln\left(1 + \dfrac{i \times FV}{PMT}\right)}{\ln(1+i)}$	(10-1n)	$n = \dfrac{\ln\left[1 + \dfrac{i \times FV(\text{due})}{PMT(1+i)}\right]}{\ln(1+i)}$	(12-1n)
$n = -\dfrac{\ln\left(1 - \dfrac{i \times PV}{PMT}\right)}{\ln(1+i)}$	(10-2n)	$n = -\dfrac{\ln\left[1 - \dfrac{i \times PV(\text{due})}{PMT(1+i)}\right]}{\ln(1+i)}$	(12-2n)

Calculating i algebraically requires the trial-and-error method described in Appendix 11B. We will use only the financial calculator method to solve for the interest rate in example problems.

The Mathematics of Vehicle Leasing In recent years, 20% to 25% of new vehicles were leased. The main elements of a typical lease contract are as follows:

• The lessee makes fixed beginning-of-month payments for the term of the lease. The most common term is four years.

- The lessee is responsible for all vehicle operating costs (including insurance) during the term of the lease. In this respect, leasing does not differ from owning a vehicle.

- Most leases are "closed-end" or "walk away" leases. At the end of the term, the lessee can simply return the vehicle to the car dealer. Alternatively, at the option of the lessee, the vehicle may be purchased for a *predetermined* amount (called the **residual value**). The residual value represents the dealer's estimate of the market value of the vehicle at the end of the lease.

We will use a particular example to develop your understanding of the economics and mathematics of leasing. Suppose your down payment on a three-year lease is $3000. The car's purchase price is $30,000 and its residual value after three years is $15,000. We will now explain how the lease payment is calculated.

From the car dealer's point of view, the $27,000 "balance" is paid by 36 beginning-of-month payments plus a projected final payment of $15,000 after three years. This final payment will come either from you (if you exercise the purchase option) or from the sale of the vehicle at the end of the lease. Since the future selling price can only be estimated, the amount of the final payment is not known with certainty. The lease payments are calculated on the assumption that the final payment will be $15,000.

Except for the uncertainty in the amount of the final payment, the situation is similar to repaying a $27,000 loan by 36 beginning-of-month payments plus a final payment of $15,000 after three years. In that case, we know that the present value of all loan payments (discounted at the interest rate on the loan) is $27,000. Similarly, the present value of all lease payments and the residual value (discounted at the interest rate charged on the lease) is $27,000. In general,

$$\begin{pmatrix} \text{Purchase} \\ \text{price} \end{pmatrix} - \begin{pmatrix} \text{Down} \\ \text{payment} \end{pmatrix} = \begin{pmatrix} \text{Present value of} \\ \text{the lease payments} \end{pmatrix} + \begin{pmatrix} \text{Present value of} \\ \text{the residual value} \end{pmatrix}$$

The interest rate on a lease is applied as a monthly compounded rate. Therefore, the monthly lease payments form a simple annuity due.

There are six variables embedded in this mathematical relationship. They are: the purchase price, the down payment, the residual value, the number of payments, the amount of the monthly payment, and the interest rate on the lease. If five of the variables are given, you can calculate the sixth. In the advertisements that car dealers place in newspapers, you may not find the values for all six variables. The most commonly omitted variable is the "residual value" (which may be called the "option to purchase at lease end"). If its value is given at all, it will be found among the details in the tiny print at the bottom of the advertisement.

EXAMPLE 12.3A   **CALCULATING THE SIZE OF LEASE PAYMENTS**

A lease that has $2\frac{1}{2}$ years to run is recorded on a company's books as a liability of $27,369. If the company's cost of borrowing was 6% compounded monthly when the lease was signed, what is the amount of the lease payment at the beginning of each month?

SOLUTION

The "book value" of the lease liability is the present value of the remaining lease payments. The discount rate employed should be the interest rate the company would have paid to borrow funds. The lease payments constitute a simple annuity due with

$$PV(\text{due}) = \$27,369 \quad n = 12(2.5) = 30 \quad \text{and} \quad i = \tfrac{6\%}{12} = 0.5\% \text{ per month}$$

Substitute the given values into formula (12-2) and solve for *PMT*.

$$PV(\text{due}) = PMT\left[\frac{1 - (1 + i)^{-n}}{i}\right] \times (1 + i)$$

$$\$27{,}369 = PMT\left(\frac{1 - 1.005^{-30}}{0.005}\right)(1.005)$$

$$= PMT(27.79405)(1.005)$$

$$= PMT(27.93302)$$

$$PMT = \$979.81$$

The monthly lease payment is $979.81.

BGN mode

6 | I/Y
P/Y | 12 | ENTER
(making *C/Y* = *P/Y* = 12)
30 | N
27369 | PV
0 | FV
CPT | PMT
Ans: −979.81

EXAMPLE 12.3B   **CALCULATING THE *PMT* NEEDED TO ATTAIN A SAVINGS GOAL**

Mr. Walters has already accumulated $104,000 in his Registered Retirement Savings Plan (RRSP). His goal is to build it to $250,000 with equal contributions at the beginning of each six-month period for the next seven years. If his RRSP earns 8.5% compounded semiannually, what must be the size of further contributions?

SOLUTION

The $250,000 target will be the combined future value of the $104,000 already in the RRSP and the simple annuity due formed by the next 14 payments. That is,

$$\$250{,}000 = \text{Future value of } \$104{,}000 + FV(\text{due}) \quad ①$$

with $n = 2(7) = 14$ and $i = \frac{8.5\%}{2} = 4.25\%$ per half *year*.

The future value of the $104,000 will be

$$FV = PV(1 + i)^n = \$104{,}000(1.0425)^{14} = \$186{,}250.84$$

The future value of the 14 contributions will be

$$FV(\text{due}) = PMT\left[\frac{(1 + i)^n - 1}{i}\right](1 + i)$$

$$= PMT\left(\frac{1.0425^{14} - 1}{0.0425}\right)(1.0425)$$

$$= PMT(19.39966)$$

Substituting these amounts into equation ①, we obtain

$$\$250{,}000 = \$186{,}250.84 + PMT(19.39966)$$

$$PMT = \frac{\$250{,}000 - \$186{,}250.84}{19.39966} = \$3286.10$$

BGN mode

8.5 | I/Y
P/Y | 2 | ENTER
(making *C/Y* = *P/Y* = 2)
14 | N
104000 | +/− | PV
250000 | FV
CPT | PMT
Ans: −3286.10

Mr. Walters must make semiannual contributions of $3286.10 to reach the $250,000 target in seven years.

EXAMPLE 12.3C **CALCULATING THE PAYMENT ON A CAR LEASE**

An automobile manufacturer is calculating the lease payments to charge on the SLX model which has a selling price of $27,900. During a month-long promotion, the manufacturer will offer an interest rate of only 1.8% compounded monthly on a three-year lease. If the residual value is $14,500, what will be the lease payments, assuming a $2500 down payment?

SOLUTION

Earlier in this section, we developed the leasing equation:

$$\left(\begin{array}{c}\text{Purchase}\\\text{price}\end{array}\right) - \left(\begin{array}{c}\text{Down}\\\text{payment}\end{array}\right) = \left(\begin{array}{c}\text{Present value of}\\\text{the lease payments}\end{array}\right) + \left(\begin{array}{c}\text{Present value of}\\\text{the residual value}\end{array}\right)$$

For the SLX lease,

$$\$27,900 - \$2500 = \left(\begin{array}{c}\text{Present value of}\\\text{the lease payments}\end{array}\right) + \left(\begin{array}{c}\text{Present value}\\\text{of }\$14,500\end{array}\right) \quad ①$$

The lease payments form a simple annuity due with $i = \frac{1.8\%}{12} = 0.15\%$ and $n = 36$.

The present value of the lease payments is

$$PV(\text{due}) = PMT\left[\frac{1 - (1 + i)^{-n}}{i}\right](1 + i)$$

$$= PMT\left[\frac{1 - 1.0015^{-36}}{0.0015}\right](1.0015)$$

$$= PMT(35.07224)$$

The present value of the $14,500 residual value is

$$PV = FV(1 + i)^{-n} = \$14,500(1.0015)^{-36} = \$13,738.32$$

Substitute these values into equation ① and solve for *PMT*.

$$\$25,400 = PMT(35.07224) + \$13,738.32$$

$$PMT = \frac{\$25,400 - \$13,738.32}{35.07224} = \$332.50$$

The beginning-of-month lease payment is $332.50.

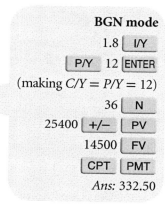

EXAMPLE 12.3D **CALCULATING *n* GIVEN THE FUTURE VALUE OF A SIMPLE ANNUITY DUE**

Rounding *n* upward to the next integer, how long will it take to accumulate $1,000,000 in an RRSP if the first quarterly contribution of $2000 is made today? Assume the RRSP earns 8% compounded quarterly.

SOLUTION

First, we need to find the number of contributions required for the future value to reach $1,000,000. Since the compounding interval equals the payment interval, the contributions form a simple annuity having

$$PMT = \$2000 \quad i = \frac{8\%}{4} = 2\% \quad \text{and} \quad FV(\text{due}) = \$1,000,000$$

Substitute these values into formula (12-1n).

$$n = \frac{\ln\left[1 + \dfrac{i \times FV(\text{due})}{PMT(1 + i)}\right]}{\ln(1 + i)}$$

$$= \frac{\ln\left[1 + \dfrac{0.02 \times \$1,000,000}{\$2000(1.02)}\right]}{\ln(1.02)}$$

$$= \frac{2.3799}{0.019803}$$

$$= 120.18$$

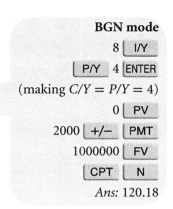

BGN mode

| 8 | I/Y |

| P/Y | 4 | ENTER |

(making $C/Y = P/Y = 4$)

| 0 | PV |

| 2000 | +/− | PMT |

| 1000000 | FV |

| CPT | N |

Ans: 120.18

The 121st contribution is required to reach $1,000,000. The time to the end of the 121st payment interval is

$$121 \text{ quarters} = \tfrac{121}{4} = 30.25 \text{ years} = 30 \text{ years and 3 months}$$

With n rounded to the next higher integer, it will take 30 years and 3 months to accumulate $1,000,000 in the RRSP. (Including accrued earnings, the $1,000,000 is actually reached quite early in the 121st interval.)

EXAMPLE 12.3E   **CALCULATING n GIVEN THE PRESENT VALUE OF A GENERAL ANNUITY DUE**

An investment fund is worth $210,000 and earns 9% compounded semiannually. If $2000 is withdrawn at the beginning of each month starting today, when will the fund become depleted?

SOLUTION

The initial amount in the account equals the present value of the future withdrawals. Since the first withdrawal occurs today, and the payment interval differs from the compounding interval, the withdrawals form a *general annuity due* having

$$PV(\text{due}) = \$210,000 \quad PMT = \$2000 \quad \text{and} \quad i = \tfrac{9\%}{2} = 4.5\%$$

The value we must use for i in formula (12-2n) is the periodic rate for the one-month payment interval. Substitute

$$c = \frac{\text{Number of compoundings per year}}{\text{Number of payments per year}} = \frac{2}{12} = 0.1\overline{6}$$

into

$$i_2 = (1 + i)^c - 1 = (1.045)^{0.1\overline{6}} - 1 = 0.00736312 \text{ per month}$$

Substitute the known values into formula (12-2n).

$$n = -\frac{\ln\left[1 - \dfrac{i \times PV(\text{due})}{PMT(1 + i)}\right]}{\ln(1 + i)}$$

$$= -\frac{\ln\left[1 - \dfrac{0.00736312(\$210,000)}{\$2000(1.00736312)}\right]}{\ln(1.00736312)}$$

$$= 198.85$$

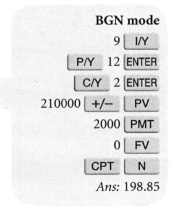

BGN mode

| 9 | I/Y |

| P/Y | 12 | ENTER |

| C/Y | 2 | ENTER |

| 210000 | +/− | PV |

| 2000 | PMT |

| 0 | FV |

| CPT | N |

Ans: 198.85

The fund will permit 199 monthly withdrawals. The final withdrawal, smaller than $2000, will occur at the *beginning* of the 199th payment interval. But that will be 198 months from now. So the fund will be depleted at the time of the 199th payment, which is 198 months or 16 years and 6 months from now.

EXAMPLE 12.3F   **CALCULATING THE INTEREST RATE FOR AN ANNUITY DUE**

Therese intends to contribute $3000 at the beginning of each six-month period to an RRSP. What rate of return must her RRSP earn in order to reach $600,000 after 25 years?

SOLUTION

The payments form an annuity due whose future value after 25 years is to be $600,000. That is,

$$FV(\text{due}) = \$600,000 \quad PMT = \$3000 \quad \text{and} \quad n = m(\text{Term}) = 2(25) = 50$$

If we set $P/Y = C/Y = 2$, we will obtain the semiannually compounded rate of return. Enter these values and compute I/Y.

Therese's RRSP must earn 9.43% compounded semiannually.

> **BGN mode**
>
> P/Y   2 ENTER
> (making $C/Y = P/Y = 2$)
> 50   N
> 0   PV
> 3000 +/–   PMT
> 600000   FV
> CPT   I/Y
> *Ans:* 9.43

EXAMPLE 12.3G   **CALCULATING THE INTEREST RATE BUILT INTO AN INSTALMENT PAYMENT OPTION**

A $100,000 life insurance policy requires an annual premium of $420 or a monthly premium of $37. In either case, the premium is payable at the beginning of the period of coverage. What is the effective rate of interest policyholders pay when they choose the monthly payment plan?

SOLUTION

In effect, the insurance company lends the $420 annual premium to policyholders choosing the monthly payment option. These policyholders then repay the "loan" with 12 beginning-of-month payments of $37. Hence, $420 is the present value of the 12 payments that form an annuity due. We have

$$PV(\text{due}) = \$420 \quad PMT = \$37 \quad n = 12 \quad \text{and} \quad P/Y = 12$$

The effective interest rate is the same as the annually compounded rate ($C/Y = 1$). Enter these values and compute I/Y.

The effective interest rate on the monthly payment plan is 13.04%.

> **BGN mode**
>
> P/Y   12 ENTER
> C/Y   1 ENTER
> 12   N
> 420   PV
> 37 +/–   PMT
> 0   FV
> CPT   I/Y
> *Ans:* 13.04

EXAMPLE 12.3H   **CALCULATING THE INTEREST RATE BUILT INTO LEASE PAYMENTS**

A car dealer advertised the Hyundai Santa Fe GL AWD sport utility vehicle for sale at $33,610. The same vehicle could also be leased for five years at $379 per month, based on a $4310 down payment. At the end of the lease, the lessee could purchase the vehicle for $10,711. What monthly compounded interest rate was built into the lease?

SOLUTION

Mathematically, the problem is the same as calculating the interest rate charged on a loan where the balance is reduced from $29,300 (= $33,610 − $4310) to $10,711 by 60 beginning-of-month payments of $379. That is, $29,300 is the combined present value of 60 payments of $379 and a terminal payment of $10,711. In effect, we are given

$$PV(\text{due}) = \$29,300 \quad PMT = \$379 \quad n = 60 \quad \text{and} \quad FV = \$10,711$$

The interest rate built into the lease was 4.13% compounded monthly.

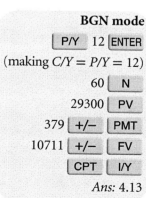

> **BGN mode**
>
> P/Y   12 ENTER
> (making $C/Y = P/Y = 12$)
> 60   N
> 29300   PV
> 379 +/–   PMT
> 10711 +/–   FV
> CPT   I/Y
> *Ans:* 4.13

POINT OF INTEREST

"Rent-to-Own" or "Rent Too Onerous?"

Rent-to-own stores offer credit-challenged consumers yet another opportunity to dig themselves into a deeper financial hole. Furniture, appliances, and home electronic products may be rented under agreements that require weekly or monthly rent payments. The renter can terminate the rental agreement at any time without further cost. If the rental payments are made for a period specified in the agreement (18 months to four years, depending on the item rented), the renter takes ownership.

A study of rent-to-own consumers found that the primary reasons for consumers using rent-to-own stores were:

1. They want to obtain the goods right away rather than wait to accumulate savings.
2. They do not need to pass a credit check at rent-to-own stores.
3. They like the flexibility of returning the goods and cancelling the contract at any time.

Critics argue that rent-to-own stores charge exorbitant rental rates. Rent-to-own business operators respond that they incur high collection and default costs because of their high-risk clientele.

Some examples of *weekly* rental rates are: $13.66 for a Samsung 32-inch LCD HD TV; $13.66 for a Moffat full-size washer-dryer combo; and $10.93 for a JVC 60 Gb Hard-Drive Camcorder. If the weekly rent is paid for 156 weeks, the renter takes ownership of the item. [The renter also pays HST (or GST plus PST) on the rental rates.]

QUESTIONS

1. In department and home entertainment stores, the Samsung 32-inch LCD HD TV mentioned above was priced in the neighbourhood of $650. Suppose we treat the rent-to-own transaction as a purchase-on-credit transaction wherein the $650 purchase price is paid off by beginning-of-week payments of $13.66 for 156 weeks. What are the imputed weekly compounded interest rate and effective interest rate? Assume there are exactly 52 weeks in a year. (Since the actual transaction is a rental transaction rather than a credit transaction, it is not subject to the Criminal Code's requirement that the effective rate of interest must not exceed 60%.)

2. The rent-to-own operation claimed in its advertising that the imputed interest rate (based on the $13.66 weekly rental rate and the retail value of the Samsung TV) was 29.9% compounded monthly. If this is correct, what retail value was used?

3. Suppose that the Samsung TV is purchased for $650 on a loan from a consumer-finance company that charges interest at 30% compounded monthly. What regular beginning-of-week payment would pay off the loan in three years?

SPREADSHEET STRATEGIES *PMT, n,* and *i* for an Annuity Due

The spreadsheet templates introduced in Sections 11.1, 11.2, and 11.3 for calculating *PMT, n,* and *i,* respectively, for *ordinary* general annuities may also be employed for simple annuities *due* and general annuities *due.* You simply enter "1" for the variable "type" when you have an annuity due.

Below we use the third of these templates to calculate the interest rate embedded in the vehicle lease described in Example 12.3H. In this problem, a vehicle priced at $33,610 can be leased for $379 per month after a down payment of $4310. The residual value at the end of the five-year lease is $10,711. The payments form a general annuity due. Obtain the template from Chapter 11 of the textbook's Web site; look for "RATE for Any Annuity."

The main features of the completed template are presented below. The formulas programmed into cells C10 and C14 are displayed in cells C11 and C15, respectively. After entering the given data in the yellow input cells, the computed interest rates for *i, j,* and *f* immediately appear in the output cells C10, C13, and C14, respectively.

	A	B	C	D
1				
2	A spreadsheet for calculating the interest rate in an annuity.			
3	Example 12.3H:			
4				
5		Number of payments, *n* or *nper*	60	
6		Regular annuity payment, *PMT* or *pmt*	-$379.00	
7		Present value, *PV* or *pv*	$29,300.00	
8		Future value, *FV* or *fv*	-$10,711.00	
9		Annuity *type*	1	
10		RATE(*nper, pmt, pv, fv, type*)	0.3442%	
11		Formula in cell C10:	=RATE(C5,C6,C7,C8,C9)	
12		Payments (& compoundings) per year	12	
13		Nominal annual rate, *j*	4.130%	
14		Effective rate of interest, *f*	4.2093%	
15		Formula in cell C14:	=EFFECT(C13,C12)	
16				

The nominal interest rate built into the lease was 4.13% compounded monthly.

CONCEPT QUESTIONS

1. An ordinary annuity and an annuity due have the same future value, *n,* and *i.* Which annuity has the larger payment? Give the reason for your answer.

2. An ordinary annuity and an annuity due have the same present value, *n,* and *i.* Which annuity has the smaller payment? Give the reason for your answer.

3. Other variables being the same, how will the amount of the down payment on a car lease affect the size of the lease payments?

4. Other variables being the same, how will the size of the residual value affect the size of the car lease payments?

5. The term of the lease on a vehicle is about to expire. Answer Parts (a) and (b) strictly on financial considerations.

   a. If the market value of the vehicle is less than the residual value, what should the lessee do?

   b. If the market value of the vehicle exceeds the residual value, what should the lessee do?

   c. In view of your answers to (a) and (b), will the interest rate on a lease contract tend to be higher or lower than the interest rate on a loan to purchase the same vehicle? Explain.

EXERCISE 12.3

connect

Spreadsheet template: The partially completed Excel templates introduced in Section 11.1, 11.2, and 11.3 for calculating an annuity's PMT, n, and i, respectively, may be used in many of the problems in Exercise 12.3. Go to Chapter 11 of the Student Edition to find "PMT for Any Annuity" or "NPER for Any Annuity" or "RATE for Annuity."

Answers to the odd-numbered problems are at the end of the book.

Calculate nominal and effective interest rates accurate to the nearest 0.01%.

1. In order to accumulate $750,000 after 25 years, calculate the amounts that must be invested at the beginning of each year if the invested funds earn:

   a. 6% compounded annually.   **b.** 7% compounded annually.

   c. 8% compounded annually.   **d.** 9% compounded annually.

   Also calculate the total earnings in each case.

2. What beginning-of-month withdrawals can a $400,000 RRIF (Registered Retirement Income Fund) sustain for 20 years if the investments within the RRIF earn:

   a. 3% compounded monthly?   **b.** 4.5% compounded monthly?

   c. 6% compounded monthly?   **d.** 7.5% compounded monthly?

   Also calculate the total earnings distributed over the life of the annuity in each case.

3. How long will it take an RRSP to grow to $600,000 if it receives a contribution of $2500 at the beginning of each quarter and it earns:

   a. 6% compounded quarterly?   **b.** 7% compounded quarterly?

   c. 8% compounded quarterly?   **d.** 9% compounded quarterly?

4. For how long will a $100,000 fund sustain beginning-of-month withdrawals of $700 if the fund earns:

   a. 4% compounded monthly?   **b.** 5% compounded monthly?

   c. 6% compounded monthly?   **d.** 7% compounded monthly?

5. Ichiro is checking potential outcomes for the growth of his RRSP. He plans to make contributions of $500 at the beginning of each month. What nominal rate of return must his RRSP earn for its future value after 25 years to be:

   a. $400,000?   **b.** $500,000?   **c.** $600,000?

6. Gina has $500,000 accumulated in her RRSP and intends to use the amount to purchase a 20-year annuity. She is investigating the size of quarterly payment she can expect to receive, depending on the rate of return earned by the funds. What nominal rate of return must the funds earn for the beginning-of-quarter payment to be:

   a. $10,000?   **b.** $11,000?   **c.** $12,000?

7. Your client currently has accumulated capital of $560,000 and hopes to retire this year. She wants to receive an annuity payment at the beginning of each year for the next 20 years. If the capital can earn 6.5% compounded annually, what maximum annual payment can she receive and just deplete the capital after 20 years? (Taken from CIFP course materials.)

8. Your client purchases an annuity for $700,000 that provides beginning-of-month payments for 15 years. If the annuity earns 4.5% compounded monthly, what monthly payment will he receive? (Taken from CIFP course materials.)

9. Your client wants to accumulate $1,000,000 over the next 25 years by investing the same amount at the beginning of each month. If she can expect a long-term rate of return of 8% compounded annually, how much must she invest each month? (Taken from CIFP course materials.)

10. To accumulate $200,000 after 20 years, what amount must be invested each year if the investment earns 9% compounded annually and the contributions are made:

    a. At the beginning of each year?   **b.** At the end of each year?

11. What maximum annual withdrawals will a $200,000 fund earning 6% compounded annually sustain for 20 years if the withdrawals are made:

    a. At the beginning of each year?   **b.** At the end of each year?

12. Triex Manufacturing wants to accumulate $500,000 for an expansion planned to begin in five years. If today Triex makes the first of equal quarterly payments into a fund earning 5.4% compounded monthly, what size should these payments be?

13. Your client has already accumulated $20,000 and plans to invest another $5000 at the beginning of each year for the next 15 years. He expects to earn a return of $7\frac{1}{4}\%$ compounded annually on his investments. How much will his investments be worth fifteen years from now? (Taken from CIFP course materials.)

14. An insurance company wishes to offer customers a monthly instalment alternative to the annual premium plan. All premiums are payable at the beginning of the period of coverage. The monthly payment plan is to include an interest charge of 12% compounded monthly on the unpaid balance of the annual premium. What will be the monthly premium per $100 of annual premium?

15. Advance Leasing calculates the monthly payments on its three-year leases on the basis of recovering the capital cost of the leased equipment and earning a 13.5% compounded monthly rate of return on its capital investment. What will be the monthly lease payment on equipment that costs $8500?

16. Shane is about to have his twenty-fifth birthday. He has set a goal of retiring at age 55 with $700,000 in an RRSP. For planning purposes he is assuming that his RRSP will earn 8% compounded annually.

    a. What contribution on each birthday from age 25 to 54 inclusive will be required to accumulate the desired amount in his RRSP?

    b. If he waits five years before starting his RRSP, what contribution on each birthday from age 30 to 54 inclusive will be required to accumulate the target amount?

17. Wendy will soon turn 33. She wants to accumulate $500,000 in an RRSP by her sixtieth birthday. How much larger will her annual contributions have to be if they are made at the end of each year (from age 33 to age 59 inclusive) instead of at the beginning of each year? Assume that her RRSP will earn 9% compounded annually.

18. CompuLease leases computers and peripheral equipment to businesses. What lease payments must CompuLease charge at the beginning of each quarter of a five-year lease if it is to recover the $20,000 capital cost of a system and earn 12% compounded quarterly on its investment?

19. Island Water Taxi has decided to lease another boat for five years rather than finance the purchase of the boat at an interest rate of 10.5% compounded monthly. It has set up a long-term lease liability of $43,000. What is the lease payment at the beginning of each month?

20. The MSRP on a Nissan Maxima 3.5 SV is $38,625. The interest rate on a 48-month lease is 1.9% compounded monthly. What is the monthly lease payment, assuming a down payment of $5400 and a residual value of $11,990?

21. The $219.40 monthly payment on a 48-month lease of a Kia SOUL was based on a down payment of $1545, an interest rate of 3.9% compounded monthly, and a residual value of $6815. What is the full price (MSRP) for the car?

22. With a down payment of $4850, the monthly payment on a four-year lease of a Ford F150 SuperCab (MSRP $27,629) is $369.27. The interest rate on the lease is 7.99% compounded monthly. What residual value was used in the calculation?

23. A Smart ForTwo cabriolet (MSRP $21,550) can be leased for $248 per month. This payment is based on an interest rate of 6.9% compounded monthly, a down payment of $1425, and a residual value of $14,794. What is the term of the lease?

24. What interest rate is being charged if the monthly payment on a 48-month lease of a Jaguar XF (MSRP $58,125) is $799? The required down payment is $2999 and the residual value is $24,059.

25. The MSRP for a BMW 528i is $58,499. The monthly payment on a 48-month lease at 1.9% compounded monthly is $697. The residual value at the end of the lease is $21,000. Rounded to the nearest dollar, what down payment was used in the lease calculation?

26. Rentown advertised a computer system at a cash price of $1699 and at a rent-to-own rate of $129 at the beginning of each month for 24 months. What effective rate of interest is a customer paying to acquire the computer in a rent-to-own transaction?

27. Kim wants to save half of the $30,000 purchase price of a new car by making monthly deposits of $700, beginning today, into a T-bill savings account earning 4.2% compounded monthly. How long will it take him to reach his goal?

28. Central Personnel's accountant set up a long-term lease liability of $11,622.73 to recognize a new contract for the lease of office furniture. She used the firm's 10.5% monthly compounded cost of borrowing as the discount rate. If the lease payment at the beginning of each month is $295, what is the term of the lease?

29. The payments required on a contractual obligation are $500 per month. The contract was purchased for $13,372 just *before* a regular payment date. The purchaser determined this price based on his required rate of return of 9.75% compounded monthly. How many payments will he receive?

30. How much longer will a $100,000 fund earning 9% compounded monthly sustain beginning-of-month withdrawals of $900 than beginning-of-month withdrawals of $1000?

31. How many fewer deposits will it take to accumulate savings of $100,000 with beginning-of-month deposits of $220 than with beginning-of-month deposits of $200? The savings earn 5.4% compounded monthly.

32. If a furniture retailer offers a financing plan on a $1500 purchase requiring four equal quarterly payments of $400 including the first payment on the purchase date, what effective rate of interest is being charged on the unpaid balance?

33. An RRSP is now worth $223,000 after contributions of $2500 at the beginning of every six months for 16 years. What effective rate of return has the plan earned?

34. Pembroke Golf Club's initiation fee is $5500. It offers an instalment payment alternative of $1000 down and $1000 at the end of each year for five years. What effective rate of interest is being charged on the instalment plan?

35. If contributions of $1500 at the beginning of every three months resulted in an RRSP worth $327,685 after 20 years, what quarterly compounded nominal rate and effective rate of return did the RRSP earn?

36. As of the date of Victory Machine Shop's most recent financial statements, three years remained in the term of a capital lease reported as a long-term liability of $13,824. If the beginning-of-month lease payments are $450, what monthly compounded annual discount rate was used in valuing the lease?

37. If a furniture store offers to sell a refrigerator priced at $1195 on a conditional sale contract requiring 12 monthly payments of $110 (including a payment on the date of sale), what effective rate of interest is being charged to the customer?

38. For the past 13 years, Ms. Perrault has contributed $2000 at the beginning of every six months to a mutual fund. If the mutual fund statement at the end of the 13 years reports that her fund units are worth a total of $91,477, what has been the semiannually compounded nominal rate and the effective rate of return on her investments over the 13 years?

○39. Advantage Leasing Ltd. is in the business of purchasing equipment, which it then leases to other companies. Advantage calculates the payments on its five-year leases so that it recovers the original cost of the equipment plus a return on investment of 15% compounded quarterly over the term of the lease. What will be the required lease payments on a machine that cost $25,000 if the lease payments will be received:

    a. At the beginning of every month?

    b. At the beginning of each six month period?

○40. Mr. and Mrs. Friedrich have just opened a Registered Education Savings Plan (RESP) for their daughter. They want the plan to pay $3000 at the beginning of each half year for four years, starting nine years from now when their daughter will enter college or university. What semiannual contributions, including one today, must they make for the next nine years if the RESP earns 8.25% compounded semiannually?

○41. Ambleside Golf Club's board of directors has set next year's membership fee at $1900, payable at the beginning of the year. The board has instructed its accountant to calculate beginning-of-quarter and beginning-of-month payment plans that provide a 15% semiannually compounded rate of return on the unpaid balance of the annual fee. What will be the amounts of the quarterly and monthly payments?

○42. RRSP contributions of $5000 are made at the beginning of every six months. How many more contributions will it take to reach $750,000 if the RRSP earns 8% compounded semiannually than if it earns 10% compounded semiannually?

○43. Mrs. McPherson wants to use $10,000 from her late husband's estate to assist her grandson when he enters college in seven years. Assume the $10,000 are invested immediately at 8% compounded monthly, and the grandson will make beginning-of-month withdrawals of $500 when he starts college. When will the final withdrawal occur?

○44. If you contribute $1000 to an RRSP at the beginning of every three months for 25 years and then use the accumulated funds to purchase an annuity paying $3000 at the beginning of each month, what will be the term of the annuity? Assume that the RRSP earns 8.5% compounded quarterly, and the funds invested in the annuity earn 7.5% compounded monthly.

○45. Quantum Research Ltd. has arranged debt financing from its parent company to complete the development of a new product. Quantum "draws down" $12,000 at the beginning of each month. If interest accumulates on the debt at 8.2% compounded quarterly, how long will it take to reach the credit limit of $1 million?

○46. Jamshid borrowed $350 from his mother at the beginning of every month for $2\frac{1}{2}$ years while he attended Seneca College.

    a. If the interest rate on the accumulating debt was 6% compounded semiannually, what amount did he owe his mother at the end of the $2\frac{1}{2}$-year period?

    b. If he made the first monthly payment of $175 on the loan at the end of the first month following the $2\frac{1}{2}$-year period, how long after the date he entered college will he have the loan repaid?

○**47.** The annual membership dues in the Rolling Meadows Golf and Country Club can be paid by four payments of $898.80 at the beginning of each calendar quarter, instead of by a single payment of $3428 at the beginning of the year. What effective rate of interest is the club charging the quarterly instalment payers on the unpaid balance of their annual dues?

○**48.** The Lifestyle Fitness and Exercise Centre charges annual membership fees of $600 (in advance) or six "easy" payments of $120 at the beginning of every two months. What effective interest rate is being charged on the instalment plan?

○**49.** A magazine offers a one-year subscription rate of $63.80 and a three-year subscription rate of $159.80, both payable at the start of the subscription period. Assuming that you intend to continue to subscribe for three years and that the one-year rate does not increase for the next two years, what rate of "return on investment" will be earned by paying for a three-year subscription now instead of three consecutive one-year subscriptions?

○**50.** Continental Life Insurance Company of Canada offered $250,000 of term life insurance to a 40-year-old female nonsmoker for an annual premium of $447.50 (in advance) or for monthly premium payments (in advance) of $38.82 by preauthorized electronic debit. What effective rate of interest is charged to those who pay monthly?

○**51.** The same disability insurance policy offers four alternative premium payment plans: an annual premium of $666.96, semiannual premiums of $341.32, quarterly premiums of $173.62, or monthly premiums of $58.85. In every case, the premiums are payable in advance. What effective rate of interest is the insurance company charging clients who pay their premiums:

    a. Semiannually?   **b.** Quarterly?   **c.** Monthly?

○**52.** A $500,000 life insurance policy for a 26-year-old offers four alternative premium payment plans: an annual premium of $470.00, semiannual premiums of $241.50, quarterly premiums of $123.37, or monthly premiums of $42.30. In every case, the premiums are payable in advance. What effective rate of interest is the insurance company charging if the premium is paid:

    a. Semiannually?   **b.** Quarterly?   **c.** Monthly?

•**53.** Mr. Ng contributed $1000 to an RRSP at the beginning of each calendar quarter for the past 20 years. The plan earned 10% compounded quarterly for the first 10 years and 12% compounded quarterly for the last 10 years. He is converting the RRSP to a Registered Retirement Income Fund (RRIF) and intends to withdraw equal amounts at the beginning of each month for 15 years. If the funds in the RRIF earn 8.25% compounded monthly, what maximum monthly amount can be withdrawn?

•**54.** As a result of the closure of the mine at which he had been employed, Les Orr received a $27,000 severance settlement on his fifty-third birthday. He "rolled" the severance pay into a new RRSP and then, at age 62, used the accumulated funds to purchase an annuity paying $491.31 at the beginning of each month. If the RRSP and the annuity earn 8.5% compounded annually, what is the term of the annuity?

•**55** Mr. van der Linden has just used the funds in his RRSP to purchase a 25-year annuity earning 8% compounded semiannually and paying $3509 at the beginning of each month. Mr. van der Linden made his last regular semiannual contribution of $2500 to his RRSP six months before purchasing the annuity. How long did he contribute to the RRSP if it earned 8% compounded annually?

12.4 COMPREHENSIVE ANNUITY PROBLEMS

The example problems and exercises in each section of the text are usually chosen to illustrate the concepts and techniques introduced in that particular section. Each problem is an application primarily within the narrow scope of the section. This makes Step 3 of the problem-solving procedure (suggested in Section 2.4) virtually self-evident. (Step 3 is: "Identify the principle, concept, or idea that can be used to construct a word equation.") However, when applications arise in business, the connections to the underlying concept and a solution idea are not usually so apparent.

The purpose of this section is to present some interesting, comprehensive, and challenging problems that may involve any type of annuity as well as individual payments. A problem's solution may call upon any topic in Chapters 8 through 12.

> **TIP** **Identify the Type of Annuity at the Outset**
>
> Before doing any calculations for an annuity, you should write down the type of annuity involved. If you intend to use the financial calculator functions, set the calculator in the proper mode (ordinary or due) at this time. By doing these small steps at the outset, you are less likely to overlook them later when you become preoccupied with more profound aspects of the solution.

The flowchart in Figure 12.3 presents a procedure for identifying the type of annuity and the relevant formulas.

FIGURE 12.3 Annuity Classification Flowchart

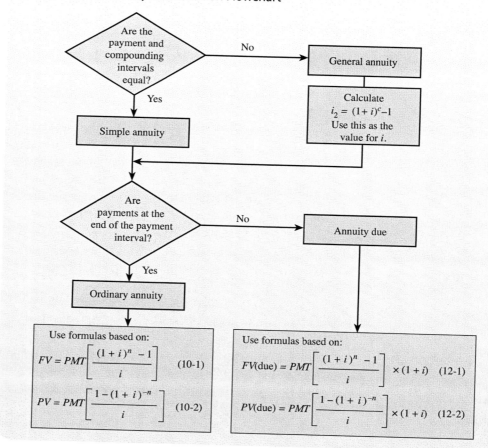

EXAMPLE 12.4A   **REDUCING A LOAN'S TERM BY MAKING MORE FREQUENT, SMALLER PAYMENTS**

Calculate the time required to pay off a $25,000 loan at 8.25% compounded monthly if the loan is repaid by:

a. Quarterly payments of $600.

b. Monthly payments of $200.

c. Semimonthly payments of $100.

d. In every case, a total of $600 is paid every three months. Explain why the time required to repay the loan shortens as smaller payments are made more frequently.

SOLUTION

In every case, the present value of the payments is $25,000 and $i = \frac{8.25\%}{12} = 0.6875\%$. The payments form an ordinary *general* annuity in Parts (a) and (c) where the payment interval differs from the compounding interval. In Part (b), the payments form an ordinary *simple* annuity.

a. $$c = \frac{\text{Number of compoundings per year}}{\text{Number of payments per year}} = \frac{12}{4} = 3$$

$$i_2 = (1 + i)^c - 1 = (1.006875)^3 - 1 = 0.020767122 \text{ per month}$$

Substitute this value and $PMT = \$600$ into formula (10-2n).

$$n = -\frac{\ln\left(1 - \frac{i \times PV}{PMT}\right)}{\ln(1 + i)}$$

$$= -\frac{\ln\left(1 - \frac{0.020767122 \times \$25,000}{\$600}\right)}{\ln(1.020767122)}$$

$$= 97.53$$

8.25	I/Y
P/Y	4 ENTER
C/Y	12 ENTER
25000	PV
600 +/−	PMT
0	FV
CPT	N

Ans: 97.53

The loan will be paid off by 98 quarterly payments requiring $\frac{98}{4} = 24.5$ years or 24 years and 6 months.

b. Substitute $i = 0.006875$ and $PMT = \$200$ into formula (10-2n).

$$n = -\frac{\ln\left(1 - \frac{0.006875 \times \$25,000}{\$200}\right)}{\ln(1.006875)}$$

$$= 286.31$$

Same I/Y, C/Y, PV, FV

P/Y	12 ENTER
200 +/−	PMT
CPT	N

Ans: 286.31

The loan will be paid off by 287 monthly payments requiring $\frac{287}{12} = 23.92$ years or 23 years and 11 months.

c. In a manner similar to Part (a), we obtain $c = 0.5$, $i_2 = 0.003431612$, and $n = 569.58$. Therefore, the loan will be paid off by 570 semimonthly payments requiring $\frac{570}{24} = 23.75$ years or 23 years and 9 months.

d. It is apparent that the loan's term shortens as a given total annual amount is allocated to smaller, more frequent payments. This happens because the more frequent the payments, the earlier the principal balance is reduced. Subsequent interest charges are then lower. Consider, for example, the cases of monthly and quarterly payments. The first $200 monthly payment will reduce the principal balance somewhat. The interest charged in the second month will be less than in the first month because it is calculated on the *reduced* principal. In contrast, the first quarterly payment must include interest on the *full* $25,000 for each of the first three months. Therefore, the interest component of the first quarterly $600 payment will be *greater* than the sum of the *interest* components of the first three $200 monthly payments. Accordingly, the *principal* component of the $600 payment will be *smaller* than the sum of the principal components of the first three $200 monthly payments. This same effect will repeat and compound every quarter. Therefore, monthly payments will reduce the principal balance faster (and pay off the loan sooner) than quarterly payments.

EXAMPLE 12.4B   **A MULTIPLE-STEP PROBLEM IN PERSONAL FINANCIAL PLANNING**

Victor and his financial adviser are checking whether Victor's savings plan will allow him to achieve his retirement goals. Victor wishes to retire in 30 years at age 58. His plan is to use some of the funds in his RRSP at age 58 to purchase a 10-year annuity paying $5000 at the end of each month. Then, at age 68, he intends to use the balance of the funds in his RRSP to purchase a 20-year annuity paying at least $7000 at each month's end.

Victor anticipates that he will be able to contribute $5000 to his RRSP at the beginning of each of the next 15 years and $10,000 at the beginning of each of the subsequent 15 years. Can Victor achieve the desired retirement income if the RRSP earns 8% compounded semiannually and the funds used to purchase the annuities earn 7.5% compounded monthly?

SOLUTION

Victor's savings plan is presented in the following time diagram.

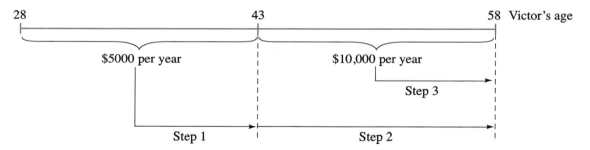

His desired retirement income stream is shown in the following time diagram.

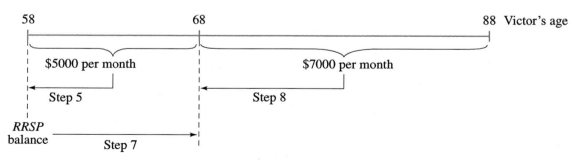

The key test to determine if Victor can achieve his objective for retirement income is whether there will be sufficient funds in his RRSP at age 68 to purchase a 20-year annuity paying $7000 at the end of each month. In general terms, our strategy for the solution is to:

- Calculate the expected amount in the RRSP at age 58. (Steps 1, 2, and 3 in the first diagram. Then in Step 4, add the results of Steps 2 and 3.)
- Determine the amount required to purchase the 10-year annuity. (Step 5 in the second diagram.) Then in Step 6, subtract the Step 5 result from the Step 4 result to obtain the "RRSP balance" after purchasing the annuity.
- Calculate the expected amount in the RRSP at age 68. (Step 7.)
- Calculate the amount required to purchase the 20-year annuity. (Step 8.) Then, in Step 9, compare the Step 8 amount to the Step 7 amount.

Step 1: Calculate the future value at age 43 of the RRSP contributions of $5000 per year. The contributions form a general annuity due for which

$$i = \frac{8\%}{2} = 4\%, n = m(\text{Term}) = 1(43 - 28) = 15, \text{ and}$$

$$c = \frac{\text{Number of compoundings per year}}{\text{Number of payments per year}} = \frac{2}{1} = 2$$

The periodic interest rate for a payment interval is

$$i_2 = (1 + i)^c - 1 = 1.04^2 - 1 = 0.0816 \text{ per year}$$

$$FV(\text{due}) = PMT\left[\frac{(1 + i)^n - 1}{i}\right](1 + i)$$

$$= \$5000\left(\frac{1.0816^{15} - 1}{0.0816}\right)(1.0816)$$

$$= \$148,680.07$$

BGN mode

	8	I/Y
P/Y	1	ENTER
C/Y	2	ENTER
	15	N
	0	PV
5000	+/−	PMT
	CPT	FV

Ans: 148,680.07

Step 2: Calculate the future value at age 58 of the Step 1 result.

$$FV = PV(1 + i)^n = \$148,680.07(1.0816)^{15} = \$482,228.57$$

BGN mode

Same *I/Y, P/Y, C/Y, N*

148680.07	+/−	PV
10000	+/−	PMT
	CPT	FV

Ans: 779,588.71

Step 3: Calculate the future value at age 58 of the 15 contributions of $10,000 per year.

$$FV(\text{due}) = \$10,000\left(\frac{1.0816^{15} - 1}{0.0816}\right) \times (1.0816)$$

$$= \$297,360.14$$

Step 4: Calculate the total amount in the RRSP at age 58.

$$\$482,228.57 + \$297,360.14 = \$779,588.71$$

Step 5: The retirement income annuities are ordinary simple annuities for which $i = \frac{7.5\%}{12} = 0.625\%$ per month. Calculate the amount required (present value) to purchase the 10-year annuity paying $5000 per month.

$$PV = PMT\left[\frac{1 - (1 + i)^{-n}}{i}\right]$$

$$= \$5000\left[\frac{1 - (1.00625)^{-120}}{0.00625}\right]$$

$$= \$421,223.71$$

	7.5	I/Y
P/Y	12	ENTER
(making *C/Y = P/Y =* 12)		
	120	N
	5000	PMT
	0	FV
	CPT	PV

Ans: −421,223.71

Step 6: The RRSP balance at age 58 is the difference between the Step 4 result and the Step 5 result.

Balance = $779,588.71 − $421,223.71 = $358,365.00

Step 7: Calculate the amount (future value) in the RRSP at age 68. The balance from Step 6 grows at 8% compounded semiannually.

$$FV = \$358,365.00(1.04)^{20} = \$785,221.85$$

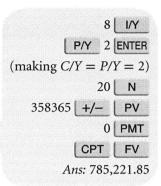

8 I/Y
P/Y 2 ENTER
(making C/Y = P/Y = 2)
20 N
358365 +/− PV
0 PMT
CPT FV
Ans: 785,221.85

Step 8: Calculate the amount (present value) required to purchase the 20-year annuity earning 7.5% compounded monthly and paying $7000 per month.

$$PV = \$7000\left[\frac{1 - (1.00625)^{-240}}{0.00625}\right] = \$868,924.92$$

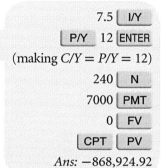

7.5 I/Y
P/Y 12 ENTER
(making C/Y = P/Y = 12)
240 N
7000 PMT
0 FV
CPT PV
Ans: −868,924.92

Step 9: Compare the Step 7 and Step 8 results.

When Victor reaches age 68, the RRSP will not have enough funds to purchase the 20-year annuity paying $7000 per month. The projected shortage is about

$868,924.92 − $785,221.85 = $83,703.07

EXERCISE 12.4   *Answers to the odd-numbered problems are at the end of the book.*

∘1. Monthly payments were originally calculated to repay a $20,000 loan at 9% compounded monthly over a 10-year period. After one year, the debtor took advantage of an option in the loan contract to increase the loan payments by 15%. How much sooner will the loan be paid off?

2. Rentown advertised a television at a cash price of $599.99 and at a rent-to-own rate of $14.79 at the beginning of each week for 78 weeks. What effective rate of interest is a customer paying to acquire the television in a rent-to-own transaction? (Assume that a year has exactly 52 weeks.)

∘3. Sheila already has $67,000 in her RRSP. How much longer must she contribute $4000 at the end of every six months to accumulate a total of $500,000 if the RRSP earns 9% compounded quarterly? (Round the time required to the next higher month.)

∘4. What amount is required to purchase an annuity that pays $5000 at the end of each quarter for the first 10 years and then pays $2500 at the beginning of each month for the subsequent 10 years? The rate of return on the invested funds is 6% compounded quarterly.

∘5. Natalie's RRSP is currently worth $133,000. She plans to contribute for another seven years, and then let the plan continue to grow through internal earnings for an additional three years. If the RRSP earns 8.25% compounded annually, how much must she contribute at the end of every six months for the next seven years in order to have $350,000 in the RRSP 10 years from now?

○**6.** Mr. Palmer wants to retire in 20 years and purchase a 25-year annuity that will make end-of-quarter payments. The payment size is to be the amount which, 20 years from now, has the purchasing power of $6000 today. If he already has $54,000 in his RRSP, what semiannual contributions must he make for the next 20 years to achieve his retirement goal? Assume that the annual rate of inflation for the next 20 years will be 2.5%, the RRSP will earn 8% compounded semiannually, and the rate of return on the fund from which the annuity is paid will be 5.6% compounded quarterly.

○**7.** Interprovincial Distributors Ltd. is planning to open a distribution centre in Calgary in five years. It can purchase suitable land now for the distribution warehouse for $450,000. Annual taxes on the vacant land, payable at the end of each year, would be close to $9000. Rounded to the nearest dollar, what price would the property have to exceed five years from now to make it financially advantageous to purchase the property now instead of five years from now? Assume that Interprovincial can otherwise earn 12% compounded semiannually on its capital.

○**8.** Canadian Pacific Class B preferred shares have just paid their quarterly $1.00 dividend and are trading on the Toronto Stock Exchange at $50. What will the price of the shares have to be three years from now for a current buyer of the shares to earn 7% compounded annually on his investment?

○**9.** If Gayle contributes $1000 to her RRSP at the end of every quarter for the next 10 years and then contributes $1000 at each month's end for the subsequent 15 years, how much will she have in her RRSP at the end of the 25 years? Assume that the RRSP earns 8.5% compounded semiannually.

○**10.** It will cost A-1 Courier $1300 to convert a van from gasoline to natural gas fuel. The remaining useful life of the van is estimated at five years. To financially justify the conversion, what must be the reduction in the monthly cost of fuel to repay the original investment along with a return on investment of 12% compounded monthly? Assume that the fuel will be purchased at the beginning of each month.

●**11.** Conrad has two loans outstanding, which he can repay at any time. He has just made the eleventh monthly payment on an $8500 loan at 10.5% compounded monthly for a three-year term. The twenty-second monthly payment of $313.69 was also made today on the second loan, which has a five-year term and an interest rate of 9.5% compounded semiannually. Conrad is finding the total monthly payments too high, and interest rates on similar loans are now down to 8.25% compounded monthly. He wishes to reduce his monthly cash outflow by obtaining a debt consolidation loan just sufficient to pay off the balances on the two loans. What would his monthly payment be on a five-year term loan at the new rate?

○**12.** Jeanette wishes to retire in 30 years at age 55 with retirement savings that have the purchasing power of $300,000 in today's dollars.

   a. If the rate of inflation for the next 30 years is 2% per year, how much must she accumulate in her RRSP?

   b. If she contributes $3000 at the end of each year for the next five years, how much must she contribute annually for the subsequent 25 years to reach her goal? Assume that her RRSP will earn 8% compounded annually.

   c. The amount in Part (a) will be used to purchase a 30-year annuity. What will the month-end payments be if the funds earn 6% compounded monthly?

•**13.** The average annual costs to support a child born today are estimated as follows:

Years 1–6	$12,000
Years 7–12	11,000
Years 13–17	10,000
Years 18–19	15,000

The costs in the early years include child care expenses or foregone earnings of the care-giving parent. Rounded to the nearest dollar:

a. What is the aggregate total cost (ignoring the time value of money) of raising a child to age 19?

b. What is the total economic value, at the date of birth of a child, of these future expenditures, if money can earn 6% compounded monthly? Assume that the annual costs are paid in equal end-of-month amounts.

c. What will be the economic value at age 19 of the past expenditures, assuming money can earn 6% compounded monthly?

•**14.** To compensate for the effects of inflation during their retirement years, the Pelyks intend to purchase a combination of annuities that will provide the following pattern of month-end income:

Calendar years, inclusive	Income ($)
2015 to 2019	7500
2020 to 2024	9000
2025 to 2029	10,500
2030 to 2040	12,000

Rounded to the nearest dollar, how much will they need in their RRSPs when they retire at the beginning of 2015 to purchase the annuities, if the annuity payments are based on a rate of return of 6% compounded semiannually?

•**15.** For its "Tenth Anniversary Salebration," Pioneer Furniture is offering terms of 10% down, no interest, and no payments for six months. The balance must then be paid in six equal payments, with the first payment due six months after the purchase date. The conditional sale contract calculates the monthly payments to include interest at the rate of 15% compounded monthly after the end of the interest-free period. Immediately after the sale of the furniture, Pioneer sells the contract to Afco Finance at a discount to yield Afco 18% compounded semiannually from the date of the sale. What cash payment will Pioneer receive from Afco on a piece of furniture sold for $2000?

•**16.** Patrick contributes $1000 at the beginning of every quarter to his RRSP. In addition, he contributes another $2000 to the RRSP each year from his year-end bonus. If the RRSP earns 9.5% compounded semiannually, what will be the value of his RRSP after 23 years?

•**17.** Reg is developing a financial plan that would enable him to retire 30 years from now at age 60. Upon reaching age 60, he will use some of the funds in his RRSP to purchase an eight-year annuity that pays $5000 at the end of each month. Then, at age 68, he will use the remaining funds to purchase a 20-year annuity paying $6000 at each month's end. What contributions must he make to an RRSP at the beginning of each quarter for 30 years to achieve his retirement goal, if the RRSP and the annuities earn 7.5% compounded monthly?

○**18.** Cynthia currently has $55,000 in her RRSP. She plans to contribute $7000 at the end of each year for the next 17 years and then use the accumulated funds to purchase a 20-year annuity making end-of-month payments.

   a. Assume that her RRSP earns 8.75% compounded annually for the next 17 years, and the fund from which the annuity is paid will earn 5.4% compounded monthly. What monthly payments will she receive?

   b. If the average annual rate of inflation for the next 17 years is 2%, what will be the purchasing power in today's dollars of the monthly payments 17 years from now?

•**19.** A major car manufacturer is developing a promotion offering new car buyers the choice between "below market" four-year financing at 1.9% compounded monthly or a cash rebate. On the purchase of a $25,000 car, what cash rebate would make a car buyer indifferent between the following alternatives?

   • Financing through the car dealer at the reduced interest rate.

   • Taking the cash rebate and obtaining bank financing at 6.6% compounded monthly for the net "cash" price.

•**20.** The monthly payments on a $30,000 loan at 10.5% compounded monthly were calculated to repay the loan over a 10-year period. After 32 payments were made, the borrower became unemployed and, with the approval of the lender, missed the next three payments.

   a. What amount paid along with the regular payment at the end of the thirty-sixth month will put the loan repayment back on the original schedule?

   b. Instead of the "make-up" arrangement in Part (a), suppose the regular loan payments (beginning with the payment at the end of the thirty-sixth month) are recalculated to put the loan back on its 10-year repayment "track." What will be the new payments?

•**21.** Martha's RRSP is currently worth $97,000. She plans to contribute $5000 at the beginning of every six months until she reaches age 58, 12 years from now. Then she intends to use half of the funds in the RRSP to purchase a 20-year annuity making month-end payments. Five years later she will use half of the funds then in her RRSP to purchase another 20-year annuity making month-end payments. Finally, at age 68, she will use all of the remaining funds to purchase a third 20-year annuity also making end-of-month payments. What will be her monthly income at age 65 and at age 70 if her RRSP and the annuities earn 7.5% compounded monthly?

KEY TERMS

Annuity due **p. 459**

Book value of a lease **p. 470**

General annuity due **p. 459**

Residual value **p. 478**

Simple annuity due **p. 459**

SUMMARY OF NOTATION AND KEY FORMULAS

$FV(\text{due}) = $ Future value of an n-payment annuity due

$PV(\text{due}) = $ Present value of an n-payment annuity due

FORMULA (12-1) $FV(\text{due}) = PMT\left[\dfrac{(1+i)^n - 1}{i}\right] \times (1+i)$ Finding the future value of an annuity due

FORMULA (12-2) $PV(\text{due}) = PMT\left[\dfrac{1 - (1+i)^{-n}}{i}\right] \times (1+i)$ Finding the present value of an annuity due

FORMULA (12-1n) $n = \dfrac{\ln\left[1 + \dfrac{i \times FV(\text{due})}{PMT(1+i)}\right]}{\ln(1+i)}$ Finding the number of payments, given $FV(\text{due})$

FORMULA (12-2n) $n = -\dfrac{\ln\left[1 - \dfrac{i \times PV(\text{due})}{PMT(1+i)}\right]}{\ln(1+i)}$ Finding the number of payments, given $PV(\text{due})$

REVIEW PROBLEMS

Answers to the odd-numbered review problems are at the end of the book.

Interest rates should be calculated accurate to the nearest 0.01%.

1. **(LO1)** Brunswick Trucking has signed a five-year lease with Ford Credit Canada Ltd. on a new truck. Lease payments of $1900 are made at the beginning of each month. To purchase the truck, Brunswick Trucking would have had to borrow funds at 8.25% compounded monthly.

   a. What initial liability should Brunswick report on its balance sheet?

   b. How much will the liability be reduced during the first year of the lease?

2. **(LO1)** What minimum amount of money earning 7% compounded semiannually will sustain withdrawals of $1000 at the beginning of every month for 12 years?

3. **(LO2)** What maximum annual withdrawals will a $300,000 fund earning 7.75% compounded annually sustain for 25 years if the withdrawals are made:

   a. At the beginning of each year?

   b. At the end of each year?

4. **(LO2)** Regular investments made at the beginning of each quarter earn 6% compounded quarterly. How many more $1000 investments than $1100 investments will it take to accumulate $100,000?

5. **(LO2)** An RRSP is now worth $316,000 after contributions of $3500 at the beginning of every six months for 17 years. What effective rate of return has the plan earned?

6. **(LO1)** Calculate the amount that will be accumulated after 20 years if:

   a. $1000 is invested at the beginning of every six months at 8.5% compounded semiannually.

   b. $2000 is invested at the beginning of every year at 8.5% compounded annually.

7. **(LO2)** A life insurance company quoted an annual premium of $387.50 (payable at the beginning of the year) for a $250,000 term insurance policy on a 35-year-old male nonsmoker. Alternatively, the insured can pay $33.71 at the beginning of each month by preauthorized electronic debit. Which

payment plan would an applicant choose solely on the basis of money being worth 7.5% compounded monthly?

8. **(LO1)** A seven-year capital lease of an executive jet requires semiannual payments of $200,000 at the beginning of each six-month period. The company can borrow funds for 5 to 10 years at 7.4% compounded semiannually.

   a. What long-term lease liability will the firm set up at the start of the term of the lease?

   b. What liability will remain halfway through the term of the lease?

9. **(LO2)** Suppose that $5000 is contributed at the beginning of each year to an RRSP that earns 8% compounded annually.

   a. How many contributions will it take to accumulate the first $500,000?

   b. How many more contributions will it take for the RRSP to reach $1,000,000?

10. **(LO2)** The membership dues at Shoreline Golf and Country Club are $2820 payable at the beginning of the year, or four payments of $736.56 payable at the beginning of each quarter. What effective rate of interest is the club charging members who pay their dues quarterly?

11. **(LO2)** Excel Leasing calculates the payments on long-term equipment leases so that it earns a rate of return of 15% compounded quarterly on its investment in the equipment. What beginning-of-month payments will Excel charge on a four-year lease of a photocopier costing $7650? (Assume the photocopier has no residual value at the end of the lease.)

12. **(LO2)** Apex Fabricating wants to accumulate $800,000 for an expansion expected to begin in four years. If today Apex makes the first of equal quarterly payments into a fund earning 6.75% compounded monthly, what should the size of these payments be?

13. **(LO2)** How many more RRSP contributions of $300 at the beginning of every month are required to reach $200,000 if the funds earn 7.5% compounded monthly than if they earn 8.5% compounded monthly?

14. **(LO2)** As of the date of Colony Farm's most recent financial statements, $3\frac{1}{2}$ years remained in the term of a lease reported as a long-term liability of $27,400. If the beginning-of-month lease payments are $750, what monthly compounded nominal discount rate was used in valuing the lease?

15. **(LO2)** If a furniture store offers to sell a washer-dryer combination priced at $1395 on a conditional sale contract requiring 12 monthly payments of $125 (including a payment on the date of sale), what effective rate of interest is being charged?

16. **(LO2)** Sovereign Life Insurance Company of Canada offers $250,000 of term life insurance to a 45-year-old male for an annual premium of $716 (in advance) or for monthly premium payments (in advance) of $62.50 by preauthorized electronic debit. What effective rate of interest is charged to those who pay monthly?

17. **(LO2)** Fred is about to have his twenty-seventh birthday. He has set a goal of retiring at age 58 with $1,000,000 in his RRSP. For planning purposes, he is assuming that his RRSP will earn 8% compounded annually.

   a. What contributions on each birthday from age 27 to 57 inclusive will be required to accumulate the desired amount in his RRSP?

   b. If he waits five years before starting his RRSP, what contributions on each birthday from age 32 to 57 inclusive will be required to reach the target?

○18. **(LO1)** What is the initial economic value of an annuity due if it consists of 19 semiannual payments of $1500? Money is worth 5% compounded semiannually for the first five years, and 6% compounded semiannually thereafter.

○19. **(LO1)** What will be the amount in an RRSP after 30 years if contributions of $4000 are made at the beginning of each year for the first 10 years, and contributions of $6000 are made at the beginning of each year for the subsequent 20 years? Assume that the RRSP will earn 8.25% compounded annually.

○20. **(LO1)** Calculate the future value of an investment plan requiring contributions of $800 at the beginning of each calendar quarter for seven years. Assume that the rate of return will be 8% compounded quarterly for the first 30 months and 7% compounded semiannually for the remainder of the annuity's term.

○21. **(LO2)** Ms. Bowers wants to be able to purchase a 20-year annuity at age 62 that will pay her $3500 at the beginning of each month. She makes her first quarterly contribution to an RRSP on her thirty-fifth birthday and continues them up to but not including her sixty-second birthday. What should be the amount of each contribution? Assume that her RRSP will earn 8% compounded quarterly and that the money used to purchase the annuity will earn 4.8% compounded monthly.

○22. **(LO2)** Mr. and Mrs. Zolob contributed $50 on the first of each month to an RESP they set up for their grandson Jeff. By the time he entered Mohawk College, 14 years and 5 months of contributions had accumulated. The grandparents' contributions stopped, and Jeff started beginning-of-month withdrawals of $500. How long will these payments last if the RESP has earned and will continue to earn 8.25% compounded monthly?

○23. **(LO1)** A rental agreement requires the payment of $1000 at the beginning of each month.

   a. What single payment at the beginning of the rental year should the landlord accept instead of twelve monthly payments if money is worth 8% compounded monthly?

   b. Show that the landlord will be equally well off at the end of the year under either payment arrangement if rental payments are invested at 8% compounded monthly.

○24. **(LO1)** Mick contributed $5000 at the beginning of each year for 25 years to his RRSP. Assume that the RRSP earned 8% compounded annually. What percentage of the RRSP's value after 25 years comes from contributions made in the first five years?

○25. **(LO1)** What amount is required to purchase an annuity that pays $4000 at the end of each quarter for the first five years and then pays $2500 at the beginning of each month for the subsequent 15 years? Assume that the annuity payments are based on a rate of return of 5.6% compounded quarterly.

○26. **(LO1) (LO2)** Suppose that $5000 is contributed at the beginning of each year for 25 years to an RRSP that earns 10% compounded annually. By what percentage would annual contributions have to be increased in order to have the same future value after 25 years if the plan earns only 8% compounded annually?

○27. **(LO1) (LO2)** Suppose you contribute $2500 to an RRSP at the beginning of every six months for 25 years, and then use the accumulated funds to purchase an annuity paying $2500 at the beginning of each month. How long after the start of the annuity will the last payment be made? Assume that the RRSP earns 8% compounded semiannually and the funds invested in the annuity earn 5.1% compounded monthly.

○28. **(LO2)** Capital Leasing leases commercial kitchen equipment to restaurants, hotels, hospitals, and other institutions. Capital Leasing calculates the payments on its four-year leases so that it recovers the purchase price of the equipment plus a return on investment of 16% compounded annually over the term of the lease. What will be the required lease payments at the beginning of each quarter on equipment purchased by Capital for $57,000?

○29. **(LO2)** New Look Fitness Centre offers a one-year membership for $500 in advance, or a three-month membership for $160 in advance. What effective rate of interest is an individual paying if she buys four consecutive three-month memberships instead of a one-year membership?

○30. **(LO2)** A life insurance company is calculating the monthly premium that it will offer clients as an alternative to paying the full annual premium. With both alternatives, premiums are payable at the beginning of the period of coverage. If the monthly payment by preauthorized electronic debit is calculated to yield the insurance company 10% compounded semiannually on the unpaid balance of the annual premium, what should be the monthly premium per $100 of annual premium?

CASE A "Lotto" Money

On October 19, 2005, the winning numbers were announced for the $340,000,000 jackpot in America's biggest lottery game, Powerball. It was soon determined that only one of the 146 million tickets sold for the draw had the winning combination of numbers! It turns out that the winning ticket had been purchased jointly by two couples in southern Oregon. The Powerball rules gave the winners a choice between receiving 30 annual payments (including one immediately) of $11,333,300 or an immediate lump payment of $227.8 million.

QUESTIONS

1. What is the nominal sum of the 30 payments in the annuity due? Strictly speaking, is it legitimate for Powerball to report a $340 million jackpot? Explain your reasoning. (Many mega-prize lotteries employ a similar approach in their promotions.)
2. The Multi-State Lottery Association (MSLA) that administers Powerball determined the amount of the annual annuity payment as follows. First the MSLA determined that, from lottery ticket sales, it could pay $227.8 million as a single lump prize. The MSLA then obtained quotes in the financial markets on 30-year annual-payment annuities due that could be purchased with the $227.8 million. The best quote was $11.3333 million per year. Rounded to the nearest 0.01%, what was the rate of return on this annuity?
3. If the Powerball winners can earn 6% compounded annually on their personal investments, what was the initial economic value of the annuity to them? Which option should they have chosen in that case?
4. Until October 2002, the annuity due option for Powerball Jackpot winners was structured for 25 rather than 30 annual payments. What annual payment in a 25-year annuity due would the October 19, 2005 Powerball cash prize ($227.8 million) purchase? (Use the rate of return you calculated in Question 2.)
5. If the 25-year annuity option were still in place, what Powerball Jackpot prize would the MSLA have reported for the October 19, 2005 draw?
6. Why do you suppose the MSLA changed from a 25-year to a 30-year term for the annuity option?

APPENDIX 12A   SETTING YOUR CALCULATOR IN THE ANNUITY DUE MODE

This appendix illustrates the keystrokes needed to set your calculator for annuity due calculations.

Sharp EL-738	Texas Instruments BA II Plus	Hewlett Packard 10B
2nd F	2nd	[ ]
BGN	BGN	BEG/END
"BGN" appears in the display when in this mode.	2nd	"BEGIN" appears in the display when in this mode.
	SET	
	2nd	
	QUIT	
	"BGN" appears in the display when in this mode.	

When you repeat these keystrokes, your calculator will "toggle" or switch back to the ordinary annuity mode (no indicator in the display). The calculator remains in the most recently selected mode, even after being turned off.

13

Annuities: Special Situations

LEARNING OBJECTIVES

After completing this chapter, you will be able to:

LO1 Calculate the present value of a perpetuity and a deferred perpetuity

LO2 Calculate the present value and future value of an annuity whose payment size grows at a constant rate

TWO SPECIAL CASES OF ANNUITIES are examined in this chapter. The first is perpetuities—annuities whose payments continue forever. For example, a college might receive a $200,000 gift or bequest to offer an annual scholarship in perpetuity. The mathematics of perpetuities turn out to be surprisingly simple.

The second special case is constant-growth annuities—annuities whose payments increase at a steady rate. We often make a "constant-growth assumption" in long-term financial planning. A growing annuity is usually a better approximation of our saving pattern than a constant payment annuity. As wages increase over time (even if only through inflation), most people are able to save more each year. Many pension plans index or link pension payments to the Consumer Price Index. The payments increase over time by the same percentage as the CPI. Again, a growing annuity is a good representation of this payment pattern.

13.1 PERPETUITIES

Suppose a $100,000 investment can earn 5% compounded annually. It will earn $5000 in the first year. If the $5000 is paid out from the investment account at the end of the year, the principal will remain at $100,000. As long as the investment continues to earn 5% compounded annually, $5000 can be paid out at the end of every year forever. The value of the investment (principal plus accrued interest) will rise steadily from $100,000 to $105,000 during any year, and then abruptly fall back to $100,000 when the $5000 is paid out on the last day of the year. Consequently, a graph of the investment's "Value" vs. "Time" has the saw-tooth pattern shown in Figure 13.1.

FIGURE 13.1   Value of $100,000 Investment that Pays Out Only Its Interest Earnings

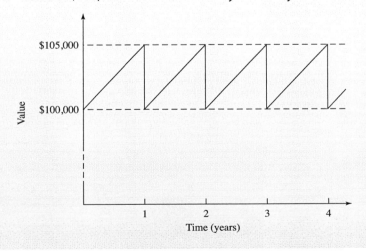

If more than $5000 is paid out at the end of each year, a portion of it will be principal. As the years go by, the principal balance will be eroded in an accelerating fashion because less and less interest is earned in each successive year. The trend is illustrated in Figure 13.2[1] where $6000 is paid each year. In conclusion, $5000 is the *maximum* amount that can be paid out at the end of every year *in perpetuity*.

---

[1]   Figures 13.1 and 13.2 were suggested by Oded Tal of Conestoga College.

FIGURE 13.2 Value of $100,000 Investment that Pays Out More than Its Interest Earnings

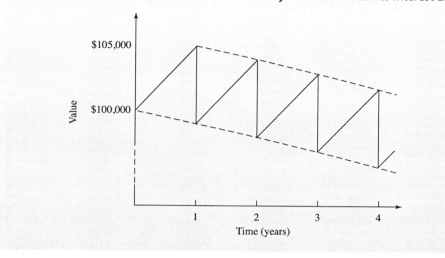

LO1 An annuity whose payments continue forever is called a **perpetuity**. Figure 13.3 presents a time diagram for an **ordinary perpetuity** with payments of size *PMT* at the *end* of each payment interval. In a **perpetuity due**, the payments will occur at the *beginning* of each payment interval.

FIGURE 13.3 Time Diagram for the Payments of an Ordinary Perpetuity

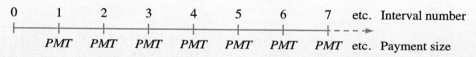

Let us use formula (10-2) to calculate the present value of annual payments of $5000 in perpetuity, discounting at 5% compounded annually. (Do you have any hunch what the present value will be?) We have *PMT* = $5000 and *i* = 5% = 0.05. But what value shall we use for *n*? To answer this question, recall that payments far in the future make a negligible contribution to present value. So let us just use *n* = 1000. (If you have any doubts about doing this, calculate the present value of the thousandth payment by itself.) We obtain

$$PV = PMT\left[\frac{1-(1+i)^{-n}}{i}\right] = \$5000\left[\frac{1-(1.05)^{-1000}}{0.05}\right] = \$100,000$$

We could have anticipated this result from our knowledge that the present value of an annuity is the amount required to purchase the annuity. If money can earn 5% compounded annually, $100,000 can purchase a perpetuity paying

$$0.05 \times \$100,000 = \$5000$$

at the end of every year. Since "0.05" is the value of *i*, "$100,000" is the value of *PV*, and "$5000" is the value of *PMT*, the general relationship among these three variables for an ordinary perpetuity is

$$i(PV) = PMT$$

That is,

PRESENT VALUE OF AN ORDINARY PERPETUITY

$$PV = \frac{PMT}{i} \qquad \text{(13-1)}$$

A perpetuity due may be viewed as the combination of a single immediate payment and an ordinary perpetuity. Therefore, the present value of a perpetuity due is just

$$PV(\text{due}) = PMT + PV = PMT + \frac{PMT}{i}$$

The future value of a perpetuity is an undefined quantity—since payments continue forever, the future value is infinite.

To this point, the perpetuity's payment interval has been equal to the compounding interval. If this is not the case, we are dealing with an ordinary *general* perpetuity or a *general* perpetuity due. Then we must make the same adjustment that we did for annuities. That is, we must use the formula $i_2 = (1 + i)^c - 1$ to calculate the periodic interest rate that matches the payment interval, and substitute this value of i_2 for i in the PV formula.

EXAMPLE 13.1A   **CALCULATING THE ENDOWMENT AND RATE OF RETURN REQUIRED TO SUSTAIN AN ORDINARY PERPETUITY**

A chartered bank is considering the establishment in perpetuity of a Visiting Professor Chair in Public Policy at a university. The ongoing cost will be $11,250 at the end of each month.

a. If money can earn 5.4% compounded monthly in perpetuity, what endowment is required to fund the position?

b. What monthly compounded nominal rate of return must an endowment of $2.25 million earn to fully fund the position?

SOLUTION

a. The payments form an ordinary simple perpetuity having

$$PMT = \$11{,}250 \quad \text{and} \quad i = \tfrac{5.4\%}{12} = 0.45\% \text{ per month.}$$

The required endowment is

$$PV = \frac{PMT}{i} = \frac{\$11{,}250}{0.0045} = \$2{,}500{,}000$$

b. With $PV = \$2{,}250{,}000$ and $PMT = \$11{,}250$ per month, the required interest rate per payment interval is

$$i = \frac{PMT}{PV} = \frac{\$11{,}250}{\$2{,}250{,}000} = 0.005 = 0.5\% \text{ per month}$$

The required nominal rate of return is

$$j = mi = 12(0.5\%) = 6\% \text{ compounded monthly}$$

EXAMPLE 13.1B   **CALCULATING THE PRICE OF A PERPETUAL PREFERRED SHARE**

Some preferred shares promise a fixed periodic dividend in perpetuity.

a. What is the fair market value of a perpetual preferred share just after payment of a quarterly $0.50 dividend? The market requires a dividend yield of 5% compounded annually on preferred shares of similar risk.

b. What will be an investor's annually compounded dividend yield if she is able to purchase these shares at $36.00 each?

SOLUTION

According to the Valuation Principle, the fair market value of a share is the present value of the expected dividend payments (discounted at the rate of return required in the financial market). Since a dividend has just been paid, the first dividend the purchaser will receive will be three months from now. Viewed from the purchase date, the dividend payments form an ordinary perpetuity. Since the payment interval is three months but the compounding interval is one year, the dividend payments form a general perpetuity.

a. Given: $PMT = \$0.50$ and $i = \frac{5\%}{1} = 5\%$

We must first calculate the equivalent periodic rate for the three-month payment interval. (It will be *about* $\frac{5\%}{4} = 1.25\%$ per quarter.)

$$c = \frac{\text{Number of compoundings per year}}{\text{Number of payments per year}} = \frac{1}{4} = 0.25$$

Then

$$i_2 = (1 + i)^c - 1 = 1.05^{0.25} - 1 = 0.0122722 = 1.22722\% \text{ per quarter}$$

and

$$PV = \frac{PMT}{i_2} = \frac{\$0.50}{0.0122722} = \$40.74$$

Thus, the fair market value of a share is $40.74.

b. If the investor can purchase the shares at a lower price than the fair market value in Part (a), her dividend yield will be greater than 5% compounded annually (because she will receive the same dividends from a smaller investment). The dividend yield per payment interval will be

$$i = \frac{PMT}{PV} = \frac{\$0.50}{\$36.00} = 0.01\overline{38} = 1.3\overline{8}\% \text{ per quarter}$$

The annually compounded nominal dividend yield is the same as the effective dividend yield. Using formula (9-3)

$$f = (1 + i)^m - 1 = (1.013\overline{8})^4 - 1 = 0.0567 = 5.67\% \text{ compounded annually}$$

EXAMPLE 13.1C   **CALCULATING THE INITIAL ENDOWMENT FOR A GENERAL PERPETUITY**

What amount must be placed in a perpetual fund today if it earns 4.8% compounded semiannually, and the first monthly payment of $500 in perpetuity will be made:

a. One month from today?

b. One year from today?

SOLUTION

In both cases, the required initial amount is the present value of the payments. Since payments are made monthly but compounding takes place semiannually, the payments form a *general* perpetuity having

$$PMT = \$500 \text{ per month} \quad \text{and} \quad i = \frac{4.8\%}{2} = 2.4\% \text{ per six months}$$

We must calculate the equivalent periodic rate for the one-month payment interval. (It will be *approximately* $\frac{4.8\%}{12} = 0.4\%$ per month.)

$$c = \frac{\text{Number of compoundings per year}}{\text{Number of payments per year}} = \frac{2}{12} = 0.1\overline{6}$$

and

$$i_2 = (1 + i)^c - 1 = (1.024)^{0.1\overline{6}} - 1 = 0.00396057687 = 0.396057687\% \text{ per month}$$

a. The required initial endowment is

$$PV = \frac{PMT}{i_2} = \frac{\$500}{0.00396057687} = \$126,244.24$$

The initial amount required to fund the perpetuity is $126,244.24.

b. The perpetuity is shown on a time line in the following diagram. Viewed from a date 11 months from now, the payments form an ordinary perpetuity. Viewed from today, the payments form a deferred ordinary perpetuity with an 11-month period of deferral.

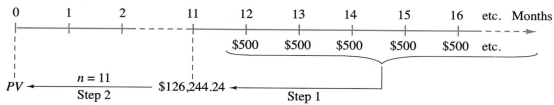

The calculation of today's present value of payments must be done in two steps. First determine the present value, 11 months from today, of the ordinary perpetuity. (This is the same as the $126,244.24 amount we calculated in Part (a).) The amount that must be placed in the fund today is the present value of $126,244.24, 11 months earlier. Using formula (8-2), this present value is

$$PV = FV(1 + i_2)^{-n} = \$126{,}244.24(1.00396057687)^{-11} = \$120{,}872.73$$

The initial amount that must be placed in the perpetual fund is $120,872.73.

EXAMPLE 13.1D   **CALCULATING THE PAYMENT IN A DEFERRED GENERAL PERPETUITY**

Mrs. Paquette is setting up a trust fund with an initial contribution of $150,000. The funds are to be immediately invested, and the first semiannual payment of a perpetuity is to be made five years from now. The payments are to be used for the care of her son for the rest of his life, and then are to be paid to the Canadian Foundation for Multiple Sclerosis. If the funds in trust earn 5% compounded annually, what is the maximum payment the trust can make in perpetuity?

SOLUTION

The data and solution idea are shown in the time diagram below. Viewed from a focal date $4\frac{1}{2}$ years from now, the payments form an ordinary perpetuity. Since the payment interval (six months) does not equal the compounding interval (one year), the payments form a general perpetuity.

The future value of the $150,000 contribution after $4\frac{1}{2}$ years will be the amount (present value) sustaining the perpetuity. That is,

$$\binom{FV \text{ of } \$150{,}000,}{4.5 \text{ years from now}} = \binom{PV \text{ of the ordinary general}}{\text{perpetuity, } 4.5 \text{ years from now}} \quad ①$$

Since

$$i = \frac{5\%}{1} = 5\% \quad \text{and} \quad c = \frac{\text{Number of compoundings per year}}{\text{Number of payments per year}} = \frac{1}{2} = 0.5$$

then

$$i_2 = (1 + i)^c - 1 = 1.05^{0.5} - 1 = 0.024695077 = 2.4695077\% \text{ per 6 months}$$

The left side of equation ① is

$$FV = PV(1 + i_2)^n = \$150{,}000(1.024695077)^9 = \$186{,}828.49$$

The right side is

$$PV = \frac{PMT}{i_2} = \frac{PMT}{0.024695077}$$

Substitute these values into ① giving

$$\$186,828.49 = \frac{PMT}{0.024695077}$$

Hence,

$$PMT = 0.024695077 \times \$186,828.49 = \$4613.74$$

The trust can make semiannual payments of $4613.74 in perpetuity.

CONCEPT QUESTIONS

1. A perpetuity and an annuity both have the same values for *PMT* and *i*. Which has the larger present value? Give a brief explanation.

2. If market interest rates rise, will it require a larger endowment to sustain a perpetuity with a particular payment size? Give a brief explanation.

3. Will the market value of a perpetual preferred share (paying a fixed periodic dividend) rise or fall if the rate of return (dividend yield) required by investors declines? Give a brief explanation.

EXERCISE 13.1   *Answers to the odd-numbered problems are at the end of the book.*

1. Mrs. O'Reilly donated $500,000 to Medicine Hat College for a perpetual scholarship fund for women in business studies. What amount can be awarded on each anniversary, if the scholarship fund earns $4\frac{1}{2}\%$ compounded annually?

2. What amount is required to fund a perpetuity that pays $10,000 at the beginning of each quarter? The funds can be invested to earn 5% compounded quarterly.

3. A perpetuity is to pay $10,000 at the end of every six months. How much less money is required to fund the perpetuity if the money can be invested to earn 5% compounded semiannually instead of 4% compounded semiannually?

4. In 1752, the British government converted all of its outstanding bonds to perpetual bonds that paid a fixed interest rate. These bonds paid only the interest every three months—the principal amount of the debt would never be repaid. The perpetual bonds have come to be known as "Consols," and they trade in the British financial markets. The owner of a £1000 face-value (or denomination) Consol receives £6.25 every three months.

   a. What is the fixed interest rate (on the face value) paid by the Consols?

   b. If the prevailing long-term interest rate in the British financial markets is 4.5% compounded quarterly, what is the fair market value of a £1000 face-value Consol? (Assume that you will receive the first interest payment in three months.)

5. How much more money is required to fund an ordinary perpetuity than a 30-year ordinary annuity if both pay $5000 quarterly and money can earn 5% compounded quarterly?

6. Ranger Oil recently donated $750,000 to the Northern Alberta Institute of Technology (NAIT) to fund (in perpetuity) five annual bursaries for students in Petroleum Engineering Technology. If the first five bursaries are to be awarded immediately, what is the maximum amount of each bursary? Assume that the bursary fund earns 4.9% compounded semiannually.

7. An old agreement requires a town to pay $500 per year in perpetuity to the owner of a parcel of land for a water well dug on the property in the 1920s. The well is no longer used, and the town wants to buy out the contract, which has become an administrative

nuisance. What amount (including the regular scheduled payment) should the landowner be willing to accept on the date of the next scheduled payment if long-term low-risk investments now earn 5.8% compounded annually?

8. The alumni association of Seneca College is initiating a one-year drive to raise money for a perpetual scholarship endowment fund. The goal is to offer ten scholarships per year, each worth $5000.

    a. How large a fund is required to begin awarding the scholarships one year after the funds are in place if the funds can be invested to earn 5% compounded annually in perpetuity?

    b. Suppose that, during its fund-raising year, the alumni association finds an insurance company that will pay 5.5% compounded annually in perpetuity. How much less money does the association need to raise?

    c. What dollar amount in scholarships can be awarded annually if the alumni association raises only $750,000? Use the interest rate from Part (b).

9. A city sells plots in its cemetery for $1000 plus an amount calculated to provide for the cost of maintaining the grounds in perpetuity. This cost is figured at $25 per plot due at the end of each quarter. If the city can invest the funds to earn 4.8% compounded annually in perpetuity, what is the price of a plot?

10. A company's preferred shares pay a $2 dividend every six months in perpetuity. What is the fair market value of the shares just after payment of a dividend if the dividend yield required by the market on shares of similar risk is

    a. 4% compounded semiannually?   b. 5% compounded semiannually?

11. A company's perpetual preferred shares pay a semiannual dividend of $1.50. The next dividend will be paid tomorrow.

    a. At what price would the shares provide an investor with a 4.5% semiannually compounded rate of return? The investor will receive tomorrow's dividend.

    b. If the shares are trading at $70, what nominal rate of return will they provide to a purchaser?

12. Mr. O'Connor set up a trust account paying $500 per month in perpetuity to the local SPCA. These payments consume all of the interest earned monthly by the trust. Between what amounts does the balance in the trust account fluctuate if it earns 6% compounded monthly?

∘13. What sum of money, invested today in a perpetual fund earning 5.5% compounded semiannually, will sustain quarterly perpetuity payments of $1000 if the first payment is made

    a. three months from today?   b. one year from today?

∘14. The common shares of Unicorp. are forecast to pay annual dividends of $2 at the end of each of the next five years, followed by dividends of $3 per year in perpetuity. What is the fair market value of the shares if the market requires an 8% annually compounded rate of return on shares having a similar degree of risk?

∘15. Mr. Chan has donated $1 million to a college to set up a perpetuity for the purchase of books and journals for a new library to be built and named in his honour. The donation will be invested and earnings will compound for three years, at which time the first of the quarterly perpetuity payments will be made. If the funds earn 6% compounded quarterly, what will be the size of the payments?

∘16. A wealthy benefactor has donated $1,000,000 to establish a perpetuity that will be used to support the operating costs of a local heritage museum scheduled to open in three years' time. If the funds earn 4.8% compounded monthly, what monthly payments, the first occurring three years from now, can the museum expect?

∘**17.** A legal dispute delayed for 18 months the disbursement of a $500,000 bequest designated to provide quarterly payments in perpetuity to a hospice. While under the jurisdiction of the court, the funds earned interest at the rate of 5% compounded semiannually. The hospice has just invested the $500,000 along with its earnings in a perpetual fund earning 5.2% compounded semiannually. What payments will the hospice receive beginning three months from now?

13.2 CONSTANT-GROWTH ANNUITIES

In many situations in real life, regular payments that we make or receive do not remain constant. As a result of inflation and wage growth, we pay more for rent, memberships, insurance, etc., as the years go by. Usually we are able to increase our saving rate and RRSP contributions from time to time. Some pension plans (including the Canada Pension Plan, the Quebec Pension Plan, and the Old Age Security program) provide annual cost-of-living increases. Many businesses grow their revenue, profit, and dividends through real economic growth as well as through inflation.

For long-range financial projections and planning, it is natural to want to incorporate some sort of growth pattern in future payments. The constant-payment annuities we have been considering so far may not provide an adequate approximation of many patterns of increasing payments. In this section we consider the case of **constant-growth annuities**—annuities in which the payments change by the *same percentage* from one payment to the next. Let

$$g = \text{Rate of growth in payment size between successive payments}$$

For example, if each quarterly payment is 1.5% larger than the preceding payment, then $g = 1.5\% = 0.015$. In general, if we let *PMT* represent the amount of the *first* payment, then

$$\text{Second payment} = PMT + g \times PMT$$
$$= PMT(1 + g)$$

$$\text{Third payment} = (\text{Second payment}) + g \times (\text{Second payment})$$
$$= (\text{Second payment}) \times (1 + g)$$
$$= PMT(1 + g) \times (1 + g)$$
$$= PMT(1 + g)^2$$

You can now see the pattern. Each payment is a factor $(1 + g)$ larger than the preceding payment. In other words, the payment's growth rate, *g*, compounds every payment interval.

LO2   The formulas for the future value and the present value of a constant-growth ordinary simple annuity are:

FUTURE VALUE OF A CONSTANT-GROWTH ORDINARY ANNUITY

$$FV = PMT\left[\frac{(1 + i)^n - (1 + g)^n}{i - g}\right] \qquad (13\text{-}2)^2$$

PRESENT VALUE OF A CONSTANT-GROWTH ORDINARY ANNUITY

$$PV = PMT\left[\frac{1 - (1 + g)^n(1 + i)^{-n}}{i - g}\right] \qquad (13\text{-}3)$$

---

[2] Formulas (13-2) and (13-3) are not programmed into financial calculators. However, there is a way to trick your calculator into using its financial functions (designed for fixed-payment annuities) to calculate the future value or present value of a constant-growth annuity. It doesn't save much time, but if you find it satisfying to make a device do something for which it was not intended, here is what you do. Make the following "adjustments" to the values entered for I/Y and PMT .

    FV Calculation: In the I/Y memory, enter the "adjusted" nominal annual rate: $m(\frac{1+i}{1+g} - 1) \times 100\%$. In the PMT memory, enter the "adjusted" payment: $PMT \times (1 + g)^{n-1}$.

    PV Calculation: Use the same I/Y value as for the *FV* calculation above. In the PMT memory, enter the "adjusted" payment: $\frac{PMT}{1 + g}$

Note that these formulas have a structure somewhat similar to formulas (10-1) and (10-2). If you substitute $g = 0$ (no growth in the size of payments) into formulas (13-2) and (13-3), you will obtain formulas (10-1) and (10-2). Hence, we can conclude that (10-1) and (10-2) are the "zero-growth case" of the more general formulas (13-2) and (13-3).

Valuation of Common Shares According to the Valuation Principle, the fair market value of common shares is the present value of all future dividends (discounted at the market's required rate of return). The further we look into the future, the more difficult it becomes to forecast the dividends. Because of this high degree of uncertainty, the rate of return at which investors discount the future dividends is appropriately high.

One approach to stock valuation is to forecast separate dividend growth rates for the short run (three to five years during which forecasts are more reliable) and the long run (where the "crystal ball" becomes cloudy). For example, an analyst might forecast dividends growing at 15% per year for four years and 5% per year thereafter. During the first four years we have a growing annuity; thereafter we have a growing perpetuity. However, at the high discount rates employed in common stock valuation, dividends beyond 30 years contribute little to the present value of the dividend stream.

POINT OF INTEREST

Such a Deal!

In the early 1990s, it was apparent that existing Canada Pension Plan (CPP) contribution levels could not sustain future benefits. In early 1998, the CPP was amended to phase in a dramatic increase in the required contribution rates. The new regulations took contribution rates from 5.85% of Pensionable Earnings in 1998 to 9.9% in 2003. (The rate was only 3.6% in 1966 when the CPP system began.) Pensionable Earnings are basically annual employment or self-employment income falling between $3500 and an upper amount that is inflation-adjusted. In 2009, this upper limit was $46,300. Therefore, if your employment income in 2009 was more than $46,300, you and your employer each paid half of the maximum CPP contribution for 2009 of:

$$0.099 \times (\$46{,}300 - \$3500) = \$4237.20$$

The primary benefit that contributors expect to receive from the CPP is the Retirement Pension. This pension is indexed to the CPI. To be eligible for the maximum CPP pension, you must be age 65 and have made the maximum annual CPP contribution for 83% of the years since 1965 or age 18, whichever is the shorter period. In 2009, the maximum annual CPP Retirement Pension was $10,905.

In this Point of Interest, we will estimate the rate of return that CPP contributions must earn to deliver the expected pension. The assumptions are:

- Shona begins to make maximum CPP contributions ($4237.20) at age 25 in 2009.
- Thereafter, the rate of inflation (and consequently, the annual increase in the CPP contribution and the Retirement Pension) will be 2%.
- Shona will retire and begin drawing the maximum Retirement Pension at age 65.
- Shona will live to age 86 (current life expectancy for a woman aged 65.)
- CPP contributions and pension payments will be made at the end of each year.

If the pension is funded by Shona's contributions,

$$\binom{\text{Future value, at age 65,}}{\text{of CPP contributions}} = \binom{\text{Present value, at age 65,}}{\text{of pension payments}}$$

Since both the contributions and the pension payments grow at the constant rate of inflation, formulas (13-2) and (13-3) must be used for these calculations.

QUESTIONS

1. What is the future value, at age 65, of Shona's CPP contributions if the rate of return they earn is:
   a. 3% compounded annually?
   b. 4% compounded annually?

2. What will be the (indexed) CPP Retirement Pension in Shona's first year of retirement? (The maximum annual CPP Retirement Pension in 2009 was $10,905.)

3. What is the present value, at age 65, of Shona's pension payments if the discount rate is:

 a. 3% compounded annually?

 b. 4% compounded annually?

4. Suppose Shona could take the amounts that she and her employer will contribute to the CPP, and instead invest these amounts to provide for a do-it-yourself pension. What is your *estimate* of the minimum rate of return Shona's investments must earn to provide the same pension payments as we have projected for the CPP Retirement Pension?

5. Are you underwhelmed? (No explanation is required.)

NET @ssets

Life expectancy tables are based on overall population averages for each age group. Your life expectancy may differ from the overall average for your age group due to factors such as genetics, health, gender, and lifestyle. To see how personal factors affect your life expectancy, answer the questions on either of the following Web sites that may be accessed through the textbook's Web site. In Chapter 13 of the Student Edition, find "Longevity Game" or "Life Expectancy Calculator."

Respond to the questions concerning factors that affect your life expectancy. The age you can expect to reach is then calculated automatically. By changing your response to just one question, you can determine that factor's statistical effect on your life expectancy.

EXAMPLE 13.2A **FUTURE VALUE OF GROWING RRSP CONTRIBUTIONS**

Monica intends to make RRSP contributions on February 28 of each year. She plans to contribute $3000 in the first year and increase the contribution by 3% every year thereafter.

a. Rounded to the nearest dollar, how much will she have in her RRSP at the time of her thirtieth contribution if the plan earns 8% compounded annually?

b. What will be the amount of her last contribution?

SOLUTION

a. The amount in the RRSP will be the future value of the 30 contributions. Viewed from the date of the thirtieth payment, the contributions form a constant-growth ordinary simple annuity having

$$PMT = \$3000 \quad i = 8\% \quad n = 30 \quad \text{and} \quad g = 3\%$$

Substitute these values into formula (13-2).

$$FV = PMT\left[\frac{(1+i)^n - (1+g)^n}{i-g}\right]$$
$$= \$3000\left(\frac{1.08^{30} - 1.03^{30}}{0.08 - 0.03}\right)$$
$$= \$3000\left(\frac{10.0626569 - 2.4272625}{0.05}\right)$$
$$= \$458,124$$

Monica will have $458,124 in her RRSP at the time of her thirtieth contribution.

b. The final contribution will be the future value of $3000 after 29 compoundings at 3%.

$$\text{Final contribution} = \$3000(1.03)^{29} = \$7069.70$$

EXAMPLE 13.2B   **AMOUNT REQUIRED TO PURCHASE AN INDEXED ANNUITY**

If money accumulated in an RRSP is used to purchase a fixed payment annuity, the payments will steadily lose purchasing power due to inflation. For this reason, some retirees purchase indexed annuities in which the payments increase at a predetermined rate.

Rounded to the nearest dollar, how much will it cost to purchase a 20-year ordinary annuity making semiannual payments that grow at the rate of 2% compounded semiannually? The first payment is $10,000 and the funds used to purchase the annuity earn 6% compounded semiannually.

SOLUTION

The cost will be the present value of the payments.

The payments form a constant-growth ordinary simple annuity having

$$PMT = \$10,000, \ i = \tfrac{6\%}{2} = 3\% \text{ per half year}, \ n = 2(20) = 40, \text{ and } g = \tfrac{2\%}{2} = 1\% \text{ per half year}$$

Substitute these values into formula (13-3).

$$PV = PMT\left[\frac{1 - (1 + g)^n(1 + i)^{-n}}{i - g}\right]$$

$$= \$10,000\left[\frac{1 - (1.01)^{40}(1.03)^{-40}}{0.03 - 0.01}\right]$$

$$= \$271,789$$

The indexed annuity will cost $271,789.

EXAMPLE 13.2C   **CALCULATING THE INITIAL PAYMENT IN A CONSTANT-GROWTH ANNUITY**

Derek is 30 years old and intends to accumulate $1 million in his RRSP by age 60. He expects his income and annual RRSP contributions to keep pace with inflation, which he assumes will be 2.5% per year. Rounded to the nearest dollar, what will be his initial contribution one year from now if he assumes the RRSP will earn 8% compounded annually?

SOLUTION

$1 million is the future value of a constant-growth ordinary simple annuity having

$$FV = \$1,000,000 \quad i = 8\% \quad n = 30 \quad \text{and} \quad g = 2.5\%$$

Substitute these values into formula (13-2).

$$FV = PMT\left[\frac{(1 + i)^n - (1 + g)^n}{i - g}\right]$$

$$\$1,000,000 = PMT\left(\frac{1.08^{30} - 1.025^{30}}{0.08 - 0.025}\right)$$

$$\$1,000,000 = PMT(144.820)$$

$$PMT = \frac{\$1,000,000}{144.820} = \$6905$$

Derek's initial contribution one year from now will be $6905.

SPREADSHEET STRATEGIES   FV and PV of a Constant-Growth Annuity

Connect provides a partially completed template for calculating the future value and the present value of an ordinary simple constant-growth annuity. In Chapter 13 of the Student Edition, find "FV & PV of Constant-Growth Annuity."

The main features of a completed future value template are presented below. The formulas programmed into cells C13 and C15 are displayed in cells C14 and C16, respectively. Data are entered to solve Example 13.2B. In this example,

we are asked to calculate the amount required to purchase a 20-year ordinary annuity in which semiannual payments start at $10,000 and subsequently grow at the rate of 2% compounded semiannually. The funds earn 6% compounded semiannually. After entering the given values into the yellow input cells, the computed present value immediately appears in the output cell C15. The annuity's future value (which we are not asked for) is also computed in C13.

	A	B	C	D
1				
2	Using a spreadsheet to calculate the present value of a constant-growth annuity.			
3	Example 13.2B:			
4				
5		Nominal annual interest rate, j	6.000%	
6		Nominal annual growth rate	2.000%	
7		Compoundings per year, m	2	
8		Periodic interest rate, i	3.0000%	
9		Periodic growth rate, g	1.0000%	
10		Number of payments, n	40.00	
11		Initial payment, PMT	$10,000.00	
12				
13		Future value, FV	$886,587.03	
14		Formula in cell C13:	=C11*((1+C8)^C10-(1+C9)^C10)/(C8-C9)	
15		Present value, PV	$271,789.32	
16		Formula in cell C15:	=C11*(1-(1+C9)^C10*(1+C8)^(-C10))/(C8-C9)	
17				

The annuity will cost $271,789 (rounded to the nearest dollar.)

CONCEPT QUESTIONS

1. In this section, does constant growth mean that each successive payment increases by the same dollar amount? If not, what does it mean?

2. How would you handle cases where successive annuity payments decrease by the same percentage every payment interval?

EXERCISE 13.2

Spreadsheet template: A partially completed Excel template for calculating the future value and present value of a constant-growth annuity is provided in Connect. You can use this template for many of the problems in Exercise 13.2. In Chapter 13 of the Student Edition, find "FV & PV of Constant-Growth Annuity."

Answers to the odd-numbered problems are at the end of the book.

1. Suppose year-end contributions to an RRSP start at $3000 and increase by 2.5% per year thereafter. What amount will be in the RRSP after 25 years if the plan earns 9% compounded annually?

2. Chantal will make year-end contributions for 30 years to an RRSP earning 8% compounded annually.

   a. How much will she have after 30 years if the annual contribution is $2000?

   b. How much more will she have after 30 years if she increases the contributions by 2% every year?

3. Randall wants to accumulate $750,000 in his RRSP by the end of his 30-year working career. What should be his initial year-end contribution if he intends to increase the contribution by 3% every year and the RRSP earns 10% compounded annually?

4. How much will it cost to purchase a 20-year indexed annuity in which the end-of-quarter payments start at $5000 and grow by 0.5% every quarter? Assume that the money used to purchase the annuity earns 6% compounded quarterly.

5. Ken Tuckie is about to buy a 25-year annuity that will deliver end-of-month payments. The first payment will be $1000. How much more will it cost to index the annuity so that payments grow at the rate of 2.4% compounded monthly? Assume the money used to purchase the annuity earns 5.4% compounded monthly.

6. Mrs. Sippy (age 65) is about to begin receiving a CPP retirement pension of $11,000 per year. This pension is indexed to the Consumer Price Index (CPI). Assume that the annual pension will be paid in a single year-end payment, the CPI will rise 3% per year, and money is worth 6% compounded annually. What is the current economic value of:

   a. 20 years of pension benefits?   **b.** 25 years of pension benefits?

○7. Ida Ho is about to retire from a government job with a pension that is indexed to the Consumer Price Index (CPI). She is 60 years old and has a life expectancy of 25 years. Estimate the current economic value of her pension, which will start at $20,000 per year. For the purpose of this estimation, assume that Ida will draw the pension for 25 years, the annual pension will be paid in a single year-end payment, the CPI will rise 2.5% per year, and money is worth 5% compounded annually. How much of the current economic value comes from indexing?

○8. Della Ware has accumulated $600,000 in her RRSP and is about to purchase a 25-year annuity from which she will receive month-end payments. The money used to purchase the annuity will earn 4.8% compounded monthly.

   a. What will be the monthly payment without indexing?

   b. What will be the initial payment if payments grow by 2.4% compounded monthly?

   c. How long will it be until the monthly payment from the indexed annuity exceeds the monthly payment from the constant-payment annuity?

○9. Dean has already implemented the first stage of his financial plan. Over a 30-year period, he will continue to increase his annual year-end RRSP contributions by 3% per year. His initial contribution was $2000. At the end of the 30 years, he will transfer the funds to an RRIF and begin end-of-month withdrawals that will increase at the rate of 1.8% compounded monthly for 25 years. Assume that his RRSP will earn 9% compounded annually and his RRIF will earn 6% compounded monthly. What will be the size of his initial RRIF withdrawal?

○10. Maritime Bank recently announced that its next semiannual dividend (to be paid six months from now) will be $1.00 per share. A stock analyst's best estimate for the growth in future dividends is 5% compounded semiannually.

   a. If you require a rate of return of 10% compounded semiannually on the stock, what maximum price should you be willing to pay per share? Ignore the present value of dividends beyond a 50-year time horizon.

   b. What price do you obtain if you do not ignore dividends beyond 50 years? (Hint: Use a large value, say 99,999, for n in the present value calculation.)

○11. The dividends on the common shares of Mosco Inc. are forecast to grow at 10% per year for the next five years. Thereafter, the best guess is that the annual dividend will grow at the same 3% annual rate as the nominal GNP. A $2.00 dividend for the past year was recently paid. Assume that the required rate of return is 9% compounded annually. What is the fair market value of the shares if we ignore all dividends beyond a 30-year time horizon?

○12. **Using the Constant-Growth Annuity Chart** The NET @ssets feature at the beginning of this section describes how to access the Constant-Growth Annuity Chart available in this textbook's Web site. Use this chart to answer the following questions. Assume in every case that you make annual end-of-year contributions to an RRSP for 25 years. The RRSP earns 7.5% compounded annually. Compared to a "base case" of constant contributions of $3000, how much larger (in percentage terms) will the value of your RRSP be after 25 years if you increase the payments by:

   a. 1% per year?   **b.** 2% per year?   **c.** 4% per year?

KEY TERMS

Constant-growth annuity **p. 510**   Perpetuity **p. 504**

Ordinary perpetuity **p. 504**   Perpetuity due **p. 504**

SUMMARY OF NOTATION AND KEY FORMULAS

g = Rate of growth in payment size between successive payments

FORMULA (13-1) $PV = \dfrac{PMT}{i}$ Finding the present value of an ordinary perpetuity

FORMULA (13-2) $FV = PMT\left[\dfrac{(1+i)^n - (1+g)^n}{i-g}\right]$ Finding the future value of a constant-growth ordinary annuity

FORMULA (13-3) $PV = PMT\left[\dfrac{1-(1+g)^n(1+i)^{-n}}{i-g}\right]$ Finding the present value of a constant-growth ordinary annuity

REVIEW PROBLEMS

Answers to the odd-numbered review problems are at the end of the book.

1. **(LO1)** If money can earn 6% compounded annually, what percentage more money is required to fund an ordinary perpetuity paying $1000 at the end of every year, than to fund an ordinary annuity paying $1000 per year for 25 years?

2. **(LO1)** A company's preferred shares pay a $1.25 dividend every three months in perpetuity. What is the fair market value of the shares just after payment of a dividend if the rate of return required by the market on shares of similar risk is:

   a. 5% compounded quarterly?

   b. 6% compounded quarterly?

3. **(LO1)** Mr. Larsen's will directed that $200,000 be invested to establish a perpetuity making payments at the end of each month to his wife for as long as she lives and subsequently to the Canadian Heart Foundation. What will the payments be if the funds can be invested to earn 5.4% compounded monthly?

4. **(LO1)** Mrs. McTavish wants to establish an annual $5000 scholarship in memory of her husband. The first scholarship is to be awarded two years from now. If the funds can earn 6.25% compounded annually, what amount must Mrs. McTavish pay now to sustain the scholarship in perpetuity?

○5. **(LO1)** What minimum amount will have to be dedicated today to a fund earning 5.6% compounded quarterly, if the first quarterly payment of $2000 in perpetuity is to occur:

a. Three months from now?

b. Five years from now?

○6. **(LO1)** The common shares of Bancorp Ltd. are forecast to pay annual dividends of $3 at the end of each of the next five years, followed by dividends of $2 per year in perpetuity. What is the fair market value of the shares if the market requires a 10% annually compounded rate of return on shares having a similar degree of risk?

○7. **(LO1)** How much more money is required to fund an ordinary perpetuity than a 25-year ordinary annuity, if the funds can earn 7% compounded quarterly, and both pay $500 monthly?

○8. **(LO1)** Dr. Pollard donated $100,000 to the Canadian National Institute for the Blind. The money is to be used to make semiannual payments in perpetuity (after a period of deferral) to finance the recording of books-on-CD for the blind. The first perpetuity payment is to be made five years from the date of the donation. If the funds are invested at 5% compounded semiannually, what will be the size of the payments?

○9. **(LO1)** What percentage more money is required to fund an ordinary perpetuity than to fund a 30-year ordinary annuity, if the funds can earn 5.8% compounded semiannually? The perpetuity and the annuity each pay $1000 semiannually.

CASE Should You Choose to Start Receiving the CPP Retirement Pension at Age 60 Instead of Age 65?

Subject to certain restrictions, you may elect to start collecting the Canada Pension Plan (CPP) monthly Retirement Pension at any time after you reach age 60. The payments are then reduced by 0.5% for each month the pension is collected before age 65. For example, if the pension starts at age 60, the monthly payment will be decreased by

$$(5 \times 12 \text{ months}) \times (0.5\%) = 30\%.$$

The reduction is permanent, extending to payments after age 65 as well.

In Example 10.3H, we compared the economic values of a pension starting at age 60 and a pension starting at age 65. At that point, we ignored an important feature of the CPP Retirement Pension. The payments are indexed to the cost-of-living—every January the payments are increased by the percent change in the CPI index during a recent one-year period.

After studying constant-growth annuities, we can do a more rigorous analysis by incorporating an estimate of the rate of inflation in future years. Turn back the clock to consider Neil as he approaches age 60 at the end of 2008. The maximum CPP Retirement Pension at age 65 in the year 2009 is $10,905 per year. If Neil elects to start receiving the pension at age 60, it will be 0.7 × $10,905 = $7633.50 per year. In our analysis, we will assume the pension is received as a single payment at each year-end. The payments then form an ordinary annuity. Also assume a 2% annual rise in the Consumer Price Index (CPI) in the years ahead. The CPP pension will then increase by 2% per year.

QUESTIONS

1. Assuming that Neil lives another 21 years (the life expectancy of a 60-year-old male), what is the economic value (at the beginning of 2009) of the reduced pension if money can earn 6% compounded annually?
2. What will Neil's initial pension be if he waits until age 65 to start receiving it?
3. What is the economic value (at the beginning of 2009) of the full pension if Neil receives it for 16 years from age 65 to age 81? Again use 6% compounded annually for the discount rate.
4. Compare the economic values. Which choice should Neil make?
5. Repeat Questions 1, 3, and 4 assuming money can earn only 4.5% compounded annually.
6. The Department of Finance Canada issued an Information Paper in May of 2009 announcing that federal and provincial finance ministers have recommended changes to the Canada Pension Plan. These changes include increasing the early-pension reduction from 0.5% to 0.6% per month. The proposed change would be phased in over a five-year period from 2012 to 2016 inclusive. Repeat Questions 1 and 4, assuming that a 0.6% per month reduction is currently in force.

CHAPTER 14

Loan Amortization; Mortgages

LEARNING OBJECTIVES

After completing this chapter, you will be able to:

LO1 Construct a loan's amortization schedule

LO2 Calculate the principal balance after any payment using both the Prospective Method and the Retrospective Method

LO3 Calculate the final loan payment when it differs from the others

LO4 Calculate the principal and interest components of any payment

LO5 Calculate mortgage payments for the initial loan and its renewals

LO6 Calculate mortgage loan balances and amortization periods to reflect prepayments of principal

LOAN AMORTIZATION IS THE PROCESS of repaying the original principal by equal periodic payments. (The final payment may differ from the others.) Although all payments are the same size, each one consists of a different combination of principal and interest. There are several applications in which we need to separate the principal and interest components of one or more payments. In Sections 1 and 2, you will learn the concepts needed to do these calculations.

The largest single amount most of us will ever borrow is a mortgage loan for the purchase of a home. In 2010, total residential mortgage debt in Canada rose above $1 trillion ($1000 billion)—about $39,000 for every person over the age of 19. This represented 69% of total household debt (mortgage loans, personal loans, line-of-credit loans, and credit-card debt.) Mortgage financing is also very common in the commercial sector. In fact, a higher proportion of commercial properties and residential rental properties have mortgage loans against them than do owner-occupied dwellings. Good management of mortgage debt is a key factor in growing your net worth.

14.1 | LOAN AMORTIZATION

A loan for a major purchase such as a vehicle, machinery, or real estate, is usually set up as a term loan. In a **term loan**, the periodic payment and usually the interest rate are fixed for the term or duration of the loan. If the loan is for the purchase of a vehicle or equipment, the term of the loan is typically three to five years. The payments are calculated so that the loan will be fully repaid (or amortized) at the end of the term.

A loan obtained to finance the purchase of real estate is typically too large for the borrower to repay within five years. Payments are usually calculated to repay the loan over a longer time period (20, 25, 30, or 35 years) called the **amortization period**. But most lenders will agree to fix the interest rate for a maximum period of only five to ten years. Typically, loans secured by real estate (mortgage loans) are set up for a *term* of five or seven years, and an *amortization period* of 25 or 30 years. At the end of the loan's term, the principal balance becomes due. Lenders will normally renew the loan (for the amount of the loan balance) at a new market-based interest rate for another term. Usually, the loan payment is recalculated to maintain the loan on its original amortization path.

AMORTIZATION SCHEDULES

LO1 A **loan amortization schedule** is a table that:

- Breaks down each payment into its interest and principal components, and

- Gives the principal balance outstanding after each payment.

Typical headings for the columns of an amortization schedule are presented in Table 14.1.

Each payment occupies a row in the schedule. The values entered in the last three columns are calculated as follows:

1. Calculate the "Interest portion" of the payment using

$$\text{Interest portion} = i \times \text{Principal balance after the previous payment}$$

where i is the periodic interest rate for one payment interval.

2. Calculate the "Principal portion" of the payment from

$$\text{Principal portion} = PMT - \text{Interest portion}$$

3. Calculate the new "Principal balance" from

$$\text{Principal balance} = \text{Previous principal balance} - \text{Principal portion}$$

TABLE 14.1   Column Headings for an Amortization Schedule

Payment number	Payment ($)	Interest portion ($)	Principal portion ($)	Principal balance ($)
0	—	—	—	Original loan
1				
etc.	etc.			

NET @ssets

An interactive Loan Amortization Chart is provided in the textbook's Web site. In Chapter 14 of the Student Edition, find "Loan Amortization Chart."

The chart has data boxes in which you enter values for key variables. You can either enter the "Loan amount" and then calculate the monthly payment, or you can enter the "Monthly payment" and then calculate the initial amount of the loan. The chart will handle only loans having *monthly* payments and *monthly* compounding of interest. After entering new data, click on the "Calculate" button to generate a new chart.

For loan terms of up to 30 months, the bar chart presents the balance *after* every payment. If you move the cursor over any bar in the chart, the balance (rounded to the nearest dollar) will be displayed. For terms of 31 to 120 months, there is a bar for every second or fourth *payment*. For terms of 121 months to 360 months, there is a bar for each *year* representing the *beginning* balance.

Boxes below the data-entry area display the sum of the payments and the total interest paid over the life of the loan. If you click on the "View Report" button, a window will open showing the complete amortization schedule.

EXAMPLE 14.1A   **CONSTRUCTING A FULL AMORTIZATION SCHEDULE**

Marpole Carpet Cleaning borrowed $7600 from Richmond Credit Union at 8% compounded quarterly. The loan is to be repaid by equal quarterly payments over a two-year term. Construct the amortization schedule for the loan.

SOLUTION

The loan payments form an ordinary simple annuity having

$$PV = \$7600 \quad n = 4(2) = 8 \quad \text{and} \quad i = \tfrac{8\%}{4} = 2\%$$

The payment amount must be calculated before beginning the amortization schedule. Substitute these values into formula (10-2) and solve for *PMT*.

$$PV = PMT\left[\frac{1 - (1 + i)^{-n}}{i}\right]$$

$$\$7600 = PMT\left[\frac{1 - (1.02)^{-8}}{0.02}\right]$$

$$PMT = \frac{\$7600}{7.32548144} = \$1037.474473$$

Rounded to the nearest cent, Marpole's quarterly payment will be $1037.47. Now construct the amortization schedule.

8 I/Y
P/Y 4 ENTER
(making C/Y = P/Y = 4)
8 N
7600 PV
0 FV
CPT PMT
Ans: −1037.474473

Payment number	Payment ($)	Interest portion ($)	Principal portion ($)	Principal balance ($)
0	—	—	—	7600.00
1	1037.47	152.00 ①	885.47 ②	6714.53 ③
2	1037.47	134.29	903.18	5811.35
3	1037.47	116.23	921.24	4890.11
4	1037.47	97.80	939.67	3950.44
5	1037.47	79.01	958.46	2991.98
6	1037.47	59.84	977.63	2014.35
7	1037.47	40.29	997.18	1017.17
8	1037.47	20.34	1017.13	0.04

① **Step 1:** Interest portion $= i \times$ Previous balance
$= 0.02(\$7600)$
$= \$152.00$

② **Step 2:** Principal portion $= PMT -$ Interest portion
$= \$1037.47 - \$152.00$
$= \$885.47$

③ **Step 3:** Balance after payment $=$ Previous balance $-$ Principal portion
$= \$7600.00 - \$885.47$
$= \$6714.53$

The balance after two years does not turn out to be zero. We will now address this point.

The Final Payment in a Loan Amortization Schedule In Example 14.1A, the loan balance at the end of the two-year term was not exactly zero (even though we calculated the payment so that it would pay off the loan after two years.) The 4¢ balance is not a significant amount, but we should aim for utmost precision in financial calculations. Why didn't we get a zero balance? (Give this question some thought before reading on.)

When we make payments in everyday commerce, we do not deal in fractions of a cent. We acknowledged this fact in Example 14.1A when we rounded the loan payment to the nearest cent. But the mathematics tells us that the quarterly payment must be $1037.474473 for eight payments to pay off the loan. Therefore, each payment was actually

$$\$1037.474473 - \$1037.47 = \$0.004473$$

(or 0.4473¢) too small. That shortfall will leave a balance after eight payments of *approximately*

$$8(\$0.004473) = \$0.03578$$

The *precise* balance will be the future value of the eight shortages. That is,

$$\text{Balance} = PMT\left[\frac{(1+i)^n - 1}{i}\right] = \$0.004473\left[\frac{(1.02)^8 - 1}{0.02}\right] = \$0.03839$$

which appears in the amortization table as $0.04 because all dollar amounts are rounded to the nearest cent.

In a case where the calculated payment is rounded *up* to the nearest cent, each actual payment includes a small *over*payment. The balance in the amortization schedule at the end of the loan's term will be a negative amount (equal to the future value of the individual overpayments.) This negative balance represents a refund owed to the borrower.

In practice, lenders adjust the size of the *final* payment to make the final balance precisely zero. In Example 14.1A, the lender would increase the final payment to $1037.51 making the principal portion $1017.17 and the final balance $0.00.

In general, Steps 2 and 3 of the three-step procedure presented earlier in this section must be altered as follows for the *final* payment.

2. The principal portion of the *final* payment is simply the previous principal balance (in order to reduce the new balance to zero).
3. Calculate the final payment using

$$\text{Final payment} = \text{Interest portion} + \text{Principal portion}$$

Using the Texas Instruments BA-II PLUS Amortization Worksheet This worksheet streamlines the calculation of the interest and principal components of a payment in the amortization schedule. Appendix 14A provides instruction on the use of the Amortization Worksheet. (Appendix 14B demonstrates the amortization functions on the Sharp EL-738 calculator.) We will employ the Amortization Worksheet in Example 14.1B.

EXAMPLE 14.1B **CONSTRUCTING A FULL AMORTIZATION SCHEDULE WHERE THE PAYMENTS FORM A GENERAL ANNUITY**

Healey Fishing obtained a $40,000 loan for a major refit of a troller. The loan contract requires seven equal annual payments including interest at 11.5% compounded semiannually. Construct the full amortization schedule for the loan. Calculate the total interest paid over the life of the loan.

SOLUTION

The loan payments form an ordinary *general* annuity in which

$$PV = \$40,000 \quad n = 7 \quad i = \tfrac{11.5\%}{2} = 5.75\% \quad \text{and} \quad c = \tfrac{2}{1} = 2$$

The periodic interest rate that matches the one-year payment interval is

$$i_2 = (1 + i)^c - 1 = 1.0575^2 - 1 = 0.11830625 \text{ per year}$$

Calculate the payment from

$$\$40,000 = \text{Present value of seven payments}$$

$$\$40,000 = PMT\left[\frac{1 - (1.11830625)^{-7}}{0.11830625}\right]$$

$$PMT = \frac{\$40,000}{4.5883725} = \$8717.69$$

11.5	I/Y
P/Y 1	ENTER
C/Y 2	ENTER
7	N
40000	PV
0	FV
CPT	PMT

Ans: −8717.688

Now construct the amortization schedule.

Payment number	Payment ($)	Interest portion ($)	Principal portion ($)	Principal balance ($)
0	—	—	—	40,000.00
1	8717.69	4732.25	3985.44	36,014.56
2	8717.69	4260.75	4456.94	31,557.62
3	8717.69	3733.46 ①	4984.23 ②	26,573.39 ③
4	8717.69	3143.80	5573.89	20,999.50
5	8717.69	2484.37	6233.32	14,766.18
6	8717.69	1746.93	6970.76	7795.42
7	8717.67 ④	922.25	7795.42	0.00
Totals:	61,023.81	21,023.81	40,000.00	

① Interest portion = 0.11830625($31,557.62) = $3733.46

② Principal portion = $8717.69 − $3733.46 = $4984.23

③ Balance after payment = $31,557.62 − $4984.23 = $26,573.39

④ Last payment = $7795.42 + $922.25 = $8717.67

$$\begin{aligned} \text{Total interest paid} &= (\text{Total of payments}) - \$40{,}000 \\ &= 6(\$8717.69) + \$8717.67 - \$40{,}000 \\ &= \$21{,}023.81 \end{aligned}$$

Same *I/Y, P/Y, C/Y, PV*

8717.69 [+/−] [PMT]

- - - - - - - - - - - - - - -

[2nd] [AMORT]

3 [ENTER]

[↓] 3 [ENTER]

[↓] *BAL* = 26,573.39

[↓] *PRN* = −4984.23

[↓] *INT* = −3733.46

PRECISE CALCULATION OF A LOAN'S BALANCE

LO2 In previous chapters we have calculated the balance owed after any payment by using the general principle that:

$$\text{Principal balance} = \left(\begin{array}{c} \text{Present value of the remaining payments} \\ (\text{discounted at the } \textit{contractual rate of interest} \text{ on the loan}) \end{array} \right)$$

This method, based on payments yet to come, is known as the **Prospective Method** for calculating a loan's balance. (The dictionary definition of "prospective" is "concerned with, or applying to, the future.")

We now know that the final payment on a term loan will usually differ from the other payments. Therefore, the Prospective Method for calculating a loan's balance will yield the precisely correct balance *only* if we *either*:

1. Use the *precisely correct* value of the final payment; *or*

2. Assume *all* the remaining payments are equal and use the *non-rounded* value for *n*, the number of remaining payments.

With either approach, the Prospective Method is less straightforward than it initially seemed. In the first approach, we must first determine the size of the final payment, and then calculate the combined present value of the final payment and the other remaining payments. (Later in this section, we will explain how to calculate the value of the final payment without working through the entire amortization schedule.) With the second approach, we must first determine the number of remaining payments, *n*, to several decimal places. Then we use this value for *n* in the present value calculation. (We will demonstrate this approach in Part (b) of Example 14.1C.)

To avoid these "messy" complications, it would be preferable to have an alternative method for calculating a loan's balance that does not depend on the final payment. We now turn our attention to such a method.

LO2 **Retrospective Method for Loan Balances** This name for our alternative method for calculating a loan's balance will make more sense after we develop the underlying concept. The loan balance immediately after any payment is the single amount that will replace all remaining payments. In Figure 14.1, the loan balance at the time of payment number *x* replaces the subsequent *n* − *x* payments. Since

$$\text{Original loan} = \left(\begin{array}{c} \text{Present value of all payments} \\ (\text{discounted at the } \textit{contractual rate of interest} \text{ on the loan}) \end{array} \right)$$

then

$$\begin{pmatrix} \text{Original} \\ \text{loan} \end{pmatrix} = \begin{pmatrix} \text{Present value of} \\ \text{the first } x \text{ payments} \end{pmatrix} + \begin{pmatrix} \text{Present value of the balance} \\ \text{just after the } x\text{th payment} \end{pmatrix}$$

This equation is really a statement that the original loan is economically equivalent to the combination of the first x payments and the balance after the xth payment. The implied focal date is the date of the original loan.

FIGURE 14.1   A Loan Is Equivalent to a Series of Payments and the Principal Balance After the Payments

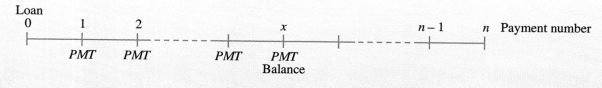

Let us now re-state this economic equivalence, but with the focal date at the xth payment as indicated in Figure 14.2.

$$\begin{pmatrix} \text{Future value of} \\ \text{the original loan} \end{pmatrix} = \begin{pmatrix} \text{Future value of the} \\ \text{first } x \text{ payments} \end{pmatrix} + \text{Balance after the } x\text{th payment}$$

FIGURE 14.2   Placing the Focal Date at the Balance Date

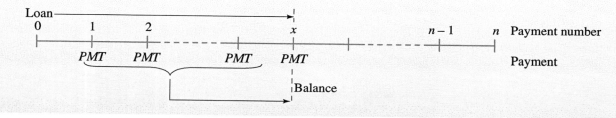

If we then rearrange this equation to isolate the "Balance after the xth payment," we have

$$\text{Balance after the } x\text{th payment} = \begin{pmatrix} \text{Future value of} \\ \text{the original loan} \end{pmatrix} - \begin{pmatrix} \text{Future value of the} \\ \text{first } x \text{ payments} \end{pmatrix}$$

or, with a minor re-wording,

$$\text{Balance} = \begin{pmatrix} \text{Future value of} \\ \text{the original loan} \end{pmatrix} - \begin{pmatrix} \text{Future value of the} \\ \text{payments already made} \end{pmatrix}$$

This method of calculating a loan's balance is based on the payments we see when *looking back* from a focal date coinciding with the balance. A dictionary definition of "retrospective" is "looking back on, or dealing with, the past." Now you see the reason for the name **Retrospective Method**. It is based on payments already made.

EXAMPLE 14.1C   COMPARISON OF PROSPECTIVE AND RETROSPECTIVE METHODS

A $57,000 mortgage loan at 6.9% compounded monthly requires monthly payments during its 20-year amortization period.

a. Calculate the monthly payment rounded to the nearest cent.

b. Calculate the balance after five years using both the Retrospective Method and the Prospective Method.

SOLUTION

The payments form an ordinary simple annuity having

$$PV = \$57{,}000 \quad i = \frac{6.9\%}{12} = 0.575\% \text{ per month} \quad \text{and} \quad n = 12(20) = 240$$

a. Substitute the given values into

$$PV = PMT\left[\frac{1 - (1 + i)^{-n}}{i}\right]$$

giving

$$\$57{,}000 = PMT\left[\frac{1 - (1.00575)^{-240}}{0.00575}\right]$$

Solving for PMT, we obtain $PMT = \$438.50545$ which we round to $438.51.

	6.9	I/Y
	P/Y 12	ENTER
(making $C/Y = P/Y = 12$)		
	240	N
	57000	PV
	0	FV
	CPT	PMT

Ans: -438.50545

b. Retrospective Method:

Balance = Future value of $57,000 − Future value of first 60 payments

Algebraic Approach:

Substitute $i = \frac{6.9\%}{12} = 0.575\%$, $PV = \$57{,}000$, $n = 60$, and $PMT = \$438.51$ into

$$\text{Balance} = PV(1 + i)^n - PMT\left[\frac{(1 + i)^n - 1}{i}\right]$$

$$= \$57{,}000(1.00575)^{60} - \$438.51\left[\frac{(1.00575)^{60} - 1}{0.00575}\right]$$

$$= \$80{,}403.940 - \$31{,}313.079$$

$$= \$49{,}090.86$$

The balance after five years is $49,090.86.

Financial Calculator Approach:

Recall that when you compute [FV] on a financial calculator, you will obtain the future value of an initial single amount stored in [PV] *plus* the future value of [N] payments stored in [PMT]. In the Retrospective Method, you want the future value of the initial loan *minus* the future value of the payments already made. To accomplish this subtraction, simply enter the payment with a negative sign as in the box at the right.

Same *I/Y, P/Y, C/Y, PV*

	60	N
438.51	+/−	PMT
	CPT	FV

Ans: $-49{,}090.86$

This reasoning is consistent with our Cash Flow Sign Convention. Our initial loan is a cash *inflow* (positive). The payments are cash *outflows* (negative). The computed future value (balance) is negative because it represents the single cash *outflow* still required to pay off the loan.

Prospective Method:

After five years, 60 payments have been made and $12(20) - 60 = 180$ payments remain. However the final payment will not be exactly \$438.51 because we rounded the calculated payment (\$438.50545) to the next higher cent. Using the rounded payment, let's calculate the non-integer number of payments for the entire loan. Substitute the given data into formula (10-2n).

$$n = -\frac{\ln\left(1 - \dfrac{i \times PV}{PMT}\right)}{\ln(1 + i)}$$

$$= -\frac{\ln\left(1 - \dfrac{0.00575 \times \$57{,}000}{\$438.51}\right)}{\ln(1.00575)}$$

$$= -\frac{\ln(0.25258261)}{\ln(1.00575)}$$

$$= 239.9946411$$

Same I/Y, P/Y, C/Y PV, FV as in Part (a)

438.51 [+/−] [PMT]

[CPT] [N]

Ans: 239.9946411

To obtain the precisely correct balance after 60 payments using the Prospective Method, we must calculate the present value of the remaining

$$239.9946411 - 60 = 179.9946411 \text{ payments of } \$438.51$$

$$\text{Balance} = PMT\left[\frac{1 - (1 + i)^{-n}}{i}\right]$$

$$= \$438.51\left[\frac{1 - (1.00575)^{-179.9946411}}{0.00575}\right]$$

$$= \$49{,}090.86$$

Same I/Y, P/Y, C/Y
Same PMT, FV

179.9946411 [N]

[CPT] [PV]

Ans: 49,090.86

This is the same answer as we obtained using the Retrospective Method. (If you had used $n = 180$ remaining payments, you would have obtained a balance of \$49,091.70, which is \$0.84 too high.) After comparing the Prospective and Retrospective Methods, you are likely to conclude that the Retrospective Method is both shorter and less prone to user errors. For these reasons, hereafter we will usually employ the Retrospective Method to calculate a loan's balance.

CALCULATING THE FINAL PAYMENT

LO3 In the process of constructing the amortization charts in Examples 14.1A and 14.1B, we noted that the final payment must cover the balance still owed after the second-to-last payment plus the interest on that balance for one payment interval. That is,

$$\left(\begin{array}{c}\text{Final}\\\text{payment}\end{array}\right) = \left(\begin{array}{c}\text{Balance after the}\\\text{second-to-last payment}\end{array}\right) + i \times \left(\begin{array}{c}\text{Balance after the}\\\text{second-to-last payment}\end{array}\right)$$

Since $\left(\begin{array}{c}\text{Balance after the}\\\text{second-to-last payment}\end{array}\right)$ is a common factor on the right side, then

$$\text{Final payment} = (1 + i) \times \left(\begin{array}{c}\text{Balance after the}\\\text{second-to-last payment}\end{array}\right)$$

If the loan payments form a *general* annuity, replace i by i_2, the equivalent periodic rate that matches the payment interval. [Recall that $i_2 = (1 + i)^c - 1$.]

EXAMPLE 14.1D   **CALCULATING A LOAN BALANCE AND THE FINAL PAYMENT**

Meditech Laboratories borrowed $28,000 at 10% compounded quarterly to purchase new testing equipment. Payments of $1500 are made every three months.

a. Calculate the balance after the tenth payment.

b. Calculate the final payment.

SOLUTION

a. The loan payments form an ordinary simple annuity having

$$PV = \$28,000, PMT = \$1500 \text{ (except for the last payment), and } i = \frac{10\%}{4} = 2.5\%$$

The loan in this example has been set up so that the regular payment is a "nice round" easily remembered number. In all likelihood, the final payment will differ substantially from $1500. Consequently, if we use the Prospective Method and assume all payments are the same, any loan balance we calculate will have a significant error. In contrast, if we use the Retrospective Method, we do not need to know either the final payment or the total number of payments.

$$\begin{pmatrix} \text{Balance after} \\ \text{10 payments} \end{pmatrix} = \begin{pmatrix} \text{Future value of \$28,000} \\ \text{after 10 quarters} \end{pmatrix} - \begin{pmatrix} \text{Future value of the} \\ \text{10 payments already made} \end{pmatrix}$$

$$= PV(1 + i)^n - PMT\left[\frac{(1 + i)^n - 1}{i}\right]$$

$$= \$28,000(1.025)^{10} - \$1500\left[\frac{(1.025)^{10} - 1}{0.025}\right]$$

$$= \$35,842.367 - \$16,805.073$$

$$= \$19,037.29$$

10 I/Y
P/Y 4 ENTER
(making C/Y = P/Y = 4)
10 N
28000 PV
1500 +/− PMT
CPT FV
Ans: −19,037.29

b. To calculate the final payment, we need to know the balance after the second-to-last payment. But before we can calculate this balance, we must determine the total number of payments. In other words, this part requires three steps: (1) calculate the number of payments using formula (10-2n), (2) calculate the balance after the second-to-last payment using the Retrospective Method, and (3) calculate the final payment.

$$n = -\frac{\ln\left(1 - \frac{i \times PV}{PMT}\right)}{\ln(1 + i)}$$

$$= -\frac{\ln\left(1 - \frac{0.025 \times \$28,000}{\$1500}\right)}{\ln(1.025)}$$

$$= 25.457357$$

Same I/Y, P/Y, C/Y
Same PV, PMT
0 FV
CPT N
Ans: 25.457357

The loan requires 26 payments. The balance after 25 payments will be

$$\begin{pmatrix} \text{Balance after} \\ \text{25 payments} \end{pmatrix} = \$28,000(1.025)^{25} - \$1500\left[\frac{(1.025)^{25} - 1}{0.025}\right]$$

$$= \$51,910.435 - \$51,236.646$$

$$= \$673.79$$

Same I/Y, P/Y, C/Y
Same PV, PMT
25 N
CPT FV
Ans: −673.79

Final payment $= (1 + i) \times$ Balance after 25 payments

$$= 1.025 \times \$673.79$$

$$= \$690.63$$

> ### TRAP An Incorrect Interpretation of the Fractional Part of "*n*"
>
> In Part (b) of Example 14.1D, it is natural to look at the value of $n = 25.457357$ and wonder if we can obtain the size of the last payment simply by multiplying *PMT* by the fractional part of *n*. Unfortunately, this calculation will give only an approximate value for the amount of the last payment. In Example 14.1D, the actual final payment was $690.63 whereas
>
> $$(\text{Fractional part of } n) \times PMT = 0.457357 \times \$1500 = \$686.04$$
>
> Notice that this amount is neither the final payment ($690.63) nor the principal component of the final payment ($673.79).

PARTIAL AMORTIZATION SCHEDULE

LO1 A particular circumstance may require only a portion of a loan's amortization schedule. Suppose, for example, you need amortization details for the monthly payments made in the fourth year of a five-year loan. The partial schedule needs to include only details of payments 37 to 48 inclusive. The key value you need to get started is the principal balance after the 36th payment. Once you have this value, you can use the same three-step routine that we outlined at the beginning of this section to obtain the interest portion, principal portion, and principal balance for each subsequent payment.

EXAMPLE 14.1E   **A PARTIAL LOAN AMORTIZATION SCHEDULE**

Kimberleigh obtained a loan from her bank for $11,000 at 10.5% compounded monthly to purchase a new car. The monthly payments were set at $250. Construct a partial amortization schedule showing details of the first two payments, Payments 27 and 28, and the last two payments. Calculate the total interest charges.

SOLUTION

The loan payments constitute an ordinary simple annuity in which

$$PV = \$11,000 \quad i = \tfrac{10.5\%}{12} = 0.875\% \quad \text{and} \quad PMT = \$250 \text{ (except for the final payment)}$$

Let us first determine how many payments will be required to pay off the loan. Using formula (10-2*n*),

$$
\begin{aligned}
n &= -\frac{\ln\!\left(1 - \dfrac{i \times PV}{PMT}\right)}{\ln(1 + i)} \\[2mm]
&= -\frac{\ln\!\left(1 - \dfrac{0.00875 \times \$11,000}{\$250}\right)}{\ln(1.00875)} \\[2mm]
&= 55.80
\end{aligned}
$$

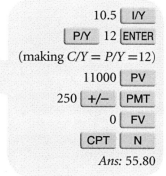

10.5 [I/Y]
[P/Y] 12 [ENTER]
(making $C/Y = P/Y = 12$)
11000 [PV]
250 [+/−] [PMT]
0 [FV]
[CPT] [N]

Ans: 55.80

Therefore, 56 payments are needed to pay off the loan. The last two payments will be Payments 55 and 56.

Notes ①, ②, and ③ under the amortization schedule on the next page present the calculations for obtaining the interest and principal components of the first payment, and the balance after the first payment. In the call-out box to the right of the notes, we show how the same quantities may be computed using the Amortization Worksheet. Similar calculations should be repeated for the second payment.

For an algebraic approach with Payment 27, we first need to determine the balance after 26 payments. Using the Retrospective Method,

$$\begin{pmatrix} \text{Balance after} \\ \text{26 payments} \end{pmatrix} = \begin{pmatrix} \text{Future value of \$11,000} \\ \text{after 26 months} \end{pmatrix} - \begin{pmatrix} \text{Future value of the} \\ \text{26 payments already made} \end{pmatrix}$$

$$= \$11,000(1.00875)^{26} - \$250\left[\frac{(1.00875)^{26} - 1}{0.00875}\right]$$

$$= \$6533.07$$

Knowing this balance, we can now proceed as we did for Payments 1 and 2. (If you use the Amortization Worksheet, you do *not* need to first obtain the balance after Payment 26.)

For an algebraic approach with Payment 55, we first need to determine the balance after 54 payments. Using the Retrospective Method,

$$\begin{pmatrix} \text{Balance after} \\ \text{54 payments} \end{pmatrix} = \begin{pmatrix} \text{Future value of \$11,000} \\ \text{after 54 months} \end{pmatrix} - \begin{pmatrix} \text{Future value of the} \\ \text{54 payments already made} \end{pmatrix}$$

$$= \$11,000(1.00875)^{54} - \$250\left[\frac{(1.00875)^{54} - 1}{0.00875}\right]$$

$$= \$444.74$$

Now the calculations for the last two payments may be completed.

Payment number	Payment ($)	Interest portion ($)	Principal portion ($)	Principal balance ($)
0	—	—	—	11,000.00
1	250	96.25 ①	153.75 ②	10,846.25 ③
2	250	94.90	155.10	10,691.15
.	.	.	.	
.	.	.	.	
26	.	.	.	6533.07
27	250	57.16	192.84	6340.23
28	250	55.48	194.52	6145.71
.	.	.	.	
.	.	.	.	
54	.	.	.	444.74
55	250	3.89	246.11	198.63
56	200.37 ④	1.74	198.63	0.00
Total	13,950.37	2950.37 ⑤	11,000.00	

① Interest portion $= i \times$ Previous balance
   $= 0.00875(\$11,000)$
   $= \$96.25$

② Principal portion $= PMT -$ Interest portion
   $= \$250 - \$96.25$
   $= \$153.75$

③ Balance after payment $=$ Former balance $-$ Principal portion
   $= \$11,000 - \$153.75$
   $= \$10,846.25$

④ Last payment $=$ Balance after 55 payments $\times (1 + i)$
   $= \$198.63(1.00875)$
   $= \$200.37$

⑤ Total interest $=$ Total of payments $-$ Initial loan
   $= 55(\$250) + \$200.37 - \$11,000$
   $= \$2950.37$

Same *I/Y, P/Y, C/Y*

Same *PV, PMT*

- - - - - - - - - - - - - -

2nd AMORT

1 ENTER

↓   1 ENTER

↓   *BAL* $= 10,846.25$

↓   *PRN* $= -153.75$

↓   *INT* $= -96.25$

POINT OF INTEREST

Just When You Thought You Had It All Figured Out ...

Jeff had been haggling with Joe, the car salesperson, for over an hour by the time they agreed on a price for the car Jeff wanted. As Joe started to write up the sale, he asked Jeff what portion of the purchase price he wished to finance. Jeff responded that he would pay cash. Joe gave him a look of disbelief. "Why pay cash? You will be better off putting your money in a GIC earning 5% and borrowing from us at 7.9% to finance the purchase of your car."

"Ya, right!" replied Jeff sarcastically.

"I'll show you," responded Joe. As Joe started to enter numbers into his computer, Jeff thought: "How can this guy make such a preposterous claim? It's a no-brainer!"

Joe's printer started to whirr. "We'll have the analysis in a jiffy."

Jeff, a business graduate from the local college, was actually looking forward to seeing Joe humbled by the self-evident outcome. He leaned forward as Joe laid the printout on his desk.

Joe started to explain. "I chose $10,000 as the amount financed—just for the purpose of discussion. The monthly loan payment for three years would be $312.90. The total of your payments comes to $11,264.40. So the total interest you pay is $1264.40."

Joe continued: "Suppose that you purchase a three-year GIC with the $10,000 you are prepared to pay in a cash deal. After three years it will be worth $11,576.25. So the interest you earn is $1576.25. That's $311.85 more than the interest you pay on the loan! So there's the proof in cold hard numbers." Joe had that look of smug satisfaction as he leaned back in his leather-upholstered chair.

"There's gotta be a mistake," muttered Jeff. He reached for the printout with one hand and his financial calculator with the other. As he started to punch in the numbers, he thought: "Here's where my business math course will really pay off." Jeff first calculated the future value of the GIC at 5% compounded annually and confirmed Joe's number. "At least he got the simple part right," thought Jeff. He then assumed monthly compounding for the 7.9% rate and was surprised to get Joe's figure for the monthly payment. Jeff started to feel a little uneasy since this calculation seemed the most likely point where Joe would make an error. Jeff went on to verify the total interest charged and the interest differential. Joe's figures were correct to the penny.

Jeff stared at his calculator in disbelief. He kept asking himself: "How can it be that you earn more interest on a $10,000 GIC at only 5% compounded annually than you pay on a $10,000 loan at 7.9% compounded monthly?"

QUESTIONS

1. Answer Jeff's vexing question.
2. Prepare a rigorous analysis of the economic gain or loss (in current dollars) from financing $10,000 as proposed by Joe. Assume that money can earn 5% compounded annually.

Connect provides partially completed Excel templates for full and partial loan amortization schedules. Instructions are provided with each template. Go to the Student Edition of Connect and find "Loan Amortization Schedules."

Here we use the template for the partial amortization schedule in Example 14.1E. The completed schedule is presented below. The number of payments required to pay off the loan and the loan balances after the 26th and 54th payments were obtained by calculations separate from the spreadsheet. A sample of the formula used in each column is provided under the schedule.

	A	B	C	D	E	F	G
1							
2	Using a spreadsheet for a Partial Loan Amortization Schedule.						
3	Example 14.1E:						
4							
5			Nominal annual interest rate, *j*			10.500%	
6			Compoundings per year, *m*			12	
7			Payments per year			12	
8			Given periodic rate of interest rate, *i*			0.8750%	
9			Compoundings per payment interval, *c*			1.0000000000	
10			Periodic rate of interest, i_2			0.875000000%	
11			Original loan, *PV*			$11,000.00	
12			Payment, *PMT*			$250.00	
13							
14		*Payment*		*Interest*	*Principal*	*Principal*	
15		*number*	*Payment*	*portion*	*portion*	*balance*	
16		0	– –	– –	– –	$11,000.00	
17		1	$250.00	$96.25	$153.75	$10,846.25	
18		2	$250.00	$94.90	$155.10	$10,691.15	
19							
20		26	– –	– –	– –	$6,533.07	
21		27	$250.00	$57.16	$192.84	$6,340.23	
22		28	$250.00	$55.48	$194.52	$6,145.71	
23							
24		54	– –	– –	– –	$444.74	
25		55	$250.00	$3.89	$246.11	$198.63	
26		56	$200.37	$1.74	$198.63	0.00	
27							
28	Sample Formulas:		Cell E17:	=C17-D17	Cell D17:	=ROUND(F$10*F16,2)	
29			Cell F17:	=F16-E17	Cell C26:	=F25+D26	
30							

EXERCISE 14.1

Spreadsheet templates: Connect provides partially completed Excel templates for full and partial loan amortization schedules. You can use one or the other of these templates in all of the problems in Exercise 14.1. Go to the Student Edition of Connect and find "Loan Amortization Schedules."

Answers to the odd-numbered problems are at the end of the book.

1. Monica bought a $1250 stereo system for 20% down, with the balance to be paid with interest at 15% compounded monthly in six equal monthly payments. Construct the full amortization schedule for the debt. Calculate the total interest paid.

2. Dr. Alvano borrowed $8000 at 8% compounded quarterly to purchase a new X-ray machine for his clinic. The agreement requires quarterly payments during a two-year amortization period. Prepare the full amortization schedule for the loan. Calculate the total interest charges.

∘**3.** Golden Dragon Restaurant obtained a $9000 loan at 9% compounded annually to replace some kitchen equipment. Prepare a complete amortization schedule if the loan is repaid by semiannual payments over a three-year term.

∘**4.** Valley Produce received $50,000 in vendor financing at 7.8% compounded semiannually for the purchase of harvesting machinery. The contract requires equal annual payments for seven years to repay the debt. Construct the amortization schedule for the debt. How much interest will be paid over the seven-year term?

∘**5.** Suppose that the loan in Problem 2 permits an additional prepayment of principal on any scheduled payment date. Prepare another amortization schedule that reflects a prepayment of $1500 with the third scheduled payment.

∘**6.** Suppose that the loan in Problem 4 permits an additional prepayment of principal on any scheduled payment date. Prepare another amortization schedule that reflects a prepayment of $10,000 with the second scheduled payment. How much interest is saved as a result of the prepayment?

∘**7.** Cloverdale Nurseries obtained a $60,000 loan at 7.5% compounded monthly to build an additional greenhouse. Monthly payments were calculated to amortize the loan over six years. Construct a partial amortization schedule showing details of the first two payments, Payments 43 and 44, and the last two payments.

∘**8.** Jean and Walter Pereira financed the addition of a swimming pool using a $24,000 home improvement loan from their bank. Monthly payments were based on an interest rate of 7.2% compounded semiannually and a five-year amortization. Construct a partial amortization schedule showing details of the first two payments, Payments 30 and 31, and the last two payments. What total interest will the Pereiras pay over the life of the loan?

The following problems are variations of the preceding eight problems. The size of the regular loan payment is given instead of the duration of the loan.

9. Monica bought a $1250 stereo system for 20% down and payments of $200 per month (except for a smaller final payment) including interest at 15% compounded monthly. Construct the full amortization schedule for the debt. Calculate the total interest paid.

10. Dr. Alvano borrowed $8000 at 8% compounded quarterly to purchase a new X-ray machine for his clinic. The agreement requires quarterly payments of $1000 (except for a smaller final payment). Prepare the full amortization schedule for the loan. Calculate the total interest charges.

∘**11.** Golden Dragon Restaurant obtained a $9000 loan at 9% compounded annually to replace some kitchen equipment. Prepare a complete amortization schedule if payments of $1800 (except for a smaller final payment) are made semiannually.

∘**12.** Valley Produce received $50,000 in vendor financing at 7.8% compounded semiannually for the purchase of harvesting machinery. The contract requires annual payments of $10,000 (except for a smaller final payment). Construct the complete amortization schedule for the debt. How much interest will be paid over the entire life of the loan?

∘**13.** Suppose that the loan in Problem 10 permits an additional prepayment of principal on any scheduled payment date. Prepare another amortization schedule that reflects a prepayment of $1000 with the third scheduled payment.

∘**14.** Suppose that the loan in Problem 12 permits an additional prepayment of principal on any scheduled payment date. Prepare another amortization schedule that reflects a prepayment of $10,000 with the second scheduled payment. How much interest is saved as a result of the prepayment?

○**15.** Cloverdale Nurseries obtained a $60,000 loan at 7.5% compounded monthly to build an additional greenhouse. Construct a partial amortization schedule for payments of $1000 per month (except for a smaller final payment) showing details of the first two payments, Payments 56 and 57, and the last two payments.

○**16.** Jean and Walter Pereira financed the addition of a swimming pool using a $24,000 home improvement loan from their bank. Monthly payments of $500 (except for a smaller final payment) include interest at 7.2% compounded semiannually. Construct a partial amortization schedule showing details of the first two payments, Payments 28 and 29, and the last two payments. What total interest will the Pereiras pay over the life of the loan?

17. Using the Loan Amortization Chart Follow the instructions in the NET @ssets box at the beginning of Section 14.1 for accessing and using the Loan Amortization Chart in this textbook's Web site. Enter $10,000 for the "Loan amount" and 7.5% for the monthly compounded "Interest rate."

    a. Compare the profiles of the bar charts for loan terms of 30 months and 30 years. Approximately what percentage of the original principal is paid off midway through the term in each case?

    b. Prepare a table presenting the total interest paid over the life of the loan for terms of 5, 10, 15, 20, 25, and 30 years.

    c. Next, vary the "Term in months" to find the term for which the total interest paid over the life of the loan equals:
    (i) the original principal, and   **(ii)** 1.5 times the original principal.

18. Using the Loan Amortization Chart Follow the instructions in the NET @ssets box at the beginning of Section 14.1 for accessing and using the Loan Amortization Chart in this textbook's Web site. Use this chart and its associated report to solve:

    a. Problem 1.   **b.** Problem 7.

14.2 DIRECT CALCULATION OF THE INTEREST AND PRINCIPAL COMPONENTS OF A PAYMENT OR GROUP OF PAYMENTS

LO4 Proper accounting procedures require a business to separate the principal and interest components of payments on amounts borrowed or loaned. Only the interest portion of a loan payment is an accounting expense for the borrower and an accounting revenue for the lender. *Individual* investors must also determine the interest portion of any loan payments they receive in order to report the interest income on their tax returns.

To calculate the total interest in a series of consecutive payments, you do not need to first construct a partial amortization table covering these payments, and then add the individual interest components. A similar statement applies to the total principal in a series of payments. In this section you will learn approaches that are more direct and more efficient.

You already know the basic concepts for calculating the interest and principal components of a *single* payment. That is,

$$\text{Interest component} = i \times \text{Balance after the previous payment}$$

$$\text{Principal component} = PMT - \text{Interest component}$$

Note that you can also obtain the principal component of a payment without first determining the interest component by using the idea:

$$\text{Principal component} = \binom{\text{Balance after the}}{\text{previous payment}} - \binom{\text{Balance after the}}{\text{current payment}}$$

How can you extend the latter idea to obtain the total of the principal components in a group of consecutive payments? The combined effect of these principal components is to reduce the balance from its value just before the first of the payments, to the value just after the last payment in the series. That is,

$$\binom{\text{Total principal in a}}{\text{series of payments}} = \binom{\text{Balance before the}}{\text{first of the payments}} - \binom{\text{Balance after the}}{\text{last of the payments}}$$

Then

$$\binom{\text{Total interest in a}}{\text{series of payments}} = \binom{\text{Total of all the}}{\text{payments in the series}} - \binom{\text{Total principal in the}}{\text{series of payments}}$$

In our example problems, we will normally use the Retrospective Method for calculating loan balances.

EXAMPLE 14.2A **CALCULATING THE INTEREST AND PRINCIPAL COMPONENTS OF A SINGLE PAYMENT AND OF A GROUP OF CONSECUTIVE PAYMENTS**

A $9500 personal loan at 7.5% compounded monthly is to be repaid over a four-year term by equal monthly payments.

a. Calculate the interest and principal components of the twenty-ninth payment.

b. How much interest will be paid in the second year of the loan?

SOLUTION

The loan payments form an ordinary simple annuity with

$$PV = \$9500 \quad n = 12(4) = 48 \quad \text{and} \quad i = \tfrac{7.5\%}{12} = 0.625\%$$

a. The size of the loan payments must be obtained before any balances can be calculated.

Solve for *PMT* in

$$PV = PMT\left[\frac{1 - (1 + i)^{-n}}{i}\right]$$

$$\$9500 = PMT\left[\frac{1 - (1.00625)^{-48}}{0.00625}\right]$$

$$= PMT(41.35837)$$

$$PMT = \frac{\$9500}{41.35837} = \$229.6996$$

7.5	I/Y
P/Y 12	ENTER
(making C/Y = P/Y = 12)	
48	N
9500	PV
0	FV
CPT	PMT
Ans: −229.6996	

Round the payment to $229.70.

We next want

$$\binom{\text{Interest component}}{\text{of Payment 29}} = i \times \binom{\text{Balance after}}{\text{28 payments}}$$

Using the Retrospective Method to calculate the balance after 28 payments,

$$\begin{pmatrix}\text{Balance after}\\28\text{ payments}\end{pmatrix}=\begin{pmatrix}\text{Future value of}\\\$9500\text{ after }28\text{ months}\end{pmatrix}-\begin{pmatrix}\text{Future value of the }28\\\text{payments already made}\end{pmatrix}$$

$$= PV(1+i)^n - PMT\left[\frac{(1+i)^n-1}{i}\right]$$

$$= \$9500(1.00625)^{28} - \$229.70\left[\frac{(1.00625)^{28}-1}{0.00625}\right]$$

$$= \$11{,}310.678 - \$7004.844$$

$$= \$4305.83$$

Same *I/Y, C/Y, P/Y, PV*

28 [N]
229.70 [+/–] [PMT]
[CPT] [FV]
Ans: −4305.83

Hence,

$$\begin{pmatrix}\text{Interest component}\\\text{of Payment 29}\end{pmatrix}=0.00625\times\$4305.83=\$26.91$$

and

$$\text{Principal component} = PMT - \text{Interest component}$$
$$= \$229.70 - \$26.91$$
$$= \$202.79$$

b. $$\text{Total }interest\text{ paid in Year 2} = 12(PMT) - \text{Total }principal\text{ paid in Year 2}$$

where

$$\text{Total }principal\text{ paid in Year 2} = \text{Balance after Year 1} - \text{Balance after Year 2}$$
$$=\begin{pmatrix}\text{Balance after}\\12\text{ payments}\end{pmatrix}-\begin{pmatrix}\text{Balance after}\\24\text{ payments}\end{pmatrix}$$

Use the Retrospective Method to calculate both balances.

$$\begin{pmatrix}\text{Balance after}\\12\text{ payments}\end{pmatrix}=\begin{pmatrix}\text{Future value of}\\\$9500\text{ after }12\text{ months}\end{pmatrix}-\begin{pmatrix}\text{Future value of the }12\\\text{payments already made}\end{pmatrix}$$

$$= \$9500(1.00625)^{12} - \$229.70\left[\frac{(1.00625)^{12}-1}{0.00625}\right]$$

$$= \$7384.36$$

Same *I/Y, P/Y, C/Y*
Same *PV, PMT*
12 [N]
[CPT] [FV]
Ans: −7384.36

$$\begin{pmatrix}\text{Balance after}\\24\text{ payments}\end{pmatrix}=\begin{pmatrix}\text{Future value of}\\\$9500\text{ after }24\text{ months}\end{pmatrix}-\begin{pmatrix}\text{Future value of the }24\\\text{payments already made}\end{pmatrix}$$

$$= \$9500(1.00625)^{24} - \$229.70\left[\frac{(1.00625)^{24}-1}{0.00625}\right]$$

$$= \$5104.47$$

Same *I/Y, P/Y, C/Y*
Same *PV, PMT*
24 [N]
[CPT] [FV]
Ans: −5104.47

Therefore,

   Total principal paid in Year 2 = $7384.36 − $5104.47 = $2279.89

and

   Total interest paid in Year 2 = 12($229.70) − $2279.89 = $476.51

Using the Texas Instruments BA-II PLUS Amortization Worksheet This worksheet streamlines the calculation of the interest and principal components of a single payment, or of a group of consecutive payments. The worksheet will be employed for the financial calculator solutions in Examples 14.2B and 14.2C.

EXAMPLE 14.2B   **INTEREST AND PRINCIPAL COMPONENTS OF LOAN PAYMENTS THAT FORM A GENERAL ANNUITY**

The monthly payments on a $10,000 loan at 7% compounded semiannually are $300. How much will Payments 21 to 30 inclusive reduce the principal balance? What is the total interest in these payments?

SOLUTION

The loan payments form an ordinary *general* annuity having

$$PV = \$10,000, PMT = \$300 \text{ (except for the final payment)}, i = \frac{7\%}{2} = 3.5\%, \text{ and}$$

$$c = \frac{\text{Number of compoundings per year}}{\text{Number of payments per year}} = \frac{2}{12} = 0.1\overline{6}$$

We must use the periodic rate that matches the one-month payment interval.

$$i_2 = (1 + i)^c - 1 = 1.035^{0.1\overline{6}} - 1 = 0.0057500395$$

Reduction in principal = Balance after Payment 20 − Balance after Payment 30

Use the Retrospective Method to calculate both balances.

$$\begin{pmatrix} \text{Balance after} \\ \text{20 payments} \end{pmatrix} = \begin{pmatrix} \text{Future value of} \\ \$10,000 \text{ after 20 months} \end{pmatrix} - \begin{pmatrix} \text{Future value of the 20} \\ \text{payments already made} \end{pmatrix}$$

$$= \$10,000(1.0057500395)^{20} - \$300 \left[\frac{(1.0057500395)^{20} - 1}{0.0057500395} \right]$$

$$= \$4875.71$$

$$\begin{pmatrix} \text{Balance after} \\ \text{30 payments} \end{pmatrix} = \begin{pmatrix} \text{Future value of} \\ \$10,000 \text{ after 30 months} \end{pmatrix} - \begin{pmatrix} \text{Future value of the 30} \\ \text{payments already made} \end{pmatrix}$$

$$= \$10,000(1.0057500395)^{30} - \$300 \left[\frac{(1.0057500395)^{30} - 1}{0.0057500395} \right]$$

$$= \$2084.60$$

Therefore,

$$\text{Reduction in principal} = \$4875.71 - \$2084.60 = \$2791.11$$

and

$$\text{Total interest paid} = 10(\$300.00) - \$2791.11 = \$208.89$$

7	I/Y
P/Y 12	ENTER
C/Y 2	ENTER
10000	PV
300 +/−	PMT

	2nd	AMORT
	21	ENTER
	30	ENTER
↓	BAL =	2,084.60
↓	PRN =	−2,791.11
↓	INT =	−208.89

LO4   Interest and Principal Components of Investment-Annuity Payments We normally think of the purchase of an annuity from a financial institution as an investment. The principal amount of the investment and the interest it earns generate the future stream of annuity payments. But the size and composition of the payments are no different if we take the following view of the transaction. In effect, the purchaser of the annuity "lends" the principal amount to the financial institution at the rate of interest earned by the annuity. The subsequent annuity payments repay the "loan." Therefore, we can use the concepts developed for loan payments to calculate an annuity's principal balance at any point, and to separate annuity payments into interest and principal components.

EXAMPLE 14.2C **CALCULATING THE INTEREST AND PRINCIPAL COMPONENTS OF PAYMENTS IN AN INVESTMENT ANNUITY**

Joanna purchased a 20-year annuity with $100,000 accumulated in her RRSP. She receives equal payments at the end of every calendar quarter. The interest rate earned by the annuity is 5.6% compounded quarterly.

a. Calculate the interest component of the 15th payment.

b. Of the payments received in the 10th year, what dollar amount represents the recovery of principal from her initial investment of $100,000?

SOLUTION

a. We must first determine the size of the quarterly payment.

Substitute $PV = \$100,000$, $n = 20(4) = 80$, and $i = \frac{5.6\%}{4} = 1.4\%$ into formula (10-2).

$$\$100,000 = PMT\left[\frac{1 - (1.014)^{-80}}{0.014}\right]$$
$$= PMT(47.941138)$$
$$PMT = \$2085.8913$$

Round PMT to $2085.89.

$$\binom{\text{Interest component}}{\text{of Payment 15}} = i \times \binom{\text{Balance after}}{14 \text{ payments}}$$

Using the Retrospective Method,

$$\binom{\text{Balance after}}{14 \text{ payments}} = \binom{\text{Future value of}}{\$100,000 \text{ after 14 quarters}} - \binom{\text{Future value of the 14}}{\text{payments already made}}$$
$$= \$100,000(1.014)^{14} - \$2085.89\left[\frac{(1.014)^{14} - 1}{0.014}\right]$$
$$= \$89,472.84$$

Hence,

Interest component of Payment 15 = $0.014 \times \$89,472.84 = \$1252.62$

b. Payments 37 to 40 inclusive will be received in the 10th year.

$$\binom{\text{Total principal in}}{\text{Payments 37 to 40}} = \binom{\text{Balance after}}{36 \text{ payments}} - \binom{\text{Balance after}}{40 \text{ payments}}$$

where

$$\binom{\text{Balance after}}{36 \text{ payments}} = \binom{\text{Future value of}}{\$100,000 \text{ after 36 quarters}} - \binom{\text{Future value of the 36}}{\text{payments already made}}$$
$$= \$100,000(1.014)^{36} - \$2085.89\left[\frac{(1.014)^{36} - 1}{0.014}\right]$$
$$= \$68,176.99$$

Similarly, the balance after 40 payments is $63,555.41. Therefore,

Principal received in Year 10 = $\$68,176.99 - \$63,555.41 = \$4621.58$

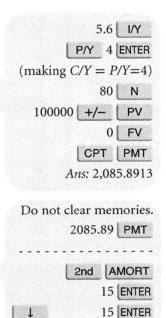

5.6 **I/Y**
P/Y 4 **ENTER**
(making $C/Y = P/Y = 4$)
80 **N**
100000 **+/-** **PV**
0 **FV**
CPT **PMT**
Ans: 2,085.8913

Do not clear memories.
2085.89 **PMT**
- - - - - - - - - - - - -
2nd **AMORT**
15 **ENTER**
↓ 15 **ENTER**
↓ $BAL = -88,639.57$
↓ $PRN =$ 833.27
↓ $INT =$ 1,252.62

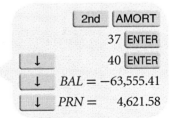

2nd **AMORT**
37 **ENTER**
↓ 40 **ENTER**
↓ $BAL = -63,555.41$
↓ $PRN =$ 4,621.58

SPREADSHEET STRATEGIES Calculating Interest and Principal Components

Connect provides a partially completed template for calculating the interest and principal components of a single payment in an annuity, or of a group of consecutive annuity payments. Go to the Student Edition of Connect and find "CUMIPMT & CUMPRINC for Any Annuity." The first page of this workbook discusses Excel's CUMIPMT and CUMPRINC functions.

We will use the CUMIPMT & CUMPRINC template here to answer Part b of Example 14.2A. In this example, we are asked to determine the total interest paid in the second year of a $9500 loan at 7.5% compounded monthly. The loan is to be repaid by equal monthly payments over a four-year term. The main features of a completed template are presented below. The formulas programmed into cells C11, C19, and C21 are displayed in cells C12, C20, and C22, respectively. After entering the known values in the yellow input cells, the answer for the interest paid in Year 2 ($476.51) appears in C19 and for the principal paid in Year 2 ($2279.88) appears in C21.

	A	B	C	D
1				
2		Using a spreadsheet to calculate interest and principal		
3		components of a single payment or a group of payments.		
4		Example 14.2A, Part b:		
5			.	
6		Nominal annual interest rate, j	7.500%	
7		Compoundings per year, m	12	
8		Given periodic rate of interest, i	0.6250%	
9		Payments per year	12	
10		Compoundings per payment interval, c	1.0000000000	
11		Periodic rate of interest, i_2 or *rate*	0.625000000%	
12		Formula in cell C11:	=(1+C8)^C10–1	
13		Number of payments, n or *nper*	48	
14		Initial principal, *PV* or *pv*	$9,500.00	
15		First payment #, *start_period*	13	
16		Final payment #, *end_period*	24	
17		Annuity *type*	0	
18				
19		CUMIPMT*(rate, nper, pv, start_period, end_period, type)*	-$476.51	
19		Formula in cell C19:	=CUMIPMT(C11,C13,C14,C15,C16,C17)	
21		CUMPRINC*(rate, nper, pv, start_period, end_period, type)*	-$2,279.88	
22		Formula in cell C21:	=CUMPRINC(C11,C13,C14,C15,C16,C17)	

Note: Part a of Example 14.2A asks for the interest and principal components of Payment 29. These may be quickly computed by entering "29" in both cells C15 and C16.

CONCEPT QUESTIONS

1. Will a loan's balance midway through its amortization period be (pick one):
   (i) more than   **(ii)** less than   or   **(iii)** equal to half of the original principal? Explain.

2. If the loan payments and interest rate remain unchanged, will it take longer to reduce a loan's balance from $20,000 to $10,000 than to reduce the balance from $10,000 to $0? Explain briefly.

3. The calculated monthly payment on a loan amortized over five years is rounded up by 0.2 cents to get to the nearest cent.
   a. Will the adjusted final payment be more than or less than the regular payment?
   b. Will the difference between the regular and the final payment be (pick one):
   (i) more than **(ii)** less than or **(iii)** equal to 0.2 cents × 60 = 12 cents? Explain.

4. The calculated monthly payment on a loan amortized over 10 years is rounded down by 0.3 cents to get to the nearest cent.
   a. Will the adjusted final payment be more than or less than the regular payment?
   b. Will the difference between the regular and the final payment be (pick one):
   (i) more than **(ii)** less than or **(iii)** equal to 0.3 cents × 120 = 36 cents? Explain.

5. A loan has a 10-year amortization period. If the interest rate is fixed, will the principal repaid in the third year be (pick one):
   (i) more than **(ii)** less than or **(iii)** equal to the principal repaid in the seventh year? Explain.

6. A loan has a five-year amortization period. If the interest rate is fixed, will the interest paid in the fourth year be (pick one):
   (i) more than **(ii)** less than or **(iii)** equal to the interest paid in the second year? Explain.

7. Loan A is for $20,000 and Loan B is for $10,000. Both have the same interest rate and amortization period. Will the total interest paid on Loan A be (pick one):
   (i) more than **(ii)** less than or **(iii)** equal to twice the total interest paid on Loan B? Explain.

EXERCISE 14.2

Connect

Spreadsheet templates: Connect provides a partially completed Excel template for calculating the principal and interest components of a single annuity payment or of a group of consecutive payments. You can use this template in many of the problems in Exercise 14.2. (You cannot use the template for a problem in which you are given the payment but not the number of payments.) Go to the Student Edition of Connect and find "CUMIPMT & CUMPRINC for Any Annuity."

Answers to the odd-numbered problems are at the end of the book.

In problems throughout this Exercise, round the calculated loan payments to the nearest cent before going on to calculate loan balances and/or interest and principal components.

1. A $40,000 loan at 6.6% compounded monthly will be repaid by monthly payments over ten years.
   a. Calculate the interest component of Payment 35.
   b. Calculate the principal component of Payment 63.
   c. Calculate the reduction of principal in Year 1.
   d. Calculate the reduction of principal in Year 10.

2. Monthly payments are required on a $45,000 loan at 6.0% compounded monthly. The loan has an amortization period of 15 years.
   a. Calculate the interest component of Payment 137.
   b. Calculate the principal component of Payment 76.
   c. Calculate the interest paid in Year 1.
   d. Calculate the interest paid in Year 14.

3. The interest rate on a $14,000 loan is 8.4% compounded semiannually. Semiannual payments will pay off the loan in seven years.
    a. Calculate the interest component of Payment 10.
    b. Calculate the principal component of Payment 3.
    c. Calculate the interest paid in Year 6.
    d. How much do Payments 3 to 6 inclusive reduce the principal balance?

4. A five-year loan of $25,000 at 7.2% compounded quarterly requires quarterly payments.
    a. Calculate the interest component of Payment 10.
    b. Calculate the principal component of Payment 13.
    c. Calculate the total interest in Payments 5 to 10 inclusive.
    d. Calculate the principal paid in Year 4.

5. A $125,000 loan at 6.0% compounded semiannually will be repaid by monthly payments over a 20-year amortization period.
    a. Calculate the interest component of Payment 188.
    b. Calculate the principal component of Payment 101.
    c. Calculate the reduction of principal in Year 1.
    d. Calculate the reduction of principal in Year 20.

6. Semiannual payments are required on an $80,000 loan at 8.0% compounded annually. The loan has an amortization period of 15 years.
    a. Calculate the interest component of Payment 5.
    b. Calculate the principal component of Payment 17.
    c. Calculate the interest paid in Year 1.
    d. Calculate the interest paid in Year 14.

7. The interest rate on a $50,000 loan is 7.6% compounded semiannually. Quarterly payments will pay off the loan in ten years.
    a. Calculate the interest component of Payment 8.
    b. Calculate the principal component of Payment 33.
    c. Calculate the total interest in Payments 21 to 30 inclusive.
    d. Calculate the reduction of principal in Year 3.

8. A five-year loan of $20,000 at 6.8% compounded quarterly requires monthly payments.
    a. Calculate the interest component of Payment 47.
    b. Calculate the principal component of Payment 21.
    c. Calculate the interest paid in Year 2.
    d. How much do Payments 40 to 45 inclusive reduce the principal balance?

9. The monthly payments on a $15,000 loan at 6.0% compounded monthly are $275.
    a. Calculate the interest component of Payment 13.
    b. Calculate the principal component of Payment 44.
    c. Calculate the final payment.

10. Quarterly payments of $3000 are required on an $80,000 loan at 8.0% compounded quarterly.
    a. Calculate the interest component of Payment 30.
    b. Calculate the principal component of Payment 9.
    c. Calculate the final payment.

11. The interest rate on a $100,000 loan is 7.2% compounded semiannually. The monthly payments on the loan are $700.

   a. Calculate the interest component of Payment 221.

   b. Calculate the principal component of Payment 156.

   c. Calculate the final payment.

12. A $30,000 loan at 6.7% compounded annually requires monthly payments of $450.

   a. Calculate the interest component of Payment 29.

   b. Calculate the principal component of Payment 65.

   c. Calculate the final payment.

13. A $37,000 loan at 8.2% compounded semiannually is to be repaid by equal semiannual payments over 10 years.

   a. What will be the principal component of the sixth payment?

   b. What will be the interest component of the sixteenth payment?

   c. How much will Payments 6 to 15 inclusive reduce the principal?

   d. How much interest will be paid in the third year?

   e. What will be the final payment?

14. A 10-year annuity providing a rate of return of 5.6% compounded quarterly was purchased for $25,000. The annuity makes payments at the end of each quarter.

   a. How much of the twenty-fifth payment is interest?

   b. What is the principal portion of the thirteenth payment?

   c. What is the total interest in Payments 11 to 20 inclusive?

   d. How much is the principal reduction in the second year?

   e. What is the final payment?

○15. Guy borrowed $8000 at 7.8% compounded monthly and agreed to repay the loan in equal quarterly payments over four years.

   a. How much of the fifth payment will be interest?

   b. What will be the principal component of the eleventh payment?

   c. How much interest will be paid by Payments 5 to 12 inclusive?

   d. How much will the principal be reduced in the second year?

   e. What will be the final payment?

○16. A 25-year annuity was purchased with $225,000 that had accumulated in a Registered Retirement Savings Plan (RRSP). The annuity provides a semiannually compounded rate of return of 5.2% and makes equal month-end payments.

   a. What amount of principal will be included in Payment 206?

   b. What will be the interest portion of Payment 187?

   c. How much will Payments 50 to 100 inclusive reduce the principal balance?

   d. How much interest will be paid in the fourteenth year?

   e. What will be the final payment?

Problems 17 to 20 are variations of Problems 13 to 16 respectively. The size of the regular payment is given instead of the duration of the loan or investment annuity.

17. A $37,000 loan at 8.2% compounded semiannually is to be repaid by semiannual payments of $2500 (except for a smaller final payment).

    a. What will be the principal component of the sixteenth payment?

    b. What will be the interest portion of the sixth payment?

    c. How much will Payments 8 to 14 inclusive reduce the principal balance?

    d. How much interest will be paid in the fifth year?

    e. What will be the final payment?

18. An annuity providing a rate of return of 5.6% compounded quarterly was purchased for $27,000. The annuity pays $800 at the end of each quarter (except for a smaller final payment).

    a. How much of the sixteenth payment is interest?

    b. What is the principal portion of the thirty-third payment?

    c. What is the total interest in Payments 20 to 25 inclusive?

    d. How much will the principal be reduced by payments in the sixth year?

    e. What will be the final payment?

○19. Guy borrowed $8000 at 7.8% compounded monthly and agreed to make quarterly payments of $500 (except for a smaller final payment).

    a. How much of the eleventh payment will be interest?

    b. What will be the principal component of the sixth payment?

    c. How much interest will be paid by Payments 3 to 9 inclusive?

    d. How much will the principal be reduced in the third year?

    e. What will be the final payment?

○20. An annuity paying $1400 at the end of each month (except for a smaller final payment) was purchased with $225,000 that had accumulated in an RRSP. The annuity provides a semiannually compounded rate of return of 5.2%.

    a. What amount of principal will be included in Payment 137?

    b. What will be the interest portion of Payment 204?

    c. How much will the principal be reduced by Payments 145 to 156 inclusive?

    d. How much interest will be paid in the twentieth year?

    e. What will be the final payment?

○21. Ms. Esperanto obtained a $40,000 home equity loan at 7.5% compounded monthly.

    a. What will she pay monthly if the amortization period is 15 years?

    b. How much of the payment made at the end of the fifth year will go towards principal and how much will go towards interest?

    c. What will be the balance on the loan after five years?

    d. How much interest did she pay during the fifth year?

○22. Elkford Logging's bank will fix the interest rate on a $60,000 loan at 8.1% compounded monthly for the first four-year term of an eight-year amortization period. Monthly payments are required on the loan.

    a. If the prevailing interest rate on four-year loans at the beginning of the second term is 7.5% compounded monthly, what will be the monthly payments for the last four years?

    b. What will be the interest portion of the twenty-third payment?

    c. Calculate the principal portion of the fifty-third payment.

•**23.** Christina has just borrowed $12,000 at 9% compounded semiannually. Since she expects to receive a $10,000 inheritance in two years when she turns 25, she has arranged with her credit union to make monthly payments that will reduce the principal balance to exactly $10,000 in two years.

    a. What monthly payments will she make?

    b. What will be the interest portion of the ninth payment?

    c. Determine the principal portion of the sixteenth payment.

•**24.** Elkford Logging's bank will fix the interest rate on a $60,000 loan at 8.1% compounded monthly for the first four years. After four years, the interest rate will be fixed at the prevailing five-year rate. Monthly payments of $800 (except for a smaller final payment) are required on the loan.

    a. If the interest rate after four years is 7.5% compounded monthly, when will the loan be paid off?

    b. What will be the amount of the final payment?

    c. What is the interest portion of the thirty-second payment?

    d. Calculate the principal portion of the fifty-eighth payment.

25. **Using the Loan Amortization Chart** Follow the instructions in the NET @ssets box at the beginning of Section 14.1 for accessing and using the Loan Amortization Chart in this textbook's Web site. Use this chart and its associated report to solve:

    a. Problem 21.   **b.** Problem 22.

26. **Using the Composition of Loan Payments Chart** An interactive chart for investigating the composition of loan payments is provided in the textbook's Web site. In Chapter 14 of the Student Edition, find "Composition of Loan Payments."

    The chart provides cells for entering the essential information about a loan (*PV, j, m, PMT*, and payments/year). You can then compare the composition (interest and principal components) of any two payments. Simply enter the serial numbers of the two payments and then click on the "Submit" button. Two bar diagrams provide a visual comparison of the interest and principal components. The actual numerical values are also displayed.

    Consider a $120,000 mortgage loan at 6.5% compounded semiannually. Monthly payments of $800 will pay off the loan in 25 years and 4 months.

    a. How much more interest is paid by the 20th payment than the 220th payment?

    b. How long does it take before the interest component of a payment drops below 50%?

    c. Which payment number is closest to being comprised of:
        (i) 75% interest?   **(ii)** 25% interest?

    d. Which payment number comes closest to having a mix of principal and interest that is the opposite of the first payment's mix?

    e. Which payment number comes closest to having double the principal component of the 5th payment?

    f. Which payment number comes closest to having half the interest component of the 10th payment?

connect

connect

14.3 MORTGAGE LOANS: FUNDAMENTALS

BASIC CONCEPTS AND DEFINITIONS

A mortgage loan is a loan secured by some *physical* property. Often the borrowed money is used to purchase the property. If the property securing the loan is not real estate, the mortgage is called a *chattel* mortgage. This section will deal only with mortgage loans secured by real property.

The **face value** of the mortgage is the original principal amount that the borrower promises to repay. In legal language, the borrower is called the **mortgagor** and the lender is called the **mortgagee**. The mortgage contract sets out the terms and conditions of the loan. It also specifies the lender's remedies should the borrower default on repayment of the loan. The key remedy is the ultimate power to foreclose on the property and cause it to be sold to recover the amounts owed. At the time a mortgage loan is granted, the lender registers the mortgage on the title of the property at the provincial government's land titles office. Anyone can search the title to determine potential claims against the property.

Even though a homeowner may already have a mortgage loan, the remaining equity in the home can sometimes be used as security for another mortgage loan. The second lender's claim will rank behind the existing claim of the first lender. If the borrower defaults on the first mortgage loan, the first lender's claim must be satisfied before any claim of the second lender. Because of this ranking of the claims, the existing mortgage is referred to as the *first mortgage* and the additional mortgage as the *second mortgage*. Since a second mortgage lender is exposed to greater risk, the interest rate on a second mortgage is significantly higher than the rate on a first mortgage. Loans advertised by financial institutions as "home equity loans" or "home improvement loans" will often be secured by a second mortgage.

The most common amortization periods for mortgage loans are 25 and 30 years. However, a lender will usually commit to a fixed interest rate for only a shorter period or term. The **term** of a mortgage loan is the length of time from the date on which the loan is advanced to the date on which the remaining principal balance is due and payable. Most institutional lenders offer terms of six months to seven years. At the expiry of the loan's term, the lender will normally renew the loan for another term, but at the prevailing market rate of interest on the date of renewal. The payments are adjusted so that the borrower continues with the original amortization period but at the new interest rate.

CALCULATING THE PAYMENT AND BALANCE

LO5 The federal *Interest Act* requires that the mortgage contract "contains a statement showing … the rate of interest chargeable, calculated yearly or half-yearly, not in advance." In our terminology, the interest rate must be disclosed as the equivalent semiannually compounded nominal rate or the equivalent annually compounded rate.[1] The semiannually compounded rate has become the industry standard for disclosure in the mortgage contract. Mortgage interest rates advertised by most financial institutions are also semiannually compounded rates (even though the compounding frequency is not usually stated). Most mortgage loans are set up for monthly payments. With interest compounded semiannually, the monthly payments form an ordinary *general* annuity having

$$c = \frac{\text{Number of compoundings per year}}{\text{Number of payments per year}} = \frac{2}{12} = \frac{1}{6} = 0.1\overline{6}$$

---

[1] The *Interest Act* makes the lender liable for a very severe penalty for failing to disclose the rate of interest as required by the Act. In that event, the Interest Act states that "no interest whatever shall be chargeable, payable, or recoverable, on any part of the principal money advanced." The borrower would be entitled to a refund of any interest already paid and consequently would have the loan on an interest-free basis.

The mortgage interest rates quoted by a minority of credit unions and a majority of independent mortgage brokers are monthly compounded rates. Monthly payments then form an ordinary *simple* annuity.

Most mortgage lenders will agree to semi-monthly, biweekly, or weekly payments instead of monthly payments. For the *same dollar total* of mortgage payments in a year, you will pay off more principal if you spread the total over more frequent smaller payments than over less frequent larger payments. With more frequent smaller payments, money is (on average) paid *sooner* resulting in *earlier* reduction of principal and *lower* subsequent interest charges.

Usually the borrower chooses a standard amortization period of 15, 20, 25, 30, or 35 years. The payments for the initial term are then calculated *as though* the interest rate is fixed for the *entire* amortization period. Occasionally, the borrower has a preference for a particular payment size. As long as the resulting amortization period is no more than 35 years, most mortgage lenders will agree to such a proposal.

The principal balance on the mortgage loan after any payment may be calculated using either the Prospective Method or (preferably) the Retrospective Method. The balance at the end of a mortgage's term becomes, in effect, the beginning loan amount for the next term. The lender calculates a new payment size based on current interest rates and (normally) a continuation of the original amortization period. Part (b) of Example 14.3A demonstrates this procedure.

The principal and interest components of any mortgage payment may be calculated as described in Section 14.2 for other term loans. Particularly when the amortization period is more than 20 years, the payments in the first few years are primarily interest. Consider a mortgage loan at 8.5% compounded semiannually with a 25-year amortization period. Figure 14.3 shows how the interest and principal components of the fixed monthly payments change over the lifetime of the loan.

NET @ssets

You can create a chart much like Figure 14.3 for any mortgage using the Amortization Calculator available on the CanadaMortgage.com Web site. Access it via the Student Edition of the textbook's Web site. In Chapter 14, find "Amortization Calculator."

After entering the data for the mortgage loan in the cells at the top of the page, click on the "Calculate" button. Scroll down the screen to view the bar chart. Each bar shows the interest and principal components of the total amount paid in a particular year. To see the precise dollar amount of the components in any year, move the cursor over the bar for that year and read the values in the box above the chart.

FIGURE 14.3   The Composition of Mortgage Payments During a 25-Year Amortization

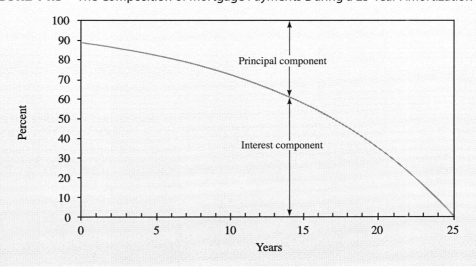

At any point in the 25-year amortization, the interest portion of a payment is the vertical distance below the curve. The principal portion of the payment is the remainder of the 100%, that is, the vertical distance above the curve. For example, the payment at the end of Year 14 is about 60% interest and 40% principal. During the first five years, more than 80% of every payment is interest. Consequently, the principal balance declines very slowly during the early years (as you will see in Figure 14.4).

Figure 14.4 illustrates how the balance owed on a $100,000 mortgage loan at 8.5% compounded semiannually declines during its 25-year amortization period. As expected from the preceding discussion, the balance decreases slowly in the early years. It takes about one-quarter of the amortization period to pay off the first $10,000 (10% of the original loan). Almost *three-quarters* of the amortization period are required to reduce the balance to *one-half* of the original principal. The principal declines at an accelerating rate in later years as an ever-increasing portion of each payment is applied to the principal.

FIGURE 14.4 A Mortgage's Declining Balance During a 25-Year Amortization

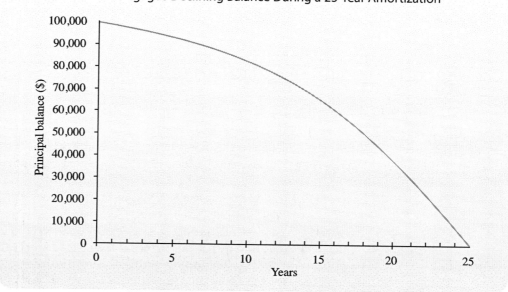

EXAMPLE 14.3A **CALCULATING THE PAYMENTS ON A MORTGAGE LOAN AT ITS BEGINNING AND AT RENEWAL**

A $50,000 mortgage loan is written with a 20-year amortization period, a three-year term, and an interest rate of 7.5% compounded semiannually. Payments are made monthly. Calculate:

a. The balance at the end of the three-year term.

b. The size of the payments upon renewal for a five-year term at 7% compounded semiannually (with the loan maintaining its original 20-year amortization).

SOLUTION

a. Before the balance can be calculated, we must obtain the monthly payment. Use the amortization period rather than the term of the mortgage when calculating the payment. That is, calculate the monthly payment that will repay the loan in 20 years if the interest rate remains at 7.5% compounded semiannually. The mortgage payments constitute an ordinary general annuity having

$$PV = \$50,000 \quad n = 12(20) = 240 \quad i = \frac{7.5\%}{2} = 3.75\% \quad \text{and} \quad c = \frac{2}{12} = 0.1\overline{6}$$

The periodic interest rate that matches the one-month payment interval is

$$i_2 = (1 + i)^c - 1 = 1.0375^{0.1\overline{6}} - 1 = 0.00615452390 \text{ per month}$$

Solve formula (10-2) for *PMT*.

$$\$50,000 = PMT\left(\frac{1 - 1.0061545239^{-240}}{0.0061545239}\right)$$
$$\$50,000 = PMT(125.2188)$$
$$PMT = \$399.30$$

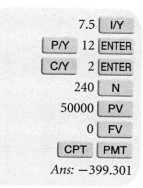

Using the Retrospective Method, the balance after three years will be

$$\begin{pmatrix} \text{Balance after} \\ \text{36 payments} \end{pmatrix} = \begin{pmatrix} \text{Future value of \$50,000} \\ \text{after 36 months} \end{pmatrix} - \begin{pmatrix} \text{Future value of the 36} \\ \text{payments already made} \end{pmatrix}$$

$$= \$50,000(1.0061545239)^{36} - \$399.30\left[\frac{1.0061545239^{36} - 1}{0.0061545239}\right]$$

$$= \$46,322.20$$

The balance after the initial three-year term will be $46,322.20.

Same I/Y, PV, P/Y, C/Y
36 N
399.30 +/- PMT
CPT FV
Ans: −46,322.20

b. The renewal is handled in the same way as a new mortgage whose original principal equals the balance from Part (a), but with a 17-year amortization period and an interest rate of 7% compounded semiannually. That is,

$$PV = \$46,322.20 \quad n = 12(17) = 204 \quad i = \tfrac{7\%}{2} = 3.5\% \quad \text{and} \quad c = \tfrac{2}{12} = 0.1\overline{6}$$

The periodic interest rate that matches the one-month payment interval is

$$i_2 = (1 + i)^c - 1 = 1.035^{0.1\overline{6}} - 1 = 0.0057500395 \text{ per month}$$

Solve formula (10-2) for *PMT*.

$$\$46,322.20 = PMT\left[\frac{1 - 1.0057500395^{-204}}{0.0057500395}\right]$$

$$\$46,322.20 = PMT(119.9164)$$

$$PMT = \$386.29$$

Same P/Y, C/Y
7 I/Y
204 N
46322.20 PV
0 FV
CPT PMT
Ans: −386.287

Upon renewal of the mortgage at 7% compounded semiannually, the payments will drop to $386.29 per month.

EXAMPLE 14.3B **CALCULATIONS WHERE THE MORTGAGE PAYMENT IS ROUNDED TO THE NEXT HIGHER $10**

The monthly payments for the first five-year term of a $20,000 mortgage loan were based on a 10-year amortization and an interest rate of 7% compounded semiannually. The payments were rounded up to the next higher $10.

a. Calculate the size of the monthly payments.

b. What is the principal balance at the end of the five-year term?

c. If the interest rate at renewal is 6.6% compounded semiannually for a second five-year term, calculate the new monthly payments also rounded to the next higher $10.

d. Calculate the size of the final payment.

SOLUTION

a. The payments form an ordinary general annuity with

$$PV = \$20,000 \quad n = 12(10) = 120 \quad i = \tfrac{7\%}{2} = 3.5\% \quad \text{and} \quad c = \tfrac{2}{12} = 0.1\overline{6}$$

The periodic rate for the one-month payment interval is

$$i_2 = (1 + i)^c - 1 = 1.035^{0.1\overline{6}} - 1 = 0.00575003948 \text{ per month}$$

Solve formula (10-2) for *PMT*.

$$\$20,000 = PMT\left[\frac{1 - 1.00575003948^{-120}}{0.00575003948}\right]$$

$$PMT = \$231.19$$

Rounded to the next higher $10, the monthly payment is $240.

7 I/Y
P/Y 12 ENTER
C/Y 2 ENTER
120 N
20000 PV
0 FV
CPT PMT
Ans: −231.19

b. The balance after five years is

$$\begin{pmatrix} \text{Balance after} \\ \text{60 payments} \end{pmatrix} = \begin{pmatrix} \text{Future value of \$20,000} \\ \text{after 60 months} \end{pmatrix} - \begin{pmatrix} \text{Future value of the 60} \\ \text{payments already made} \end{pmatrix}$$

$$= \$20,000(1.00575003948)^{60} - \$240\left[\frac{1.00575003948^{60} - 1}{0.00575003948}\right]$$

$$= \$11,074.06$$

> Same I/Y, PV, P/Y, C/Y
>
> 60 [N]
> 240 [+/−] [PMT]
> [CPT] [FV]
>
> *Ans:* −11,074.06

c. The balance from Part (b) becomes the initial loan amount for the second five-year term. With

$$PV = \$11,074.06, \ n = 60, \text{ and } i = \tfrac{6.6\%}{2} = 3.3\%, \text{ we obtain}$$

$$i_2 = (1 + i)^c - 1 = 1.033^{0.1\overline{6}} - 1 = 0.00542586532$$

and

$$\$11,074.06 = PMT\left[\frac{1 - 1.00542586532^{-60}}{0.00542586532}\right]$$

$$PMT = \$216.73$$

> Same P/Y, C/Y
>
> 6.6 [I/Y]
> 60 [N]
> 11074.06 [PV]
> 0 [FV]
> [CPT] [PMT]
>
> *Ans:* −216.73

Rounded to the next higher \$10, the monthly payment on renewal will be \$220.

d. Since the payment size has been rounded up, it may require less than 60 payments to pay off the debt, and the final payment will be less than \$220. The number of payments is

$$n = -\frac{\ln\left(1 - \dfrac{i \times PV}{PMT}\right)}{\ln(1 + i)}$$

$$= -\frac{\ln\left(1 - \dfrac{0.00542586532 \times \$11,074.06}{\$220}\right)}{\ln(1.00542586532)}$$

$$= 58.95$$

> Same I/Y, PV, P/Y, C/Y
>
> 220 [+/−] [PMT]
> 0 [FV]
> [CPT] [N]
>
> *Ans: =* 58.95

There will be 59 payments in the second term. The final payment will be the balance after 58 payments plus one month's interest. That is,

$$\text{Final payment} = \text{Balance after 58 payments} \times (1 + i)$$

$$\begin{pmatrix} \text{Balance after} \\ \text{58 payments} \end{pmatrix} = \begin{pmatrix} \text{Future value of \$11,074.06} \\ \text{after 58 months} \end{pmatrix} - \begin{pmatrix} \text{Future value of the 58} \\ \text{payments already made} \end{pmatrix}$$

$$= \$11,074.06(1.00542586532)^{58} - \$220\left[\frac{1.00542586532^{58} - 1}{0.00542586532}\right]$$

$$= \$208.04$$

> Same I/Y, P/Y, C/Y
> Same PV, PMT
>
> 58 [N]
> [CPT] [FV]
>
> *Ans:* −208.04

Hence,

$$\text{Final payment} = \$208.04 \times 1.00542586532 = \$209.17$$

QUALIFYING FOR A MORTGAGE LOAN

Mortgage lenders must determine whether a mortgage loan is adequately secured by the property, and whether the borrower has the financial capacity to make the mortgage payments. To do this, they calculate and set upper limits on three ratios:[2]

1. *Loan-to-Value Ratio* $= \dfrac{\text{Principal amount of the loan}}{\text{Lending value of the property}} \times 100\% \leq 80\%$

---

[2] The indicated upper limits are typical for what are called "conventional first mortgages."

The 80% *maximum* for this ratio means the borrower's *minimum* down payment is 20% of the "lending value." (The lending value is the lesser of the purchase price and the market value as determined by a certified appraiser.)

2. *Gross Debt Service Ratio* (GDS ratio):

$$\text{GDS ratio} = \frac{\left(\begin{array}{c}\text{Total monthly payments for mortgage,}\\ \text{condo fees, property taxes, and heat}\end{array}\right)}{\text{Gross monthly income}} \times 100\% \leq 32\%$$

The upper limit on this ratio means that the major costs of home ownership should not require more than 32% of the borrower's gross income.

3. *Total Debt Service Ratio* (TDS ratio):

$$\text{TDS ratio} = \frac{\left(\begin{array}{c}\text{Total monthly payments for mortgage,}\\ \text{property taxes, heat, and other debt}\end{array}\right)}{\text{Gross monthly income}} \times 100\% \leq 40\%$$

The upper limit on this ratio means that payments related to home ownership *and all other debt* should not require more than 40% of the borrower's gross income.

A borrower must qualify on *all* three ratios. The upper limits for the GDS and TDS ratios vary somewhat from one lender to another. Depending on the lender, the maximum GDS ratio can range from 30% to 33% and the maximum TDS ratio from 37% to 42%.

NET @ssets

The Canadian Imperial Bank of Commerce (CIBC) provides an online calculator that enables you to determine the maximum mortgage loan and maximum house purchase price for which you qualify.

To access the calculator, go to the Student Edition of the textbook's Web site. In Chapter 14, find "Calculate What You Can Afford."

Based on the financial information that you enter, the calculator determines the maximum loan and home purchase price at which you first reach CIBC's upper limit for one of the key ratios (32% for the Gross Debt Service Ratio, GDS, and 40% for Total Debt Service Ratio, TDS). The calculator will allow you to exceed the normal 80% limit on the loan-to-value ratio for a "conventional mortgage"—you may go as high as 95%. But you should understand that you are required to purchase mortgage default insurance if you go over the normal 80% limit. The lender treats the insurance premiums as part of your monthly debt payments when calculating the GDS and TDS ratios.

EXAMPLE 14.3C | **DETERMINING THE MAXIMUM MORTGAGE LOAN FOR WHICH A BORROWER QUALIFIES**

The Schusters have saved $55,000 for the down payment on a home. Their gross monthly income is $6300. They want to know the maximum conventional mortgage loan for which they can qualify in order to determine the highest price they can pay for a home. They have 18 payments of $600 per month remaining on their car loan. Their bank has upper limits of 32% for the GDS ratio and 40% for the TDS ratio.

a. Allowing for property taxes of $300 per month and heating costs of $225 per month, what maximum monthly mortgage payment do the GDS and TDS ratios permit?

b. What is the maximum mortgage loan for which the Schusters can qualify? (Use a 25-year amortization and an interest rate of 7% compounded semiannually for a five-year term. Round the answer to the nearest $100.)

c. Based on a $55,000 down payment and the maximum loan from Part (b), what is the highest price they can pay for a home? Round the answer to the nearest $100.

SOLUTION

a. The GDS ratio allows

$$\frac{\left(\begin{array}{c}\text{Maximum mortgage payment} \\ \text{+ property taxes + heating costs}\end{array}\right)}{\text{Gross income}} = 0.32$$

That is,

$$\frac{\text{Maximum mortgage payment + \$300 + \$225}}{\$6300} = 0.32$$

Hence,

$$\text{Maximum mortgage payment + \$300 + \$225} = 0.32(\$6300)$$

$$\text{Maximum mortgage payment} = 0.32(\$6300) - \$525 = \$1491$$

The TDS ratio allows

$$\frac{\left(\begin{array}{c}\text{Maximum payments on all debt} \\ \text{+ property taxes + heating costs}\end{array}\right)}{\text{Gross income}} = 0.40$$

Hence,

$$\text{Maximum mortgage payment + \$300 + \$225 + \$600} = 0.40(\$6300)$$

$$\text{Maximum mortgage payment} = 0.40(\$6300) - \$1125 = \$1395$$

For the Schusters' situation, the TDS ratio is the more restrictive ratio. It limits the maximum mortgage payment to $1395 per month.

b. The TDS ratio restricts the Schusters to a maximum mortgage payment of $1395 per month. For a loan at 7% compounded semiannually with a 25-year amortization,

$$n = 12(25) = 300 \quad i = \tfrac{7\%}{2} = 3.5\% \quad c = 0.1\overline{6} \quad \text{and} \quad i_2 = 1.035^{0.1\overline{6}} - 1 = 0.0057500395$$

The maximum loan permitted by the TDS ratio is

$$PV = \text{Present value of 300 payments of \$1395}$$
$$= \$1395\left[\frac{1 - 1.0057500395^{-300}}{0.0057500395}\right]$$
$$= \$199,200 \text{ rounded to the nearest \$100}$$

c. Combining the maximum loan with the $55,000 down payment, the Schusters would have

$$\$199,200 + \$55,000 = \$254,200$$

available to purchase a home, subject to satisfying the criterion for a conventional mortgage. If they purchase a home for $254,200, the loan-to-value ratio[3] would be

$$\frac{\$199,200}{254,200} \times 100\% = 78.4\%$$

Since the ratio is less than 80%, the Schusters meet the loan-to-value criterion for a conventional mortgage. Therefore, $254,200 is the maximum price they can pay for a home.

---

[3]   Mortgage lenders usually base the loan-to-value ratio on the *lesser* of the purchase price or the market value placed on the property by an independent appraiser. In this example, the appraised value would have to be at least $199,200 ÷ 0.8 = $249,00 for the Schusters to qualify for a $199,200 mortgage loan.

   The Schusters also need to keep in mind that they will have significant legal, appraisal, survey, and registration costs in connection with the purchase of the home. A general rule-of-thumb is to allow 1.5% of the purchase price for these "closing costs".

POINT OF INTEREST

An Analysis of the Interest "Savings" from Choosing a Shorter Amortization Period

Many financial planners and commentators make a great ballyhoo about the large amount of interest that can be saved by choosing a shorter mortgage amortization period. Their typical analysis goes as follows. (We will use monthly compounding rather than semiannual compounding to simplify the math.)

Suppose you obtain a $100,000 mortgage loan at 7.2% compounded monthly. The following table compares 20- and 25-year amortizations.

Amortization period	Monthly payment ($)	Total of all payments ($)	Total interest ($)
25 years	719.59	215,877	115,877
20 years	787.35	188,964	88,964
Difference:	(67.76)	26,913	26,913

By choosing a 20-year amortization, you will have "interest savings" of $26,913. The "savings" result from eliminating payments of $719.59 per month during Years 21 to 25 by spending an extra $67.76 per month during Years 1 to 20. That is,

$$\text{Interest savings} = (5 \times 12 \times \$719.59) - (20 \times 12 \times \$67.76) = \$26,913$$

It seems quite astounding—increasing the monthly mortgage payment by less than 10% reduces the total interest costs by over 23%! The usual conclusion is that reduction of your mortgage's amortization period should be one of your highest financial priorities because of the amazing "interest savings." In the present example, you will be "$26,913 ahead" by choosing the 20-year amortization.

Do you see any flaws in this conventional analysis? Is it complete? Does it violate any basic concept you have learned? (Clearly, the analysis must be problematic—otherwise, we would not be making an issue of it. But before reading on, cover up the remainder of the discussion and take five minutes to see if you can identify the error made by so many "experts.")

The main flaw in the analysis is that a basic concept in finance—the time value of money—has been ignored. Whenever you add nominal dollar amounts that are paid on different dates, you are ignoring the time value of money. The longer the time frame over which the payments are spread, the more serious the resulting error will be. In the preceding analysis, a dollar in Year 25 is treated as having the same value as a dollar in Year 1. In fact, individual dollars saved in Years 21 to 25 have, on average, significantly less economic value than extra dollars spent in Years 1 to 20.

Let us do a rigorous analysis to determine the amount of the economic advantage of the shorter amortization period.

QUESTIONS

1. For the first 20 years, the monthly payments on the 25-year amortization are $67.76 lower than the payments on the 20-year amortization loan. Suppose you invest this difference each month to earn the same rate of interest that you pay on either mortgage. How much will you accumulate after 20 years?

2. What will be the balance owed after 20 years on the 25-year mortgage? Compare this balance to the Question 1 result. Which mortgage alternative puts you in a better financial position 20 years from now? Where did all of the "interest savings" go?

3. How will the outcome differ if the rate of return on your investments is higher than the interest rate you pay on your mortgage?

4. Write a "decision rule" that your friends (who have not had the good fortune to take this course) can use to decide whether to select a longer or a shorter mortgage amortization period.

Postscript: We do not disagree with the advice that paying off your mortgage as fast as possible should be a high financial priority. We merely make the point that the usual analysis is flawed and overstated. Legitimate reasons for the advice are:

- When you use extra money to reduce the principal on your mortgage, you are *certain* of earning an *after-tax* rate of return equal to the interest rate on the mortgage. After you adjust returns from alternative investments for their *risk* and *tax exposure*, the mortgage "investment" is usually very attractive in comparison.

- Human nature is such that we are more readily motivated to accelerate mortgage repayment than to undertake some other investment plan.
- Reduction of household debt improves our ability to absorb financial shocks such as loss of income due to sickness or job loss.

Post-postscript: In the next section, you will learn about other possibilities for accelerating the repayment of a mortgage loan. Some books present calculations of the resulting "interest savings." We play down this fundamentally flawed perspective for the reasons discussed in this Point of Interest.

COMMON PREPAYMENT PRIVILEGES AND PENALTIES

LO6

NET @ssets

An interactive Mortgage Payoff Chart is provided in the textbook's Web site. In Chapter 14 of the Student Edition, find "Mortgage Payoff Chart."

The chart plots the mortgage balance and the cumulative interest over the full amortization period. You can also select from a variety of accelerated payment and prepayment options. If you enter a non-zero "Prepayment amount," the chart shows additional graphs for the balance and cumulative interest with prepayments. These graphs enable you to see how much the prepayments reduce both the cumulative interest cost and the time required to pay off the loan.

Any payments other than the regular contractual payments on a mortgage loan are called **prepayments**. Unless they include a penalty, prepayments are applied entirely to the reduction of principal, since the regular payments already cover interest charges. Mortgages that place no restrictions or penalties on extra payments by the borrower are called **open mortgages**. At the other extreme are **closed mortgages**, which do not allow any prepayment without a penalty. A borrower must pay a higher interest rate on an open mortgage than on a closed mortgage having the same term—about 2% higher for a one-year-term open mortgage.

Between the two extremes just described are closed mortgages with prepayment options. These mortgages grant limited penalty-free prepayment privileges. The more common prepayment options are one or more of the following.

- **Individual (or Lump) Payments** Once each year the borrower can prepay without penalty up to 15% of the original amount of the mortgage loan. Mortgage "years" are measured from the date of the loan.

- **Increasing the Regular Payment** Once each year, the borrower can permanently increase the size of the regular payments. There is usually an upper limit (such as 15%) on the increase in any year.

- **"Double-Up"** On any payment date, the borrower can pay up to twice the regular monthly payment. Taken to the extreme, the borrower could double *every* payment.

If the mortgage contract allows more than one of these options, the borrower can take advantage of two or more simultaneously. However, unused privileges cannot be carried forward. For example, if you do not use a 15% lump prepayment privilege in the first year, you cannot carry it forward to enable you to prepay up to 30% in the second year.

Details of these prepayment privileges vary among lending institutions. For example, single prepayments may be permitted only once each year or several times (subject to the 10% or 15% annual limit).

Another increasingly common feature of mortgages is a "skip-a-payment" provision. This allows the borrower to miss one monthly payment each year. Whereas a prepayment will shorten the time required to ultimately pay off a mortgage, skipping a payment will lengthen the time.

It is not unusual for homeowners to sell their house partway through the term of a closed mortgage. If a mortgage has a *portability* clause, the balance owed may be transferred to the next property purchased by the borrower. Some mortgages are *assumable*. An assumable mortgage loan may be transferred to (or "assumed by") the purchaser of the property securing the mortgage *if* the purchaser satisfies the lender's GDS and TDS ratios. The most typical scenario, however, is for the vendor to "pay out" the balance owed on the mortgage. The mortgage contract provides for a financial penalty on any prepayment not specifically permitted by the contract. The most common prepayment penalty is the *greater* of:

- Three months' interest on the amount prepaid, or

- The lender's reduction in interest revenue from the prepaid amount (over the remainder of the mortgage's term).[4]

EXAMPLE 14.3D   **THE CONSEQUENCES OF A 10% LUMP PREPAYMENT**

The interest rate for the first five-year term of a $100,000 mortgage loan is 7.5% compounded semiannually. The mortgage requires monthly payments over a 25-year amortization period. The mortgage contract gives the borrower the right to prepay up to 15% of the original mortgage loan, once each year, without interest penalty. Suppose that, at the end of the second year of the mortgage, the borrower makes a prepayment of $10,000.

a. How much will the amortization period be shortened?

b. What will be the principal balance at the end of the five-year term?

SOLUTION

a. The $10,000 prepayment at the time of the twenty-fourth regular monthly payment will be applied entirely to reducing the principal. To answer Part (a), we must take the following steps:

Step 1.   Calculate the payments based on a 25-year amortization.

Step 2.   Calculate the balance after 24 payments.

Step 3.   Reduce this balance by $10,000.

Step 4.   Calculate the number of monthly payments needed to pay off this new balance.

Step 5.   Calculate the reduction in the original 25-year amortization period.

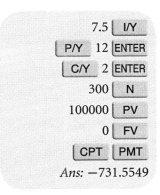

Step 1:   The periodic rate for the one-month payment interval is

$$i_2 = (1 + i)^c - 1 = 1.0375^{0.1\overline{6}} - 1 = 0.0061545239 \text{ per month}$$

Solve formula (10-2) for *PMT*.

$$\$100,000 = PMT\left[\frac{1 - 1.0061545239^{-300}}{0.0061545239}\right]$$

$$PMT = \$731.55$$

The monthly payment is $731.55.

---

[4]   The following is an extract from a mortgage contract describing this penalty.

"The amount, if any, by which interest at the rate on this mortgage exceeds interest at the current reinvestment interest rate, calculated on the amount prepaid by you, for the remaining term of the mortgage. The 'current reinvestment interest rate' at the time of prepayment means the rate at which we would lend to you on the security of a similar mortgage of your property for a term starting on the date of prepayment and ending on the balance due date of the mortgage."

Step 2: $\begin{pmatrix}\text{Balance after}\\24\text{ payments}\end{pmatrix}$

$= \begin{pmatrix}\text{Future value of }\$100,000\\ \text{after 24 months}\end{pmatrix} - \begin{pmatrix}\text{Future value of the 24}\\ \text{payments already made}\end{pmatrix}$

$= \$100,000(1.0061545239)^{24} - \$731.55\left[\dfrac{1.0061545239^{24} - 1}{0.0061545239}\right]$

$= \$97,007.25$

The balance after 24 payments is $97,007.25.

Step 3:   The balance after the $10,000 prepayment is $87,007.25.

Step 4:   Calculate the number of payments of $731.55 required to pay off the balance of $87,007.25.

$n = -\dfrac{\ln\left(1 - \dfrac{i \times PV}{PMT}\right)}{\ln(1 + i)}$

$= -\dfrac{\ln\left(1 - \dfrac{0.0061545239 \times \$87,007.25}{\$731.55}\right)}{\ln(1.0061545239)}$

$= 214.60$

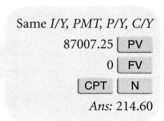

Same *I/Y, PMT, P/Y, C/Y*

87007.25 ⎿ PV ⏌

0 ⎿ FV ⏌

⎿ CPT ⏌ ⎿ N ⏌

Ans: 214.60

After the $10,000 prepayment, 215 additional payments will pay off the loan.

Step 5:   With the prepayment, a total of 24 + 215 = 239 monthly payments are required. Therefore, the $10,000 prepayment reduces the amortization period by

$300 - 239 = 61 \text{ months} = 5 \text{ years and 1 month}$

b. Beginning with the balance of $87,007.25 after the $10,000 prepayment, calculate the new balance after another 36 payments.

$\begin{pmatrix}\text{Balance after}\\36\text{ payments}\end{pmatrix} = \begin{pmatrix}\text{Future value of }\$87,007.25\\ \text{after 36 months}\end{pmatrix} - \begin{pmatrix}\text{Future value of the 36}\\ \text{payments already made}\end{pmatrix}$

$= \$87,007.25(1.0061545239)^{36} - \$731.55\left[\dfrac{1.0061545239^{36} - 1}{0.0061545239}\right]$

$= \$79,133.00$

Same *I/Y, P/Y, C/Y*

Same *PV, PMT*

36 ⎿ N ⏌

⎿ CPT ⏌ ⎿ FV ⏌

Ans: −79,133.00

The balance at the end of the five-year term will be $79,133.00.

EXAMPLE 14.3E   **THE CONSEQUENCES OF A 10% INCREASE IN THE PAYMENT SIZE**

Two and one-half years ago the Simpsons borrowed $90,000 secured by a mortgage against the home they purchased at the time. The monthly payments, based on an interest rate of 7.25% compounded semiannually for a five-year term, would amortize the debt over 25 years. The mortgage has a prepayment clause that allows the Simpsons to increase the monthly payments by up to 10% once in each year. Any increase is to be a permanent increase. If the Simpsons increase payments by 10% starting with the thirty-first payment:

a. How much will the amortization period be shortened?

b. What will be the principal balance at the end of the first five-year term?

SOLUTION

a. The following steps are required to answer the question.

Step 1:   Calculate the original size of the payments.

Step 2:   Calculate the balance after $2\frac{1}{2}$ years (30 payments).

Step 3:   Calculate the size of the payments after a 10% increase.

Step 4:   Calculate the number of the new larger payments needed to amortize the balance from Step 2.

Step 5:   Calculate the reduction from the original 25-year amortization period.

Step 1:   The periodic rate for the one-month payment interval is

$$i_2 = (1 + i)^c - 1 = 1.03625^{0.1\overline{6}} - 1 = 0.00595238334 \text{ per month}$$

Solve formula (10-2) for *PMT*.

$$\$90,000 = PMT\left[\frac{1 - 1.00595238334^{-300}}{0.00595238334}\right]$$

$$PMT = \$644.33$$

The monthly payment is $644.33.

7.25	I/Y
P/Y 12	ENTER
C/Y 2	ENTER
300	N
90000	PV
0	FV
CPT	PMT

Ans: −644.327

Step 2: $\begin{pmatrix}\text{Balance after}\\ \text{30 payments}\end{pmatrix}$

$= \begin{pmatrix}\text{Future value of }\$90,000\\ \text{after 30 months}\end{pmatrix} - \begin{pmatrix}\text{Future value of the 30}\\ \text{payments already made}\end{pmatrix}$

$= \$90,000(1.00595238334)^{30} - \$644.33\left[\dfrac{1.00595238334^{30} - 1}{0.00595238334}\right]$

$= \$86,444.03$

The balance after 30 payments is $86,444.03.

Same *I/Y, PV, P/Y, C/Y*

30	N
644.33 +/−	PMT
CPT	FV

Ans: −86,444.03

Step 3:   The higher payment is 1.1($644.33) = $708.76.

Step 4:   Calculate the number of payments of $708.76 required to pay off the balance of $86,444.03.

$$n = -\frac{\ln\left(1 - \dfrac{i \times PV}{PMT}\right)}{\ln(1 + i)}$$

$$= -\frac{\ln\left(1 - \dfrac{0.00595238334 \times \$86,444.03}{\$708.76}\right)}{\ln(1.00595238334)}$$

$$= 218.13$$

Same *I/Y, P/Y, C/Y*

86444.03	PV
708.76 +/−	PMT
0	FV
CPT	N

Ans: 218.13

219 additional payments are needed to pay off the loan.

Step 5:   The total time to amortize the loan will be 30 + 219 = 249 months instead of the original 300 months. Therefore, the amortization period will be shortened by

$$300 - 249 = 51 \text{ months, or 4 years and 3 months.}$$

b. By the end of the five-year term, the balance in Step 2 will be reduced by an additional 30 payments of $708.76.

$$\begin{pmatrix} \text{Balance after 30} \\ \text{more payments} \end{pmatrix}$$

$$= \begin{pmatrix} \text{Future value of \$86,444.03} \\ \text{after 30 months} \end{pmatrix} - \begin{pmatrix} \text{Future value of the 30} \\ \text{additional payments made} \end{pmatrix}$$

$$= \$86,444.03(1.00595238334)^{30} - \$708.76\left[\frac{1.00595238334^{30} - 1}{0.00595238334}\right]$$

$$= \$80,085.70$$

Same *I/Y, P/Y, C/Y*
Same *PV, PMT*
30 [N]
[CPT] [FV]
Ans: −80,085.70

The balance at the end of the five-year term will be $80,085.70.

EXERCISE 14.3   *Answers to the odd-numbered problems are at the end of the book.*

1. A $100,000 mortgage loan at 7.2% compounded semiannually requires monthly payments based on a 25-year amortization. Assuming that the interest rate does not change for the entire 25 years, complete the following table.

Interval	Balance at the end of the interval ($)	Principal reduction during the interval ($)	Interest paid during the interval ($)
0 to 5 years			
5 to 10 years			
10 to 15 years			
15 to 20 years			
20 to 25 years			

2. The interest rate on a $100,000 mortgage loan is 7% compounded semiannually.

   a. Calculate the monthly payment for each of 20-year, 25-year, and 30-year amortizations.

   b. By what percentage must the monthly payment be increased for a 25-year amortization instead of a 30-year amortization?

   c. By what percentage must the monthly payment be increased for a 20-year amortization instead of a 30-year amortization?

   d. For each of the three amortization periods in Part (a), calculate the total interest paid over the entire amortization period. Assume that the interest rate and payments do not change and the final payment equals the others.

3. A $100,000 mortgage loan has a 25-year amortization.

   a. Calculate the monthly payment at interest rates of 6%, 7%, and 8% compounded semiannually.

   b. By what percentage does the monthly payment on the 8% mortgage exceed the monthly payment on the 7% mortgage?

   c. Calculate the total interest paid over the entire 25-year amortization period at each of the three interest rates. (Assume the final payment equals the others.)

4. The Graftons can afford a maximum mortgage payment of $1000 per month. The current interest rate is 7.2% compounded semiannually. What is the maximum mortgage loan they can afford if the amortization period is:

   a. 15 years?   **b.** 20 years?   **c.** 25 years?   **d.** 30 years?

5. The Tarkanians can afford a maximum mortgage payment of $1000 per month. What is the maximum mortgage loan they can afford if the amortization period is 25 years and the interest rate is:

   a. 6.5% compounded semiannually?   **b.** 7.5% compounded semiannually?

6. A $100,000 mortgage loan at 7.6% compounded semiannually has a 25-year amortization period.

   a. Calculate the monthly payment.

   b. If the interest rate were 1% lower (that is, 6.6% compounded semiannually), what loan amount would result in the same monthly payment?

○7. The Switzers are nearing the end of the first five-year term of a $100,000 mortgage loan with a 25-year amortization. The interest rate has been 6.5% compounded semiannually for the initial term. How much will their monthly payments increase if the interest rate upon renewal is 7.5% compounded semiannually?

○8. The Melnyks are nearing the end of the first three-year term of a $100,000 mortgage loan with a 20-year amortization. The interest rate has been 7.7% compounded semiannually for the initial term. How much will their monthly payments decrease if the interest rate upon renewal is 6.7% compounded semiannually?

○9. The interest rate for the first three years of an $80,000 mortgage loan is 7.4% compounded semiannually. Monthly payments are calculated using a 25-year amortization.

   a. What will be the principal balance at the end of the three-year term?

   b. What will be the monthly payments if the loan is renewed at 6.8% compounded semiannually (and the original amortization period is continued)?

○10. Five years ago, Ms. Halliday received a mortgage loan from the Scotiabank for $60,000 at 7.8% compounded semiannually for a five-year term. Monthly payments were based on a 25-year amortization. The bank is agreeable to renewing the loan for another five-year term at 6.8% compounded semiannually. Calculate the principal reduction that will occur in the second five-year term if:

   a. The payments are recalculated based on the new interest rate and a continuation of the original 25-year amortization.

   b. Ms. Halliday continues to make the same payments as she made for the first five years (resulting in a reduction of the amortization period).

○11. A $40,000 mortgage loan charges interest at 6.6% compounded *monthly* for a four-year term. Monthly payments were calculated for a 15-year amortization and then rounded up to the next higher $10.

   a. What will be the principal balance at the end of the first term?

   b. What will be the monthly payments on renewal for a three-year term if they are calculated for an interest rate of 7.2% compounded monthly and an 11-year amortization period, but again rounded to the next higher $10?

○12. Many mortgage lenders offer the flexibility of dividing a mortgage loan between a fixed-interest-rate portion and a variable-interest-rate portion. (A variable-rate mortgage is sometimes referred to as an adjustable-rate mortgage, abbreviated ARM.) The variable interest rate changes from time to time, following the trend of short-term interest rates in the capital markets. On average, quoted variable interest rates on mortgages are lower than quoted fixed rates for most terms. But at times variable rates can rise above (even substantially above) fixed rates, especially fixed rates that may have been "locked in" two or three years earlier.

   Suppose a $100,000 mortgage loan with a 25-year amortization is divided equally between a fixed-rate portion at 6.6% compounded semiannually and a variable-rate portion at 5.4% compounded monthly. (Quoted rates on variable-rate mortgages are normally monthly compounded rates.)

   a. What is the initial (combined) monthly payment?

   b. What will be the combined monthly payment if the variable rate jumps to 6.6% compounded monthly after two years?

○13. The interest rate for the first five years of a $27,000 mortgage loan was 7.25% compounded semiannually. The monthly payments computed for a 10-year amortization were rounded to the next higher $10.

    a. Calculate the principal balance at the end of the first term.

    b. Upon renewal at 6.75% compounded semiannually, monthly payments were calculated for a five-year amortization and again rounded up to the next $10. What will be the amount of the last payment?

○14. The Delgados have a gross monthly income of $6000. Monthly payments on personal loans total $500. Their bank limits the gross debt service ratio at 33% and the total debt service ratio at 42%.

    a. Rounded to the nearest $100, what is the maximum 25-year mortgage loan for which they can qualify on the basis of their income? Assume monthly heating costs of $200 and property taxes of $220 per month. Current mortgage rates are 6.8% compounded semiannually.

    b. Rounded to the nearest $100, what minimum down payment must they have to qualify for the maximum conventional mortgage (80% loan-to-value ratio) on a new home?

○15. The Archibalds are eligible for Canada Mortgage and Housing Corporation's Mortgage Loan Insurance. Consequently, their limits are 95% for the loan-to-value ratio, 32% for the GDS ratio, and 40% for the TDS ratio.

    a. Rounded to the nearest $100, what is the maximum 25-year mortgage loan for which they can qualify if their gross monthly income is $5000 and their payments on personal debt amount to $600 per month? Assume monthly heating costs of $150 and property taxes of $200 per month. Current mortgage rates are 6.6% compounded semiannually.

    b. If they make the minimum down payment, what is the maximum price (rounded to the nearest $100) they can pay for a home? (Assume the purchase price equals the appraised value.)

○16. Marge and Homer Sampson have saved $95,000 toward the purchase of their first home. Allowing $7000 for legal costs and moving expenses, they have $88,000 available for a down payment.

    a. Based only on a loan-to-value ratio of 80%, what is the maximum purchase price they can consider?

    b. After thorough investigation, the Sampsons made a $360,000 offer on a townhouse subject to arranging financing. Next they met with their banker. With an $88,000 down payment, the Sampsons will need a mortgage loan of $272,000. The current interest rate on a five-year term fixed-rate mortgage with a 25-year amortization is 5.4% compounded semiannually. The banker gathered data for calculating the Sampsons' GDS and TDS ratios. Annual property taxes will be $3000. Annual heating costs will be about $2400. The Sampsons make monthly payments of $800 on a car loan ($14,000 balance). Their gross monthly income is $7000. Calculate the GDS and TDS ratios for the Sampsons.

    c. Note that the Sampsons meet the GDS criterion ($\leq 32\%$) but exceed the TDS limit (40%). The item causing the problem is the $800 per month car payment. Suppose the Sampsons use $14,000 of their down-payment savings to pay off the car loan. They will still have enough to make the minimum down payment (0.2 × $60,000 = $72,000) but will have to increase the mortgage loan by $14,000 to $286,000. Re-calculate the GDS and TDS ratios. Do the Sampsons satisfy all three ratios by taking this approach?

○**17.** The interest rate on a $100,000 mortgage loan is 7% compounded semiannually.

  a. What are the monthly payments for a 25-year amortization?

  b. Suppose that the borrower instead makes weekly payments equal to one-fourth of the monthly payment calculated in Part (a). (In mortgage terminology, these are referred to as accelerated weekly payments.) When will the loan be paid off if the interest rate does not change? Assume there are exactly 52 weeks in a year.

○**18.** A $200,000 mortgage at 6.6% compounded semiannually with a 25-year amortization requires monthly payments. The mortgage allows the borrower to prepay up to 10% of the original principal once each year. How much will the amortization period be shortened if, on the first anniversary of the mortgage, the borrower makes (in addition to the regular payment) a prepayment of:

  a. $10,000?   **b.** $20,000?

○**19.** A $200,000 mortgage at 6.6% compounded semiannually with a 30-year amortization requires monthly payments. The mortgage allows the borrower to prepay up to 10% of the original principal once each year. How much will the amortization period be shortened if, on the first anniversary of the mortgage, the borrower makes (in addition to the regular payment) a prepayment of:

  a. $10,000?   **b.** $20,000?

○**20.** A $100,000 mortgage at 6.9% compounded semiannually with a 25-year amortization requires monthly payments. The mortgage entitles the borrower to increase the amount of the regular payment by up to 15% once each year. How much will the amortization period be shortened if, after the twelfth payment, the payments are increased by:

  a. 7.5%?   **b.** 15%?

○**21.** A $100,000 mortgage at 6.9% compounded semiannually with a 30-year amortization requires monthly payments. The mortgage allows the borrower to increase the amount of the regular payment by up to 10% once each year. How much will the amortization period be shortened if payments are increased by 10% after the twelfth payment, and by another 10% after Payment 24?

○**22.** A $100,000 mortgage at 6.2% compounded semiannually with a 25-year amortization requires monthly payments. The mortgage allows the borrower to "double up" on a payment once each year. How much will the amortization period be shortened if the borrower doubles the tenth payment?

○**23.** A $100,000 mortgage at 6.8% compounded semiannually with a 30-year amortization requires monthly payments. The mortgage allows the borrower to "double up" on a payment once each year. How much will the amortization period be shortened if the borrower doubles the eighth payment?

○**24.** A $100,000 mortgage at 6.75% compounded semiannually with a 20-year amortization requires monthly payments. The mortgage allows the borrower to miss a payment once each year. How much will the amortization period be lengthened if the borrower misses the ninth payment? (The interest that accrues during the ninth month is converted to principal at the end of the ninth month.)

○**25.** A $100,000 mortgage at 7.3% compounded semiannually with a 25-year amortization requires monthly payments. The mortgage allows the borrower to miss a payment once each year. How much will the amortization period be lengthened if the borrower misses the twelfth payment? (The interest that accrues during the twelfth month is converted to principal at the end of the twelfth month.)

○**26.** A $100,000 mortgage at 7.1% compounded semiannually with a 30-year amortization requires monthly payments. How much will the amortization period be shortened if a $10,000 lump payment is made along with the twelfth payment and payments are increased by 10% starting in the third year?

○**27.** A $100,000 mortgage at 6.8% compounded semiannually with a 25-year amortization requires monthly payments. How much will the amortization period be shortened if payments are increased by 10% starting in the second year, and a $10,000 lump payment is made along with the twenty-fourth payment?

○**28.** Monthly payments on a $150,000 mortgage are based on an interest rate of 6.6% compounded semiannually and a 30-year amortization. If a $5000 prepayment is made along with the thirty-second payment:

   a. How much will the amortization period be shortened?

   b. What will be the principal balance after four years?

○**29.** The interest rate for the first five years of a $120,000 mortgage is 7% compounded semiannually. Monthly payments are based on a 25-year amortization. If a $5000 prepayment is made at the end of the second year:

   a. How much will the amortization period be shortened?

   b. What will be the principal balance at the end of the five-year term?

○**30.** A $130,000 mortgage loan at 7.2% compounded *monthly* has a 25-year amortization.

   a. What prepayment at the end of the first year will reduce the time required to pay off the loan by one year? (Assume the final payment equals the others.)

   b. Instead of the prepayment in Part (a), what prepayment at the end of the tenth year will reduce the time required to pay off the loan by one year?

○**31.** After three years of the first five-year term at 6.3% compounded semiannually, Dean and Cindy decide to take advantage of the privilege of increasing the payments on their $200,000 mortgage loan by 10%. The monthly payments were originally calculated for a 30-year amortization.

   a. How much will the amortization period be shortened?

   b. What will be the principal balance at the end of the five-year term?

○**32.** The MacLellans originally chose to make payments of $1600 per month on a $138,000 mortgage written at 7.4% compounded semiannually for the first five years. After three years they exercised their right under the mortgage contract to increase the payments by 10%.

   a. If the interest rate does not change, when will they extinguish the mortgage debt?

   b. What will be the principal balance at the end of the five-year term?

•**33.** The monthly payments on the Wolskis' $166,000 mortgage were originally based on a 25-year amortization and an interest rate of 7% compounded semiannually for a five-year term. After two years, they elected to increase their monthly payments by $100, and at the end of the fourth year they made a $10,000 prepayment.

   a. How much have they shortened the amortization period?

   b. What was the principal balance at the end of the five-year term?

•**34.** A marketing innovation is the "cash-back mortgage" wherein the lender gives the borrower an up-front bonus cash payment. For example, if you borrow $100,000 on a 3% cash-back mortgage loan, the lender will give you $3000 in addition to the $100,000 loan. You pay back only the $100,000 principal over the amortization period. The $3000 can be immediately applied as a prepayment to reduce the principal balance (to $97,000) or it can be used for any other purpose. You must keep your mortgage with the lender for at least five years.

The cash-back mortgage seems like a good deal but there is more you need to know about advertised mortgage interest rates. The rates you see posted in your local financial institution are just a starting point for negotiations. You can get $\frac{1}{4}$% knocked off just by asking for it. With some firm negotiating, you can probably get a $\frac{1}{2}$% reduction. If the institution really wants your business, you can get a $\frac{3}{4}$% or even 1% reduction. However, if you take advantage of some other promotion such as a cash-back offer, you will not get any rate discount. So the cash-back offer is not as good as it initially appears.

Which of the following loans should be chosen by the borrower?

- A standard $100,000 mortgage loan at 6.5% compounded semiannually?

- A 3% cash-back mortgage loan for $100,000 at 7.25% compounded semiannually?

In both cases, the interest rate is for a five-year term and the payments are based on a 25-year amortization. For the cash-back mortgage, assume that the $3000 cash bonus is immediately applied to reduce the balance to $97,000. (Since the monthly payments are based on the $100,000 face value, the prepayment will shorten the time required to pay off the loan.) Assume money can earn 4.8% compounded monthly.

35. **Using the Mortgage Payoff Chart** To access this chart, go to the Student Edition of the textbook's Web site. In Chapter 14, find "Mortgage Payoff Chart." Over the full amortization period, the chart plots graphs of both the mortgage balance and the cumulative interest paid. Note the "Definitions" section below the chart.

You can select from a variety of accelerated payment and prepayment options. If you enter a non-zero "Prepayment amount," the chart presents additional graphs for the balance and cumulative interest under the prepayment plan. (Round prepayment amounts to the nearest dollar before entry.) These graphs enable you to see how much the prepayments reduce both the cumulative interest cost and the time required to pay off the loan. Use this chart (and its associated report) to answer the following problems from this Exercise. In Parts (b) through (f), round the answer to the nearest 0.1 year. Also note that the reduction (referred to as "savings") in the total interest paid is over the life of the loan.

a. Problem 1   b. Problem 17   c. Problem 19
d. Problem 23   e. Problem 29   f. Problem 31

KEY TERMS

Amortization period **p. 519**

Closed mortgage **p. 552**

Face value **p. 544**

Loan amortization schedule **p. 519**

Mortgagee **p. 544**

Mortgagor **p. 544**

Open mortgage **p. 552**

Prepayments **p. 552**

Prospective Method **p. 523**

Retrospective Method **p. 524**

Term **p. 544**

Term loan **p. 519**

SUMMARY OF NOTATION AND KEY FORMULAS

In all but the last of the following equations, the relevant interest rate or discount rate is the loan's contractual rate of interest.

$$\text{Original loan} = \left[\frac{\text{Present value of all payments}}{\text{(discounted at the } contractual\ rate\ of\ interest \text{ on the loan)}} \right]$$

We frequently use this concept to calculate the payment size or the amortization period.

$$\text{Principal balance} = \left[\frac{\text{Present value of the remaining payments}}{\text{(discounted at the } contractual\ rate\ of\ interest \text{ on the loan)}} \right]$$

Prospective Method for calculating a loan's balance.

$$\text{Balance} = \left(\begin{array}{c} \text{Future value of} \\ \text{the original loan} \end{array} \right) - \left(\begin{array}{c} \text{Future value of the} \\ \text{payments already made} \end{array} \right)$$

Retrospective Method for calculating a loan's balance.

$$\text{Final payment} = (1 + i) \times \left(\begin{array}{c} \text{Balance after the} \\ \text{second-to-last payment} \end{array} \right)$$

The final loan payment usually differs from the others.

$$\text{Interest component} = i \times \text{Balance after the previous payment}$$

$$\text{Principal component} = \left(\begin{array}{c} \text{Balance after the} \\ \text{previous payment} \end{array} \right) - \left(\begin{array}{c} \text{Balance after the} \\ \text{current payment} \end{array} \right)$$

The interest and principal components of a loan payment may be calculated from nearby balances.

REVIEW PROBLEMS

Answers to the odd-numbered review problems are at the end of the book.

1. **(LO1)** Jessica bought a $1150 television set for 25% down and the balance to be paid with interest at 11.25% compounded monthly in six equal monthly payments. Construct the full amortization schedule for the debt. Calculate the total interest paid.

2. **(LO1)** Givens, Hong, and Partners obtained a $7000 term loan at 8.5% compounded annually for new boardroom furniture. Prepare a complete amortization schedule in which the loan is repaid by equal semiannual payments over three years.

3. **(LO4) (LO2)** A $28,000 loan at 8% compounded quarterly is to be repaid by equal quarterly payments over a seven-year term.

    a. What will be the principal component of the sixth payment?

    b. What will be the interest portion of the twenty-second payment?

    c. How much will the loan's balance be reduced by Payments 10 to 15 inclusive?

    d. How much interest will be paid in the second year?

4. **(LO4) (LO2)** A 20-year annuity was purchased with $180,000 that had accumulated in an RRSP. The annuity provides a semiannually compounded rate of return of 5% and makes equal month-end payments.

    a. What will be the principal portion of Payment 134?

    b. What will be the interest portion of Payment 210?

    c. How much will the annuity's balance be reduced by Payments 75 to 100 inclusive?

    d. How much interest will be paid in the sixth year?

5. **(LO1)** Metro Construction received $60,000 in vendor financing at 10.5% compounded semiannually for the purchase of a loader. The contract requires semiannual payments of $10,000 until the debt is paid off. Construct the complete amortization schedule for the debt. How much total interest will be paid over the life of the loan?

6. **(LO1)** Suppose that the loan in Problem 5 permits an additional prepayment of principal on any scheduled payment date. Prepare another amortization schedule that reflects a prepayment of $5000 with the third scheduled payment. How much interest is saved as a result of the prepayment?

7. **(LO4) (LO2) (LO3)** An annuity providing a rate of return of 4.8% compounded monthly was purchased for $45,000. The annuity pays $400 at the end of each month.

    a. How much of Payment 37 will be interest?

    b. What will be the principal portion of Payment 92?

    c. How much interest will be paid by Payments 85 to 96 inclusive?

    d. How much principal will be repaid in the fifth year?

    e. What will be the amount of the final payment?

8. **(LO1) (LO2)** The interest rate on a $6400 loan is 10% compounded semiannually. If the loan is to be repaid by monthly payments over a four-year term, prepare a partial amortization schedule showing details of the first two payments, Payments 34 and 35, and the last two payments.

9. **(LO3) (LO4) (LO2)** A $255,000 amount from an RRSP is used to purchase an annuity paying $6000 at the end of each quarter. The annuity provides an annually compounded rate of return of 6%.

    a. What will be the amount of the final payment?

    b. What will be the interest portion of the twenty-seventh payment?

    c. What will be the principal portion of the fifty-third payment?

    d. How much will the principal balance be reduced by Payments 14 to 20 inclusive?

    e. How much interest will be received in the sixth year?

∘10. **(LO5) (LO2)** A mortgage contract for $45,000 written 10 years ago is just at the end of its second five-year term. The interest rates were 8% compounded semiannually for the first term and 7% compounded semiannually for the second term. If monthly payments throughout have been based on the original 25-year amortization, calculate the principal balance at the end of the second term.

∘11. **(LO5) (LO6)** The interest rate for the first three years of an $87,000 mortgage is 7.4% compounded semiannually. Monthly payments are based on a 20-year amortization. If a $4000 prepayment is made at the end of the sixteenth month:

    a. How much will the amortization period be shortened?

    b. What will be the principal balance at the end of the three-year term?

∘12. **(LO1) (LO2)** Niagara Haulage obtained an $80,000 loan at 7.2% compounded monthly to build a storage shed. Construct a partial amortization schedule for payments of $1000 per month showing details of the first two payments, Payments 41 and 42, and the last two payments.

∘13. **(LO5) (LO2)** The interest rate for the first five years of a $90,000 mortgage loan is 7.25% compounded semiannually. Monthly payments are calculated using a 20-year amortization.

    a. What will be the principal balance at the end of the five-year term?

    b. What will be the new payments if the loan is renewed at 6.5% compounded semiannually (and the original amortization period is continued)?

∘14. **(LO5)** A mortgage calls for monthly payments of $887.96 for 25 years. If the loan was for $135,000, calculate the semiannually compounded nominal rate of interest on the loan.

∘15. **(LO5)** A $25,000 home improvement (mortgage) loan charges interest at 6.6% compounded monthly for a three-year term. Monthly payments are based on a 10-year amortization and rounded up to the next $10. What will be the principal balance at the end of the first term?

∘16. **(LO5) (LO6)** The interest rate for the first five years of a $95,000 mortgage is 7.2% compounded semiannually. Monthly payments are based on a 25-year amortization. If a $3000 prepayment is made at the end of the third year:

    a. How much will the amortization period be shortened?

    b. What will be the principal balance at the end of the five-year term?

∘17. **(LO5) (LO6)** After two years of the first five-year term at 6.7% compounded semiannually, Dan and Laurel decide to take advantage of the privilege of increasing the payments on their $110,000 mortgage loan by 10%. The monthly payments were originally calculated for a 25-year amortization.

    a. How much will the amortization period be shortened?

    b. What will be the principal balance at the end of the five-year term?

APPENDIX 14A

INSTRUCTIONS FOR THE TEXAS INSTRUMENTS BA-II PLUS AMORTIZATION WORKSHEET

The Amortization Worksheet enables you to quickly obtain the interest and principal components of any loan payment, or to quickly obtain the total of the interest components and the total of the principal components in a group of consecutive payments.

Let us use an example to demonstrate the use of the Amortization Worksheet. A $10,000 loan at 6% compounded monthly is repaid by monthly payments over a five-year term. Suppose we want to determine the total interest and total principal in Payments 11 to 20 inclusive.

The basic information about the loan must be entered in the usual manner in the | I/Y |, | PV |, | PMT |, | P/Y |, and | C/Y | memories. In the present example, we do not know the value for | PMT | at the outset. Therefore, we must first calculate it. Then we must re-enter the *rounded* value in the | PMT | memory *before* accessing the Amortization Worksheet.

Find "AMORT" located above the | PV | key. To access the Amortization Worksheet, press | 2nd | | AMORT |. Recall that a worksheet can be thought of as a column of items that you can view one-at-a-time in the calculator's display. The "AMORT" worksheet's column contains the five items listed below. You see the top item when you first access the worksheet. Other items may be viewed using the scroll keys | ↓ | and | ↑ |.

6 | I/Y |
| P/Y | 12 | ENTER |
(making C/Y = P/Y = 12)
60 | N |
10000 | PV |
0 | FV |
| CPT | | PMT |
Ans: −193.3280
193.33 | +/− | | PMT |

P1 =	nn
P2 =	nn
BAL =	n,nnn.nn
PRN =	n,nnn.nn
INT =	n,nnn.nn

P1 represents the serial number of the *first* payment in the group of consecutive payments. *P2* represents the serial number of the *last* payment in the group. *BAL* represents the principal balance *after* Payment number *P2*. *PRN* and *INT* represent the total principal and total interest in Payments *P1* to *P2 inclusive*. Where the letters nn and n,nnn.nn are indicated above, you will see numerical values in your display.

We want the total interest and total principal in Payments 11 to 20 inclusive. After accessing the worksheet,

Press		11	ENTER		to set *P1* = 11
Press		↓		20	ENTER		to scroll down and set *P2* = 20
Press		↓			to scroll down and view "*BAL* = 6,993.06"
Press		↓			to scroll down and view "*PRN* = −1,540.95"
Press		↓			to scroll down and view "*INT* = −392.35"
Press		2nd			QUIT		to exit from the worksheet

The balance after Payment 20 is $6993.06, the total principal in Payments 11 to 20 inclusive is $1540.95, and the total interest in the same group of payments is $392.35.

The computation took place at the moment you pressed the ⌊ ↓ ⌋ key after entering the value for *P2*. The calculator uses the Retrospective Method. Consequently, it ignores whatever value may be residing in the ⌊ FV ⌋ memory.

If you want the interest and principal components of a *single* payment (and the balance after that payment), enter the payment's serial number for *both P1 and P2*.

| APPENDIX 14B |

AMORTIZATION FUNCTIONS ON THE SHARP EL-738 CALCULATOR

We will use the following example to demonstrate the use of the amortization functions on the Sharp EL-738 calculator. A $10,000 loan at 6% compounded monthly must be repaid by monthly payments over a five-year term. Suppose we want to determine: (a) the total interest and total principal in Payments 11 to 20 inclusive, and (b) the interest and principal components of Payment 15.

The basic information about the loan must be entered in the usual manner in the ⌊ I/Y ⌋, ⌊ P/Y ⌋, ⌊ C/Y ⌋, ⌊ N ⌋, ⌊ PV ⌋, ⌊ PMT ⌋, and ⌊ FV ⌋ memories. Since the payment is not given in the current example, you must first calculate it. In this example, you obtain *PMT* = $193.3280. Then re-enter the value of *PMT rounded* to the nearest cent (and with the proper sign for the direction of the cash flow) in the ⌊ PMT ⌋ memory.

a. Press ⌊AMORT⌋ — to access the amortization worksheet. The first line in the display reads "*AMRT P1 =*"

Press 11 ⌊ ENT ⌋ — to set the first payment's serial number at *P1* = 11

Press ⌊ ↓ ⌋ 20 ⌊ ENT ⌋ — to scroll down and set the second payment's serial number at *P2* = 20

Press ⌊ ↓ ⌋ — to scroll down and view the balance after Payment 20: "*BALANCE* = 6993.06"

Press ⌊ ↓ ⌋ — to scroll down and view the total principal in Payments 11 to 20: "*ΣPRINCIPAL* = −1540.95"

Press ⌊ ↓ ⌋ — to scroll down and view the total interest in Payments 11 to 20: "*ΣINTEREST* = −392.35"

b. Scroll back to the initial "*AMRT P1 =*" line.

Press 15 ⌊ ENT ⌋ — to set the first payment's serial number at *P1* = 15

Press ⌊ ↓ ⌋ 15 ⌊ ENT ⌋ — to scroll down and also set the second payment's serial number at *P2* = 15

Press ⌊ ↓ ⌋ — to scroll down and view the balance after Payment 15: "*BALANCE* = 7773.15"

Press ⌊ ↓ ⌋ — to scroll down and view the principal component of Payment 15: "*ΣPRINCIPAL* = −153.70"

Press ⌊ ↓ ⌋ — to scroll down and view the interest component of Payment 15: "*ΣINTEREST* = −39.63"

Press ⌊ON/C⌋ — when you are ready to exit from the worksheet.

LEARNING OBJECTIVES

After completing this chapter, you will be able to:

LO1 Calculate the market price of a bond on any date

LO2 Calculate the yield to maturity of a bond on an interest payment date

LO3 Calculate the payment for a sinking fund

LO4 Prepare a sinking fund schedule

THE PRIMARY MEANS BY WHICH our three levels of government and publicly listed corporations finance their long-term debt is by issuing the type of bonds described in this chapter. At the end of 2009, $356 billion of the government of Canada's $565 billion net federal debt was financed by these "marketable" bonds. In comparison, about $183 billion was financed by Treasury Bills and $12.1 billion by Canada Savings Bonds. The total of provincial, territorial, and municipal bonds outstanding exceeded that of Government of Canada bonds. Corporate bonds totalling over $603 billion represented about three-quarters of all corporate long-term debt in 2009.

Even though you may never directly own marketable bonds, you will probably indirectly invest in them at some point in the future. Marketable bonds form a significant portion of many managed portfolios such as bond mutual funds, balanced mutual funds, and pension plans. The Canada Pension Plan had almost $33.5 billion invested in provincial and federal government bonds at the end of 2009.

The purchaser of a bond is not "locked in" for the entire lifetime of the bond. There is an active, efficient "bond market" for the sale and purchase of bonds after their initial issue. In this chapter, you will learn how to calculate bond prices that are reported in the financial news.

15.1 | BASIC CONCEPTS AND DEFINITIONS

A bond is a certificate representing the borrower's debt obligation to the bond holder. The borrower is usually called the bond issuer. We will adopt the widespread practice of using the term *bond* loosely to refer to both true bonds and debentures. The technical distinction between a bond and a debenture is that a **bond** is secured by specific assets of the borrower, whereas a **debenture** is backed only by the general credit of the borrower. Therefore, Government of Canada "bonds" are, in fact, debentures since no particular assets secure them. The distinction is not important for the mathematics of bonds.

Unlike term loans, where each payment includes a principal portion that reduces the debt, bonds require that the borrower make periodic payments of interest only. Then, on the **maturity date** of the bond, the full principal amount is repaid along with the final interest payment. Bonds are issued with maturities ranging from 2 to 30 years.

The bond certificate sets out the main features of the loan contract. The following items are part of the information you need to calculate a bond's market price.

- The **issue date** is the date on which the loan was made and on which interest starts to accrue.

- The **face value** (or *denomination*) is the principal amount of the debt represented by the bond. The most common face values are $1000, $5000, and $25,000, although larger denominations are often issued to institutional investors. Normally, the issuer of a bond will redeem the bond on its maturity date at a **redemption price** equal to its face value. There are special circumstances under which a bond may be redeemed on or before its maturity date at a redemption price different from the face value. These circumstances are beyond the scope of coverage in this textbook. We assume that bonds will be redeemed on their maturity date for their face value.

- The **coupon rate**[1] is the contractual rate of interest paid on the face value of the bond. It is a *semiannually* compounded rate and is normally fixed for the life of the bond. The vast majority of bonds pay interest at six-month intervals, measured from the issue date.[2] Therefore, such interest payments form an ordinary *simple* annuity.

You should be clear on the distinction between *savings* bonds (such as Canada Savings Bonds described in Section 8.5) and the *marketable* bonds discussed in this chapter. You can cash in a *savings* bond before its scheduled maturity date and receive the full face value plus accrued interest. *Marketable* bonds such as Government of Canada bonds do not have this open-redemption privilege. If you want to liquidate a marketable bond before it matures, you must sell it through an investment dealer who participates in the "bond market." Let us now address the question of what determines the market value of a bond.

BOND PRICE ON AN INTEREST PAYMENT DATE

Most bonds pay interest semiannually, offer no early redemption privileges, and are redeemed for their face value at maturity. In this section we are concerned with pricing bonds that have these typical features. But before we begin discussing the mathematics of bond pricing, you should understand *why* bond prices change in the bond market.[3]

DEPENDENCE OF BOND PRICE ON PREVAILING INTEREST RATES

On the date a bond is issued, its coupon rate must be a competitive rate of return. The bond issuer cannot expect a prudent investor to buy a new 6% coupon bond (for the full face value) if the investor can earn a 7% rate of return from other investments of similar risk.

Subsequent to the issue date, prevailing interest rates in the financial markets change (and the coupon rate offered on *subsequent new* bond issues must change accordingly). However, the coupon rate on a previously issued bond is *fixed* for the life of the bond. If its coupon rate *exceeds* the current competitive rate of return, investors will be willing to pay *more* than the face value to acquire the bond. If the bond's coupon rate is *less* than the current competitive rate of return, investors will not buy the bond unless its price is a suitable amount *below* face value.

To make our discussion more specific, consider the four hypothetical Government of Canada bonds listed in Table 15.1. The issue dates and initial terms have been chosen so that, as of today's date, every bond has five years remaining until maturity. Consequently, the four $1000 face-value bonds represent identical investments except for differing coupon rates. The coupon rate on the *newly issued* Bond A is 6% compounded semiannually. Therefore, we can conclude that the prevailing competitive rate of return for five-year maturity bonds is also 6% compounded semiannually.

---

[1] This term originated many years ago when it was customary for the bond certificate to have interest coupons attached to its margin. At each interest payment date, the bond holder would clip off the matured coupon and present it at a bank to receive payment in cash. Most bonds are now registered in the owner's name, and interest payments are made by direct deposit to an investment account or by cheque sent through the mail.

[2] If a bond's maturity date is the last day of a month, both semiannual coupons are paid on the *last* days of the appropriate months. For example, a bond maturing on September 30 pays its March coupon on March 31 (rather than on March 30). A bond maturing on October 31 pays an April coupon on April 30. If a bond's maturity date is August 29 or 30, it pays a February coupon on February 28 (or February 29 in a leap year).

[3] For the most part, bonds are not bought and sold at a particular physical location corresponding to the stock exchanges for common shares. The "bond market" consists of investment dealers who are linked by telecommunications networks and who act as intermediaries between bond buyers and sellers.

TABLE 15.1   Relative Prices of $1000 Face Value Bonds

Bond	Issue date	Initial term (years)	Couponrate (%)	Bond price
A	Today	5	6	$1000
B	5 years ago	10	7	More than $1000
C	10 years ago	15	6	$1000
D	15 years ago	20	5	Less than $1000

We will now develop the reasoning for the relative bond prices indicated in the last column. Bonds C and A both carry a 6% coupon and have five years remaining until maturity. Therefore, Bond C is identical to Bond A from this point onward. Its market value will always be the same as the market value of Bond A. Today that value is $1000. When a bond trades at its face value, it is said to trade "at par." Any bond will trade at par if its coupon rate equals the prevailing rate of return required in the bond market.

Bond B carries a coupon rate that is 1% above the current competitive rate. It will pay $70 interest per year ($35 every six months), whereas Bond A will pay only $60 per year. If you could buy Bond B for $1000, you would earn a 7% rate of return on your investment. Since the prevailing rate of return is only 6%, investors will prefer Bond B and bid its price above $1000. As the purchase price rises, the rate of return on the purchase price declines (because the future interest payments to the bond holder remain fixed, regardless of the amount paid for the bond).

TRAP   Don't Overlook the Capital Gain or Loss Component of Total Return

You might think that bond B's price will rise to the level at which the $70 interest received each year provides the required 6% rate of return. This price would be about $1167 since $\frac{\$70}{\$1167} \times 100\% = 6.00\%$. But this line of reasoning misses part of the broader picture. Suppose you buy bond B for $1167 and hold the bond until it matures. In addition to the final interest payment on the maturity date, you will be paid the $1000 face value, not the $1167 you paid for the bond. Therefore, you will suffer a $167 capital loss for the entire holding period. This reduces your annual rate of *total* return (Section 9.5) below the 6% we calculated for the income yield. For your rate of *total* return to be 6%, you can pay more than $1000 but not as much as $1167. Then the capital loss will be smaller and the income yield will exceed 6%. We will learn how to calculate the precise price point at which the extra income yield offsets the capital loss, leaving a 6% rate of total return.

Bond D pays only $50 interest per year ($25 every six months). Investors will not buy Bond D until its price falls to an appropriate level below $1000. If you buy a bond for *less* than its face value, you will realize a capital *gain* when the face value is received at maturity. The market value of Bond D is the price at which the interest payments, combined with the capital gain, provide a rate of *total* return equal to 6% compounded semiannually.

Summary The market value of Bond B is more than its face value because its coupon rate exceeds the required rate of return in the bond market. In other words, if the market rate *falls below* the coupon rate, the bond's price *rises above* its face value. The market value of Bond D is less than its face value because its coupon rate is less than the required rate of return in the bond market. In other words, if the market rate *rises above* the coupon rate, the bond's price *falls below* its face value. This inverse relation between market rate of return and market value is easily remembered using the "teeter-totter model" shown in Figure 15.1.

FIGURE 15.1 Effects of Interest Rate Changes on Bond Prices

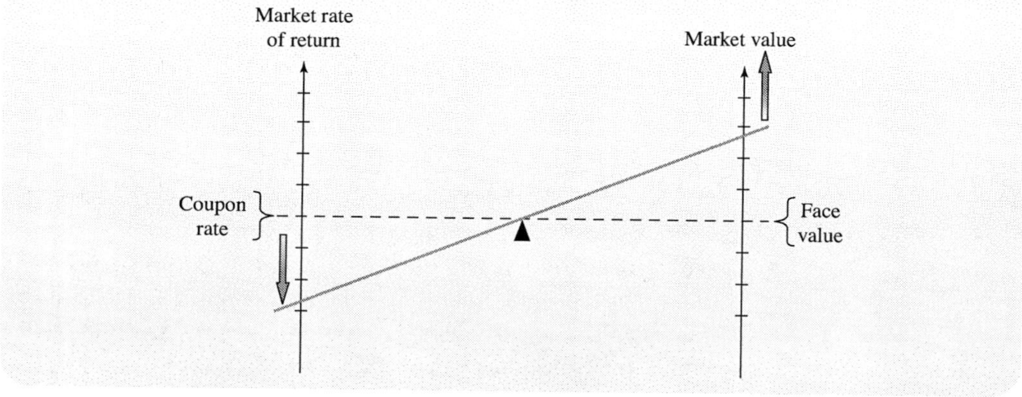

In the particular case shown in the diagram, the market rate of return has fallen below the bond's coupon rate. Pushing the market-rate-of-return end of the teeter-totter down below the coupon rate raises the market-value end above the bond's face value. (This is the Bond B case.) The more the market rate falls below the coupon rate, the higher the bond price will rise above the face value. If prevailing rates in the bond market start to rise (from the level depicted in the diagram), all bond prices will start to decline. But a particular bond's price will not fall below face value until the market's required rate of return rises above that bond's coupon rate.

Later in this section we will add another feature to the model that will make it particularly helpful.

CALCULATING A BOND'S PRICE ON AN INTEREST PAYMENT DATE

LO1 The pricing or valuation of bonds is yet another application where we use the Valuation Principle to determine an investment's fair market value. To apply the Valuation Principle to bonds, we need to:

1. Determine the amount and timing of future payments.
2. Determine the rate of return currently required in the bond market.
3. Calculate the present value of the future payments using this rate of return as the discount rate.

If we let

$2b$ = Coupon rate (compounded semiannually) and
FV = Face value of the bond

then the interest rate for the six-month interest payment interval is b and the semi-annual interest payment is:

$$b \times (\text{Face value}) = b \times FV$$

In this section we consider the special case where a bond is being sold on an interest payment date (with the interest payment going to the seller). Figure 15.2 illustrates the future payments that a prospective purchaser/investor can expect to receive. There are n interest payments remaining until the bond matures. Each interest payment is $b(FV)$. At the time of the final interest payment, the face value FV will also be received. According to the Valuation Principle, the fair market value of the bond is the present value of these future payments discounted at the *prevailing rate of return* in the bond market. That is,

$$\begin{pmatrix}\text{Fair market}\\ \text{value of a bond}\end{pmatrix} = \begin{pmatrix}\text{Present value of the}\\ \text{interest payments}\end{pmatrix} + \begin{pmatrix}\text{Present value of}\\ \text{the face value}\end{pmatrix}$$

NET @ssets

The current market rates of return for selected maturities of Government of Canada bonds are posted on the Bank of Canada's Web site. The relevant Web page may be accessed by going to the Student Edition of the textbook's Web site. In Chapter 15, find "Canada Bond Yields." For each maturity, the market-determined rate of return over the past year is displayed in a graph, and the rates for the most recent five business days are presented in a table.

The term *yield* is used on the Web page and in everyday "bond talk" to mean *yield to maturity*, which we will discuss in Section 15.3. It actually represents the bond's *total* rate of return, rather than just the interest-income yield.

An inspection of the diagrams and tables on the Web page will give you a sense of the month-to-month and day-to-day variations in the rate of return required in the financial markets from these low-risk bonds.

FIGURE 15.2 Expected Payments from a Bond

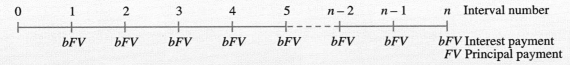

Since the interest payments form an ordinary annuity, we will use formula (10-2) to obtain the present value of the interest payments. The present value of the face value can be calculated using $PV = FV(1 + i)^{-n}$. Hence, the combined present value is

BOND PRICE (ON AN INTEREST PAYMENT DATE)

$$\text{Bond price} = b(FV)\left[\frac{1 - (1 + i)^{-n}}{i}\right] + FV(1 + i)^{-n} \tag{15-1}$$

where i is the prevailing six-month periodic rate of return in the bond market.

> **TIP** **Different Roles of Coupon Rate and Bond Market Rate of Return**
>
> The bond's coupon rate is used only to determine the size of the periodic interest payments. The prevailing rate of return in the bond market is used to discount the future payments when calculating the bond's price.

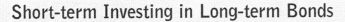

POINT OF INTEREST

Short-term Investing in Long-term Bonds

In the year 2008, $1100 billion ($1,100,000,000,000) worth of Government of Canada bonds changed hands in the Canadian bond market! The following information may be helpful in gaining a sense of the importance of the bond market and the volume of its transactions.

Stocks and the stock market receive vastly more coverage in the media than bonds and the bond market. The aggregate value of shares traded on the Toronto Stock Exchange in 2008 was almost $1850 billion. Therefore, trading in Government of Canada bonds alone represented 60% of the value of all stocks traded on the TSX. (About 75% of all bond trading is in Government of Canada issues.)

The average total face value of Government of Canada bonds outstanding during 2008 was $228 billion. How can the value of transactions in the year ($1100 billion) exceed the value of bonds potentially available for sale? The most important factor by far is the following. If a particular bond is sold three times in the year, its selling price will be counted three times in the figure for the total value of trading. To get the $1100 billion figure for the value of Government of Canada bonds sold/bought in 2008, the entire $228 billion of outstanding Government of Canada bonds were, in effect, sold $\frac{\$1100}{\$228} \approx 4.8$ times during the year! This makes the average holding period only about 75 days! Now you understand the stereotype of the bond dealer holding a telephone handset in each hand and speaking into both.

EXAMPLE 15.2A   **CALCULATING THE PRICE OF A BOND ON AN INTEREST PAYMENT DATE**

Calculate the market value of Bonds B, C, and D in Table 15.1 (reproduced below).

Bond	Issue date	Initial term (years)	Coupon rate (%)	Bond price
A	Today	5	6	$1000
B	5 years ago	10	7	More than $1000
C	10 years ago	15	6	$1000
D	15 years ago	20	5	Less than $1000

SOLUTION

Since the new issue of five-year bonds carries a 6% coupon rate, the current competitive rate of return on five-year bonds is 6% compounded semiannually. Therefore, we will use $i = \frac{6\%}{2} = 3\%$ to discount the remaining payments from bonds B, C, and D.

For Bond B, $FV = \$1000,$ $n = 2(5) = 10,$ $b = \frac{7\%}{2} = 3.5\%,$ $b(FV) = 0.035(\$1000) = \$35$

Similarly, for Bond C, $FV = \$1000,$ $n = 10,$ $b = 3\%,$ $b(FV) = \$30$

and for Bond D, $FV = \$1000,$ $n = 10,$ $b = 2.5\%,$ $b(FV) = \$25$

$$\text{Price of Bond B} = b(FV)\left[\frac{1 - (1 + i)^{-n}}{i}\right] + FV(1 + i)^{-n}$$

$$= \$35\left(\frac{1 - 1.03^{-10}}{0.03}\right) + \$1000(1.03^{-10})$$

$$= \$298.56 + \$744.09$$

$$= \$1042.65$$

> 6 I/Y
> P/Y 2 ENTER
> (making $C/Y = P/Y = 2$)
> 10 N
> 35 PMT
> 1000 FV
> CPT PV
> *Ans:* −1042.65

$$\text{Price of Bond C} = \$30\left(\frac{1 - 1.03^{-10}}{0.03}\right) + \$1000(1.03^{-10})$$

$$= \$255.91 + \$744.09$$

$$= \$1000.00$$

> Same I/Y, P/Y, C/Y, N, FV
> 30 PMT
> CPT PV
> *Ans:* −1000.00

$$\text{Price of Bond D} = \$25\left(\frac{1 - 1.03^{-10}}{0.03}\right) + \$1000(1.03^{-10})$$

$$= \$213.26 + \$744.09$$

$$= \$957.35$$

> Same I/Y, P/Y, C/Y, N, FV
> 25 PMT
> CPT PV
> *Ans:* −957.35

The prices of Bonds B, C, and D are $1042.65, $1000, and $957.35, respectively. These prices confirm the relative prices we deduced in the last column of Table 15.1.

Postscript: Let us be clear on how the purchaser of Bond B will earn the market rate of return (6%) that the present value calculation builds into the bond's price. The $70 annual interest by itself represents an *income yield* of

$$\frac{\$70}{\$1042.65} \times 100\% = 6.7\%$$

However, over the entire five years there will be a *capital loss* of $1042.65 − $1000 = $42.65. The capital loss per year is

$$\frac{\$42.65}{5} = \$8.53 \text{ representing a loss of } \frac{\$8.53}{\$1042.65} \times 100\% = 0.8\% \text{ per } year$$

Rate of total return = Income yield + Capital loss yield $\approx 6.7\% + (-0.8\%) \approx 5.9\%$

(The reason we do not get exactly 6% compounded semiannually is that our crude calculation ignores the timing of payments and the effect of semiannual compounding.)

EXAMPLE 15.2B **CALCULATING A BOND'S PRICE CHANGE RESULTING FROM A CHANGE IN THE PREVAILING INTEREST RATE**

A $5000 face value bond has a coupon rate of 6.6% and a maturity date of March 1, 2027. Interest is paid semiannually. On September 1, 2011, the prevailing interest rate on long-term bonds abruptly rose from 6% to 6.2% compounded semiannually. What were the bond's prices before and after the interest rate change?

SOLUTION

Given: $FV = \$5000$, $b = \frac{6.6\%}{2} = 3.3\%$

September 1, 2011 was an interest payment date, after which $15\frac{1}{2}$ years remain until maturity of the bond ($n = 31$). The semiannual interest from the bond is

$$b(FV) = 0.033(\$5000) = \$165$$

On September 1, 2011, the prevailing periodic market rate rose from

$$i = \frac{6\%}{2} = 3\% \quad \text{to} \quad i = \frac{6.2\%}{2} = 3.1\%$$

$$\text{Bond price before rate increase} = b(FV)\left[\frac{1 - (1 + i)^{-n}}{i}\right] + FV(1 + i)^{-n}$$

$$= \$165\left(\frac{1 - 1.03^{-31}}{0.03}\right) + \$5000(1.03^{-31})$$

$$= \$3300.07 + \$1999.94$$

$$= \$5300.01$$

$$\text{Bond price after rate increase} = \$165\left(\frac{1 - 1.031^{-31}}{0.031}\right) + \$5000(1.031^{-31})$$

$$= \$3256.71 + \$1940.67$$

$$= \$5197.38$$

The bond's price dropped from $5300.01 to $5197.38 as a result of the interest rate increase. [Although the bond's price remained above the face value (since $b > i$), the bond price decreased by $102.63.]

6 I/Y
P/Y 2 ENTER
(making $C/Y = P/Y = 2$)
31 N
165 PMT
5000 FV
CPT PV
Ans: −5300.01

Same *P/Y, C/Y*
Same *N, PMT, FV*
6.2 I/Y
CPT PV
Ans: −5197.38

EXAMPLE 15.2C **CALCULATING THE CAPITAL GAIN FROM AN INVESTMENT IN BONDS**

Mr. Manhas purchased 10 bonds, each with a face value of $1000 and paying a 6% coupon rate. On the purchase date, the bonds still had $9\frac{1}{2}$ years remaining until maturity, and the market rate of return for bonds of this maturity was 7% compounded semiannually. Two and one-half years later, when the interest rate had declined to 5.5% compounded semiannually, he sold the bonds. What was the capital gain (or loss) on the bond investment?

SOLUTION

Capital gain = 10(Selling price per bond − Purchase price per bond)

For calculating the purchase price of each bond,

$FV = \$1000 \quad b = \frac{6\%}{2} = 3\% \quad b(FV) = \$30 \quad n = 2(9.5) = 19 \quad \text{and} \quad i = \frac{7\%}{2} = 3.5\%$

For calculating the selling price of each bond,

$FV = \$1000 \quad b = 3\% \quad b(FV) = \$30 \quad n = 2(7) = 14 \quad \text{and} \quad i = \frac{5.5\%}{2} = 2.75\%$

$$\text{Purchase price} = b(FV)\left[\frac{1 - (1 + i)^{-n}}{i}\right] + FV(1 + i)^{-n}$$

$$= \$30\left(\frac{1 - 1.035^{-19}}{0.035}\right) + \$1000(1.035^{-19})$$

$$= \$411.295 + \$520.156$$

$$= \$931.45$$

$$\text{Selling price} = \$30\left(\frac{1 - 1.0275^{-14}}{0.0275}\right) + \$1000(1.0275^{-14})$$

$$= \$344.730 + \$683.997$$

$$= \$1028.73$$

Capital gain = 10(\$1028.73 − \$931.45) = \$972.80

7	I/Y
P/Y	2 ENTER

(making $C/Y = P/Y = 2$)

19	N
30	PMT
1000	FV
CPT	PV

Ans: −931.45

Same *P/Y, C/Y, PMT, FV*

14	N
5.5	I/Y
CPT	PV

Ans: −1028.73

Bond Premium and Bond Discount Figure 15.3 shows graphs of bond price versus the prevailing market rate of return for two 7% coupon, $1000 face value bonds. One bond has five years remaining until maturity, and the other has 10 years until maturity. For the reasons discussed earlier, the market values of both bonds are *below* their $1000 face value when the market rate of return *exceeds* the 7% coupon rate. In this circumstance, we say that each bond trades at a discount. The amount of the discount is

$$\text{Bond discount} = \text{Face value} - \text{Bond price} \quad \text{when } i > b$$

The discount is larger for the bond with the longer maturity.

FIGURE 15.3   Bond Price versus Market Rate of Return for Two Maturities of 7% Coupon Bonds

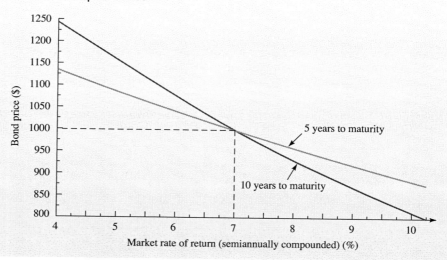

Similarly, the market values of both bonds are *above* their face value when the market rate of return is *less* than the 7% coupon rate. In this circumstance, we say that each bond trades at a premium. The amount of the premium is

$$\text{Bond premium} = \text{Bond price} - \text{Face value} \quad \text{when } i < b$$

The premium is larger for the bond with the longer maturity.

The dependence of the discount or premium on the time remaining until maturity can be added to our teeter-totter model as shown in Figure 15.4. Think of bonds with longer maturities as "sitting" further out from the pivot point on the right arm of the teeter-totter. For a given interest rate movement of the left arm, bonds further away from the pivot point will move through a larger vertical distance. That is, longer-term bonds will undergo a greater change in market value than shorter-term bonds.

FIGURE 15.4   Dependence of Bond Premium on Time to Maturity

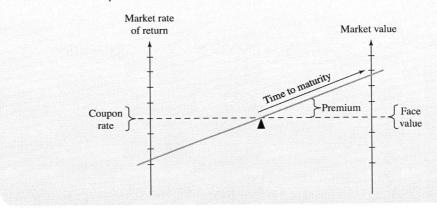

CONCEPT QUESTIONS

1. Name four variables that affect a bond's price. Which ones, if any, have an inverse effect on the bond's price? That is, for which variables does a lower value of the variable result in a higher bond price?

2. Under what circumstance can you realize a capital gain on a bond investment?

3. Assuming that the bond issuer does not default on any payments, is it possible to lose money on a bond investment? Discuss briefly.

4. On a recent interest payment date, a bond's price exceeded its face value. If the prevailing market rate of return does not change thereafter, will the bond's premium be different on later interest payment dates? Explain.

5. If you are firmly convinced that prevailing interest rates will decline, how should you change the relative weighting of short-term and long-term bonds in your bond portfolio?

EXERCISE 15.2

☰ connect

Spreadsheet template: The Excel workbook "PV of Any Annuity" may be used for many of the problems in Exercise 15.2. Go to Chapter 10 of the Student Edition of Connect and find "PV of Any Annuity."

Answers to the odd-numbered problems are at the end of the book.

Note: Unless otherwise indicated, assume that:
- **Bond interest is paid semiannually.**
- **The bond was originally issued at its face value.**
- **Bonds are redeemed at their face value at maturity.**
- **Market rates of return are compounded semiannually.**

Calculate the purchase price of each of the $1000 face value bonds in Problems 1 through 8.

Problem	Issue date	Maturity date	Purchase date	Coupon rate (%)	Market rate (%)
1.	June 1, 2000	June 1, 2020	June 1, 2006	5.75	4.5
2.	June 15, 2005	June 15, 2030	Dec 15, 2011	5.0	6.0
3.	Dec 15, 1998	Dec 15. 2023	June 15, 2001	4.75	5.9
4.	Jan 1, 1997	Jan 1, 2017	July 1, 2005	7.3	3.8
5.	May 15, 2000	May 15, 2020	Nov 15, 2006	6.0	4.0
6.	Jan 31, 2009	Jan 31, 2039	July 31, 2011	5.1	6.0
7.	Mar 15, 1977	Mar 15, 2002	Sept 15, 1981	8.8	17.0
8.	Oct 31, 1981	Oct 31, 2006	Apr 30, 1998	16.0	5.7

9. Denis purchased a $10,000 face value Ontario Hydro Energy bond maturing in five years. The coupon rate was 6.5% payable semiannually. If the prevailing market rate at the time of purchase was 5.8% compounded semiannually, what price did Denis pay for the bond? (Taken from CIFP course materials.)

10. Bernard purchased a $50,000 bond carrying a 4.5% coupon rate when it had 8 years remaining until maturity. What price did he pay if the prevailing rate of return on the purchase date was 5.2% compounded semiannually? (Taken from CIFP course materials.)

11. A $1000, 6.5% coupon bond has $13\frac{1}{2}$ years remaining until maturity. Calculate the bond premium if the required return in the bond market is 5.5% compounded semiannually.

12. A $1000, 5.5% coupon bond has $8\frac{1}{2}$ years remaining until maturity. Calculate the bond discount if the required return in the bond market is 6.3% compounded semiannually.

13. A $5000, 5.75% coupon bond has 16 years remaining until maturity. Calculate the bond discount if the required return in the bond market is 6.5% compounded semiannually.

14. A $25,000, 6.25% coupon bond has $21\frac{1}{2}$ years remaining until maturity. Calculate the bond premium if the required return in the bond market is 5.2% compounded semiannually.

15. Eight years ago, Yan purchased a $20,000 face value, 6% coupon bond with 15 years remaining to maturity. The prevailing market rate of return at the time was 7.2% compounded semiannually; now it is 4.9% compounded semiannually. How much more or less is the bond worth today?

16. Bond A and Bond B both have a face value of $1000, each carries a 5% coupon, and both are currently priced at par in the bond market. Bond A matures in 2 years and Bond B matures in 10 years. If the prevailing required rate of return in the bond market suddenly drops to 4.7% compounded semiannually, how much will the market price of each bond change? What general rule does this outcome demonstrate?

17. Bond C and Bond D both have a face value of $1000, and each carries a 4.2% coupon. Bond C matures in 3 years and Bond B matures in 23 years. If the prevailing required rate of return in the bond market suddenly rises from the current 4.5% to 4.8% compounded semiannually, how much will the market price of each bond change? What general rule does this outcome demonstrate?

18. Using the "Market Value of Bonds" Chart This textbook's Web site provides an interactive chart for comparing the response of the prices of two bonds to a given change in the bond market's required rate of return. In Chapter 15 of the Student Edition, find "Market Value of Bonds." Follow the instructions provided with this chart to solve:

    a. Problem 16.   **b.** Problem 17.

19. Bonds A, B, C, and D all have a face value of $1000 and carry a 7% coupon. The time remaining until maturity is 5, 10, 15, and 25 years for A, B, C, and D, respectively. Calculate their market prices if the rate of return required by the market on these bonds is 6% compounded semiannually. Summarize the observed pattern or trend in a brief statement.

20. Bonds E, F, G, and H all have a face value of $1000 and carry a 7% coupon. The time remaining until maturity is 5, 10, 15, and 25 years for E, F, G, and H, respectively. Calculate their market prices if the rate of return required by the market on these bonds is 8% compounded semiannually. Summarize the observed pattern or trend in a brief statement.

21. Bonds J, K, and L all have a face value of $1000 and all have 20 years remaining until maturity. Their respective coupon rates are 6%, 7%, and 8%. Calculate their market prices if the rate of return required by the market on these bonds is 5% compounded semiannually. Summarize the observed pattern or trend in a brief statement.

22. Bonds M, N, and Q all have a face value of $1000 and all have 20 years remaining until maturity. Their respective coupon rates are 7%, 6%, and 5%. Calculate their market prices if the rate of return required by the market on these bonds is 8% compounded semiannually. Summarize the observed pattern or trend in a brief statement.

○**23.** A $1000, 7% coupon bond has 15 years remaining until maturity. The rate of return required by the market on these bonds has recently been 7% (compounded semiannually). Calculate the price change if the required return abruptly:

    a. Rises to 8%.   **b.** Rises to 9%.   **c.** Falls to 6%.   **d.** Falls to 5%.

    e. Is the price change caused by a 2% interest rate increase twice the price change caused by a 1% interest rate increase?

    f. Compare the magnitude of the price change caused by a 1% interest rate increase to the price change caused by a 1% interest rate decrease.

○**24.** This problem investigates the sensitivity of the prices of bonds carrying differing coupon rates to interest rate changes. Bonds K and L both have a face value of $1000 and 15 years remaining until maturity. Their coupon rates are 6% and 8% respectively. If the prevailing market rate decreases from 7.5% to 6.5% compounded semiannually, calculate the price change of each bond:

    a. In dollars.

    b. As a percentage of the initial price.

    c. Are high-coupon or low-coupon bonds more sensitive to a given interest rate change? Justify your response using the results from Part (b).

○**25.** Three years after the issue of a $10,000, 6.5% coupon, 25-year bond, the rate of return required in the bond market on long-term bonds is 5.6% compounded semiannually.

   a. At what price would the bond sell?

   b. What capital gain or loss (expressed as a percentage of the original investment) would the owner realize by selling the bond at that price?

○**26.** Four and one-half years ago Gavin purchased a $25,000 bond in a new Province of Ontario issue with a 20-year maturity and a 6.1% coupon. If the prevailing market rate is now 7.1% compounded semiannually:

   a. What would be the proceeds from the sale of Gavin's bond?

   b. What would be the capital gain or loss (expressed as a percentage of the original investment)?

○**27.** Three years ago Quebec Hydro sold an issue of 20-year, 6.5% coupon bonds. Calculate an investor's percent capital gain for the entire three-year holding period if the current semiannually compounded return required in the bond market is:

   a. 5.5%.   **b.** 6.5%.   **c.** 7.5%.

○**28.** Two and one-half years ago the Province of Saskatchewan sold an issue of 25-year, 6% coupon bonds. Calculate an investor's percent capital gain for the entire $2\frac{1}{2}$-year holding period if the current rate of return required in the bond market is:

   a. 6.5%.   **b.** 6%.   **c.** 5.5%.

•**29.** During periods of declining interest rates, long-term bonds can provide investors with impressive capital gains. An extraordinary example occurred in the early 1980s. In September 1981, the bond market was pricing long-term bonds to provide a rate of return of 18.5% compounded semiannually. Suppose you had purchased 10% coupon bonds in September 1981 with 20 years remaining until maturity. Four and one-half years later (in March 1986) the bonds could have been sold at a prevailing market rate of 9.7% compounded semiannually. What would have been your semiannually compounded rate of total return on the bonds during the $4\frac{1}{2}$-year period?

•**30.** The downside of the long-term bond investment story occurs during periods of rising long-term interest rates, when bond prices fall. During the two years preceding September 1981, the market rate of return on long-term bonds rose from 11% to 18.5% compounded semiannually. Suppose that in September 1979 you had purchased 10% coupon bonds with 22 years remaining until maturity, and then sold them in September 1981. What would have been your semiannually compounded rate of total return on the bonds during the two-year period?

15.3 YIELD TO MATURITY ON AN INTEREST PAYMENT DATE

LO2   Suppose you purchase a bond at the price given by formula (15-1). If you intend to *keep the bond until it matures,* your future rate of return can be predicted with certainty. It is the market rate of return used on the purchase date to calculate the purchase price. In the language of bonds, this rate of return is called the **yield to maturity** (YTM).[4] It is standard practice to quote the YTM as a semiannually compounded nominal rate. The yield to maturity is "locked in" by the price you pay for the bond—the higher the purchase price, the lower the bond's YTM.

---

[4]   The yield to maturity is sometimes called simply the "yield" or the "bond yield." For example, quotations of bond yields to maturity in newspapers' financial pages use just "yield" or "bond yield" to mean yield to maturity. However, "yield" is also used to refer to a bond's "current yield" (defined as the annual coupon interest as a percentage of the bond's market price). Therefore, use of the simple term "yield" to mean "yield to maturity" should be discouraged because of this ambiguity.

If you purchase a bond at the price given by formula (15-1) and intend to *sell it before it matures,* your future rate of return *cannot* be predicted with certainty. Your actual rate of return will depend on the ultimate selling price, which in turn will depend on the market rate of return on the date of sale. The prevailing market rate of return on a future date is not known in advance.

In Section 15.2, we learned how to answer the following question. Given the prevailing market rate of return (that is, given the yield to maturity required by the bond market), what is the market value of a bond? The other question a bond investor commonly faces is: What yield to maturity will a bond provide if it is purchased at its offered price?

To answer the second question, the mathematical task is to solve formula (15-1) for i given the bond price. The (semiannually compounded) yield to maturity is then $2i$. The algebraic approach requires the trial-and-error method (Appendix 11B in the textbook's Web site). In this method, you substitute estimates of i into the formula until you find an estimate that comes close to satisfying the formula. Since the financial calculator method for calculating the yield to maturity is more accurate and much more efficient, the algebraic method will be demonstrated in only one of the following examples.

EXAMPLE 15.3A   **CALCULATING THE YIELD TO MATURITY OF A BOND**

A $1000 face value Province of Manitoba bond, bearing interest at 5.8% payable semiannually, has 11 years remaining until maturity. What is the bond's yield to maturity (YTM) at its current market price of $972?

SOLUTION

This bond's yield to maturity is the discount rate that makes the combined present value of all remaining interest payments and the face value equal to the bond's market value. We are given:

$FV = \$1000$, $b = \frac{5.8\%}{2} = 2.9\%$, $b(FV) = \$29$, $n = 22$, and bond price = $972

Substitute these values into

$$\text{Bond price} = b(FV)\left[\frac{1 - (1 + i)^{-n}}{i}\right] + FV(1 + i)^{-n}$$

The YTM is the value of $2i$, where i is the solution to

$$\$972 = \$29\underbrace{\left[\frac{1 - (1 + i)^{-22}}{i}\right]}_{\text{Term 1}} + \underbrace{\$1000(1 + i)^{-22}}_{\text{Term 2}}$$

| P/Y 2 ENTER |
| (making $C/Y = P/Y = 2$) |
| 22 N |
| 972 +/− PV |
| 29 PMT |
| 1000 FV |
| CPT I/Y |

Ans: 6.154
The bond's YTM is 6.154% compounded semiannually.

In the trial-and-error method, we try various values for i on the right-hand side (RHS) until we get a value for the RHS sufficiently close to $972. For an initial estimate, we can deduce that i will be greater than $b = 2.9\%$ because the bond price is less than its face value. Let us try $i = 3\%$. The results of the substitution are shown as Trial 1 in the table below.

With $i = 3\%$, the value of the RHS is $984.06. This is higher than the actual bond price of $972. For our second trial, we should choose a larger i because bond prices fall when market rates rise. Try $i = 3.1\%$ for Trial 2.

Trial number	Estimated i (%)	Term 1 ($)	Term 2 ($)	RHS ($)	Deviation from $972 (in $)
1	3.0	462.17	521.89	984.06	12.06
2	3.1	457.57	510.87	968.44	−3.56
3	3.07	458.95	514.15	973.10	1.10

Substitution of $i = 3.1\%$ gives RHS = \$968.44. After a couple of trials, we can use the "Deviation" values in the last column to make a more intelligent estimate for the third trial. In the present case, $i = 3.0\%$ makes the RHS too large and $i = 3.1\%$ makes the RHS too small. Therefore, the value of i that makes the RHS = \$972 is between $i = 3.0\%$ and $i = 3.1\%$. Furthermore, it is closer to 3.1% than to 3.0% because 3.1% produces a smaller deviation. Let us use $i = 3.07\%$ in Trial 3.

The Trial 3 deviation indicates that our estimate of $i = 3.07\%$ is a little too low because it makes RHS a little too large. By comparing the size of the deviations for Trials 2 and 3, we can see that the correct value of i to the nearest 0.01% is 3.08%.

The bond's YTM is $2i \approx 2(3.08\%) \approx 6.16\%$ compounded semiannually.

EXAMPLE 15.3B   **CALCULATING THE YIELD TO MATURITY OF A HIGH-RISK OR "DEEP-DISCOUNT" BOND**

A corporation's financial condition may deteriorate to the point where there is some doubt about its ability to make future interest payments on its bonds or to redeem the bonds at maturity. Investors are then unwilling to buy the bonds at a price based on market rates of return on bonds of healthy corporations. The price of bonds of the financially distressed corporation will fall to a level determined more by the perceived risk than by the prevailing market rates of return. It is still useful to calculate the YTM on such "deep-discount" bonds. The YTM represents the rate of return the bond purchaser will realize if (1) the corporation does manage to meet all scheduled payments on time, and (2) the bond is held until the maturity date.

Calculate the YTM on the \$1000, 9% coupon bonds of Beaucamp Corp., which are trading at \$500. The bonds have $7\frac{1}{2}$ years remaining until maturity.

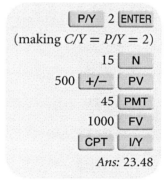

SOLUTION

Given: $FV = \$1000$, $b = \frac{9\%}{2} = 4.5\%$, $b(FV) = \$45$,
        $n = 2(7.5) = 15$, and bond price = \$500

The YTM is the value of $2i$, where i is the solution to

$$\$500 = \$45\left[\frac{1 - (1 + i)^{-15}}{i}\right] + \$1000(1 + i)^{-15}$$

The bond's YTM is $2i = 23.48\%$ compounded semiannually.

EXERCISE 15.3

Spreadsheet template: The partially completed Excel template introduced in Section 11.3 for calculating the interest rate in an annuity may be used for most of the problems in Exercise 15.3. To access the template, go to Chapter 11 of the Student Edition of the Web site, and find "RATE for Any Annuity."

Answers to the odd-numbered problems are at the end of the book.

Note: Unless otherwise indicated, assume that:
• **Bond interest is paid semiannually.**
• **The bond was originally issued at its face value.**
• **Bonds are redeemed at their face value at maturity.**
• **Market rates of return and yields to maturity are compounded semiannually.**

1. A bond with a face value of \$1000 and 15 years remaining until maturity pays a coupon rate of 5%. Calculate its yield to maturity if it is priced at \$900.

2. A bond with a face value of \$1000 and 15 years remaining until maturity pays a coupon rate of 10%. Calculate its yield to maturity if it is priced at \$1250.

3. Manuel bought a $100,000 bond with a 4% coupon for $92,300 when it had five years remaining to maturity. What was the prevailing market rate at the time Manuel purchased the bond? (Taken from CIFP course materials.)

4. Pina bought a 6% coupon, $20,000 face value corporate bond for $21,000 when it had 10 years remaining until maturity. What are her nominal and effective yields to maturity on the bond? (Taken from CIFP course materials.)

5. Bonds A and C both have a face value of $1000 and pay a coupon rate of 6.5%. They have 5 and 20 years, respectively, remaining until maturity. Calculate the yield to maturity of each bond if it is purchased for $950.

6. Bonds D and E both have a face value of $1000 and pay a coupon rate of 7%. They have 5 and 20 years, respectively, remaining until maturity. Calculate the yield to maturity of each bond if it is purchased for $1050.

∘7. A $5000 Government of Canada bond carrying a 6% coupon is currently priced to yield 6% compounded semiannually until maturity. If the bond price abruptly rises by $100, what is the change in the yield to maturity if the bond has:

   a. 3 years remaining to maturity?

   b. 15 years remaining to maturity?

∘8. A $10,000 Nova Chemicals Corp. bond carrying an 8% coupon is currently priced to yield 7% compounded semiannually until maturity. If the bond price abruptly falls by $250, what is the change in the yield to maturity if the bond has:

   a. 2 years remaining to maturity?

   b. 12 years remaining to maturity?

∘9. In the spring of 1992 it became apparent that Olympia & York (O&Y) would have serious difficulty in servicing its debt. Because of this risk, investors were heavily discounting O&Y's bond issues. On April 30, 1992 an Olympia & York bond issue, paying an 11.25% coupon rate and maturing on October 31, 1998, traded at $761.50 (per $1000 of face value). (This was at a time when Government of Canada bonds with a similar coupon and maturity date were trading at a premium of about 10% above par.) If O&Y had managed to make the contractual payments on these bonds, what yield to maturity would investors who purchased those bonds on April 30, 1992 have realized? (P.S. They didn't!)

15.4 | BOND PRICE ON ANY DATE

In Section 15.2, we learned how to calculate a bond's price on an interest payment date. This limits us to valuing a particular bond on just the two days in a year when the interest payments are made. But bonds trade in the financial markets *every* business day. We need to develop the further steps required to calculate a bond's price on any date.

CALCULATING A BOND'S PRICE ON ANY DATE

LO1   Regardless of the date of sale, a bond's market value will be the present value of the future payments discounted at the market's required rate of return. For a date of sale lying between interest payment dates, it appears that each payment must be discounted over a non-integral number of compounding intervals. We can, however, use our understanding of equivalent values to develop a simpler procedure. The present value of all payments on the date of sale may be obtained by the two steps indicated in Figure 15.5.

Step 1:   Calculate the present value of the remaining payments on the *preceding* interest payment date. For the discount rate, use the market rate of return as of the date of sale.

Step 2:   The bond price is the future value, on the date of sale, of the Step 1 result. Use $FV = PV(1 + i)^n$ with

$$i = \frac{\text{Market's required rate of return}}{2}$$

and

$$n = \frac{\text{Number of days since the preceding interest payment}}{\text{Total number of days in the full payment interval}}$$

FIGURE 15.5   Calculating a Bond's Price on Any Date

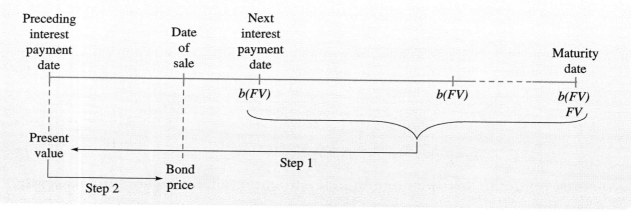

EXAMPLE 15.4A   **PRICING A BOND BETWEEN INTEREST PAYMENT DATES**

A $1000, 20-year, 6% coupon bond was issued on August 15, 2008. It was sold on November 3, 2010, to yield the purchaser 6.5% compounded semiannually until maturity. At what price did the bond sell?

SOLUTION

Given: $FV = \$1000$, $b = \frac{6\%}{2} = 3\%$, $b(FV) = \$30$, and $i = \frac{6.5\%}{2} = 3.25\%$

The two steps in the solution are indicated in the diagram below. First, determine the present value of the remaining payments at the most recent interest payment date (August 15, 2010). Then calculate the future value of this amount on the date of sale (November 3, 2010).

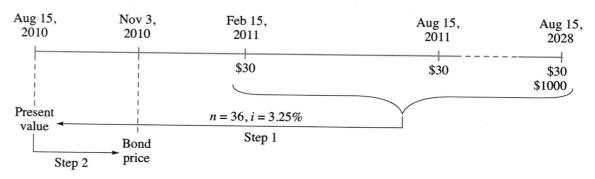

Step 1:   Using formula (15-1) with $n = 2(18) = 36$ interest payments of $30,

$$\text{Present value} = \$30\left(\frac{1 - 1.0325^{-36}}{0.0325}\right) + \$1000(1.0325^{-36})$$

$$= \$631.203 + \$316.197$$

$$= \$947.40$$

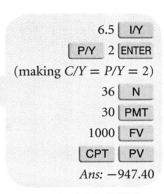

6.5 I/Y

P/Y 2 ENTER

(making $C/Y = P/Y = 2$)

36 N

30 PMT

1000 FV

CPT PV

Ans: −947.40

Step 2:   The interval from August 15 to November 3, 2010 is 80 days long. The total length of the interest payment interval from August 15, 2010 to February 15, 2011 is 184 days.

Same I/Y, P/Y, C/Y

0.4347826 N

947.40 +/− PV

0 PMT

CPT FV

Ans: 960.67

On the date of sale, the fraction of the payment interval that had elapsed was

$$n = \tfrac{80}{184} = 0.4347826$$

Price (Nov. 3) $= PV(1 + i)^n = \$947.40(1.0325)^{0.4347826} = \$960.67$

The bond sold for $960.67 on November 3, 2010. (It sold at a discount because the coupon rate was less than the market's required rate of return.)

EXAMPLE 15.4B   **PRICING A BOND BETWEEN INTEREST PAYMENT DATES**

On January 15, 2001, Westcoast Terminals Inc. issued 20-year bonds having a 7.6% coupon rate. At what price did $1000 face value bonds trade on April 10, 2011, if the required return was 6.2% compounded semiannually?

SOLUTION

Given: $FV = \$1000$, $b = \tfrac{7.6\%}{2} = 3.8\%$, $b(FV) = \$38$, and $i = \tfrac{6.2\%}{2} = 3.1\%$.

6.2 I/Y

P/Y 2 ENTER

(making $C/Y = P/Y = 2$)

20 N

38 PMT

1000 FV

CPT PV

Ans: −1103.19

Step 1:   Calculate the present value of the remaining payments at the most recent interest payment date (January 15, 2011). At that point, $n = 2(10) = 20$ interest payments remain.

$$\text{Present value (Jan. 15)} = \$38\left(\frac{1 - 1.031^{-20}}{0.031}\right) + \$1000(1.031^{-20})$$

$$= \$560.152 + \$543.034$$

$$= \$1103.19$$

Step 2:   Calculate the future value on the date of sale (April 10, 2011) of the amount from Step 1. The interval from January 15 to April 10, 2011 is 85 days long. The total length of the interest payment interval from January 15 to July 15, 2011 is 181 days.

Same I/Y, P/Y, C/Y

0.4696133 N

1103.19 +/− PV

0 PMT

CPT FV

Ans: 1119.12

On the date of sale, the fraction of the payment interval that had elapsed was

$$n = \tfrac{85}{181} = 0.4696133$$

Price (April 10) $= PV(1 + i)^n = \$1103.19(1.031)^{0.4696133} = \$1119.12$

The bonds traded at $1119.12 on April 10, 2011. (They traded at a premium because the coupon rate was greater than the market's required rate of return.)

QUOTATION OF BOND PRICES

Even if prevailing interest rates do not change, the price of a bond will change as time passes, for two reasons. First, the accrual of interest causes a bond's price to steadily rise after an interest payment. Then the price will abruptly fall by the amount $b \times FV$ on the day interest is paid. The result of this cycle repeating every six months is a "sawtooth" pattern for the graph of bond price versus time. Figure 15.6 illustrates the pattern for the case of a bond selling at a premium. Figure 15.7 presents the corresponding graph for a bond selling at a discount. The graphs show how the market value of a $1000 face value bond changes over the final six interest payment intervals before the maturity date (assuming that prevailing market rates of return do not change). Note that much of the bond price axis between $0 and $1000 has been omitted to reveal the details of bond price changes on a larger scale. Keep in mind that $b \times FV$ will be in the $20 to $50 range for coupon rates in the 4% to 10% range.

FIGURE 15.6 Price Change Over Time for a Bond Trading at a Premium

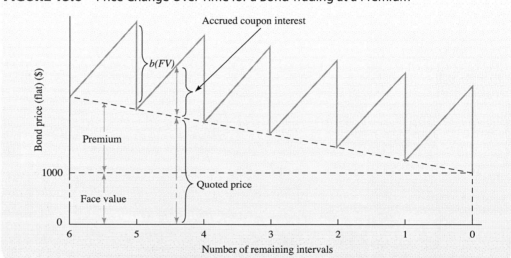

The second reason the bond's price will change is that the premium or discount will diminish over time. The premium on any date in Figure 15.6 is the distance between the downward-sloping dashed line and the horizontal line at $1000. The discount on any date in Figure 15.7 is the distance between the horizontal line at $1000 and the upward-sloping dashed line. The premium or discount decreases as time passes because the number of remaining payments decreases. It is the same reason that causes a long-term bond to sell at a larger premium or discount than a short-term bond (other variables being the same for both bonds). By the time a bond reaches its maturity date, any bond premium or discount has shrunk to zero.

FIGURE 15.7   Price Change Over Time for a Bond Trading at a Discount

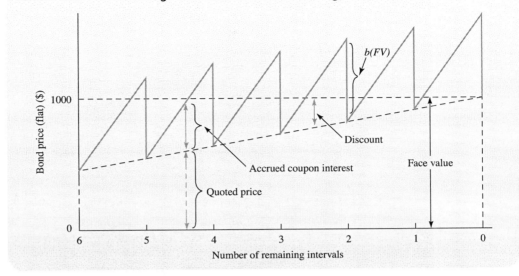

Flat Price vs. Quoted Price In bond terminology, the bond price we have been calculating (and plotting in Figures 15.6 and 15.7) is called the **flat price**. It is the *actual* amount paid by the purchaser and received by the seller (ignoring transaction charges). The flat price includes coupon interest that has accrued since the preceding interest payment date.

Before an investor can make meaningful comparisons among bond prices, the prices must be adjusted for their differing amounts of accrued coupon interest. As an extreme example, the flat prices of two otherwise identical bonds will differ by almost $b \times FV$ if one bond paid its coupon interest yesterday and the other bond will pay interest tomorrow. Accrued interest should be deducted from the flat prices of both bonds to obtain prices that may be fairly compared. For this reason, bond prices are quoted in the financial media and in the bond market with the accrued coupon interest already deducted from the flat price. That is,

$$\text{Quoted price} = \text{Flat price} - \text{Accrued coupon interest}$$

In Figures 15.6 and 15.7, the flat price on one particular date is broken down into its "accrued coupon interest" and "quoted price" components. The quoted price includes the premium or discount but does not include accrued coupon interest. When they purchase bonds, investors are aware that accrued coupon interest will be *added* to the quoted price, giving the flat price they will pay.

Table 15.2 lists some bond quotations at the close of the bond market on September 22, 2009. Since there can be several face value denominations in any bond issue, bond prices are quoted as a *percentage* of face value. The dollar price of any denomination can readily be calculated using this information. For example, the price of a $5000 face value bond quoted at 102.25(%) is

$$\$5000 \times 1.0225 = \$5112.50$$

Even though the bond yield (meaning yield to maturity) can be calculated from the other information in the table, it is nevertheless quoted in lists of this type because many bond investors are unable to perform the calculation. Since prevailing interest rates were near 40-year lows in September 2009, virtually all bonds were trading at a premium.

TABLE 15.2 Bond Price Quotations (September 22, 2009)

Issuer	Coupon rate (%)	Maturity Date	Quoted price (%)	Bond yield (%)
Government of Canada	5.0	June 1, 2037	118.29	3.912
Province of New Brunswick	4.4	June 3, 2019	102.17	4.126
Province of Ontario	5.85	March 8, 2033	115.47	4.749
Province of British Columbia	5.7	June 18, 2029	113.24	4.666
Newfoundland Municipal Financing Corporation	5.1	March 29, 2018	105.15	4.370
City of Toronto	4.375	October 28, 2015	105.55	3.361
TransCanada Pipelines Ltd.	8.29	February 5, 2026	127.59	5.678
ING Canada Inc.	5.41	September 3, 2019	100.08	5.399

Calculating the Accrued Coupon Interest We have mentioned that the buyer of a bond pays accrued coupon interest in addition to the quoted price. The prevailing practice is to calculate accrued coupon interest on a *simple-interest* basis. Therefore,

$$\text{Accrued coupon interest} = Prt = (FV)bt$$

where t is the fraction of the payment interval (containing the date of sale) that has elapsed since the preceding interest payment. That is,

$$t = \frac{\text{Number of days since the preceding interest payment}}{\text{Total number of days in the full payment interval}}$$

EXAMPLE 15.4C CALCULATING THE ACCRUED COUPON INTEREST AND QUOTED PRICE, GIVEN THE FLAT PRICE

In Example 15.4B, we calculated the (flat) price on April 10, 2011, of a $1000 face value, 7.6% coupon Westcoast Energy Inc. bond maturing January 15, 2021. The calculated price for a yield to maturity of 6.2% compounded semiannually was $1119.12.

a. How much of that price was interest that had accrued (in favour of the previous owner) since the preceding interest payment date?

b. What price did the financial media and securities brokers quote for these bonds on April 10, 2011?

SOLUTION

a. The period from the preceding interest payment on January 15, 2011 to the April 10, 2011 date of sale was 85 days long.

The number of days in the full payment interval (from January 15 to July 15) was 181.

The coupon interest that accrued over these 85 days was

$$I = Prt = (FV)bt = \$1000 \times 0.038 \times \tfrac{85}{181} = \$17.85$$

Hence, $17.85 of the $1119.12 flat price was accrued interest.

b. Brokers and financial media report the quoted price. (Bond investors understand that they must pay the accrued interest of $17.85 in addition to the quoted price.)

$$\begin{aligned}\text{Quoted price} &= \text{Flat price} - \text{Accrued interest} \\ &= \$1119.12 - \$17.85 \\ &= \$1101.27\end{aligned}$$

Using the Texas Instruments BA-II PLUS Bond Worksheet This worksheet enables you to compute either a bond's quoted price or its yield to maturity on any date. Appendix 15A provides instructions on the use of the Bond Worksheet. The worksheet will be used for the financial calculator solution in Example 15.4D.

EXAMPLE 15.4D **CALCULATING THE ACCRUED COUPON INTEREST AND QUOTED PRICE GIVEN THE YIELD TO MATURITY**

For the Government of Canada bond listed in Table 15.2, show how the quoted price may be calculated from the other information provided in the table. What accrued interest (in addition to the quoted price) did an investor have to pay on September 22, 2009 to purchase a $10,000 denomination bond?

SOLUTION

From the table, we see that the Government of Canada bond matures on June 1, 2037. The bond market was pricing these bonds on September 22, 2009 to yield 3.912% (compounded semiannually) until maturity. We have

$$FV = \$10,000 \quad b = \tfrac{5.0\%}{2} = 2.5\% \quad b(FV) = \$250 \quad i = \tfrac{3.912\%}{2} = 1.956\%$$

The steps in the algebraic solution are:

Step 1: Calculate the present value of the remaining payments on the preceding interest payment date (June 1, 2009.) After that date, $n = 2(28) = 56$ interest payments remain.

Step 2: Calculate the *flat* price on September 22, 2009 by calculating the future value of the Step 1 result with interest at 3.912% compounded semiannually.

Step 3: Calculate the coupon interest that accrues from June 1, 2009 to September 22, 2009.

Step 4: Deduct the accrued coupon interest from the flat price (Step 2 result) to get the *quoted* price.

If we use the Bond Worksheet on the Texas Instruments BA-II PLUS calculator, we can directly obtain both the quoted price and the accrued interest.

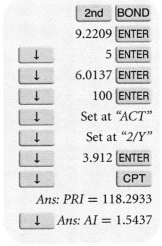

Step 1: Present value (June 1) $= \$250\left(\dfrac{1 - 1.01956^{-56}}{0.01956}\right) + \$10,000(1.01956^{-56})$

$= \$8461.472 + \$3379.744$

$= \$11,841.216$

Step 2: We need the fraction of the June 1 to December 1 payment interval that has elapsed as of September 22, 2009. There are 113 days from June 1, 2009 to September 22, 2009, and 183 days from June 1, 2009 to December 1, 2009. Therefore, the fraction of the payment interval that had elapsed was

$$n = \tfrac{113}{183} = 0.61748634$$

Flat price (Sept. 22) $= \$11,841.216(1.01956^{0.61748634}) = \$11,983.70$

Step 3: Accrued coupon interest $= Prt$

$= (FV)bt$

$= \$10,000 \times 0.025 \times \tfrac{113}{183}$

$= \$154.37$

Step 4: Quoted price $=$ Flat price $-$ Accrued interest

$= \$11,983.70 - \$154.37$

$= \$11,829.33$

By both methods, we obtain a quoted price of 118.293% of the $10,000 face value. The quoted price in Table 15.2 is 118.29% of face value. Note that the yield we used in our calculations was quoted with only four-figure accuracy. Therefore, our calculated price can have a rounding error showing up in the fourth or fifth figure.

In addition to the quoted price, the purchaser of the $10,000 face value bond must pay accrued interest of $154.37. (In the Bond Worksheet approach, we obtained $AI = \$1.5437$ per $100 of face value. For a face value of $10,000, the accrued interest is $\frac{\$10,000}{\$100} \times \$1.5437 = \$154.37$.)

SPREADSHEET STRATEGIES   Calculating the Quoted Price of a Bond

Connect provides a partially completed template for calculating the quoted price of a bond on any date. Go to the Student Edition of Connect and find "PRICE of a Bond." The "Introduction" page of this workbook discusses Excel's PRICE function.

We will use the PRICE template here to answer Example 15.4D. In this example, we are asked to calculate the quoted price on September 22, 2009 of a $10,000 face value

Government of Canada bond that carries a 5% coupon rate and matures on June 1, 2037. The bond market's required rate of return on September 22, 2009 was 3.912% compounded semiannually. The main features of the completed template are presented below. The formula programmed into cell C13 is displayed in Row 14. After entering the known values in the yellow input cells, the quoted price appears in cell C13.

	A	B	C	D	E
1					
2		Using a spreadsheet to calculate the quoted price of a bond.			
3	Example 15.4D:				
4					
5		Purchase date, *settlement_date*	22-Sep-09		
6		Maturity date, *maturity_date*	1-Jun-37		
7		Coupon rate (%), *rate*	5.0000%		
8		Market rate of return (%), *yield*	3.9120%		
9		Redemption price, *redemption_price*	100		
10		Coupon payments/year, *frequency*	2		
11		Basis code, *basis* ("1" in Canada)	1		
12					
13		PRICE *(set_date,mat_date,rate,yield,red_price,freq,basis)*	118.29333		
14		Formula in cell C13:	= PRICE (C5,C6,C7,C8,C9,C10,C11)		
15					

The quoted price is $118.2933 per $100 of redemption price. Since the redemption price of this bond is the $10,000 face value, the full quoted price is $\dfrac{\$10,000}{\$100} \times \$118.2933 = \$11,829.33$.

EXERCISE 15.4

Spreadsheet template: A partially completed Excel template for calculating the quoted price of a bond on any date is provided in Connect. You can use this template for some of the problems in Exercise 15.4. Go to the Student Edition of Connect and find "PRICE of a Bond."

Answers to the odd-numbered problems are at the end of the book.

Note: Unless otherwise indicated, assume that:
- **Bond interest is paid semiannually.**
- **The bond was originally issued at its face value.**
- **Bonds will be redeemed for their face value at maturity.**
- **Market rates of return and yields to maturity are compounded semiannually.**

Calculate the purchase price (flat) of each of the $1000 face value bonds in Problems 1 through 8.

Problem	Issue date	Maturity date	Purchase date	Coupon rate (%)	Market rate (%)
1.	June 1, 1995	June 1, 2015	June 15, 2004	8.0	5.25
2.	March 15, 2002	March 15, 2027	Oct 5, 2008	5.5	6.0
3.	Jan 1, 2006	Jan 1, 2021	April 15, 2006	4.0	4.5
4.	Sept 20, 2008	Sept 20, 2028	June 1, 2011	5.0	5.8
5.	Aug 1, 2005	Aug 1, 2025	Dec 15, 2009	6.1	4.9
6.	July 1, 2009	July 1, 2029	April 9, 2010	4.3	5.5
7.	Dec 1, 2002	Dec 1, 2022	Mar 25, 2004	5.2	5.7
8.	April 1, 2003	April 1, 2027	June 20, 2005	5.4	6.1

○9. A $1000, 6.5% coupon bond issued by Bell Canada matures on October 15, 2029. What was its flat price on June 11, 2010 if its yield to maturity was 4.75% compounded semiannually?

○10. A $1000, 6% coupon, 25-year Government of Canada bond was issued on June 1, 2005. At what flat price did it sell on April 27, 2009 if the market's required return was 4.6% compounded semiannually?

○11. A $1000, 10% coupon bond issued by Ontario Hydro on July 15, 1994 matures on July 15, 2019. What was its flat price on June 1, 2003 when the required yield to maturity was 5.5% compounded semiannually?

○12. A $1000, 6.75% coupon, 25-year Government of Canada bond was issued on March 15, 1971. At what flat price did it trade on July 4, 1981, when the market's required return was 17% compounded semiannually?

○13. A $1000, 5.2% coupon, 20-year Province of Ontario bond was issued on March 15, 2009. Calculate its flat price on March 15, April 15, May 15, June 15, July 15, August 15, and September 15, 2010, if the yield to maturity on every date was 6% compounded semiannually.

○14. A $1000, 7% coupon, 15-year Province of Saskatchewan bond was issued on May 20, 2001. Calculate its (flat) price on May 20, June 20, July 20, August 20, September 20, October 20, and November 20, 2003, if the yield to maturity on every date was 5.9% compounded semiannually.

•15. A $5000, 7% coupon, 20-year bond issued on January 21, 2006, was purchased on January 25, 2007, to yield 6.5% to maturity, and then sold on January 13, 2008, to yield the purchaser 5.2% to maturity. What was the investor's capital gain or loss:

a. In dollars? **b.** As a percentage of her original investment?

•16. A $10,000, 14% coupon, 25-year bond issued on June 15, 1984, was purchased on March 20, 1987, to yield 9% to maturity, and then sold on April 20, 1990, to yield the purchaser 11.5% to maturity. What was the investor's capital gain or loss:

a. In dollars? **b.** As a percentage of his original investment?

Problems 17 through 22 require the calculation of quoted bond prices and accrued interest.

○17. A $1000 face value, 7.6% coupon bond pays interest on May 15 and November 15. If its flat price on August 1 was $1065.50, at what price (expressed as a percentage of face value) would the issue have been reported in the financial pages?

○18. A $5000 bond was sold for $4860 (flat) on September 17. If the bond pays $200 interest on June 1 and December 1 of each year, what price (expressed as a percentage of face value) would have been quoted for bonds of this issue on September 17?

○19. If a broker quotes a price of 108.50 for a bond on October 23, what amount will a client pay per $1000 face value? The 7.2% coupon rate is payable on March 1 and September 1 of each year. The relevant February has 28 days.

○**20.** Calculate the quoted price on April 15, 2006 of the bond described in Problem 3.

○**21.** Calculate the quoted price on June 1, 2011 of the bond described in Problem 4.

○**22.** Using the bond yield given in the final column of Table 15.2, verify the September 22, 2009, quoted price for the Province of New Brunswick 4.4% coupon bond, maturing June 3, 2019.

○**23.** Using the bond yield given in the final column of Table 15.2, verify the September 22, 2009, quoted price for the Province of Ontario 5.85% coupon bond, maturing March 8, 2033.

○**24.** Using the bond yield given in the final column of Table 15.2, verify the September 22, 2009, quoted price for the Province of British Columbia 5.7% coupon bond, maturing June 18, 2029.

○**25.** Using the bond price given in the second-to-last column of Table 15.2, verify the September 22, 2009 yield (to maturity) for the Newfoundland Municipal Financing Authority 5.1% coupon bond, maturing March 29, 2018.

○**26.** Using the bond price given in the second-to-last column of Table 15.2, verify the September 22, 2009, yield (to maturity) for the City of Toronto 4.375% coupon bond, maturing October 28, 2015.

○**27.** Using the bond price given in the second-to-last column of Table 15.2, verify the September 22, 2009, yield (to maturity) for the TransCanada Pipelines Ltd. 8.29% coupon bond, maturing February 5, 2026.

○**28.** Using the bond price given in the second-to-last column of Table 15.2, verify the September 22, 2009, yield (to maturity) for the ING Canada Inc. 5.41% coupon bond, maturing September 3, 2019.

15.5   SINKING FUNDS

A **sinking fund** is an interest-earning account into which periodic deposits are made for the purpose of accumulating a required amount of money by a particular date. The accumulated funds are typically used for a capital expenditure or to retire the principal amount of a debt.

SINKING FUND FOR A CAPITAL EXPENDITURE

A sinking fund can be established by a business to accumulate funds for a future project, replacement of equipment, expansion of production facilities, or an acquisition.

LO3   The simplest sinking fund arrangement requires *equal periodic* contributions. The payment size is calculated so that, at the expected rate of return, the *future value* of the payments on the target date equals the amount needed. We will deal only with cases where the interval between contributions equals the compounding interval. The payments then form a *simple annuity*. If the sinking fund payments are made at the *end* of each payment interval, you calculate their size by solving for *PMT* in:

$$FV = PMT\left[\frac{(1+i)^n - 1}{i}\right] \tag{10-1}$$

If the sinking fund payments are made at the *beginning* of each payment interval, solve for *PMT* in:

$$FV(\text{due}) = PMT\left[\frac{(1+i)^n - 1}{i}\right] \times (1+i) \tag{12-1}$$

LO4   A table presenting details of the increase in the sinking fund each period is called a **sinking fund schedule**. The balance or accumulated amount in the sinking fund at the *end* of any interval is the future value of payments already made. The following relationships are used in constructing a sinking fund schedule.

$$\begin{pmatrix} \text{Balance at the end of} \\ \text{any payment interval} \end{pmatrix} = \begin{pmatrix} \text{Future value of the} \\ \text{payments already made} \end{pmatrix}$$

$$\begin{pmatrix} \text{Interest earned in} \\ \text{any payment interval} \end{pmatrix} = i \times \begin{pmatrix} \text{Amount in the sinking fund} \\ \text{at the beginning of the interval} \end{pmatrix}$$

TRAP   Interest Earned When Payments Form an Annuity Due

Be careful when using the preceding idea to calculate the interest earned during a payment interval of an annuity due. The interest-earning amount at the beginning of an interval is the previous interval's ending balance *plus* the new contribution at the beginning of the current interval.

$$\begin{pmatrix} \text{Increase in the sinking fund's balance} \\ \text{during any payment interval} \end{pmatrix} = PMT + \begin{pmatrix} \text{Interest earned} \\ \text{during the interval} \end{pmatrix}$$

This increase can be added to the balance from the end of the preceding interval to obtain the new balance. The format for a sinking fund schedule is presented in the following examples.

EXAMPLE 15.5A   **PREPARATION OF A COMPLETE SINKING FUND SCHEDULE IN WHICH THE PAYMENTS FORM AN ORDINARY ANNUITY**

Borland Engineering plans to undertake a $900,000 expansion six years from now. By that time, Borland wants to accumulate half of the cost of the expansion by making payments into a sinking fund at the end of each of the next six years. It is anticipated that the money in the sinking fund will earn 7% compounded annually.

a. What should be the size of the annual payments?

b. How much of the money in the sinking fund at the end of the six years will be interest earnings?

c. Prepare a sinking fund schedule. Verify the answer to Part (b) by summing the "interest earned" column.

SOLUTION

a. The future value of the six sinking fund payments, invested at 7% compounded annually, must be $450,000. Substitute $FV = \$450,000$, $i = \frac{7\%}{1} = 7\%$ and $n = 1(6) = 6$ into formula (10-1). Then solve for PMT.

$$FV = PMT\left[\frac{(1+i)^n - 1}{i}\right]$$

$$\$450,000 = PMT\left[\frac{(1.07)^6 - 1}{0.07}\right]$$

$$= PMT(7.1532907)$$

$$PMT = \$62,908.11$$

The annual sinking fund payment should be $62,908.11.

| 7 | I/Y |
| P/Y 1 | ENTER |

(making $C/Y = P/Y = 1$)

6	N
0	PV
450000	FV
CPT	PMT

Ans: −62,908.11

b. The total of the payments to the sinking fund will be

$$6 \times \$62,908.11 = \$377,448.66$$

The remainder of the $450,000 will be interest earned. That is,

$$\text{Interest earned} = \$450,000 - \$377,448.66 = \$72,551.34$$

c.

Payment interval number	Payment (at end) ($)	Interest earned ($)	Increase in the fund ($)	Balance in fund (end of interval) ($)
0	—	—	—	0
1	62,908.11	0	62,908.11	62,908.11
2	62,908.11	4403.57 ①	67,311.68 ②	130,219.79 ③
3	62,908.11	9115.39	72,023.50	202,243.29
4	62,908.11	14,157.03	77,065.14	279,308.43
5	62,908.11	19,551.59	82,459.70	361,768.13
6	62,908.11	25,323.77	88,231.88	450,000.01
	377,448.66	72,551.35 ④	450,000.01 ⑤	

① Interest earned = 0.07(Amount at the beginning of the interval) = 0.07($62,908.11) = $4403.57
② Increase in the fund = Interest earned + Payment = $4403.57 + $62,908.11 = $67,311.68
③ Balance = Previous balance + Increase in the fund = $62,908.11 + $67,311.68 = $130,219.79
④ Column total = $72,551.35 = Total interest earned (confirming the answer in Part (b)
⑤ The total of the increases to the fund should equal the final total in the sinking fund.

EXAMPLE 15.5B **PREPARATION OF A COMPLETE SINKING FUND SCHEDULE IN WHICH THE PAYMENTS FORM AN ANNUITY DUE**

Repeat Example 15.5A, with the change that the sinking fund payments are made at the beginning of each year.

SOLUTION

a. The future value of the six sinking fund payments, invested at 7% compounded annually, must be $450,000. Substitute $FV(\text{due}) = \$450,000$, $i = \frac{7\%}{1} = 7\%$ and $n = 1(6) = 6$ into formula (12-1). Then solve for PMT.

$$FV(\text{due}) = PMT\left[\frac{(1+i)^n - 1}{i}\right] \times (1+i)$$

$$\$450,000 = PMT\left[\frac{(1.07)^6 - 1}{0.07}\right](1.07)$$

$$= PMT(7.6540211)$$

$$PMT = \$58,792.63$$

The annual sinking fund payment should be $58,792.63.

BGN mode

7 | I/Y

P/Y 1 ENTER

(making $C/Y = P/Y = 1$)

6 | N

0 | PV

450000 | FV

CPT | PMT

Ans: −58,792.63

b. Interest earned = $450,000 − Total of payments
= $450,000 − (6 × $58,792.63)
= $97,244.22

c.

Payment interval number	Payment (at start) ($)	Interest earned ($)	Increase in the fund ($)	Balance in fund (end of interval) ($)
0	—	—	—	0
1	58,792.63	4115.48	62,908.11	62,908.11
2	58,792.63	8519.05 ①	67,311.68 ②	130,219.79 ③
3	58,792.63	13,230.87	72,023.50	202,243.29
4	58,792.63	18,272.51	77,065.14	279,308.43
5	58,792.63	23,667.07	82,459.70	361,768.13
6	58,792.63	29,439.25	88,231.88	450,000.01
	352,755.78	97,244.23	450,000.01	

① Interest earned = 0.07(Amount at the beginning of the interval)
= 0.07(Balance at end of previous interval + PMT)
= 0.07($62,908.11 + $58,792.63)
= $8519.05
② Increase in the fund = Interest earned + Payment = $8519.05 + $58,792.63 = $67,311.68
③ Balance = Previous balance + Increase in the fund = $62,908.11 + $67,311.68 = $130,219.79

EXAMPLE 15.5C **PREPARATION OF A PARTIAL SINKING FUND SCHEDULE**

The board of directors of Borland Engineering decides that the firm's cash flows can be managed better if the sinking fund payments are made quarterly instead of annually (as in Example 15.5A). The goal is still to accumulate $450,000 after six years, but now with end-of-quarter payments. The sinking fund would earn 6.8% compounded quarterly. Construct a partial sinking fund schedule showing details of Payments 1, 2, 15, 16, 23, and 24.

SOLUTION

The first step is to calculate the size of the payments so that their future value will be $450,000. The payments form an ordinary simple annuity with $FV = \$450,000$, $n = 4(6) = 24$, and $i = \frac{6.8\%}{4} = 1.7\%$. Solve for PMT in

$$FV = PMT\left[\frac{(1+i)^n - 1}{i}\right]$$

$$\$450,000 = PMT\left[\frac{(1.017)^{24} - 1}{0.017}\right]$$

$$= PMT(29.332891)$$

$$PMT = \$15,341.14$$

6.8	I/Y
P/Y 4	ENTER

(making $C/Y = P/Y = 4$)

24	N
0	PV
450000	FV
CPT	PMT

Ans: −15,341.14

In order to deal with Payments 15 and 16 in a sinking fund schedule, we need to determine the balance (future value) after 14 payments.

Future value after 14 payments $= \$15,341.14\left[\frac{(1.017)^{14} - 1}{0.017}\right]$

$$= \$240,200.61$$

Same I/Y, P/Y, C/Y, PV

14	N
15341.14 +/−	PMT
CPT	FV

Ans: 240,200.61

In order to deal with the last two payments (Payments 23 and 24), we need to calculate the balance after 22 payments.

Future value after 22 payments $= \$15,341.14\left[\frac{(1.017)^{22} - 1}{0.017}\right]$

$$= \$405,164.24$$

Same I/Y, P/Y, C/Y, PV, PMT

22	N
CPT	FV

Ans: 405,164.24

Payment interval number	Payment (at end) ($)	Interest earned ($)	Increase in the fund ($)	Balance in fund (end of interval) ($)
0	—	—	—	0
1	15,341.14	0	15,341.14	15,341.14
2	15,341.14	260.80 ①	15,601.94 ②	30,943.08 ③
•	•	•	•	•
14	•	•	•	240,200.61
15	15,341.14	4083.41	19,424.55	259,625.16
16	15,341.14	4413.63	19,754.77	279,379.93
•	•	•	•	•
22	•	•	•	405,164.24
23	15,341.14	6887.79	22,228.93	427,393.17
24	15,341.14	7265.68	22,606.82	449,999.99
	368,187.36	81,812.63	449,999.99	

① $0.017 \times \$15,341.14 = \$260.80$
② $\$260.80 + \$15,341.14 = \$15,601.94$
③ $\$15,601.94 + \$15,341.14 = \$30,943.08$

SINKING FUND FOR DEBT RETIREMENT

Recall from the discussion of bonds earlier in this chapter that no principal is repaid to the bond investor before the maturity of the bond. In some circumstances, bond investors may have concerns about the ability of the borrower (bond issuer) to repay the full principal amount at a maturity date several years in the future. To ease this concern, many corporate, regional government, and municipal government bonds carry a sinking fund provision.[5] The purpose of the sinking fund is to provide for the repayment of all or a substantial portion of the principal amount of the bond issue.

A trust company is usually appointed as the trustee to administer the sinking fund. The bond issuer does not have access to the money in the sinking fund; the funds are accumulated for the express purpose of repaying the principal amount of the debt. There are two ways of setting up a sinking fund for a bond issue:

- The borrower makes periodic payments to the trustee. The trustee invests the funds in low-risk securities (such as federal government bonds and Treasury bills). On the maturity date of the bond issue, the accumulated funds are used to repay all or a substantial portion of the principal amount of the debt.

- The trustee uses the periodic payments received from the bond issuer to retire a portion of the bond issue each year. To do this in any particular year, the trustee chooses the cheaper of the following two alternatives:
  (i) A specified percentage of the issue may be called and redeemed at a predetermined redemption price per bond.
  (ii) If, however, the bonds can be purchased in the bond market for less than the redemption price, the trustee will buy enough bonds for the year's prescribed debt retirement.

The second sinking fund arrangement is more common. However, the first involves the more interesting mathematics, which we will discuss in the remainder of this section.

The simplest contribution arrangement requires *equal* regular payments to the sinking fund after the initial issue[6] of the bonds. The payment size is calculated so that

$$\left(\begin{matrix} \text{Future value of the} \\ \text{sinking fund payments} \end{matrix}\right) = \left(\begin{matrix} \text{Principal amount of} \\ \text{the debt to be retired} \end{matrix}\right)$$

A conservative compound rate of return is assumed for the sinking fund. We will consider only cases where contributions are made at the end of every six months and compounding occurs semiannually. In these cases, the sinking fund contributions form an ordinary simple annuity.

The sinking fund schedule for a debt retirement usually includes an additional column for the **book value of the debt** defined as:

$$\left(\begin{matrix} \text{Book value} \\ \text{of the debt} \end{matrix}\right) = \left(\begin{matrix} \text{Principal amount} \\ \text{of the debt} \end{matrix}\right) - \left(\begin{matrix} \text{Balance in the} \\ \text{sinking fund} \end{matrix}\right)$$

The book value of a debt can be interpreted as the balance that would still be owed on the debt if the money in the sinking fund were immediately applied to reduce the debt.

Keep in mind that, under a sinking fund arrangement for debt retirement, the borrower is making *two* series of payments, each one constituting an annuity. One is the sinking fund payments to the fund's trustee. The other is the interest payments to the lenders or

---

[5] Sinking funds are primarily associated with debentures rather than with true bonds because debentures are not secured by specific fixed assets of the borrower. A debt issue that has a sinking fund provision usually includes the words "sinking fund" in its full title.

[6] In cases where the sinking fund is structured to retire only a portion of the debt, there may be an initial five- or 10-year "contribution holiday" during which the issuer makes no sinking fund payments.

bondholders. The combined total of a year's interest payments and a year's sinking fund payments is called the **annual cost of the debt**. It represents the total annual cash outflow arising from the debt obligation.

> **TIP** **The Different Roles of the Coupon Rate and the Sinking Fund Rate of Return**
>
> Distinguish the roles of the two interest rates that are involved in sinking fund debt. The contractual rate of interest on the debt determines the regular interest expense paid by the borrower to the lender. The rate of return earned by the sinking fund determines the revenue earned by the sinking fund. Although the lender does not directly receive the earnings of the sinking fund, the lender still benefits from the interest earnings: they will eventually be used to repay the principal amount of the debt.

EXAMPLE 15.5D **CALCULATING THE SINKING FUND PAYMENT SIZE, ANNUAL COST OF DEBT, AND BOOK VALUE OF DEBT**

Abacus Corp. raised $20 million from an issue of sinking fund bonds. The bonds have a 12-year term and a 9% coupon rate. The bond indenture requires Abacus to make equal semiannual contributions to a sinking fund to provide for the retirement of the full principal amount of the bond issue at its maturity.

a. If the sinking fund earns 6.5% compounded semiannually, what is the size of the semiannual sinking fund payments?

b. What is the annual cost of the debt?

c. What is the book value of the debt after six years?

SOLUTION

a. We want the future value of the sinking fund payments invested at 6.5% compounded semiannually for 12 years to be $20 million. The payments form an ordinary simple annuity having

$FV = \$20,000,000$, $i = \frac{6.5\%}{2} = 3.25\%$, and $n = 2(12) = 24$.

Substitute into formula (10-1) and solve for *PMT*.

$$FV = PMT\left[\frac{(1+i)^n - 1}{i}\right]$$

$$\$20,000,000 = PMT\left[\frac{(1.0325)^{24} - 1}{0.0325}\right]$$

$$= PMT(35.525359)$$

$$PMT = \$562,978.13$$

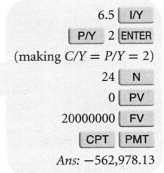

6.5 I/Y
P/Y 2 ENTER
(making C/Y = P/Y = 2)
24 N
0 PV
20000000 FV
CPT PMT
Ans: −562,978.13

b. The annual cost of the debt is the total of the bond interest and sinking fund payments made in a year. The semiannual interest paid on the debt is

$$\frac{0.09}{2} \times \$20,000,000 = \$900,000$$

Hence,

$$\text{Annual cost of the debt} = 2(\$562,978.13 + \$900,000) = \$2,925,956.26$$

c. The book value of the debt after six years is the principal amount of the debt less the amount in the sinking fund. The amount in the sinking fund is

$$FV = \$562{,}978.13\left[\frac{(1.0325)^{12} - 1}{0.0325}\right] = \$8{,}104{,}230.90$$

Book value = $\$20{,}000{,}000 - \$8{,}104{,}230.90 = \$11{,}895{,}769.10$

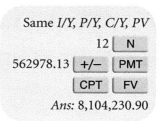

Same *I/Y, P/Y, C/Y, PV*

12 [N]

562978.13 [+/–] [PMT]

[CPT] [FV]

Ans: 8,104,230.90

EXAMPLE 15.5E   **CONSTRUCTING A PARTIAL SINKING FUND SCHEDULE**

In order to construct a secondary sewage treatment system, the town of Port Barlow has received approval to borrow $12 million through the provincial government's Municipal Finance Authority (MFA). The MFA is the central borrowing agency for financing the capital requirements of member municipalities and regional governments. It enters the capital markets to borrow the funds needed by its members. It also manages the collection of money from its members for both the payment of interest and the accumulation of sinking funds to retire the principal portion of each debt issue.

Bond coupon interest at the rate of 10% compounded semiannually is payable every six months. In addition, Port Barlow must make payments at the end of every six months into a sinking fund that will accumulate the full principal amount of the debt after 15 years. The sinking fund earns 8% compounded semiannually. Round sinking fund payments and interest earnings to the nearest dollar.

a. Calculate the combined interest and sinking fund payment that Port Barlow must send to the MFA every six months.

b. What will be the balance in the sinking fund halfway through the term of the debt?

c. How much will the balance in the sinking fund increase during the tenth year?

d. How much interest will the sinking fund earn in the first half of the seventh year?

e. Construct a partial sinking fund schedule showing details of the first two and the last two payments.

SOLUTION

a. The future value of the sinking fund payments after 15 years at 8% compounded semiannually must be $12,000,000. Substitute $FV = \$12{,}000{,}000$, $n = 2(15) = 30$, and $i = \frac{8\%}{2} = 4\%$ into formula (10-1) and solve for *PMT*.

$$FV = PMT\left[\frac{(1 + i)^n - 1}{i}\right]$$

$$\$12{,}000{,}000 = PMT\left[\frac{(1.04)^{30} - 1}{0.04}\right]$$

$$PMT = \$213{,}961$$

8 [I/Y]

[P/Y] 2 [ENTER]

(making *C/Y = P/Y =* 2)

30 [N]

0 [PV]

12000000 [FV]

[CPT] [PMT]

Ans: −213,961

The semiannual interest payment is $\$12{,}000{,}000(0.05) = \$600{,}000$

The combined semiannual payment is $\$213{,}961 + \$600{,}000 = \$813{,}961$

b. The amount in the sinking fund at any point will be the future value of the payments already contributed. After $7\frac{1}{2}$ years (15 payments), the sinking fund balance will be

$$FV = \$213{,}961\left[\frac{(1.04)^{15} - 1}{0.04}\right] = \$4{,}284{,}267$$

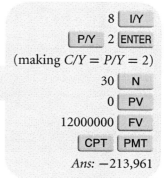

Same *I/Y, P/Y, C/Y, PV*

15 [N]

213961 [+/–] [PMT]

[CPT] [FV]

Ans: 4,284,267

c. The increase in the balance during the tenth year

$$= \text{Balance after 10 years} - \text{Balance after 9 years}$$

$$= \$213{,}961\left[\frac{(1.04)^{20} - 1}{0.04}\right] - \$213{,}961\left[\frac{(1.04)^{18} - 1}{0.04}\right]$$

$$= \$6{,}371{,}347.5 - \$5{,}487{,}118.2$$

$$= \$884{,}229$$

> Same I/Y, P/Y, C/Y
> Same PV, PMT
>
> 18 | N |
> | CPT | | FV |
> *Ans:* 5,487,118
> | STO | 1
> 20 | N |
> | CPT | | FV |
> *Ans:* 6,371,347
> | − | | RCL | 1 | = |
> *Ans:* 884,229

d. The interest earned in the first half of Year 7

$$= 0.04(\text{Amount in the fund at the end of Year 6})$$

$$= 0.04 \times \$213{,}961\left[\frac{(1.04)^{12} - 1}{0.04}\right]$$

$$= 0.04(\$3{,}214{,}936)$$

$$= \$128{,}597$$

> Same I/Y, P/Y, C/Y
> Same PV, PMT
>
> 12 | N |
> | CPT | | FV |
> *Ans:* 3,214,936
> | × | 0.04 | = |
> *Ans:* 128,597

e. Partial sinking fund schedule:

Payment interval number	Payment ($)	Interest earned ($)	Increase in the fund ($)	Balance in fund (end of interval) ($)	Book value of the debt ($)
0	—	—	—	0	12,000,000
1	213,961	0	213,961	213,961	11,786,039
2	213,961	8558 ①	222,519 ②	436,480 ③	11,563,520 ④
.	.	.	.	.	.
.	.	.	.	.	.
.	.	.	.	.	.
28				10,691,114 ⑤	1,308,886
29	213,961	427,645	641,606	11,332,720	667,280
30	213,961	453,309	667,270	11,999,990	10
	6,418,830	5,581,160	11,999,990		

① Interest earned $= 0.04(\text{Amount at the beginning of the interval})$
    $= 0.04(\$213{,}961)$
    $= \$8558$

② Increase in the fund $=$ Interest earned $+$ Payment
    $= \$8558 + \$213{,}961$
    $= \$222{,}519$

③ Balance $=$ Previous balance $+$ Increase in the fund
    $= \$213{,}961 + \$222{,}519$
    $= \$436{,}480$

④ Book value $=$ Debt principal $-$ Sinking fund balance
    $= \$12{,}000{,}000 - \$436{,}480$
    $= \$11{,}563{,}520$

⑤ Balance in the sinking fund $=$ Future value of the first 28 payments
    $= \$213{,}961\left[\frac{(1.04)^{28} - 1}{0.04}\right]$
    $= \$10{,}691{,}114$

SPREADSHEET STRATEGIES   Full Sinking Fund Schedule

Connect provides five partially completed Excel templates for a variety of sinking fund schedules. Instructions are provided with each template. Go to the Student Edition of Connect and find "Sinking Fund Schedules."

Here we use the template for the *full* sinking fund schedule (in which the payments constitute an ordinary simple

annuity) to answer Part c of Example 15.5A. In this example, end-of-year payments of $62,908.11 are made for six years to a sinking fund earning 7% compounded annually. The formulas used in Rows 14 and 20 are presented in Rows 21 and 22.

	A	B	C	D	E	F	G
1							
2	Using a spreadsheet to prepare a full sinking fund schedule.						
3	Example 15.5A, Part c:						
4							
5			Nominal annual interest rate, *j*			7.000%	
6			Compoundings and payments per year, *m*			1	
7			Interest rate per compounding interval, *i*			7.0000%	
8			Payment, *PMT*			$62,908.11	
9							
10		Payment				Balance in	
11		interval	Payment	Interest	Increase	fund (end	
12		number	(at end)	earned	in the fund	of interval)	
13		0	---	---	---	$0	
14		1	$62,908.11	$0.00	$62,908.11	$62,908.11	
15		2	$62,908.11	$4,403.57	$67,311.68	$130,219.79	
16		3	$62,908.11	$9,115.39	$72,023.50	$202,243.29	
17		4	$62,908.11	$14,157.03	$77,065.14	$279,308.43	
18		5	$62,908.11	$19,551.59	$82,459.70	$361,768.13	
19		6	$62,908.11	$25,323.77	$88,231.88	$450,000.01	
20		Total:	$377,448.66	$72,551.35	$450,000.01		
21	Row 14 formulas:	=F$8	=ROUND(F13*F$7,2)	=D14+C14		=F13+E14	
22	Row 20 formulas:	=SUM(C14:C19)	=SUM(D14:D19)	=SUM(E14:E19)			
23							

The total interest earned in the sinking fund is $72,551.35.

EXERCISE 15.5

Spreadsheet templates: *Connect provides five partially completed Excel templates for various full and partial sinking fund schedules. You can use one or another of these templates in Problems 17 to 24 and 27 to 30 of Exercise 15.5. Go to the Student Edition of Connect and find "Sinking Fund Schedules."*

Answers to the odd-numbered problems are at the end of the book.

For each of the sinking funds in Problems 1 through 8, calculate (rounded to the nearest dollar):

a. The size of the periodic sinking fund payment.

b. The balance in the sinking fund at the time indicated in the last column. (Round the sinking fund payment to the nearest dollar before calculating the balance.)

Problem	End-of-term amount of sinking fund ($ millions)	Term (years)	Sinking fund rate of return (%)	Payment and compounding interval	Payment at beginning or end of interval?	Calculate balance at the end of interval
1.	12	10	7	6 months	End	12
2.	7	5	6	3 months	End	6
3.	15	15	6.5	1 year	End	11
4.	8	10	7.5	1 month	End	65

Problem	End-of-term amount of sinking fund ($ millions)	Term (years)	Sinking fund rate of return (%)	Payment and compounding interval	Payment at beginning or end of interval?	Calculate balance at the end of interval
5.	6	5	5.25	1 month	Beginning	27
6.	10	10	6.5	3 months	Beginning	28
7.	18	15	6.75	6 months	Beginning	19
8.	5	10	5.75	1 year	Beginning	8

Each of the bond issues in Problems 9 through 16 has a sinking fund requirement for retiring the entire principal amount of the issue on its maturity date. The coupon rates and rates of return on the sinking fund investments are compounded semiannually. In each case calculate (to the nearest dollar):
a. The size of the sinking fund payment at the end of every six months.
b. The annual cost of the debt.
c. The book value of the debt at the end of the indicated interval. (Round the sinking fund payment to the nearest dollar **before** *calculating the book value.)*

Problem	Principal amount of bond issue ($ millions)	Term (years)	Sinking fund rate of return (%)	Coupon rate (%)	Calculate book value at the end of interval
○**9.**	10	10	7	10	12
○**10.**	8	5	6	8.5	6
○**11.**	15	15	6.5	9	21
○**12.**	12	10	7.5	10.5	15
○**13.**	7	5	5.75	8	7
○**14.**	9	10	6.5	9.25	18
○**15.**	11	15	7.5	10.25	19
○**16.**	10	10	7	9.75	11

For Problems 17 through 20, construct the complete sinking fund schedule. Calculate the total interest earned by adding up the "interest earned" column and by calculating the difference between the final balance in the fund and the total of the contributed payments. Round the sinking fund payments and periodic interest earnings to the nearest dollar.

Problem	End-of-term amount of sinking fund ($)	Term (years)	Sinking fund rate of return (%)	Payment and compounding interval	Payment at beginning or end of interval?
○**17.**	800,000	3	7	6 months	End
○**18.**	675,000	6	6	1 year	End
○**19.**	1,000,000	5	6.75	1 year	Beginning
○**20.**	550,000	4	5.75	6 months	Beginning

○**21.** For the sinking fund described in Problem 2, prepare a partial sinking fund schedule showing details of Payments 1, 2, 11, 12, 19, and 20. Round the sinking fund payments and periodic interest earnings to the nearest dollar.

○**22.** For the sinking fund described in Problem 5, prepare a partial sinking fund schedule showing details of Payments 1, 2, 39, 40, 59, and 60. Round the sinking fund payments and periodic interest earnings to the nearest dollar.

○**23.** For the bond sinking fund described in Problem 9, prepare a partial sinking fund schedule (including the book value of the debt) showing details of the first two and the last two payments. Round the sinking fund payments and periodic interest earnings to the nearest dollar.

○**24.** For the bond sinking fund described in Problem 10, prepare a partial sinking fund schedule (including the book value of the debt) showing details of the first two and the last two payments. Round the sinking fund payments and periodic interest earnings to the nearest dollar.

○**25.** To provide for the automation of a production process in five years, Dominion Chemicals is starting a sinking fund to accumulate $600,000 by the end of the five years. Round the sinking fund payments and the periodic interest earnings to the nearest dollar.

   a. If the sinking fund earns 7.5% compounded monthly, what monthly payments starting today should be made to the fund?

   b. How much interest will be earned in the fourth year?

   c. In what month will the fund pass the halfway point?

   d. How much interest will be earned in the thirty-fifth month?

○**26.** Repeat Problem 25, with the change that the sinking fund payments are to be made at the end of every month.

•**27.** Thermo-Tech Systems recently sold a $20 million bond issue with a 20-year maturity and a coupon rate of 7% compounded semiannually. The bond indenture contract requires Thermo-Tech to make equal payments at the end of every six months into a sinking fund administered by National Trust. The sinking fund should accumulate the full $20 million required to redeem the bonds at their maturity. Round the sinking fund payments and periodic interest earnings to the nearest dollar.

   a. What must the size of the sinking fund payments be if the fund earns 4.5% compounded semiannually?

   b. How much interest will the fund earn in the sixth year?

   c. How much will the fund increase in the twenty-seventh payment interval?

   d. Construct a partial sinking fund schedule showing details of the first two and the last two payments, and the total of the interest earned.

•**28.** The town of Mount Hope is financing a $4.5 million upgrade to its water system through the province's Municipal Finance Authority. The MFA obtained financing via a bond issue with interest at 7.5% per annum payable semiannually. Also, at the end of every six months, the town is to make equal payments into a sinking fund administered by the MFA so that the necessary funds will be available to repay the $4.5 million debt when it matures in 17 years. The sinking fund earns 4% compounded semiannually. Round the sinking fund payments and periodic interest earnings to the nearest dollar.

   a. Calculate the size of the sinking fund payments.

   b. How much will the fund increase in the eighteenth payment interval?

   c. How much interest will the fund earn in the tenth year?

   d. Construct a partial sinking fund schedule showing details of the ninth, tenth, and last two payments, and the total of the interest earned.

•**29.** A sinking fund is to be set up to provide for the repayment of 80% of the principal amount of a $1 million debt in 10 years. Equal payments are to be made at the beginning of each quarter. The sinking fund will earn 7% compounded quarterly. Round the sinking fund payments and periodic interest earnings to the nearest dollar.

   a. Calculate the size of the sinking fund payments.

   b. Construct a partial sinking fund schedule showing details of the first two and the last two payments, and the total of the interest earned.

•**30.** Repeat Problem 29, with the change that the sinking fund payments are to be made at the end of every quarter.

KEY TERMS

Annual cost of a debt **p. 595**

Bond **p. 567**

Bond discount **p. 574**

Bond premium **p. 575**

Book value of a debt **p. 594**

Coupon rate **p. 568**

Debenture **p. 567**

Face value **p. 567**

Flat price **p. 585**

Issue date **p. 567**

Maturity date **p. 567**

Quoted price **p. 585**

Redemption price **p. 567**

Sinking fund **p. 590**

Sinking fund schedule **p. 590**

Yield to maturity **p. 578**

SUMMARY OF NOTATION AND KEY FORMULAS

In the context of bond pricing,

FV = Face value of the bond

b = Coupon rate per interest payment interval (normally six months)

i = The bond market's required rate of return per payment interval

n = Number of interest payments remaining until the maturity date

FORMULA (15-1) $$\text{Bond price} = b(FV)\left[\frac{1-(1+i)^{-n}}{i}\right] + FV(1+i)^{-n}$$ Finding the price of a bond on a coupon interest payment date

The following relationships were developed for sinking funds.

$$\left(\begin{array}{c}\text{Balance at the end of}\\\text{any payment interval}\end{array}\right) = \left(\begin{array}{c}\text{Future value of the}\\\text{payments already made}\end{array}\right)$$

$$\left(\begin{array}{c}\text{Interest earned in}\\\text{any payment interval}\end{array}\right) = i \times \left(\begin{array}{c}\text{Amount in the sinking fund}\\\text{at the beginning of the interval}\end{array}\right)$$

$$\left(\begin{array}{c}\text{Increase in the sinking fund's balance}\\\text{during any payment interval}\end{array}\right) = PMT + \left(\begin{array}{c}\text{Interest earned}\\\text{during the interval}\end{array}\right)$$

$$\left(\begin{array}{c}\text{Book value}\\\text{of the debt}\end{array}\right) = \left(\begin{array}{c}\text{Principal amount}\\\text{of the debt}\end{array}\right) - \left(\begin{array}{c}\text{Balance in the}\\\text{sinking fund}\end{array}\right)$$

REVIEW PROBLEMS

Answers to the odd-numbered review problems are at the end of the book.

1. **(LO1)** A $1000, 7.5% coupon bond has $19\frac{1}{2}$ years remaining until maturity. Calculate the bond discount if the required return in the bond market is 8.6% compounded semiannually.

2. **(LO1)** Four years after the issue of a $10,000, 9.5% coupon, 20-year bond, the rate of return required in the bond market on long-term bonds was 7.8% compounded semiannually.

   a. At what price did the bond then sell?

   b. What capital gain or loss (expressed in dollars) would the original owner have realized by selling the bond at that price?

3. **(LO1)** Four and one-half years ago, Glenda purchased fifteen $1000 bonds in a Province of New Brunswick issue carrying an 8.5% coupon and priced to yield 9.8% (compounded semiannually). The bonds then had 18 years remaining until maturity. The bond market now requires a yield to maturity on the bonds of 8.0% compounded semiannually. If Glenda sells the bonds today, what will be the dollar amount of her capital gain or loss?

4. **(LO1)** A $1000 face value, 6.8% coupon, Province of Ontario bond with 18 years to run until maturity is currently priced to yield investors 6.5% compounded semiannually until maturity. How much lower would the bond's price have to be to make the yield to maturity 7% compounded semiannually?

5. **(LO1)** Two and one-half years ago, Nova Scotia Power sold an issue of 25-year, 8% coupon bonds. If the current semiannually compounded return required in the bond market is 6.9%, calculate the percent capital gain or loss on the bonds over the entire $2\frac{1}{2}$-year holding period.

6. **(LO2)** Calculate the yield to maturity on a $1000 face value bond purchased for $1034.50 if it carries a 7.9% coupon and has $8\frac{1}{2}$ years remaining until maturity.

∘7. **(LO1)** A New Brunswick Power bond issue carrying a 7.6% coupon matures on November 1, 2020. At what price did $1000 face value bonds trade on June 10, 2008, if the yield to maturity required by the bond market on that date was 5.9% compounded semiannually?

8. **(LO1)** Calculate the quoted price on June 10, 2008, of the bond in Problem 7.

∘9. **(LO3) (LO4)** The Cowichan Regional District borrowed $500,000 through the Provincial Finance Authority to purchase fire-fighting equipment. At the end of every six months, the regional district must make a sinking fund payment of a size calculated to accumulate $500,000 after seven years to repay the principal amount of the debt. The sinking fund earns 7% compounded semiannually. Construct a partial sinking fund schedule showing details of the first two and the last two payments. Round the sinking fund payments and periodic interest earnings to the nearest dollar.

∘10. **(LO2)** A $1000, 9.5% coupon Government of Canada bond has 10 years remaining until its maturity. It is currently priced at 108.25 (percent of face value).

a. What is the bond's yield to maturity?

b. If the bond price abruptly rises by $25, what is the change in its yield to maturity?

∘11. **(LO1)** A $1000, 6.5% coupon, 20-year Government of Canada bond was issued on June 15, 2006. At what price did it trade on December 10, 2010, when the market's required return was 5.2% compounded semiannually?

∘12. **(LO1)** If a broker quotes a price of 111.25 for a bond on September 10, what amount will a client pay per $1000 face value? The 7% coupon rate is payable on May 15 and November 15 of each year.

∘13. **(LO3) (LO4)** Laurentian Airways is preparing for the replacement of one of its passenger jets in three years by making payments to a sinking fund at the beginning of every six months for the next three years. The fund can earn 6% compounded semiannually, and the capital required in three years is $750,000. Prepare a complete sinking fund schedule. Round the sinking fund payments and periodic interest earnings to the nearest dollar.

∘14. **(LO3) (LO4)** The municipality of Duncan has financed a sewage treatment plant by issuing $18 million worth of sinking fund debentures. The debentures have a 15-year term and pay a coupon rate of 9% compounded semiannually. Rounding the sinking fund payments, interest payments, and periodic interest earnings to the nearest dollar,

a. What equal payments at the end of every six months will be necessary to accumulate $18 million after 15 years if the sinking fund can earn 6.25% compounded semiannually?

b. What is the annual cost of the debt to Duncan taxpayers?

c. Construct a partial sinking fund schedule (including the book value of the debt) showing details of the first three and the last three payments.

APPENDIX 15A | ## INSTRUCTIONS FOR THE TEXAS INSTRUMENTS BA-II PLUS BOND WORKSHEET

This worksheet enables you to quickly compute either a bond's *quoted* price or its yield to maturity on any date.

Find "BOND" located above the [9] key. To access the Bond Worksheet, press [2nd] [BOND]. Recall that a worksheet can be thought of as a column of items that you can view one-at-a-time in the calculator's display. The Bond Worksheet's column contains the nine items listed below. You see the top item when you first access the worksheet. You can view other items using the scroll keys ⌊ ↓ ⌋ and ⌊ ↑ ⌋ . (You may get an "Error 6" message if you scroll to the last item without first entering legitimate data for other variables.)

STD =	mm-dd-yyyy
CPN =	n.nn
RDT =	mm-dd-yyyy
RV =	nnn
ACT	
2/Y	
YLD =	n.nn
PRI =	nnn.nn
AI =	nnn.nn

STD is the label for the date of the sale or purchase (sometimes called the *SettlemenT Date*.) The formats for data entry and display are the same as for the Date Worksheet (Appendix 6A.) That is, mm, dd, and yyyy represent the digits for the month, day, and year, respectively. To enter the date June 9, 2008, the keystrokes are

06.0908 ⌊ENTER⌋

CPN is the label for the coupon rate. To enter 5.75%, the keystrokes are

5.75 ⌊ENTER⌋

RDT is the label for the bond's maturity date (also known as the *Redemption DaTe*.) Enter this date in the same manner as for *STD*.

RV is the label for the *Redemption Value*. Enter it as a percentage of face value. (In this chapter, we consider only the most common case where the redemption value equals the face value. For this case, set *RV* = 100.)

ACT is a label meaning "*ACT*ual." It means that the calculator will use the actual number of days in intervals. By repeatedly pressing ⌊ 2nd ⌋ ⌊ENTER⌋, you can toggle between *ACT* and *360*, the two possible settings for this variable. For problems in this text, always use *ACT*.

2/Y is a label meaning "two coupon payments per year." By repeatedly pressing ⌊ 2nd ⌋ ⌊ENTER⌋, you can toggle between *2/Y* and *1/Y*, the two possible settings for this variable. For problems in this text, always use *2/Y*.

YLD (standing for *YieLD*) and *PRI* (for *PRIce*) are the next two items. *You enter one of them and compute the other.* *YLD* must be entered as a semiannually compounded rate in percent equivalent form. The value for *PRI* is the *quoted* price entered as a percentage of face value. For example, a $5000 face value bond with a quoted price of $5210.50 would be entered as 104.21 (= $\frac{\$5210.50}{\$5000} \times 100\%$).

After entering the preceding values and settings, you compute the unknown *YLD* or *PRI* by scrolling to it and then pressing the ⌊ CPT ⌋ key. This also causes the computation of the last item in the list, *AI* (standing for *Accrued Interest*.) The accrued interest is displayed as a percentage of face value. To obtain the flat price of the bond, add *AI* and *PRI*. If you use the worksheet to calculate a bond's price on an interest payment date (Section 15.2 problems), *AI* will be zero.

Answers to Odd-Numbered Problems

CHAPTER 1 REVIEW AND APPLICATIONS OF BASIC MATHEMATICS

Exercise 1.1

1. 4
3. 24
5. 20
7. 49
9. 0.5
11. 6
13. 255
15. 9
17. $100.74
19. $453.51
21. $204.00

Concept Questions (Section 1.2)

1. You must retain at least one more figure than you require in the answer. To achieve four-figure accuracy in the answer, you must retain a minimum of five figures in the values used in the calculations.
3. We want seven-figure accuracy in the answer. Therefore, values used in the calculations must be accurate to a minimum of eight figures.
5. Any value that represents a count of discrete units, such as the number of months in a year, is an example. Prescribed payments or values (in contrast to calculated payments or values that have been rounded) are known with perfect accuracy. For example, the GST rate of 5% and a prescribed monthly payment of $10 may be treated as numbers having complete accuracy.

Exercise 1.2

1. $0.87500 = 87.500\%$
3. $2.3500 = 235.00\%$
5. $-1.4000 = -140.00\%$
7. $0.025000 = 2.5000\%$
9. $2.0200 = 202.00\%$
11. $0.75000 = 75.000\%$
13. $0.8\overline{3} = 83.\overline{3}\%$
15. $7.\overline{7} = 777.\overline{7}\%$
17. $1.\overline{1} = 111.\overline{1}\%$
19. $-0.0\overline{259} = -2.\overline{592}\%$
21. 11.38
23. 0.5545
25. 1.002
27. 40.10
29. $0.16667 = 16.667\%$
31. $0.016667 = 1.6667\%$
33. $0.68493 = 68.493\%$
35. $0.0091667 = 0.91667\%$
37. $94.68
39. $410.99
41. $3384.52
43. $720.04
45. $14,435.88
47. $6648.46
49. $7159.48
51. $1830.07

Concept Questions (Section 1.3)

1. If a quantity equals the base, it is 100% of the base. If a quantity is twice the base, it is 200% of the base, and so on. If a quantity is four times the base, it is 400% of the base.
3. By the same line of reasoning as in Question 1, the Portion is 10 times the Base.

Exercise 1.3

1. $6.13
3. 13.0%
5. $75.00
7. $174.98
9. 200%
11. $90.00

13. $19.47

15. 62.1%

17. $105.26

19. 1.00%

21. $0.05

23. $150.00

25. $593.78

27. $125.00

29. $2000.00

31. a. 168%
  b. 50.1%

33. 80

35. $252,100

37. 20.9%

39. 840 mg

41. 83.0%

43. 1.10%

45. 5600

47. $5,225,000

49. a. 170
  b. 41

Exercise 1.4

1. $1324.65

3. $2474.06

5. $796.50

7. $405.00

9. $7239.03

11. $4200 from Supreme
  $4050 from Buy-Right

13. $6050.00

15. 7.267%

17. 3.50%

19. $70,833.33

Concept Questions (Section 1.5)

1. You should calculate a weighted average when some of the values being averaged are more important or occur more frequently than other values.

3. If you invest the same amount of money in each investment, each rate of return has the same importance. The portfolio's rate of return will then equal the simple average of the individual rates of return.

Exercise 1.5

1. 1.53

3. 3.50

5. 7.65%

7. 7.53

9. 43.74 days

11. a. $10.67
  b. $10.66
  c. $2547.74

13. 226.25%; 44.20%

15. 25.50

17. 6,250,000

Exercise 1.6

1.

Quarter	GST remittance (Refund)
1	$7768.25
2	(17,015.25)
3	20,432.40
4	8240.90

3. a. $40,975.00
  b. $42,950.00
  c. $44,548.13

5. a. 11.50%
  b. $19.71

7. $3827.88

9. $4317.16

11. a. 7.4837
  b. 7.1273

Review Problems

1. a. 23
  b. −40
  c. $205.39
  d. $2275.40
  e. $343.08
  f. $619.94
  g. $457.60
  h. $1549.56

3. 256.5%

5. $133.33

7. $26,000.00

9. a. $29.03
  b. $2372.87

11. $2231.25

13. 4.50%

15. $110,000

17. 7.96%

19. 26.1

CHAPTER 2   REVIEW AND APPLICATIONS OF ALGEBRA

Exercise 2.1

1. 0
3. $6x^2y$
5. $7x^2 + 7xy - 4y^2$
7. $8x + 3y$
9. $25x - 16$
11. $-0.7x + 3.45$
13. $18.8x - 8.5$
15. $3.0509P$
17. $2.9307k$
19. $12a^2b - 20a^2 + 24ab$
21. $-10x^3y + 5x^2y^2 + 15xy^3$
23. $20r^2 - 7rt - 6t^2$
25. $2a^2 + 34a + 99$
27. $6x$
29. $x - y$
31. $\dfrac{x^2 - 2x + 3}{4}$
33. $2ab - 3a^2$
35. 23.75
37. -44.8
39. $315.11
41. $346.22
43. $2430.38
45. $1378.42
47. $1794.22
49. $1071.77

Exercise 2.2

1. $500.00
3. $3500.00
5. 0.175
7. $15.00
9. $2400.00
11. 0.0270
13. $575.00
15. 0.0450
17. $i = \dfrac{PMT}{PV}$
19. $CM = \dfrac{NI + FC}{X}$
21. $r = \dfrac{S + P}{Pt}$
23. $d_1 = 1 - \dfrac{N}{L(1 - d_2)(1 - d_3)}$
25. $PV = FV(1 + i)^{-n}$
27. a^5
29. b^4

31. $(1 + i)^{13}$
33. x^{28}
35. t^2
37. x^2
38. $4(1 + i)^2$
41. $\dfrac{t^3}{2r}$
43. 16.0000
45. 18.5203
47. 1,000,000
49. 1.07006
51. 1.00990
53. -4.00000
55. -0.197531
57. 20.1569
59. 15.9637
61. 1.00908

Exercise 2.3

1. 2
3. 43
5. 200
7. 0.5
9. 9
11. 30
13. $286.66
15. $699.47
17. $391.01
19. $(x, y) = (4, 2)$
21. $(a, b) = (3, 5)$
23. $(x, y) = (7, 14)$
25. $(c, d) = (500, 1000)$
27. $(v, w) = \left(\dfrac{3}{2}, -\dfrac{1}{3}\right)$
29. $(x, y) = (17.0, 6.24)$
31. $(e, f) = (250, 125)$

Exercise 2.4

1. 2065
3. $4.55
5. $25.00
7. $125\frac{3}{4}$ hours
9. Radio: $44,444
   TV: $26,667
   Newspaper: $88,889
11. 60.0%
13. Technician: 3082
    Scientist: 4623
    Executive: 6623
15. Peanuts: 32.0 kg
    Raisins: 18.0 kg

17. Joan will invest $10,800
    Sue will invest $12,960
    Stella will invest $9000
19. 42 units of product Y
21. **a.** $18,000
    b. $105,000
23. 1057
25. 238 student members
    345 regular members.
27. 230 km at 50 km/h and
    770 km at 100 km/h
29. $38.00 per hour plus $0.35
    per km
31. Canada Savings Bonds: 4.2%
    Ontario Savings Bonds: 4.5%
33. 37 units of X and 56 units of Y
35. 25 litres of milk
    15 cans of orange juice
37. 843
39. Partner: $117,000 per year
    Technician: $67,500 per year
41. $73,451.62 per child
    $24,483.87 per grandchild
43. $12,040
45. 18 minutes for cutting
    11 minutes for assembly
    6 minutes for painting

Exercise 2.5

1. 5.26%
3. 285.71%
5. 18.18%
7. $118.26
9. 105.2 cm
11. $25.00
13. 11.11%
15. $80.00
17. $42.86
19. −0.62%
21. $131.25
23. $125.00
25. $658.80
27. $99.96
29. 200.00%
31. $10,075
33. $230.00
35. $375.00
37. $124.90(GST); $174.86(PST)

39. **a.** −15.28%
    b. 2.65%
    c. −13.03%
41. 11.11% increase
43. 4.96% increase
45. $4.20
47. $311,400
49. −40.00% in Year 1
    66.67% in Year 2
51. 7,040,000
53. 16.67% reduction
55. $1.43
57. $80,000
59. 42.86% more
61. 18.70% less
63. 25.00% increase
65. 150%
67. 23.08% less
69. 1.90%

Review Problems

1. $-22a^2 + 21ab + 16b^2$
3. **a.** $0.7y + 2.2\overline{6}$
   b. $2.996843P$
5. $4505.14
7. **a.** $-\dfrac{9}{x}$
   b. $-\dfrac{8b^3}{a^9}$
9. **a.** 1.19641
   b. 0.00816485
   c. 41.1527
   d. 9.11858
11. **a.** $280.97
    b. $436.96
13. 0.120
15. $(x, y) = (7, -2)$
17. $i_1 = \dfrac{FV}{PV(1 + i_2)} - 1$
19. **a.** 238.24%
    b. $7.48
21. **a.** 79.27%
    b. −79.27%
23. $12,203.39 (Kajsa)
    $14,644.07 (Grace)
    $9152.54 (Mary Anne)
25. Base salary: $1600 per month
    Commission rate: 4.5%
27. $10.92 (reds), $7.80 (blues)
29. 456

CHAPTER 3 RATIOS AND PROPORTIONS

Exercise 3.1

1. 3:16
3. 3:1:2
5. 2:3
7. 3:5:7
9. 8:13:5
11. 1:6
13. 7:10
15. 3:4
17. 15:8
19. 2:6:3
21. 2.53:1
23. 1:4.58
25. 1:2.61
27. 3.35:1:1.78
29. 1:1.54:2.29
31. 1:2.47:1.37
33. 5:7:8
35. 3.36:1:2.18
37. 8:7:5
39. 20:1

Exercise 3.2

1. 42.0
3. 233
5. 28.7
7. 0.0155
9. $\frac{1}{3}$
11. $n = 90.0$; $m = 75.0$
13. $g = 5.00$; $f = 375$
15. $r = 11.2$; $s = 19.0$
17. $4723.06
19. 31 hours & 7 minutes
21. $32,602.50
23. Ford: $8.21 billion
    Hyundai: $3.12 billion
25. Wholesale cost: $2.95 million
    Overhead expenses: $1.55 million
27. 29 outlets
    $43.13 million

Exercise 3.3

1. $75.85
3. $406.85
5. a. $3184.00
   b. $3444.98
7. a. $168,750 to A
      $450,000 to B
      $281,250 to C

b. $7,237,500 to A
   $19,300,000 to B
   $12,062,500 to C
9. a. Harry: $80,000
      Draco: $108,000
      Hermione: $68,000
   b. $25,920
11. a. $389,838.38 to Industrial Products
       $265,798.90 to Fine Paper
       $183,362.72 to Containers & Packaging
    b. $480,724.32 to Industrial Products
       $189,341.89 to Fine Paper
       $168,933.78 to Containers & Packaging
13. A: $5256.41
    B: $3269.23
    D: $1474.36
15. Executive: $4127.73
    Supervisor: $2889.41
    Production worker: $2063.86

Exercise 3.4

1. C$2014.13
3. ¥1,275,290
5. C$5041.00
7. C$8595.72
9. £52,436.90
11. €32,181.01
13. a. Sw kr 6.662
    b. US$0.8163
    c. Mex peso 0.1349
    d. C$0.02275
15. C$3616.59
17. C$11,313.15
19. C$4713.61 gain
21. £49.50
23. C$9.04
25.

	Royal	ICE
a.	2.67%	8.18%
b.	2.01%	19.03%

27. Direct conversion: €741.65
    Indirect conversion: €741.66
    These are equal to four-figure accuracy.
29. 8.29% more expensive in Canada.
31. Personally designed travel is C$1471.29 cheaper.
33. 33.7%

Concept Questions (Section 3.5)

1. If the number of units of currency N per unit of currency M decreases, it then requires *less* of currency N to purchase 1 unit of M. Therefore, currency N has strengthened.

2. If currency G weakens relative to currency H, it will require more of currency G to purchase 1 unit of H. Therefore, the exchange rate expressed as units of G per unit of H will increase.

Exercise 3.5

1. £ has depreciated by 8.86%
3. €0.6417 per C$1.00
  C$1.5584 per €1.00
5. £0.5563 per C$1.00
7. C$1.7925 per £1.00
9. Increase of US$0.0043 per C$1.00
11. Decrease of A$0.000153 per ¥1
13. C$25.87 decrease
15. Decrease of C$898.77

Exercise 3.6

1. 151.3
3. $9001
5. 9.374
7. $3646
9. 122.2
11. $1024.46
13. a. $1157.02
  b. $1209.03
  c. 5.20%
15. Portfolio increased 175.93%
  Consumer prices increased 41.98%
17. a. $161.16
  b. 8.90% for 1978
    9.60% for 1979
    11.95% for 1980
    11.42% for 1981
    8.25% for 1982

Review Problems

1. a. 6 : 20 : 15
  b. 3 : 2 : 4
  c. 3 : 6 : 2
  d. 5 : 4 : 7
3. a. $x = 18.06$
  b. $a = 332.8; b = 205.4$
5. 11 : 14 : 8
7. $23.51 per hour
9. 13,380,910 rupiah
11. Decrease of C$691.00
13. Gain of $8.95
15. Ms. L received $4000.00
  Mr. M received $2666.67
  Mr. P received $1333.33

17. Wife to receive $148,798.17
  Son to receive $106,284.40
  Stepson to receive $75,917.43
19. C$36.96 increase
21. Alberta coal is C$10.73 cheaper per metric tonne

CHAPTER 4   MATHEMATICS OF MERCHANDISING

Exercise 4.1

1. $83.00, $166.00
3. $21.33, $16\frac{2}{3}$%
5. $1750.00, $1137.50
7. $27.40, 45.0%
9. $3256.00, $407.00
11. $41.25, $57.75
13. $149.00, $55.97
15. $83.70
17. $371.90
19. 17.8%
21. 26.55%
23. $339,800.00
25. a. $5197.50
  b. $374.00
27. 236 points
29. a. $697.68 million
  b. 401 people
31. a. $7579.22
  b. $646.88
  c. $398.91
33. 6.00%
35. a. $300.00
  b. $105.00

Exercise 4.2

1. $2317.70
3. $799.18
5. a. $4975.11
  b. $5025.87
  c. $5025.87
7. $1337.70
9. $515.46
11. a. $8772.37
  b. $8684.65
13. $642.00
15. a. $3778.78
  b. April 20
17. $2878.15
19. $1557.67
21. $374.90

23. $2127.36
25. $975.61

Concept Questions (Section 4.3)

1. Both quantities have the same numerator, but the rate of markup on cost has the smaller denominator (since $C < S$). Therefore, the rate of markup on cost is larger than the rate of markup on selling price.

3. Yes. If an item is marked up (M) by more than the unit cost (C), then

   Rate of markup on cost $= \dfrac{M}{C} \times 100\% > 100\%$

5. No. At the break-even point, there is no profit. The selling price at the break-even point must cover E as well as C. If an item is sold at cost, the merchant will *lose E* per unit sold.

Exercise 4.3

1. **a.** 31.1%
   b. 23.7%
3. Rate of markup on cost $= 106.2\%$
   Rate of markup on selling price $= 51.5\%$
5. **a.** $49.50
   b. 65.0%
   c. 39.4%
7. **a.** 50.0%
   b. $24.99
   c. 100.0%
9. **a.** $231.00
   b. 42.9%
   c. $34.65
11. **a.** $1.73
    b. 185.7%
13. **a.** $22.16
    b. 44.4%
15. Rate of markup on cost $= 209.5\%$
    Rate of markup on selling price $= 67.7\%$
17. **a.** $S = \$383.40$
    b. Rate of markup on cost $= 34.8\%$
    c. Rate of markup on selling price $= 25.8\%$
    d. S(Break-even) $= \$343.40$
19. **a.** $37.90
    b. 31.0%
21. 150.0%
23. $7.80
25. $52.81
27. $108.90

Concept Questions (Section 4.4)

1. No. The base for the rate of markup on cost is the unit cost, C. The base for the markdown is the selling price, S. Since $C < S$, a 40% markup on cost represents a smaller dollar amount than a 40% markdown from the item's selling price. A 40% markup on cost followed by a 40% markdown will give a reduced selling price that is less than C.

Exercise 4.4

1. **a.** $277.50
   b. 21.6%
3. **a.** 100.0%
   b. 50.0%
5. $22.21
7. **a.** Rate of markup on selling price $= 28.46\%$
   b. Rate of markdown $= 28.46\%$
9. $398.07
11. **a.** 25.7%
    b. 13.8%
13. 15.6%

Exercise 4.5

1. $2.98 loss
3. $2.45 loss
5. **a.** $216.00
   b. $259.20
   c. $118.80
   d. $475.20
   e. $285.12
   f. 32.0%
   g. Loss of $49.68
7. $108.00
9. 34.0%
11. **a.** 15%
    b. $19.76 loss per unit
13. 23.6%
15. **a.** 25.0%
    b. $6.12 loss
    c. 25.0%
17. **a.** $950.00
    b. $1187.50
19. **a.** $2945.25
    b. $35.70 loss

Review Problems

1. Source B is $1.30 cheaper
3. $352.08

5. $338,600

7. a. $825.80
   b. $33,852.07

9. a. $289.00
   b. 31.1%

11. a. $780.48
    b. $720.00
    c. 34.7%
    d. $34.38

13. a. $6.94
    b. $2.50

15. 122.2%

17. a. $67.30
    b. $61.24

19. a. 153.3% of cost
    b. 6.5%

21. a. $20.65
    b. 76.5%
    c. $18.59

23. $30.48

25. $574.00

27. a. $59.63
    b. 26.8%

Appendix 4A

1. $3765.25

3. $1450.61

5. Payment = $1400.00

7. 1.50%

9. a. May 15
   b. June 4
   c. $788.00
   d. $1066.32
   e. $262.33

11. a. $8163.27
    b. $6608.73

13. $15,828.35

CHAPTER 5   APPLICATIONS OF LINEAR EQUATIONS

Exercise 5.1

1.
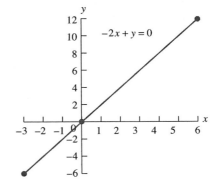

3.

x:	−3	0	6
y:	10	4	−8

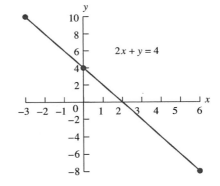

5.

x:	−8	0	12
y:	−3	3	12

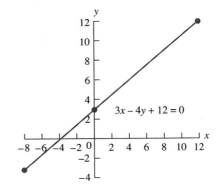

7.

x:	0	3000	6000
y:	5000	18,500	32,000

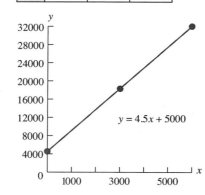

$y = 4.5x + 5000$

9. a. Slope $= \frac{5}{2}$; b-intercept $= -\frac{3}{2}$
b. Slope $= \frac{3}{4}$; b-intercept $= -3$
c. Slope $= -\frac{4}{5}$; b-intercept $= 480$
d. Slope $= -\frac{7}{8}$; b-intercept $= 0$

11. $E = 0.05R + \$1500$
Slope $= 0.05$
E-intercept $= \$1500$

13. a. Slope $= \$6$
    TR-intercept $= \$0$
b. Slope $= \$2$
    TC-intercept $= \$80,000$
c. Slope $= \$4$
    NI-intercept $= -\$80,000$
d. TR line is steepest
e. $\$4$
f. Slope of TR vs. X stays the same
    Slope of TC vs. X decreases
    Slope of NI vs. X increases

15. $x - 3y = 3$

x:	−6	3
y:	−3	0

$y = -2$

x:	−6	3
y:	−2	−2

The solution is
$(x, y) = (-3, -2)$.

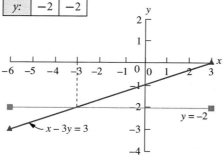

17. $x - 3y = 0$

x:	−6	3
y:	−2	1

$x + 2y = -5$

x:	−6	3
y:	0.5	−4

The solution is
$(x, y) = (-3, -1)$.

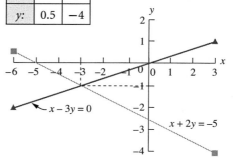

19. $y - 3x = 11$

x:	−4	2
y:	−1	17

$5x + 30 = 4y$

x:	−4	2
y:	2.5	10

The solution is
$(x, y) = (-2, 5)$.

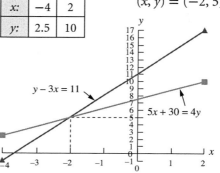

21. $7p - 3q = 23$

p:	0	6
q:	−7.67	6.33

$-2p - 3q = 5$

p:	0	6
q:	−1.67	−5.67

The solution is
$(p, q) = (2, -3)$.

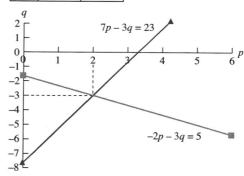

Exercise 5.2

1. **a.** Variable cost
   b. Fixed cost
   c. Mixed cost
   d. Variable cost
   e. Fixed cost
   f. Mixed cost
   g. Variable cost
   h. Fixed cost
3. $1,840,000

Exercise 5.3

1. **a.** 5000 toys per year
   b. $150,000 per year
3. **a.** 1500 jars
   b. $3000
5. **a.** 40,000 CDs per month
   b. 45,000 CDs per month
7. **a.** 6000 copies per month
   b. $50 per month
9. **a.** 150 units per week
   b. (i) $240 loss per month
      (ii) $800 profit per month
   c. 200 units per week
11. **a.** 75% of capacity
    b. $666,667 loss
13. **a.** 2000 composters per month
    b. $13,500 per month
    c. $10,800 loss per month
    d. 84.4% of capacity
    e. Decreases by 71 composters per month
15. $S = \$75$ per tire
    $TR = \$3,750,000$
    $VC = \$55$ per tire
    $FC = \$300,000$
17. **a.** $800,000
    b. $90,000
    c. $40,000
    d. $60,000
19. **a.** 28 participants
    b. $400 profit
    c. 20 participants
21. **a.** 311 tickets at $46
       205 tickets at $56
    b. $1560 at $46
       $2520 at $56
23. **a.** $40.97
    b. $40.58
25. **a.** 12.72 tonnes per hectare
    b. 1.03 tonnes per hectare

c. (i) $260 per hectare profit
   (ii) $310 per hectare loss

Exercise 5.4

1. $TR = (S)X$
   $= \$2.50X$
   $TC = (VC)X + FC$
   $= \$1.00X + \$60,000$

X:	20,000	60,000
TR:	$50,000	$150,000
TC:	$80,000	$120,000

   a. 40,000 CDs per month
   b. 45,000 CDs per month

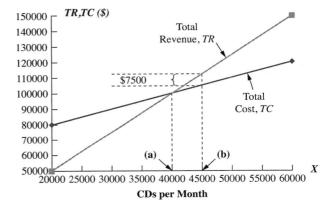

3. $TR = (S)X$
   $= \$0.10X$
   $TC = (VC)X + FC$
   $= \$0.05X + \$300$

X:	4000	8000
TR:	$400	$800
TC:	$500	$700

   a. 6000 copies/month
   b. $50 per month

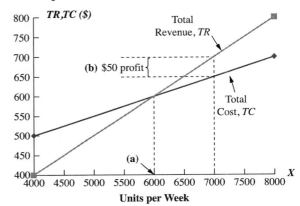

5. $TR = (S)X$
$\quad\quad = \$20X$
$\quad TC = (VC)X + FC$
$\quad\quad = \$12X + \$1200$

X:	0	250
TR:	$0	$5000
TC:	$1200	$4200

a. 150 units/week
b. (i) $240 loss
  (ii) $800 profit
c. 200 units/week

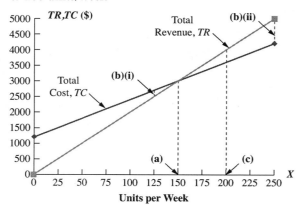

7. $TR = (S)X$
$\quad\quad = \$70X$
$\quad TC = (VC)X + FC$
$\quad\quad = \$43X + \$54,000$

X:	1000	3200
TR:	$70,000	$224,000
TC:	$97,000	$191,600

a. 2000 composters/month
b. $13,500/month
c. $10,800/month loss

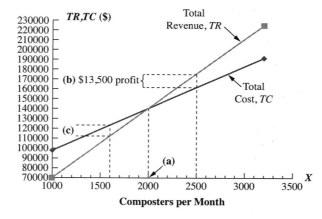

9. a. No effect on the *FC* line.
b. No effect on the *TC* line.
c. The slope of the *TR* line increases.
d. The break-even point occurs at a lower sales volumes.

Concept Questions (Section 5.5)

1. a. Since $CM = S - VC$, *CM* will increase if *S* is increased.
b. Raw materials are part of *VC*. *VC* will decrease if the cost of raw materials decreases. Therefore, *CM* will increase.
c. The property tax is part of *FC*. There will be no change in *CM*.
d. The salaries of executives are part of *FC*. There will be no change in *CM*.
e. Wages of production workers are part of *VC*. *VC* will increase and *CM* will decrease.

3. a. The break-in volume will be lowered since fewer units need to be sold to cover the reduced fixed costs.
b. If unit variable costs (*VC*) increase, the contribution margin ($CM = S - VC$) decreases, and more units must be sold to cover the unchanged fixed costs. Therefore, the break-even point is higher.
c. No change—the actual sales volume does not affect the break-even point.
d. If *S* decreases, the contribution margin ($CM = S - VC$) decreases, and more units must be sold to cover the unchanged fixed costs. Therefore, the break-even point is higher.
e. If the contribution rate (or ratio) *CR* increases, a larger portion of each unit's selling price is available to pay fixed costs. Therefore, the break-even point is lower.

Exercise 5.5

1. a. 5000 toys per year
b. $150,000 per year
3. a. 1500 jars
b. $3000
5. a. 40,000 CDs per month
b. 45,000 CDs per month
7. a. 6000 copies per month
b. $50 per month
9. a. 150 units per week
b. (i) $240 loss per month
  (ii) $800 profit per month
c. 200 units per week

11. a. 75% of capacity
   b. $666,667 loss
13. a. 2000 composters per month
   b. $13,500 per month
   c. $10,800 loss per month
   d. 84.4% of capacity
   e. Decreases by 71 composters per month
15. $S = \$75$ per tire
   $TR = \$3,750,000$
   $VC = \$55$ per tire
   $FC = \$300,000$
17. a. $800,000
   b. $90,000
   c. $40,000
   d. $60,000
19. a. 28 participants
   b. $400 profit
   c. 20 participants
21. a. 311 tickets at $46
     205 tickets at $56
   b. $1560 at $46 per ticket
     $2520 at $56 per ticket
23. a. $40.97
   b. $40.58
25. a. 12.72 tonnes per hectare
   b. 1.03 tonnes per hectare
   c. **(i)** $260 per hectare profit
     (ii) 310 per hectare loss

Review Problems

1. a. 18,000 units
   b. $3,240,000
   c. $140,000 profit
     $35,000 loss
3. a. 2479 books
   b. $56,160
   c. Select $35 price. (*NI* will fall to $54,264 at the reduced price.)
   d. 323 books
5. a. $120 million
   b. $24 million
7. a. 5000 units
   b. 7500 units
   c. $120,000
   d. **(i)** $10,000 lower
     (ii) $20,000 higher
   e. **(i)** $48,000 lower
     (ii) $24,000 higher
   f. **(i)** $40,000 higher
     (ii) $80,000 lower
   g. $28,000 lower

9. a. 36.2%
   b. **(i)** Profit of $2960 per month
     (ii) Loss of $4780 per month
   c. The owner should reduce the rental rate because it will increase the net income by $540 per month.

CHAPTER 6   SIMPLE INTEREST

Exercise 6.1

1. $83.13
3. $825.00
5. 7 months
7. 8.75%
9. $114.58
11. $6500.00
13. 4.20%
15. 11 months
17. $97.50, $98.45

Exercise 6.2

1. $118.63
3. $2892.33
5. $1171.28
7. 8.50%
9. $22.09
11. 1.50%
13. 41 days
15. January 29, 2012
17. March 9, 2011
19. March 18
21. $196.03
23. $3112.28

Exercise 6.3

1. $3027.44
3. $5169.38
5. $780.00
7. $14,100.00; $1279.58
9. 10.70%
11. 18.50%
13. 182 days
15. 8 months
17. $19,619.04
19. 9.00%
21. 7.82%
23. January 8
25. $5452.13
27. $235,423.32

Concept Questions (Section 6.4)

1. "Equivalent payments" are alternative payments (on different dates) that will put the recipient in the same economic position.
3. Calculate the future value of the earlier payment at the date of the later payment. If the future value is equal to the later payment, the two payments are equivalent.
5. Calculate the equivalent values of all three payments at the same focal date. The payment with the highest equivalent value on that focal date is the one with the largest economic value.

Exercise 6.4

1. $535.99
3. $5460.62
5. $990.87
7. $457.49
9. 7.25%
11. 90 days
13. 251 days early
15. $5500; 1.03%
17. $560 now; 10.86%
19. The two alternatives are essentially equivalent.
21. $2902.06 today
    $2933.99 in two months
    $2966.63 in four months
    $3000.00 in six months
    $3033.75 in eight months
    $3067.50 in 10 months
    $3101.25 in 12 months
23. **a.** Smith offer: $142,799.51
    Kim offer: $143,832.54
    b. Kim offer is worth $1033.03 more.
25. 7.71%

Concept Questions (Section 6.5)

1. The economic value of a nominal amount of money depends on the date when it is paid. This property of money is called the time value of money.
3. Calculate the sum of the equivalent values of the payments on the chosen date.
5. Today's economic value is lower. This economic value is the lump amount today that is equivalent to the payment stream. In other words, the lump amount along with its interest earnings could pay the series of scheduled payments. (The last payment would reduce the remaining funds to zero.) When interest rates are higher, a smaller lump amount will be sufficient to generate the payment stream because more interest will be earned to help meet the payments.

Exercise 6.5

1. $830.88
3. $1886.62
5. $4442.98
7. **a.** $3722.94
   b. $3904.76
   c. The equivalent value of a given payment stream will be higher at a later date because of the time value of money.
9. $1923.57
11. $2364.29, $2350.80
    Stream 1 has a $13.49 greater economic value (in today's dollars).
13. $1856.32
15. $2719.68

Exercise 6.6

1. $1083.45
3. $876.21
5. $505.54
7. $859.48
9. $1291.81
11. $2165.97
13. $1419.61

Review Problems

1. $9872.20
3. September 8
5. 4.75%
7. $59,729.01
9. $1028.14
11. **a.** $9709.65
    b. $9804.34
13. $237.65
15. $8459.14
17. **a.** Offer A: $193,846.15
        Offer B: $193,235.29
    b. Accept A—worth $610.86 more
    c. Accept B—worth $707.09 more
19. $2173.14

CHAPTER 7 APPLICATIONS OF SIMPLE INTEREST

Exercise 7.1

1. **a.** $15,110.96
   b. $15,191.07
3. $88.77

5. $14.16

7. $16.51 more

9. $3.49

11. $18.12

Concept Questions (Section 7.2)

1. We need to know:
  • The amounts of the future payments;
  • The dates of the future payments;
  • The prevailing (or market) rate of return on similar investments.

3. Estimate the amounts and dates of the future cash flows from the investment. Decide on the *minimum* rate of return you are prepared to accept from the investment. Calculate the sum of the present values of the forecast cash flows, discounting them at the minimum acceptable rate of return.

Exercise 7.2

1. a. $967.47

b. $974.54

c. The closer the purchase date to the payments, the smaller the discount will be for a given time value of money.

3. a. $1944.28

b. $1935.26

c. The payments from B are received one month later. This makes their value today less than the value of the payments from A.

5. $10,974.71

7. $7854.11

Concept Questions (Section 7.2)

1. The price of the 98-day T-bill is higher because less time remains until the $100,000 face value is received. You do not need as large a difference between the face value and the purchase price to provide the required rate of return.

3. The fair market value will steadily rise, reaching the T-bill's face value on the maturity date.

Exercise 7.3

1. $24,773

3. $993,084

5. $99,550 for the 30-day maturity
$99,104 for the 60-day maturity
$98,662 for the 90-day maturity

7. $629.54

9. 4.702%

11. 71 days

13. a. $98,593
  b. (i) $99,233
  (ii) $99,300
  (iii) $99,367
  c. (i) 2.787%
  (ii) 3.079%
  (iii) 3.371%

Exercise 7.4

1.

Date	Number of days	Interest rate	Interest	Accrued interest	Payment (Advance)	Principal portion	Balance
5-Feb	—	—	—	—	($15,000)	($15,000)	$15,000
29-Feb	24	8.50%	$83.84	$83.84	83.84		15,000
15-Mar	15	8.50%	52.40	52.40	10,000	10,000	5,000
31-Mar	16	8.50%	18.63	71.03	71.03		5,000
30-Apr	30	8.50%	34.93	34.93	34.93		5,000
1-May	1	8.50%	1.16	1.16	(7,000)	(7,000)	12,000
31-May	30	8.50%	83.84	85.00	85.00		12,000

The interest charged to Dr. Robillard's account was $83.84 on February 29, $71.03 on March 31, $34.93 on April 30, and $85.00 on May 31.

3.

Date	Number of days	Interest rate	Interest	Accrued interest	Payment (Advance)	Principal portion	Balance
3-Jul	—	—	—	—	($25,000)	($25,000)	$25,000
20-Jul	17	10.00%	$116.44	~~$116.44~~	116.44		25,000
29-Jul	9	10.00%	61.64	61.64	(30,000)	(30,000)	55,000
5-Aug	7	10.00%	105.48	167.12			55,000
20-Aug	15	9.75%	220.38	~~387.50~~	387.50		55,000

The amounts of interest charged on July 20 and August 20 were $116.44 and $387.50, respectively.

5.

Date	Number of days	Interest rate	Interest	Accrued interest	Payment (Advance)	Principal portion	Balance
7-Oct	—	—	—	—	($30,000)	($30,000)	$30,000
15-Oct	8	7.75%	$ 50.96	~~$ 50.96~~	50.96		30,000
15-Nov	31	7.75%	197.47	~~197.47~~	197.47		30,000
24-Nov	9	7.75%	57.33	57.33	(15,000)	(15,000)	45,000
15-Dec	21	7.75%	200.65	~~257.98~~	257.98		45,000
17-Dec	2	7.75%	19.11	19.11			45,000
23-Dec	6	7.50%	55.48	74.59	(20,000)	(20,000)	65,000
15-Jan	23	7.50%	307.19	~~381.78~~	381.78		65,000

7.

Date	Number of days	Interest rate	Interest	Accrued interest	Payment (Advance)	Principal portion	Balance
31-Mar	—	—	—	—	($30,000.00)	($30,000)	$30,000
18-Apr	18	7.50%	$110.96	$110.96	110.96		30,000
28-Apr	10	7.50%	61.64	61.64	(10,000.00)	(10,000)	40,000
14-May	16	7.50%	131.51	193.15			40,000
18-May	4	7.75%	33.97	~~227.12~~	227.12		40,000
1-Jun	14	7.75%	118.90	118.90	(15,000.00)	(15,000)	55,000
18-Jun	17	7.75%	198.53	~~317.43~~	5317.43	5000	50,000
3-Jul	15	7.75%	159.25	159.25	10,000.00	10,000	40,000
18-Jul	15	7.75%	127.40	~~286.65~~	286.65		40,000

9.

Date	Number of days	Interest rate	Interest	Accrued interest	Payment (Advance)	Principal portion	Balance
15-Aug	—	—	—	—	—	—	$3,589.80
31-Aug	16	8.75%	$13.77	$13.77	$300.00	$300.00	3,289.80
15-Sep	15	8.75%	11.83	~~25.60~~	100.00	74.40	3,215.40
30-Sep	15	8.75%	11.56	11.56	300.00	300.00	2,915.40
11-Oct	11	8.75%	7.69	19.25			2,915.40
15-Oct	4	8.50%	2.72	~~21.97~~	100.00	78.03	2,837.37
31-Oct	16	8.50%	10.57	10.57	300.00	300.00	2,537.37
15-Nov	15	8.50%	8.86	~~19.43~~	100.00	80.57	2,456.80

11.

Date	Number of days	Interest rate	Interest	Accrued interest	Payment (Advance)	Principal portion	Balance
1-Apr	—	—	—	—	—	—	$6000.00
1-May	30	8.25%	$ 40.68	~~$40.68~~	$1000.00	$959.32	5040.68
1-Jun	31	8.25%	35.32	~~35.32~~	1000.00	964.68	4076.00
7-Jun	6	8.25%	5.53	5.53			4076.00
1-Jul	24	8.00%	21.44	~~26.97~~	1000.00	973.03	3102.97
1-Aug	31	8.00%	21.08	~~21.08~~	1000.00	978.92	2124.05
27-Aug	26	8.00%	12.10	12.10			2124.05
1-Sep	5	8.25%	2.40	~~14.50~~	1000.00	985.50	1138.55
1-Oct	30	8.25%	7.72	~~7.72~~	1000.00	992.28	146.27
1-Nov	31	8.25%	1.02	~~1.02~~	147.29	146.27	0.00

Total of the interest charges = $147.29

13.

Date	Number of days	Interest rate	Interest	Accrued interest	Payment (Advance)	Principal portion	Balance
23-Feb	—	—	—	—	—	—	$5000.00
15-Apr	51	5.25%	$36.68	$36.68	$1000.00	$963.32	4036.68
15-May	30	5.25%	17.42	17.42	1000.00	982.58	3054.10
15-Jun	31	5.25%	13.62	13.62	1000.00	986.38	2067.72
15-Jul	30	5.50%	9.35	9.35	1000.00	990.65	1077.07
31-Jul	16	5.50%	2.60	2.60			1077.07
15-Aug	15	5.75%	2.55	5.15	1000.00	994.85	82.22
15-Sep	31	5.75%	0.40	0.40	82.62	82.22	0.00

Exercise 7.5

1. Grace period interest = $430.21

Date	Number of days	Interest rate	Interest	Accrued interest	Payment (Advance)	Principal portion	Balance
1-Dec	—	—	—	—	—	—	$9830.21
31-Dec	30	9.00%	$72.72	$72.72	$135.00	$62.28	9767.93
17-Jan	17	9.00%	40.95	40.95		0.00	9767.93
31-Jan	14	9.25%	34.66	75.61	135.00	59.39	9708.54
28-Feb	28	9.25%	68.89	68.89	135.00	66.11	9642.43

3. Grace period interest = $286.67

Date	Number of days	Interest rate	Interest	Accrued interest	Payment (Advance)	Principal portion	Balance
1-Jan	—	—	—	—	—	—	$7086.67
31-Jan	30	8.25%	$48.05	$48.05	$200.00	$151.95	6934.72
28-Feb	28	8.25%	43.89	43.89	200.00	156.11	6778.61
2-Mar	2	8.25%	3.06	3.06			6778.61
25-Mar	23	7.75%	33.10	36.16	500.00	500.00	6278.61
31-Mar	6	7.75%	8.00	44.16	200.00	155.84	6122.77

5. Grace period interest = $254.19

Date	Number of days	Interest rate	Interest	Accrued interest	Payment (Advance)	Principal portion	Balance
1-Dec	—	—	—	—	—	—	$5454.19
31-Dec	30	9.75%	$43.71	$43.71	$110.00	$66.29	5387.90
31-Jan	31	9.75%	44.62	44.62	110.00	65.38	5322.52
14-Feb	14	9.50%	19.39	19.39	300.00	300.00	5022.52
28-Feb	14	9.50%	18.30	37.69	110.00	72.31	4950.21

Review Problems

1. $49,472.95
3. 4.304%
5. $2.88
7. $18.41
9. a. $98,325.50
b. (i) $99,098.61
   (ii) $99,165.65
   (iii) $99,232.78
c. (i) 3.376%
   (ii) 3.669%
   (iii) 3.962%
11. $3780.22

13. Accrued interest = $284.70

Date	Number of days	Interest rate	Interest	Accrued interest	Payment (Advance)	Principal portion	Balance
1-Nov	—	—	—	—	—	—	$7484.70
30-Nov	29	7.75%	$46.09	~~$46.09~~	$120.00	$73.91	7410.79
13-Dec	13	7.75	20.46	20.46			7410.79
31-Dec	18	7.50	27.41	~~47.87~~	120.00	72.13	7338.66
31-Jan	31	7.50	46.75	~~46.75~~	120.00	73.25	7265.41

15.

Date	Number of days	Interest rate	Interest	Accrued interest	Payment (Advance)	Principal portion	Balance
23-May	—	—	—	—	($15,000.00)	($15,000.00)	$15,000.00
15-Jun	23	9.50%	$ 89.79	$ 89.79	700.00	610.21	14,389.79
15-Jul	30	9.50%	112.36	~~112.36~~	700.00	587.64	13,802.15
26-Jul	11	9.50%	39.52	39.52			13,802.15
15-Aug	20	9.25%	69.96	~~109.48~~	700.00	590.52	13,211.63
14-Sep	30	9.25%	100.44	100.44			13,211.63
15-Sep	1	9.75%	3.53	~~103.97~~	700.00	596.03	12,615.60

17.

Date	Number of days	Interest rate	Interest	Accrued interest	Payment (Advance)	Principal portion	Balance
3-Jun	—	—	—	—	($50,000.00)	($50,000.00)	$50,000.00
26-Jun	23	9.00%	$283.56	$283.56	283.56		50,000.00
30-Jun	4	9.00%	49.32	49.32	(40,000.00)	(40,000.00)	90,000.00
5-Jul	5	9.00%	110.96	160.28			90,000.00
17-Jul	12	9.25%	273.70	433.98	(25,000.00)	(25,000.00)	115,000.00
26-Jul	9	9.25%	262.29	~~696.27~~	696.27		115,000.00
31-Jul	5	9.50%	149.66	149.66	30,000.00	30,000.00	85,000.00
18-Aug	18	9.50%	398.22	547.88	35,000.00	35,000.00	50,000.00
26-Aug	8	9.50%	104.11	~~651.99~~	651.99		50,000.00

Exercise 7A

1. September 19
3. 100 days
5. October 25
7. March 3
9. $1032.53
11. $2600.00
13. 9.0%
15. 45 days
17. $988.09
19. $2760.61
21. 7.5%
23. a. March 3, 2011
  b. March 1, 2011
25. $1036.23
27. $3257.12
29. $763.17
31. $3000.90

CHAPTER 8 COMPOUND INTEREST: FUTURE VALUE AND PRESENT VALUE

Concept Questions (Section 8.1)

1. We compound interest when we convert it to principal and calculate subsequent interest on both the principal and the converted interest.
3. The "periodic rate of interest" is the percent interest earned in a single compounding period. The "nominal rate of interest" is the *annual* interest rate you obtain if you *extend* the periodic interest rate to a full year. This extension is done by multiplying the periodic rate of interest by the number of compounding periods in a year.

Exercise 8.1

1. a. 0.5% per month
  b. 1.5% per quarter
  c. 3.0% per half-year

3. **a.** 1.35% per quarter
   b. 0.45% per month
5. **a.** 7.2% compounded semiannually
   b. 7.2% compounded quarterly
   c. 7.2% compounded monthly
7. **a.** 5.00% compounded quarterly
   b. 5.00% compounded monthly
9. **a.** quarterly compounding
   b. semiannual compounding
   c. monthly compounding
11. **a.** 4 per year
    b. 12 per year

Concept Questions (Section 8.2)

1. The future value of an investment at a future date is the combined value of the investment's principal and interest on that date.
3. The more frequent the compounding of the 6% nominal rate, the more interest will be earned by the investment. Therefore, 6% compounded quarterly is the preferred rate. (The other two rates both earn 3% interest in the 6-month term.)
   (1) 6% compounded quarterly
   (2) 6% compounded semiannually and 6% simple interest (tied)
5. Quadrupling is the result of two successive doublings. If an investment doubles in 9 years, it will quadruple in 18 years.
7. The fundamental reason is that money can be invested to earn interest. $100 received today can earn interest for a longer period than $100 received at a future date.

Exercise 8.2

1. $7562.95
3. $15,428.20
5. **a.** $32,810.31
   b. $48,754.39
   c. $72,446.46
   d. $107,651.63
7. **a.** $86,230.81
   b. $90,326.36
   c. $92,540.46
   d. $94,084.15
9. **a.** $108.30
   b. $108.35
   c. $108.37
   d. $108.30
   Choose 8.2% compounded semiannually

11. Maturity value = $13,355.74
    Interest charged = $1355.74
13. $17,746.06; 25.91%
15. $21,875.18; 46.93%
17. **Interest**

rate	20 years	25 years	30 years
8%	$4660.96	$6848.48	$10,062.66
10%	$6727.50	$10,834.71	$17,449.40

19. $6865.65
21. $12,454.51
23. $3707.78
25. $11,544.93
27. Donna will receive $8340.04.
    Tim will receive $10,045.40.
    Gary will receive $12,099.48.
29. **a.** $108,366.67
    b. $113,743.60
    c. $103,219.59
31. $8206.23
33. $2766.14
35. $5617.79

Concept Questions (Section 8.3)

1. The "discount rate" is the interest rate used in a present value calculation.
3. Discounting is the opposite of compounding.
5. We are told that the present value of $100 discounted back 8 years is just half of the $100. Since 16 years contains two 8-year intervals, there will be two "halvings" of the payment amount. The present value of $100, 16 years earlier, will be
$$\frac{1}{2} \times \frac{1}{2} \times \$100 = \$25.$$

Exercise 8.3

1. **a.** $5327.26
   b. $2837.97
   c. $1511.86
3. **a.** $1460.18
   b. $1407.13
   c. $1380.33
   d. $1362.37
5. $6439.28
7. $7500.00
9. $8072.17
11. $4494.57
13. $4706.90
15. $2241.95
17. $3271.75
19. $2247.35
21. $1302.79

23. $4374.78
25. $145,000-cash offer is worth $1158.46 more
27. $61,559,000
29. $3365.06 in 3.5-year certificate
    $4003.64 in 4.5-year certificate
    $4418.92 in 5.5-year certificate
31. $2804.31
33. $14,977.31
35. $4694.63
37. $2345.50
39. $2945.55
41. $1200.00

Concept Questions (Section 8.5)

1. The future value will be the same in both cases. Mathematically, this happens because the order of multiplication in a product does not matter. In this particular case,
$$(1.04)(1.05)(1.06) = (1.06)(1.05)(1.04)$$
3. We should not reach this conclusion. It is true that the strip bond owner does not receive any payments from year to year. However, the market value of the bond increases as the time remaining until maturity decreases. This year-to-year change in market value is the owner's return on investment. The investor can choose to capture the increased value at any time by selling the bond.
5. The overall decrease will be less than $2x\%$ because the second $x\%$ decrease acts on a smaller base than the first $x\%$ decrease. Consider, for example, two successive 50% decreases. These do not make the final value zero (corresponding to a decrease of $2 \times 50\% = 100\%$). Rather, we reduce the original amount by 50% $\left(\text{or } \frac{1}{2}\right)$ twice. This leaves $\frac{1}{2} \times \frac{1}{2} = \frac{1}{4}$ or 25% of the initial value.

Exercise 8.5

1. $378.00
3. $43,118.70
5. 4.9% compounded semiannually
7. Earn $88.01 more at 5% compounded annually than at 4.75% compounded monthly
9. $371.31 from the Manulife GIC
   $369.51 from the Sun Life GIC
11. **a.** $5559.32
    b. $5576.00
13. $339.01
15. $2445.03
17. $10,209.09

19. $678.79 on the Rate Optimizer GIC
    $726.37 on the fixed-rate GIC
21. Escalating Rate GIC: $349.98
    Fixed-rate GIC: $298.32
23. **a.** $148.59
    b. $180.61
    c. $219.11
25. $21.16 per hour
27. **a.** $47,105.39
    b. $54,528.86
    c. $72,762.49
29. $34,425,064
31. $244.81
33. $1886.84
35. **a.** $7094.18
    b. $8338.08
    c. $8338.08
37. 25 bonds can be purchased
39. $10,489.74
41. $4108.05

Concept Questions (Section 8.6)

1. No. Think of the simplest case where one payment stream consists of a single payment and the other payment stream consists of a single (different) payment on a different date. These two payments are equivalent at only one discount rate.
3. Compare the future values of the two streams at a focal date 5 (or more) years from now (assuming that money is invested at 7% compounded semiannually as soon as it is received.) The two future values will be equal.

Exercise 8.6

1. $3902.32
3. $911.91
5. $1418.58
7. $4937.12
9. $2750.55; $1375.28
11. $1492.77
13. **a.** Alternative (2) is worth $770.97 more
    b. Alternative (1) is worth $560.60 more
15. $3711.68; $7423.35
17. $2845.27; $8535.81
19. $2163.49

Review Problems

1. $3372.42
3. 59.05%
5. 16.32%

7. Principal = $2012.56;
   Interest = $285.22
9. a. $13,915.66
   b. $632.04
11. a. $12,160.59 for Springboard GIC;
   $11,876.86 for fixed-rate GIC
   b. Springboard GIC will earn $394.94;
   Fixed-rate GIC will earn $374.93
13. Offer 1 is worth $37,180.13;
   Offer 2 is worth $38,164.23
   Accept Offer 2
15. $2980.82
17. a. $564.27
   b. $565.21
19. $11,106.47
21. a. $1300.21
   b. $1266.41
   c. 2.67%
23. $4327.07
25. $2311.51
27. Current price = $331.28;
   Increase in value = $25.03
29. a. $75.75
   b. 18.28%
31. $6499.99

CHAPTER 9   COMPOUND INTEREST: FURTHER TOPICS AND APPLICATIONS

Concept Questions (Section 9.1)

1. If $FV < PV$, the quantity is decreasing in size as time passes. Therefore, the rate of growth is negative. That is, the value for i is negative.
3. Since the time interval is the same for both cases, the relative size of the periodic rates of return is indicated by the overall *percent* increase rather than the overall *dollar* increase. In the case "$1 grew to $2," the final value is twice the initial value (100% increase). In the case of "$3 grew to $5," the final value is 1.667 times the initial value (66.7% increase). Therefore, the periodic rate of return was higher in the "$1 grew to $2" scenario.

Exercise 9.1

1. 8.13% compounded annually
3. 9.00% compounded quarterly
5. 8.50% compounded monthly
7. 4.37% compounded annually
9. 5.25% compounded annually

11. 4.25% compounded semiannually
13. 3.90% compounded monthly
15.
Province	Axnnual Growth
Alberta	1.81%
British Columbia	1.78%
Newfoundland	−0.40%
Nova Scotia	0.38%
Ontario	1.53%
17. a. 7.60% compounded annually
   b. 7.39% compounded quarterly
   c. 7.35% compounded monthly
19. 9.36% compounded semiannually
21. 8.04% compounded annually
23. 1.98% compounded annually
25. a. $2159.63
   b. 6.72% compounded annually
   c. 2.18% compounded annually
27. 10.80% compounded monthly
29. 6.11% compounded annually
31. −1.62% compounded annually
33. −1.45% compounded annually (3 yr.)
   5.94% compounded annually (5 yr.)
   9.50% compounded annually (10 yr.)
35. −8.58% compounded annually (3 yr.)
   0.30% compounded annually (5 yr.)
   −5.51% compounded annually (10 yr.)

Concept Questions (Section 9.2)

1. In the case of annual compounding, the value calculated for n will equal the number of years in the term of the loan or investment.

Exercise 9.2

1. 23 years
3. 4 years
5. May 1 of the following year
7. 7.00 years
9. a. 7 years
   b. 6 years and 10 months
11. a. 12 years, 9 months
   b. 13 years, 10 months
13. 14 years, 3 months
15. 3 years and 11 months
17. a. 28 years and 1 month
   b. 20 years and 2 months
19. 23 months
21. 2 years, 11 months, and 24 days
23. 11 years and 129 days
25. 1 year, 9 months, and 57 days

27. **a.** $55.404
    b. $74.87
29. **a.** 5.887% compounded semiannually
    b. 6.159% compounded semiannually

Concept Questions (Section 9.3)

1. The effective rate of interest is the *equivalent annually compounded* rate.
3. Yes. The effective interest rate equals the nominal rate for annual compounding.
5. If compounding is more frequent than annual, the effective rate exceeds the nominal rate. Lenders would prefer to disclose the lower nominal rate since most borrowers do not understand the distinction between nominal and effective rates.

Exercise 9.3

1. **a.** 6.09%
   b. 6.14%
   c. 6.17%
3. **a.** 9.20%
   b. 9.31%
   c. 9.38%
5. **a.** 10% compounded annually
   b. 9.76% compounded semiannually
   c. 9.65% compounded quarterly
   d. 9.57% compounded monthly
7. 11.7% compounded monthly ($f = 12.35\%$)
9. 9.3% compounded annually ($f = 9.3\%$)
11. 26.82%
13. 12.55%
15. 11.21%
17. Choose the semiannually compounded GIC (effective rate is 0.06% higher)
19. 16.77% for ABC; 16.99% for DEF
21. 6.78% compounded monthly;
    6.88% compounded semiannually;
    7.00% compounded annually
23. 1.49% per month.

Concept Questions (Section 9.4)

1. If two nominal interest rates are equivalent, they will produce the same future value of an investment after 1 year.
3. The equivalent periodic rate for 6 months is more than six times the equivalent periodic rate for 1 month because the 1-month rate achieves extra growth through the compounding of interest earnings at the end of each month. Therefore, the answer is: (iii) "Greater than 3%."

Exercise 9.4

1. **a.** 9.76% compounded semiannually
   b. 9.65% compounded quarterly
   c. 9.57% compounded monthly
3. **a.** 10.38% compounded annually
   b. 10.13% compounded semiannually
   c. 9.92% compounded monthly
5. **a.** 6.09% compounded annually
   b. 6.14% compounded annually
   c. 6.17% compounded annually
7. **a.** 5.87% compounded quarterly
   b. 5.96% compounded quarterly
   c. 6.03% compounded quarterly
9. 4.03% compounded semiannually
11. 5.97% compounded monthly
13. 10.59% compounded quarterly
15. 5.58% compounded annually
17. 6.41% compounded monthly
19. 4.95% compounded monthly
21. **a.** 7.76% compounded annually
    b. 7.62% compounded semiannually
    c. 7.55% compounded quarterly

Concept Questions (Section 9.5)

1. A "capital loss" is the reduction in the market value of an investment during the holding period.
3. Yes. If the expenses associated with an investment exceed the income from the investment, then the net income and the income yield will be negative. For example, if you hold a piece of raw land as an investment, you will have no income from the property but you must pay property taxes each year. The net income and income yield are then negative.
5. Yes. Suppose, for example, you bought a $160,000 condominium as an investment property using $40,000 of your own money and $120,000 borrowed on a mortgage loan. Subsequently, the condo's market value fell to $100,000 because "leaky condo" problems were discovered in the building. At that point, you have lost more than 100% of your initial $40,000 investment because the condo's market value is less than the amount owed on the mortgage loan. You must still repay the balance on the loan after the proceeds of the sale are applied to the loan.
7. For a 25% increase, $1 + c = 1.25$. For a 20% decrease, $1 + c = 1 - 0.20 = 0.8$. Note that $1.25 \times 0.8 = 1.00$. That is, a 20% decrease exactly offsets a 25% increase. Since we have the same number of 25% increases as 20% decreases, the investment's value will be unchanged (at $100) after 20 years.

9. The magnitude of the overall percent change is smaller than the sum. To illustrate, consider two successive 10% decreases from a beginning value of $1000. The first 10% decrease causes a $100 decrease to $900. The second 10% decrease acts on $900 rather than on the initial $1000. The dollar amount of the second reduction is only $90. The overall reduction is $190, which is only 19% (not 20%) of the original $1000.

Exercise 9.5

1. Income yield = 10.00%
Capital gain yield = 10.00%
Rate of total return = 20.00%
3. Income yield = 3.19%
Capital gain yield = 75.09%
Rate of total return = 78.27%

Security	Income yield (%)	Capital gain yield (%)	Rate of total return (%)
5. Postash shares ('08)	0.29	−37.60	−37.31
Postash shares ('09)	0.47	27.75	28.22
Mawer Fund ('08)	5.65	−44.60	−38.95
Mawer Fund ('09)	3.94	47.14	51.08
7. RIM shares ('08)	0.0	−56.02	−56.02
RIM shares ('09)	0.0	43.49	43.49
PH&N Bond Fd ('08)	4.38	−1.22	3.16
PH&N Bond Fd ('09)	5.47	4.02	9.49

9. Income yield = 3.44%
Capital gain yield = 5.81%
Rate of total return = 9.25%
11. Income yield = 1.36%
Capital gain yield = −12.24%
Rate of total return = −10.88%
13. $70.02
15. $1.50
17. a. 295.9%
b. $10.96
19. 56.25%
21. Decline of 33.$\bar{3}$%
23. 100% gain
25. 7.44% gain
27. a. $25,959.69
b. $11,953.13
29. a. $12.82
b. $3.00
31. 17.14% underperformance
33. 17.00% overperformance

Review Problems

1. 7.40%
3. 7.5% compounded monthly
5. a. −57.54%
b. $7.51
7. 14.43% compounded annually
9. 10.73% compounded semiannually
11. 15.39%
13. 7.02%
15. a. $25.26
b. $5.13
17. Choose bank mortgage.
(Interest rate is 0.006% lower.)
19. 12.73%
21. 13 years and 9 months
23. 6.58%
25. −0.27% compounded annually (3 years)
13.70% compounded annually (5 years)
27. 16 years and 6 months
29. 6 years, 2 months
31. a. 11.11%
b. 5 years and 6 months
33. $5500.00

Exercise 9B

1. Simple rate = 3.00%
Effective rate = 3.04%
3. Simple rate = 9.75%
Effective rate = 10.20%
5. 8.72%
7. 4.67%
9. Simple rate = −9.33%
Effective rate = −9.01%
11. Current yield = 5.06%
Effective yield = 5.19%
13. 4.64%
15. a. 972.7%
b. 227.5%

CHAPTER 10   ORDINARY ANNUITIES: FUTURE VALUE AND PRESENT VALUE

Concept Questions (Section 10.1)

1. The two types of annuities are distinguished by comparing the payment intervals to the compounding interval. If the payment interval *equals* the compounding interval, the annuity is a *simple* annuity. Otherwise, it is a *general* annuity.

3. No. Insurance premiums are paid at the beginning of the period of coverage. In the present case, the monthly payments will be made at the beginning of each month of coverage. To qualify as an ordinary annuity, the monthly payments would have to occur at the end of each month of coverage.

Concept Questions (Section 10.2)

1. Subtract the nominal sum of the payments from the annuity's future value.
2. G's future value will be (ii) more the double H's future value. From the pattern of the contributions of individual payments to the annuity's future value, we see that the earlier half of an annuity's payments contribute more to the future value than the later half of the payments. If follows that doubling the number of payments will more than double an annuity's future value.

Exercise 10.2

1. **a.** $73,105.94
   b. $146,211.88
   c. $219,317.82
3. **a.** $51,160.12
   b. $57,275.00
   c. $64,202.83
   d. $72,052.44
5. $2886.29
7. $80,542.25
9. $30,901.26
11. $3246.40
13. $59,942.63
15. **a.** $96,885.98
    b. $124,191.36
17. $57,277.75
19. $30,014.43
21. $188,830.08
23. na
25. $40,177
27. $176,937

Concept Questions (Section 10.3)

1. A's present value will be (i) double B's present value. When we inspect the present value formula

$$PV = PMT\left[\frac{1 - (1 + i)^{-n}}{i}\right]$$

we note that, for given values of i and n, the present value is proportional to PMT. Therefore, doubling the size of the payment will double the annuity's present value.

3. G's present value is (iii) less than double H's present value. The later half of G's payments will be discounted more heavily (and therefore contribute less to G's present value) than the earlier half of G's payments.

Exercise 10.3

1. **a.** $10,674.78
   b. $21,349.55
   c. $32,024.33
3. **a.** $12,462.21
   b. $8513.56
   c. $7963.33
   d. $6259.33
5. $2033.16
7. $13,638.69
9. $15,047.05
11. $14,047.16
13. $56,816.79
15. $154,093.30
17. $5442.17
19. $130,872.90
21. $14,047.16
23. **a.** $22,500.00
    b. $16,369.18
25. $12,899.99
27. $3304.30
29. $64,550.64
31. $2,893,312.18
33. $8779.95
35. Mr. Lindberg's offer is worth $65.80 more.
37. 3.97% discount
39. The pension-at-age-55 option has a 31.9% higher economic value.
41. **a.** **(i)** 21.45% larger
       (ii) 466.10% larger
    b. **(i)** 8.74% smaller
       (ii) 20.32% larger

Concept Questions (Section 10.4)

1. A deferred annuity is an ordinary annuity that does not begin until a specified time period (called the period of deferral) has passed.
3. The payments form an ordinary annuity when viewed from a focal date at the end of the period of deferral. We can then use the formula for the present value of an ordinary annuity to obtain the present value of the payments at the *end* of the period of deferral.

5. The future values of both annuities are calculated at a focal date coinciding with the final payment. The future values are the same since the deferred annuity payments form an ordinary annuity when viewed from a focal date at the final payment.

Exercise 10.4

1. $20,150.88
3. $14,032.77
5. 4 years
7. 1 year and 4 months
9. $32,365.24
11. The $2000 annuity has $470.52 greater economic value.
13. $2861.16
15. 2 years and 6 months
17. 8 years and 3 months

Concept Questions (Section 10.5)

1. The payments are at the end of each payment interval (ordinary annuity) and the payment interval is not equal to the compounding interval (general annuity).

3. $c = \dfrac{\text{No. of compoundings}}{\text{year/No. of payments/year}} = \dfrac{2}{12} = 0.1\overline{6}$

i_2 is the interest rate per payment intervals. In this case, it is the interest rate per month. It will be approximately equal to

$\dfrac{\text{Nominal annual rate}}{12} = \dfrac{6\%}{12} = 0.5\%$ per month.

The correct value will be smaller than 0.5% because i_2 compounded 6 times must equal $i = \dfrac{6\%}{2} = 3\%$ per half year.

Exercise 10.5

1. **a.** 3.441% per half year
   b. 1.706% per quarter
   c. 0.565% per month
3. **a.** 8.243% per year
   b. 4.040% per half year
   c. 0.662% per month
5. **a.** $54,864.51
   b. $55,564.96
   c. $55,929.71
   d. $56,178.55
7. **a.** $12,598.41
   b. $25,186.12
9. **a.** $16,464.70
   b. $21,764.70

11. **a.** $38,367.94
    b. $93,482.61
13. $20,035.79
15. $14,074.16
17. **a.** $10,111.85
    b. $9998.73
    c. $9939.94
19. $333,998.96
21. $11,600.00
23. **a.** A:B:C = 2:3:4
    b. A:B:C = 1.65:1.33:1
25. $188,316.36
27. $73,953.35
29. $195,703.17
31. $195,760.96
33. $35,567.10
35. $71,795
37. 2 years and 6 months
39. 5 years and 6 months
41. $313,490.72

Review Problems

1. **a.** $100,822.83
   b. $96,754.03
3. $2376.15
5. $146,297.53
7. $97,745.91
9. $18,858.53
11. $21,901.45
13. $82,819.01
15. $108,158.40
17. $2390.05
19. 59.56%
21. $50,239.95
23. $85,804.68

CHAPTER 11 ORDINARY ANNUITIES: PERIODIC PAYMENT, NUMBER OF PAYMENTS, AND INTEREST RATE

Concept Questions (Section 11.1)

1. The monthly payments will be (ii) *more* than half as large because you will pay more total interest if you pay off the loan over 10 years instead of 5 years. (The total of the principal components of the payments will be the same in both cases.)

Exercise 11.1

1. **a.** $5903.13; $352,421.75
   b. $3668.18; $389,954.60
3. **a.** $7287.54; $183,003.20
   b. $7938.61; $235,088.80
   c. $8619.33; $289,546.40
   d. $9328.37; $346,269.60
5. **a.** $2410.76; $316,063.20
   b. $1477.73; $395,344.80
   c. $957.80; $462,660.00
   d. $641.33; $519,121.20
7. **a.** $760.86
   b. $764.09
   c. $765.77
   d. $766.91
9. $3230.33
11. $294.93; $6543.70
13. $14,839.78; $587,182.40
15. $2222.05
17. **a.** $720.87
    b. 2727.19
19. $3261.26
21. $1185.51
23. $1962.61
25. **a.** $905,680.79
    b. $1708.17
27. $3241.66
29. **a.** $177,435.91
    b. $2,323,077.30
31. $5681.03
33. $12,554.29
35. $2875.94

Concept Questions (Section 11.2)

1. You will pay off the loan in (ii) less than half the time. If payments are doubled, you will pay less interest over the life of the loan. Therefore, the total of the nominal payments (principal + interest) will be reduced and you will pay off the loan in less than half the time.

Exercise 11.2

1. 8 years and 6 months
3. 25 years
5. 15 years and 6 months
7. 10 years
9. **a.** 25 years, 2 months
   b. 23 years, 4 months
   c. 21 years, 10 months
   d. 20 years, 6 months
11. **a.** 23 years, 6 months
    b. 24 years, 3 months
    c. 24 years, 8 months
    d. 24 years, 11 months
13. 12 years
15. 25 years
17. 18 years and 7 months
19. 13 months
20. 4 years and 8 months
23. 14 years and 9 months
25. 2 years and 9 months
27. To at least age 79 years and 8 months
29. 51
31. 18 years and 9 months
33. 10 years and 11 months
35. 26 years

Exercise 11.3

1. 4.80% compounded quarterly; 4.89%
3. 8.50% compounded semiannually; 8.68%
5. **a.** 6.92% compounded monthly
   b. 8.31% compounded monthly
   c. 9.41% compounded monthly
7. 7.90% compounded monthly; 8.19%
9. 8.50% compounded semiannually; 8.68%
11. 8.25% compounded monthly; 8.57%
13. 7.67%
15. 41.30%
17. 5.57%
19. 5.27%

Review Problems

1. $5418.78
3. 7.45% compounded monthly; 7.71%
5. 8.78%
7. 18 months longer
9. 20 years and 9 months
11. $7206.60
13. 1 year sooner; $3094
15. $322.29
17. 18
19. $946.39 (Lena)
    $1421.64 (Axel)
21. **a.** $741,577.64
    b. $2598.90
23. 86 years
25. 23
27. $9055.67
29. $4270.26

CHAPTER 12 ANNUITIES DUE

Concept Questions (Section 12.1)

1. Insurance premium payments, rent payments, lease payments, newspaper and magazine subscriptions, membership dues.
3. Each payment in an annuity due earns interest for *one more* payment interval than the corresponding payment in an ordinary annuity.

Exercise 12.1

1. **a.** $63,249.04
   b. $67,676.47
   c. 7.0%
3. **a.** $69,645.89
   b. $95,736.66
5. $285,926.54
7. $64,273.29
9. **a.** $16,803.44
   b. $3803.44
11. $326,252.08; $243,752.08
13. $280,678.01
15. **a.** $505,315
    b. $335,315
17. Fay: $642,566.44
    Fred: $513,950.41
    Fay will have $128,616.03 (20%) more in her RRSP at age 65.
19. **a.** 20 years
    b. Compound earnings: 11.59%
       Simple earnings: 31.37%
       Amount invested: 57.04%
    c. Compound earnings: 46.85%
       Simple earnings: 30.04%
       Amount invested: 23.11%
    d. $65,940
    e. $40,506 (37.4%) less

Concept Questions (Section 12.2)

1. The focal date is at the beginning of the first payment interval. Since payments are at the beginning of each payment interval, the focal date coincides with the first payment.
3. Since $PV(\text{due}) = PV \times (1 + i)$, then $PV(\text{due})$ is $i\%$ larger than PV. In the particular case at hand, $PV(\text{due})$ will exceed PV by 3%.

Exercise 12.2

1. **a.** $23,748.69
   b. $24,223.66
   c. 2.0%
3. **a.** $26,501.66
   b. $22,341.47
5. $23,142.25
7. **a.** $1468.90
   b. $338.90
9. Save $39.12 on Atlantic Life policy
11. Ms. Senario's offer is worth $137.31 more.
13. $428,489.96
15. $120,339.78
17. **a.** $131,043.62
    b. $21,730.97
19. **a.** Highest value: $1700 annuity
       Lowest value: $850 annuity
    b. Highest value: $850 annuity
       Lowest value: $1700 annuity
21. Accept the lease on the new location (saving of $2754.54).

Concept Questions (Section 12.3)

1. If *PMT*, *n* and *i* are the same for an ordinary annuity and an annuity due, the ordinary annuity will have the smaller *FV*. Therefore, if *FV*, *n*, and *i* are the same, the ordinary annuity has the larger *PMT*.
3. The larger the down payment, the smaller the lease payment.
5. **a.** The lessee should not exercise the purchase option. If the lessee wishes to purchase the vehicle, an equivalent vehicle can be purchased at a lower price in the "used-car market."
   b. The lessee should exercise the purchase option. If the lessee does not wish to own the vehicle, it can be sold for more than the residual value in the "used-car market."
   c. If the lessee does the rational thing, the lessor *loses*
       Residual value − Market value
   in case *a*, but *does not gain* or capture the difference
       Market value − Residual value
   in case *b*. The lessor's exposure to this market value risk is one reason why the interest rate on a lease contract is normally higher than the interest rate on a loan to purchase the same vehicle.

Exercise 12.3

1. a. $12,896.26; $427,593.50
    b. $11,082.14; $472,946.50
    c. $9499.15; $512,521.25
    d. $8123.57; $546,910.75
3. a. 25 years, 3 months
    b. 23 years, 6 months
    c. 21 years, 9 months
    d. 20 years, 6 months
5. a. 6.88% compounded monthly
    b. 8.27% compounded monthly
    c. 9.36% compounded monthly
7. $47,721.67
9. $1093.09
11. a. $16,449.92
    b. $17,436.91
13. $194,524.43
15. $285.24
17. $401.90
19. $916.22
21. $17,145.01
23. 36 months
25. $51,707.03
27. 20 months from today (21st deposit)
29. 30 payments
31. 14
33. 11.54%
35. 8.80% compounded quarterly; 9.09%
37. 24.79%
39. a. $585.12
    b. $3405.38
41. $501.07 quarterly;
    $169.04 monthly
43. 3 years and 3 months
45. 5 years and 6 months
47. 13.74%
49. 21.26% compounded annually
51. a. 9.86%
    b. 11.52%
    c. 13.45%
53. $2919.74
55. 27 years

Exercise 12.4

1. 1 year and 8 months
3. 15 years
5. $2412.64
7. $863,467
9. $572,376.63
11. $335.88

13. a. $218,000
    b. $130,178
    c. $405,883
15. $1643.51
17. $1692.37
19. $2219.49
21. $3031.42 at age 65
    $4885.46 at age 70

Review Problems

1. a. $93,794.81
    b. $15,807.53
3. a. $25,527.54
    b. $27,505.93
5. 10.36%
7. Single payment plan worth $3.48 less.
9. a. 28 contributions
    b. 8 additional contriubutions
11. $209.61
13. 16
15. 17.43%
17. a. $7506.74
    b. $11,580.67
19. $615,447.79
21. $1417.86
23. a. $11,572.42
    b. Future value after one year = $12,532.93
25. $301,010.58
27. 20 years and 10 months
29. 103.54%

CHAPTER 13   ANNUITIES: SPECIAL SITUATIONS

Concept Questions (Section 13.1)

1. The perpetuity has the larger present value. The greater the number of payments in an annuity, the larger the annuity's present value. Hence, PV(perpetuity) $>$ PV(annuity). Alternatively, the perpetuity may be viewed as a combination of an annuity identical to the given annuity and a deferred perpetuity. Then PV of given perpetuity $=$ (PV of given annuity) $+$ (PV of deferred perpetuity). Therefore, (PV of given perpetuity) $>$ (PV of given annuity).

3. The market value will rise. The rate of return (dividend yield) is the (fixed) annual dividend calculated as a percentage of the market value. If investors will accept a lower rate of return, they will pay a higher price for the shares.

Exercise 13.1

1. $22,500
3. $100,000
5. $90,085.76
7. $9120.69
9. $3120.47
11. **a.** $68.17
    b. 4.38% compounded semiannually
13. **a.** $73,223.88
    b. $70,303.99
15. $17,669.23
17. $6954.87

Concept Questions (Section 13.2)

1. No. In this section constant growth means that each successive payment increases by the same percentage.

Exercise 13.2

1. $312,421.69
3. $3494.84
5. $46,155.28
7. $362,020.14; $80,141.25
9. $1949.10
11. $37.49

Review Problems

1. 30.38%
3. $900.00
5. **a.** $142,857.14
    b. $109,693.48
7. $15,209.95
9. 21.94%

CHAPTER 14   LOAN AMORTIZATION; MORTGAGES

Exercise 14.1

1. $PMT = \$174.03$

Payment number	Payment	Interest portion	Principal portion	Principal balance
0	—	—	—	$1000.00
1	$174.03	$12.50	$161.53	838.47
2	174.03	10.48	163.55	674.92
3	174.03	8.44	165.59	509.33
4	174.03	6.37	167.66	341.67
5	174.03	4.27	169.76	171.91
6	174.06	2.15	171.91	0.00
	Total:	$44.21		

3. $PMT = \$1739.45$

Payment number	Payment	Interest portion	Principal portion	Principal balance
0	—			$9000.00
1	$1739.45	$396.28	$1343.17	7656.83
2	1739.45	337.14	1402.31	6254.52
3	1739.45	275.39	1464.06	4790.46
4	1739.45	210.93	1528.52	3261.94
5	1739.45	143.63	1595.82	1666.12
6	1739.48	73.36	1666.12	0.00

5. $PMT = \$1092.08$

Payment number	Payment	Interest portion	Principal portion	Principal balance
0	—	—	—	$8000.00
1	$1092.08	$160.00	$932.08	7067.92
2	1092.08	141.36	950.72	6117.20
3	2592.08	122.34	2469.74	3647.46
4	1092.08	72.95	1019.13	2628.33
5	1092.08	52.57	1039.51	1588.82
6	1092.08	31.78	1060.30	528.52
7	539.09	10.57	528.52	0.00
	Total:	$591.57		

7. $PMT = \$1037.41$

Payment number	Payment	Interest portion	Principal portion	Principal balance
0	—	—	—	$60,000.00
1	$1037.41	$375.00	$662.41	59,337.59
2	1037.41	370.86	666.55	58,671.04
⋮	⋮	⋮	⋮	⋮
42	—	—	—	28,298.14
43	1037.41	176.86	860.55	27,437.59
44	1037.41	171.48	865.93	26,571.66
⋮	⋮	⋮	⋮	⋮
70	—	—	—	2055.24
71	1037.41	12.85	1024.56	1030.68
72	1037.12	6.44	1030.68	0.00

9. $PMT = \$200$

Payment number	Payment	Interest portion	Principal portion	Principal balance
0	—	—	—	$1000.00
1	$200.00	$12.50	$187.50	812.50
2	200.00	10.16	189.84	622.66
3	200.00	7.78	192.22	430.44
4	200.00	5.38	194.62	235.82
5	200.00	2.95	197.05	38.77
6	39.25	0.48	38.77	0.00
	Total:	$39.25		

11. $PMT = \$1800$

Payment number	Payment	Interest portion	Principal portion	Principal balance
0	—	—	—	$9000.00
1	$1800.00	$396.28	$1403.72	7596.28
2	1800.00	334.47	1465.53	6130.75
3	1800.00	269.94	1530.06	4600.69
4	1800.00	202.57	1597.43	3003.26
5	1800.00	132.24	1667.76	1335.50
6	1394.30	58.80	1335.50	0.00

13. *PMT* = $1000

Payment number	Payment	Interest portion	Principal portion	Principal balance
0	—	—	—	$8000.00
1	$1000.00	$160.00	$840.00	7160.00
2	1000.00	143.20	856.80	6303.20
3	2000.00	126.06	1873.94	4429.26
4	1000.00	88.59	911.41	3517.85
5	1000.00	70.36	929.64	2588.21
6	1000.00	51.76	948.24	1639.97
7	1000.00	32.80	967.20	672.77
8	686.23	13.46	672.77	0.00
	Total:	$686.23		

15. *PMT* = $1000

Payment number	Payment	Interest portion	Principal portion	Principal balance
0	—	—	—	$60,000.00
1	$1000.00	$375.00	$625.00	59,375.00
2	1000.00	371.09	628.91	58,746.09
⋮	⋮	⋮	⋮	⋮
55	—	—	—	19,128.18
56	1000.00	119.55	880.45	18,247.73
57	1000.00	114.05	885.95	17,361.78
⋮	⋮	⋮	⋮	⋮
74	—	—	—	1424.49
75	1000.00	8.90	991.10	433.39
76	436.10	2.71	433.39	0.00

17. a. 47.7% for a 30-month term; 24.6% for a 30-year term

b.

Terms (yrs)	Total interest ($)
5	2022.77
10	4244.27
15	6686.49
20	9334.07
25	12,169.49
30	15,173.35

c. (i) 254 months
(ii) 357 months

Concept Questions (Section 14.2)

1. The balance midway through the amortization period will be (i) more than half the original principal. With each successive payment, the interest component becomes smaller and the principal component becomes larger. Therefore, the total principal repaid in the first half of the amortization period will be less than the total principal repaid in the second half of the amortization period. It follows that: (1) less than half of the original principal will be repaid in the first half of the amortization period; and (2) the loan's balance midway through the amortization period will be more than half the original principal.

3. a. Each regular payment includes a 0.2¢ *over*payment. Therefore, the adjusted final payment will be less than the regular payment.
b. The reduction in the final payment will be the future value of the 60 overpayments of 0.2¢. This will be (i) more than 60(0.2¢) = 12¢.

5. The principal paid in the 3rd year will be (ii) less than the principal paid in the 7th year. With each successive payment, the interest component becomes smaller and the principal component becomes larger. Therefore, the total principal paid in each successive year will increase.

7. The total interest paid on loan A will be (iii) equal to twice the interest paid on loan B. This follows from notionally splitting the $20,000 principal into two halves. Each half of loan A is identical to loan B.

Exercise 14.2

1. a. $171.57
b. $331.91
c. $2922.10
d. $5283.96
3. a. $249.69
b. $819.66
c. $359.71
d. $3491.06
5. a. $204.57
b. $446.66
c. $3365.38
d. $10,345.79
7. a. $822.74
b. $1542.15
c. $4474.70
d. $4055.64
9. a. $62.66
b. $247.84
c. $233.79
11. a. $302.03
b. $271.30
c. $562.08
13. a. $1503.31
b. $499.93
c. $18,132.85
d. $2545.96
e. $2746.60
15. a. $122.21
b. $522.79
c. $711.75
d. $1916.49
e. $587.49

17. a. $1796.03
 b. $1298.27
 c. $10,317.16
 d. $2233.04
 e. $584.80
19. a. $83.43
 b. $377.99
 c. $852.07
 d. $1650.55
 e. $197.28
21. a. $370.80
 b. $174.47; $196.33
 c. $31,238.73
 d. $2426.05
23. a. $164.85
 b. $83.73
 c. $85.39

Exercise 14.3

1.

Interval	Balance at end	Principal reduction	Interest paid
0 to 5 years	$91,271.80	$ 8728.20	$34,040.40
5 to 10 years	78,840.35	12,431.45	30,337.15
10 to 15 years	61,134.38	17,705.97	25,062.63
15 to 20 years	35,916.00	25,218.38	17,550.22
20 to 25 years	0.00	35,916.00	6850.39

3. a. $639.81 for 6% compounded semiannually
 $700.42 for 7% compounded semiannually
 $763.21 for 8% compounded semiannually
 b. 8.96%
 c. $91,943 for 6% compounded semiannually
 $110,126 for 7% compounded semiannually
 $128,963 for 8% compounded semiannually
5. a. $149,293.00
 b. $136,695.14
7. $52.56
9. a. $76,216.85
 b. $552.88
11. a. $32,333.43
 b. $360.00
13. a. $15,554.01
 b. $299.11
15. a. $155,300
 b. $163,500
17. a. $700.42
 b. 20 years and 27 weeks
19. a. 3 years and 9 months
 b. 6 years and 10 months
21. 10 years and 4 months
23. 6 months
25. 6 months

27. 7 years and 11 months
29. a. 2 years and 2 months
 b. $103,107.15
31. a. 5 years and 4 months
 b. $183,476.71
33. a. 5 years and 10 months
 b. $136,434.77

Exercise 14.4

1. 9.995%
3. a. 12.607%
 b. 12.144%
 c. 12.068%
5. a. The trust company's loan has an effective rate that is 0.38% lower.
 b. The trust company's loan has an effective rate that is 0.19% lower.
7. a. $34,488.28
 b. $36,699.09
9. a. $58,605.77
 b. $57,348.31
 c. $56,276.22
11. $161,588.89
13. $141,749.57
15. $3026.81

Review Problems

1.

Payment number	Payment	Interest portion	Principal portion	Principal balance
0	—	—	—	$862.50
1	$148.50	$ 8.09	$140.41	722.09
2	148.50	6.77	141.73	580.36
3	148.50	5.44	143.06	437.30
4	148.50	4.10	144.40	292.90
5	148.50	2.75	145.75	147.15
6	148.53	1.38	147.15	0.00
		$28.53		

3. a. $834.36
 b. $170.31
 c. $5697.14
 d. $1891.34

5.

Payment number	Payment	Interest portion	Principal portion	Principal balance
0	—	—	—	$60,000.00
1	$10,000.00	$ 3150.00	$6850.00	53,150.00
2	10,000.00	2790.38	7209.62	45,940.38
3	10,000.00	2411.87	7588.13	38,352.25
4	10,000.00	2013.49	7986.51	30,365.74
5	10,000.00	1594.20	8405.80	21,959.94
6	10,000.00	1152.90	8847.10	13,112.84
7	10,000.00	688.42	9311.58	3801.26
8	4,000.83	199.57	3801.26	0.00
	$14,000.83			

7. **a.** $146.00
    b. $316.37
    c. $1025.91
    d. $3268.88
    e. $303.33
9. **a.** $497.92
    b. $2702.05
    c. $4816.52
    d. $19,964.68
    e. $11,643.57
11. **a.** 1 year and 9 months
    b. $76,018.77
13. **a.** $77,798.79
    b. $674.02
15. $18,947.10
17. **a.** 4 years and 2 months
    b. $96,786.36

CHAPTER 15 BONDS AND SINKING FUNDS

Concept Questions (Section 15.2)

1. Four variables affecting a bond's price are:
    • the face value of the bond
    • the bond's coupon rate
    • the prevailing market rate of return on bonds
    • the time remaining until maturity of the bond
    Only the prevailing market rate of return *always* has an inverse effect on the bond's price.
3. Yes. If, during the holding period, the capital loss (due to a rise in the prevailing market rate of return) exceeds the coupon interest paid on the bond, you will suffer a net loss on the bond investment.
5. If prevailing interest rates decline, the prices of all bonds will rise. However, the prices of long-term bonds will rise more than the prices of short-term bonds. Therefore, you will improve the portfolio's capital gain if, prior to the interest rate decline, you increase the relative weighting of long-term bonds (by selling short-term bonds and using the proceeds to purchase long-term bonds).

Exercise 15.2

1. $1128.80
3. $857.77
5. $1207.07
7. $534.66
9. $10,300.09
11. $94.41
13. $369.61

15. $3470.12 more
17. Bond C: Price falls $8.25
    Bond D: Price falls $40.30
    This outcome demonstrates that bond prices fall when market rates rise, and the price of a longer-term bond falls more than the price of a shorter-term bond.
19. Bond A: $1042.65
    Bond B: $1074.39
    Bond C: $1098.00
    Bond D: $1128.65
    For a given spread of the coupon rate above the market rate, longer maturity bonds have a larger premium.
21. Bond J: $1125.51
    Bond K: $1251.03
    Bond L: $1376.54
    The greater the difference, "Coupon rate − Market rate," the greater the price premium.
23. **a.** Price drops $86.46
    b. Price drops $162.89
    c. Price rises $98.00
    d. Price rises $209.30
    e. No − less than twice.
    f. Change for 1% rise is smaller than change for 1% decline.
25. **a.** $11,130.32
    b. 11.30%
27. **a.** 10.95%
    b. 0%
    c. −9.52%
29. 28.49% compounded semiannually

Exercise 15.3

1. 6.02% compounded semiannually
3. 5.80% compounded semiannually
5. Bond A: 7.72% compounded semiannually
    Bond C: 6.97% compounded semiannually
7. **a.** 0.73% decrease
    b. 0.20% decrease
9. 17.54% compounded semiannually

Exercise 15.4

1. $1230.03
3. $958.06
5. $1152.45
7. $959.22
9. $1229.88
11. $1514.74

13. March 15: $910.03
April 15: $914.57
May 15: $918.99
June 15: $923.58
July 15: $928.04
August 15: $932.67
September 15: $911.33

15. a. $937.61
 b. 17.78%
17. 104.94%
19. $1095.34
21. $913.27
23. $115.47
25. 4.369%
27. 5.678%

Exercise 15.5

	Payment	Balance
1.	$424,333	$6,196,094
3.	$620,292	$9,534,856
5.	$ 87,284	$2,506,640
7.	$344,297	$9,268,208

	Payment	Annual cost of debt	Book value
9.	$353,611	$1,707,222	$4,836,586
11.	$302,726	$1,955,452	$6,081,667
13.	$614,137	$1,788,274	$2,311,969
15.	$204,464	$1,536,428	$5,478,509

17.

Payment interval number	Payment (at end)	Interest earned	Increase in the fund	Balance in fund (end of interval)
0	—	—	—	$ 0
1	$122,135	$ 0	$122,135	122,135
2	122,135	4275	126,410	248,545
3	122,135	8699	130,834	379,379
4	122,135	13,278	135,413	514,792
5	122,135	18,018	140,153	654,945
6	122,135	22,923	145,058	800,003
		$67,193	$800,003	

19.

Payment interval number	Payment (at end)	Interest earned	Increase in the fund	Balance in fund (end of interval)
0	—	—	—	$ 0
1	$163,710	$ 11,050	$ 174,760	174,760
2	163,710	22,847	186,557	361,317
3	163,710	35,439	199,149	560,466
4	163,710	48,882	212,592	773,058
5	163,710	63,232	226,942	1,000,000
		$181,450	$1,000,000	

21.

Payment interval number	Payment (at end)	Interest earned	Increase in the fund	Balance in fund (end of interval)
0	—	—	—	$ 0
1	$302,720	$ 0	$302,720	302,720
2	302,720	4541	307,261	609,981
·	·	·	·	·
·	·	·	·	·
·	·	·	·	·
10				3,239,928
11	302,720	48,599	351,319	3,591,247
12	302,720	53,869	356,589	3,947,836
·	·	·	·	·
·	·	·	·	·
·	·	·	·	·
18				6,202,544
19	302,720	93,038	395,758	6,598,302
20	302,720	98,975	401,695	6,999,997

23.

Payment interval number	Payment (at end)	Interest earned	Increase in the fund	Balance in fund (end of interval)	Book value of the debt
0	—	—	—	$ 0	$10,000,000
1	$353,611	$ 0	$353,611	353,611	9,646,389
2	353,611	12,376	365,987	719,598	9,280,402
·	·	·	·	·	·
·	·	·	·	·	·
·	·	·	·	·	·
18				8,663,360	1,336,640
19	353,611	$303,218	656,829	9,320,189	679,811
20	353,611	326,207	679,818	$10,000,007	(7)

25. a. $8221

b. $29,938

c. The 33rd month

d. $2003

27. a. $313,548

b. $165,087

c. $559,178

d.

Payment interval number	Payment (at end)	Interest earned	Increase in the fund	Balance in fund (end of interval)	Book value of the debt
0	—	—	—	$ 0	$20,000,000
1	$313,548	$ 0	$313,548	313,548	19,686,452
2	313,548	7,055	320,603	634,151	19,365,849
·	·	·	·	·	·
·	·	·	·	·	·
·	·	·	·	·	·
38	—	—	—	18,522,966	1,477,034
39	313,548	416,767	730,315	19,253,281	746,719
40	313,548	433,199	746,747	20,000,028	(28)
Total:		$7,458,108			

Total Interest = $20,000,028 − 40($313,548) = $7,458,108

29. a. $13,737

b.

Payment interval number	Payment (at end)	Interest earned	Increase in the fund	Balance in fund (end of interval)	Book value of the debt
0	—	—	—	$ 0	$800,000
1	$13,737	$ 240	$13,977	13,977	786,023
2	13,737	485	14,222	28,199	771,801
.	.	.	.	.	.
.	.	.	.	.	.
.	.	.	.	.	.
38	—	—	—	745,465	54,535
39	13,737	13,286	27,023	772,488	27,512
40	13,737	13,759	27,496	799,984	16
		$250,504			

Review Problems

1. $103.14

3. $2246.55

5. 12.48%

7. $1156.12

9.

Payment interval number	Payment	Interest earned	Increase in the fund	Balance in fund (end of interval)	Book value of the debt
0	—	—	—	$ 0	$500,000
1	$28,285	$ 0	$28,285	28,285	471,715
2	28,285	990	29,275	57,560	442,440
.	.	.	.	.	.
.	.	.	.	.	.
.	.	.	.	.	.
12				413,016	86,984
13	28,285	14,456	42,741	455,757	44,243
14	28,285	15,951	44,236	499,993	7

11. $1168.86

13.

Payment interval number	Payment (at end)	Interest earned	Increase in the fund	Balance in fund (end of interval)
0	—	—	—	$ 0
1	$112,571	$ 3377	$115,948	115,948
2	112,571	6856	119,427	235,375
3	112,571	10,438	123,009	358,384
4	112,571	14,129	126,700	485,084
5	112,571	17,930	130,501	615,585
6	112,571	21,845	134,416	750,001
		$74,575	$750,001	

CHAPTER 16   BUSINESS INVESTMENT DECISIONS

Exercise 16.1

1. a. Vencap should make the investment since the present value ($40,306) exceeds the required investment.

b. Increase by $3306.

3. $29,805

5. a. Yes. Buy the timber rights because *PV* of cash flows = $221,373.

b. Increase by $1373.

7. a. Purchasing saves $1160 in current dollars.

b. Leasing saves $1021 in current dollars.

9. a. Lease.

b. $1201

11. a. $3273 advantage to renting.

b. $4740 advantage to buying.

Exercise 16.2

1. a. Yes ($NPV = \$22,651$).
   b. No ($NPV = -\$848$).
   c. No ($NPV = -\$21,994$).
3. $71,744
5. No ($NPV = -\$109,521$).
7. No ($NPV = -\$144,864$).
9. No ($NPV = -\$16,653$).
11. Yes ($NPV = \$295,258$).

Exercise 16.3

1. Select B and D.
3. Select F, E, and A (having a combined NPV of $11,639).
5. The Deere's NPV is $8964 larger.
7. Project D is worth $3576 more today.
9. Model H has a $392 higher equivalent annual cash flow.
11. The 25-ton truck has a $276 higher equivalent annual cash flow.
13. The Falcon has a $1958 lower equivalent annual cost.
15. The International has a $4123 lower equivalent annual cost.

Exercise 16.4

1. 15.1%
3. Approve phase 1 ($IRR = 27.3\%$).
   Approve phase 2 ($IRR = 22.7\%$).
   Approve phase 3 ($IRR = 14.6\%$).
   Reject phase 4 ($IRR = 12.1\%$).

5. No (since $IRR = 11.7\% < 12\%$).
7. Yes since the IRR of 12.7% exceeds the cost of capital.
9. Yes. The IRR of 15.0% equals the cost of capital.
11. The IRR of 12.4% is less than the cost of capital. The mine should not be developed.
13. $IRR = 13.4\%$. Reject expansion since IRR < cost of capital (14%).

Exercise 16.5

1. a. Select D because its IRR (19.9%) is larger than C's IRR (18.1%).
   b. Select D because its NPV ($13,534) is larger than C's NPV ($12,733).
   c. Select C because its NPV ($26,791) is larger than D's NPV ($23,342).
3. a. Select X because its IRR (20.8%) is larger than Y's IRR (17.3%).
   b. Select X because its NPV ($66,712) is larger than Y's NPV ($58,720).
   c. Select Y because its NPV ($117,751) is larger than X's NPV ($100,085).
5. a. Select Y because its IRR (17.5%) is larger than X's IRR (16.0%).
   b. Select Y because its NPV ($5825) is larger than X's NPV ($3587).
   c. Select X because its NPV ($14,884) is larger than Y's NPV ($13,834).

Exercise 16.6

1. a. 4.67 years.
   b. No.

3.

Project	NPV	Payback
X	$8882	4 years
Y	$10,646	5 years

Prefer X on payback; prefer Y on NPV.

5.

Project	NPV	IRR	Payback
A	$4893	19.14%	2.64 years
B	$4589	20.02%	2.67 years

Project rankings:

Project	NPV	IRR	Payback
A	1	2	1
B	2	1	2

Review Problems

1. **a.** Leasing produces a $621 saving.
   b. Buying produces a $657 saving.
3. No ($NPV = -\$132{,}817$ at a 14% cost of capital).
5. $17,549 advantage to purchasing.
7. Select A, D, and C.
9. Yes ($NPV = \$15{,}677$).
11. Machine X has a $235 higher equivalent annual cash flow.
13. The Boston Wailer has a $4781 lower equivalent annual cost.
15. C has an annual economic advantage of $996.
17. 2.7 years.
19. **a.** A: $IRR = 30.46\%$
    B: $IRR = 34.23\%$
    B is preferred on the basis of the IRR.
    b. A has a $540 larger NPV.
    c. B has a $179 larger NPV.
21. $IRR = 16.65\%$. Undertake the investment since $IRR >$ cost of capital.
23. **a.** 4.25 years
    b. No, since 4.25 years $>$ required payback
    c. Yes, because $NPV = \$1380$

Glossary

Algebraic expression A statement of the mathematical operations to be carried out on a combination of numbers and variables.

Amortization period The total length of time over which equal regular payments will repay a loan.

Annual cost of a debt The combined total of the annual interest payments on the debt and the annual payments into a sinking fund for retirement of the principal amount of the debt.

Annualized rate of return The annual rate of return that results if a short-term rate of return continues for an entire year.

Annuity A series of equal payments at regular intervals.

Annuity due An annuity in which the periodic payments occur at the beginning of each payment interval.

Base (1) The quantity that is multiplied by itself in a power. (2) The initial amount to which a percent change is applied.

Binomial An expression containing two terms.

Bond A debt instrument secured by specific assets. The bond issuer (borrower) promises to periodically pay accrued interest, and to repay the full principal amount of the debt on the maturity date. The term "bond" is sometimes used in a generic sense to refer to both true bonds and debentures.

Bond discount The amount by which a bond's face value exceeds its quoted price.

Bond premium The amount by which a bond's quoted price exceeds its face value.

Book value of a debt The amount by which the principal balance owed on the debt exceeds the funds accumulated in a sinking fund for retiring the debt.

Book value of a lease The present value of the remaining lease payments (discounted at the interest rate on debt financing).

Break-even chart A graph presenting both total costs and total revenue as a function of sales volume so that the break-even point may be determined.

Break-even point The sales volume at which net income is zero; the intersection of the total cost and total revenue lines on a break-even chart.

Buy rate (for a currency) The exchange rate a currency dealer uses when buying a currency from you.

Capital gain The amount by which an investment's value increases during the holding period.

Capital gain yield The capital gain as a percentage of the initial investment.

Capital loss The amount by which an investment's value decreases during the holding period.

Capital rationing The circumstance wherein the total amount of capital funds that a firm may invest during a period is limited.

Cash discount A discount allowed for a payment within the discount period.

Cash flow A cash disbursement (cash outflow) or a cash receipt (cash inflow).

Cash flow sign convention Rules for using an algebraic sign to indicate the direction of cash movement. Cash *inflows* (receipts) are positive, and cash *outflows* (disbursements) are negative.

Closed mortgage A mortgage that does not permit any penalty-free prepayments.

Commercial paper Promissory notes issued by large corporations to borrow funds for a short term.

Complex fraction A fraction containing one or more other fractions in its numerator or denominator.

Compound interest method The procedure for calculating interest wherein interest is *periodically* calculated and *added* to principal.

Compounding Applying each successive percent change to the cumulative amount after the preceding percent change.

Compounding frequency The number of compoundings that take place per year.

Compounding period The time interval between two successive conversions of interest to principal.

Constant-growth annuity An annuity in which the payments increase by the *same percentage* from one payment to the next.

Contribution margin The amount by which the unit selling price exceeds the unit variable cost.

Contribution rate The contribution margin expressed as a percentage of the unit selling price.

Cost function The total costs expressed in terms of the number of units sold.

Cost of capital The average of the rates of return required by a firm's various sources of financing.

Cost-volume-profit analysis A procedure for estimating a firm's *operating profit* (or net income before taxes) at any sales *volume* given the firm's *cost structure*.

Coupon rate The nominal annual rate of interest paid on the face value of a bond.

Credit period The time period granted to a customer for paying an invoice.

Debenture A debt instrument having most of the characteristics of a bond except that no *specific* assets secure the debt.

Deferred annuity An annuity where the start of the periodic payments is delayed by more than one payment interval.

Demand loan A loan wherein the lender is entitled to demand full repayment at any time without notice.

Denominator The number under the division line in a fraction. The denominator is also known as the *divisor*.

Discount period The time period within which a payment on an invoice qualifies for a prompt payment discount.

Discounting a payment The process of calculating a payment's present value.

Discount rate The interest rate used in calculating the present value of future cash flows.

Economically equivalent payments Alternative payments that will result in the same future value at a later date.

Effective interest rate The equivalent annually compounded rate of interest.

Equation A statement of the equality of two algebraic expressions.

Equivalent discount rate The single discount rate that gives the same net price as the combined effect of multiple discounts.

Equivalent fractions Fractions that have the same value.

Equivalent interest rates Different nominal interest rates that produce the same maturity value of a given principal after one year.

Equivalent payments Alternative payments that will result in the same future value at a later date.

Equivalent ratio A ratio obtained from another ratio by multiplying each term by the same number, or by dividing each term by the same number.

Exchange rate (between two currencies) The amount of one currency required to purchase one unit of another currency.

Exponent The number of times that the base is used as a factor in repeated multiplication.

Face value (1) The amount paid at maturity of a Treasury Bill or commercial paper. (2) The principal amount that the issuer will pay to the owner of a marketable bond on its scheduled maturity date. (3) The initial principal amount of a mortgage. (4) The principal amount specified on a promissory note.

Factors The components of a term in an algebraic expression that are separated by multiplication or division signs; the components of a product.

Fair market value A price established by competitive bidding among many buyers and sellers.

Fixed cost A cost that does not change with the volume of sales.

Flat price The actual or full amount paid by a bond purchaser and received by the seller. It is the quoted price plus the accrued coupon interest.

Focal date The date selected for the calculation of equivalent values.

Future value (1) A payment's equivalent value at a *subsequent* date, allowing for the time value of money. (2) The total of principal plus interest due on the maturity date of a loan or investment.

Future value of an annuity The single amount, at the end of the annuity, that is economically equivalent to the annuity.

General annuity An annuity in which the payment interval does not equal the compounding interval.

General annuity due An annuity in which the payment interval does *not* equal the compounding interval, and payments occur at the *beginning* of each payment interval.

General perpetuity A perpetuity in which the compounding interval differs from the payment interval.

Gross profit The difference between the selling price and the unit cost of an item of merchandise. (Also called *markup*.)

Guaranteed Investment Certificate (GIC) A fixed-term non-redeemable deposit investment that earns a predetermined rate of interest.

Holding period The time period over which investment income or a capital gain is being calculated.

Improper fraction A fraction in which the numerator is larger than or equal to the denominator.

Income Revenue earned from an investment without selling any portion of the investment.

Income yield An investment's income expressed as a percentage of the amount invested at the beginning of the period.

Interest The fee or rent that lenders charge for the use of their money.

Internal rate of return The discount rate that makes the net present value of an investment's cash flows equal to zero.

Issue date The date on which a loan was made and on which interest starts to accrue.

Like terms Terms having the same literal coefficient.

Linear equation An equation in which the variable is raised only to the first power.

List price The price quoted by a supplier of a product before any trade discounts.

Literal coefficient The non-numerical factor in a term.

Loan amortization schedule A table presenting details of the interest and principal components of each payment, and the balance after each payment.

Loan repayment schedule A table presenting details of interest charges, payments, and outstanding balances on a loan.

Lowest terms (of a ratio) The equivalent ratio having the smallest possible integers for its terms.

Markdown The amount that the price of an item is reduced from the regular selling price.

Markup The difference between the selling price and the unit cost of an item of merchandise. (Also called *gross profit*.)

Maturity date The date on which the principal and accrued interest on an investment or loan are due.

Maturity value The total of principal plus interest due on the maturity date of a loan or investment.

Mid-rate (for currency exchange) The exchange rate when no charge is embedded in the exchange rate. It is approximately mid-way between the buy rate and the sell rate.

Mill rate The amount of property tax per $1000 of taxable value.

Mixed number A number consisting of a whole number plus a fraction.

Monomial An expression containing only one term.

Mortgagee The party lending money on the security of a mortgage.

Mortgagor The party borrowing money and giving a mortgage as security on the loan.

Mutually exclusive projects Alternative capital investments, any one of which will substantially satisfy the same need or purpose.

Net present value The present value of cash inflows minus the present value of cash outflows.

Net price The price paid after the deduction of trade discounts.

Nominal interest rate The stated *annual* interest rate on which the compound-interest calculation is based.

Non-linear equation An equation in which the variable appears with an exponent other than "1," or appears as part of a mathematical function.

Numerator The number above the division line in a fraction. The numerator is also known as the *dividend*.

Numerical coefficient The numerical factor in a term.

Open mortgage A mortgage loan that places no restrictions or penalties on extra payments by the borrower.

Ordinary annuity An annuity in which the payments are made at the *end* of each payment interval.

Ordinary dating Terms of payment wherein the credit period and the discount period start on the date of the invoice.

Ordinary general annuity An annuity in which the payment interval does *not* equal the compounding interval, and payments are made at the *end* of each payment interval.

Ordinary perpetuity A perpetuity in which the payments are at the end of each payment interval.

Ordinary simple annuity An annuity in which the payment interval *equals* the compounding interval, and payments are made at the *end* of each payment interval.

Partial payment Any payment that is smaller than the initial amount required to fully settle an invoice.

Payback period The number of years it will take to recover an initial investment outlay from the investment's future operating profits.

Payment interval The length of time between successive payments in an annuity.

Payment stream A series of two or more payments required by a single transaction or contract.

Period of deferral The time interval before the beginning of the first payment *interval* in a deferred annuity.

Periodic interest rate The rate of interest earned in one compounding period.

Perpetuity An annuity whose payments continue forever.

Perpetuity due A perpetuity in which the payments are at the beginning of each payment interval.

Polynomial An expression containing more than one term.

Power A mathematical operation indicating the multiplication of a quantity (the *base*) by itself a certain number (the *exponent*) of times.

Prepayments Any loan payments in addition to the regular contractual payments.

Present value A payment's economically equivalent amount at a *prior* date, allowing for the time value of money.

Present value of an annuity The single amount, at the beginning of the annuity, that is economically equivalent to the annuity.

Prime rate of interest A chartered bank's lowest lending rate.

Principal The original amount borrowed or invested.

Proper fraction A fraction in which the numerator is less than the denominator.

Proportion A statement of the equality of two ratios.

Proration A procedure in which an amount is subdivided and allocated on a proportionate basis.

Prospective Method A method for calculating a loan's balance based on payments still to be made.

Quoted price The full purchase price (flat price) of a bond less any accrued coupon interest.

Rate of interest The percentage of the principal that will be charged for a particular period of time, normally one year.

Rate of markdown The markdown expressed as a percentage of the regular price.

Rate of markup on cost The markup expressed as a percentage of the cost of the merchandise.

Rate of markup on selling price The markup expressed as a percentage of the selling price of the merchandise.

Rate of total return The investment's combined income and capital gain expressed as a percentage of the beginning investment.